1968

Calculus

BLAISDELL MATHEMATICS SERIES

CONSULTING EDITORS

George Springer, *University of Kansas*

George F. Carrier, *Harvard University*

BLAISDELL PUBLISHING COMPANY
A Division of Ginn and Company
501 Madison Avenue, New York 22, New York

Publishers of college textbooks in the pure and applied sciences

TOM M. APOSTOL

CALCULUS

VOLUME II

CALCULUS OF SEVERAL
VARIABLES WITH APPLICATIONS
TO PROBABILITY AND
VECTOR ANALYSIS

BLAISDELL PUBLISHING COMPANY

NEW YORK · LONDON · TORONTO

A DIVISION OF GINN AND COMPANY

First Edition, 1962

Second Printing, 1964

© Copyright 1962, by Blaisdell Publishing Company, a Division of Ginn and Company.

All rights reserved.

Library of Congress Catalog Card Number: 61-11601

To
Jane and Stephen

PREFACE

This book is a continuation of the author's *Calculus, Volume I*. The present volume has been written with the same underlying plan that prevailed in the first. Sound training in technique is combined with a strong theoretical development. Every effort has been made to convey to the student the spirit of modern mathematics without undue emphasis on formalization. As in Volume I, historical discussions are included to give the student a sense of participation in the evolution of ideas.

Chapter 1 is divided into two parts. Part I contains an introduction to the mathematics of sets, with special emphasis on the notion of a set function. In Part II, the foundations of probability theory are discussed as an illustration of the concepts introduced in Part I. Those who wish to omit or postpone the material on probability may skip Part II and proceed directly to the second chapter. In Chapter 2 the concept of a set function is illustrated again in connection with the study of multiple integration. The double integral is introduced via step functions and its existence is demonstrated for piecewise monotonic integrands. The discussion of the transformation formula for double integrals emphasizes the geometric significance of Jacobian determinants.

Chapter 3, an introduction to the calculus of probabilities, continues the study of probability initiated in Chapter 1. It treats topics such as random variables, distribution functions, and density functions, and it shows the use of the calculus in the study of both one- and two-dimensional random variables. Like Part II of Chapter 1, this material may be omitted or postponed. Of course, Chapter 3 presupposes a knowledge of all the introductory material on probability discussed in Chapter 1.

Derivative theory for functions of several variables is discussed in Chapter 4. This includes chain rules and differentiation of functions defined implicitly. Applications are given to geometry and to extremum problems. The treatment is unified and simplified throughout with the use of vector notation.

Chapter 5 deals with line integrals and includes a discussion of Green's theorem in the plane. This chapter also introduces the concepts of curl and divergence of a vector field. The study of vector and scalar fields is continued in Chapter 6 with the aid of surface integrals. The interrelationships between line, surface, and volume integrals are discussed in detail.

Chapter 7 extends the study of differential equations begun in Volume I and deals primarily with linear differential equations. For linear equations with constant coefficients the treatment is complete and includes both the existence and uniqueness theorems. Linear equations with nonconstant coefficients are also discussed, but the proofs of the existence and uniqueness theorems are postponed until Chapter 9. A special study is made of the Legendre and Bessel equations.

An introduction to numerical analysis is presented in Chapter 8. The emphasis here is primarily on different kinds of polynomial approximations. The ideas are unified by the terminology and notation of normed linear spaces. Approximate integration formulas, including Simpson's rule and Euler's summation formula, are also discussed.

Chapter 9, which concludes Volume II, contains proofs of the existence and uniqueness theorems referred to earlier in Chapter 7. These are deduced as consequences of existence and uniqueness theorems for the first-order vector differential equation $\vec{y}' = \vec{f}(x, \vec{y})$ which, in turn, is discussed by the use of Picard's method of successive approximations. The method of successive approximations is also cast in the language of contraction operators.

There is ample material in this volume for a full year's course meeting three times per week. (Such a course presupposes a knowledge of the material in Volume I, or its equivalent.) This second volume has been planned so that many parts can be omitted for a variety of shorter courses. A course following more or less traditional lines would cover, as a minimum, Part I of Chapter 1, Chapter 2, and Chapter 4. Beyond that, the choice of topics would vary according to the needs and preferences of individual instructors. For example, in addition to the minimum mentioned above, the following pairs of chapters could be taught:

5 and 6; 5 and 7; 5 and 8; 7 and 8; 7 and 9;
or the following combinations of three further chapters:

5, 6, 7; 5, 6, 8; 5, 7, 8; 5, 7, 9; 7, 8, 9.

The number of possibilities increases further with the inclusion of probability. As in Volume I, some sections are "starred" to indicate that they may be omitted or postponed without disrupting the continuity of the presentation. The author has taught this material in the order in which it appears in the book (omitting most of the starred sections) and also in the following order: Part I of Chapter 1, Chapters 2, 4, 5, 6, Part II of Chapter 1, Chapters 3, 7, 8, and 9.

It is with pleasure that I again acknowledge the generous help of many friends and colleagues. In particular I would like to thank Roger Hill of the California Institute of Technology, Professor Kenneth Hoffman of the Massachusetts Institute of Technology, and Professor George Springer of the University of Kansas who read most of the manuscript and made many helpful suggestions. Mr. Hill also aided in the preparation of the answers to the exercises. Professor Herbert S. Zuckerman of the University of Washington read the entire manuscript, both in preliminary form and in final draft. His detailed comments, always pertinent and valuable, led to a number of substantial improvements. I feel deep gratitude to him, not only for this help but also for the genuine interest he has shown in this work from its inception.

Once again it has been a pleasure to work with the creative and skillful staff of the Blaisdell Publishing Company. I especially thank Mr. Warren Blaisdell for his sympathetic consideration of all my wishes and for the honor he has shown me by launching his new series with these two volumes.

Finally, it gives me special pleasure to express my gratitude to my wife for the many ways in which she has contributed during the preparation of this work. In grateful acknowledgement I happily dedicate this book to her.

TOM M. APOSTOL

California Institute of Technology
March 14, 1962

CONTENTS

1. SET FUNCTIONS AND ELEMENTARY PROBABILITY

Part I. Set Functions

Part II. Elementary Probability Theory

2. MULTIPLE INTEGRATION

3. INTRODUCTION TO CALCULUS OF PROBABILITIES

† For the meaning of the symbol⋆, see the preface.

4. DIFFERENTIAL CALCULUS OF SCALAR FIELDS

5. LINE INTEGRALS

6. SURFACE INTEGRALS

7. LINEAR DIFFERENTIAL EQUATIONS

8.   INTRODUCTION TO NUMERICAL ANALYSIS

9.   EXISTENCE THEOREMS FOR DIFFERENTIAL EQUATIONS

1

SET FUNCTIONS AND ELEMENTARY PROBABILITY

Part I. Set Functions

1.1 Introduction

A great deal of scientific work involves the measurement or determination of "how much" of something is present. The simplest and most primitive type of measurement occurs in counting the number of objects in a given finite set; in fact, it was for this purpose that the human mind created the positive integers. But counting with positive integers is inadequate to measure the size or content of an *infinite* set—that is, a set containing more than a finite number of objects. More complicated sets require more complicated measures. Geometric and physical objects, for example, are associated with measures such as *area*, *length*, *volume*, and *mass*. Another type of measure, *probability*, is a concept that can be thought of as a measure of the "likelihood of occurrence" of an event.

All these measures have certain properties in common. From the purely mathematical point of view they are simply special cases of *finitely additive set functions*. The study of such functions forms a part of the *theory of measure*, an important and far-reaching branch of mathematics that is largely a product of the 20th century. Part I of this chapter introduces the concept of a set function and Part II shows how this concept leads to some of the elementary notions of probability theory. Another application of set functions (to multiple integration) is discussed in Chapter 2, and Chapter 3 develops the theory of probability further with the aid of integral and differential calculus.

Those who wish to omit or postpone the material on probability may skip most of Part II of Chapter 1 and proceed directly to Chapter 2 after reading the introductory account of set functions in Part I. Chapter 3, of course, requires a knowledge of all the material in Chapter 1.

To discuss set functions or any of their applications intelligently one must have some acquaintance with the basic concepts of the mathematics of sets. These concepts are outlined in the next few sections.

1.2 Some basic notions of set theory

The subject that has most profoundly influenced the development of mathematics in the 20th century is the *theory of sets.* As developed by Boole, Cantor,† and others in the latter part of the 19th century, it has unified many seemingly disconnected ideas, and has helped to reduce many mathematical concepts to their logical foundations in an elegant and systematic way. Although an exhaustive and rigorous treatment of the theory of sets would require a fairly large treatise, the basic notions are few in number; it is possible to develop a working knowledge of the methods and ideas of set theory with very little effort. Actually, we shall discuss not so much a new theory as an agreement about the precise terminology that we wish to apply to more or less familiar ideas.

In mathematics, the word "set" is used to represent a collection of objects viewed as a single entity. The collections called to mind by such nouns as "flock," "tribe," "crowd," "team," and "electorate" are all examples of sets. The individual objects in the collection are called *elements* or *members* of the set and they are said to *belong to* or to be *contained in* the set. The set, in turn, is said to *contain* or be *composed of* its elements.

Volume I contained many examples of sets of mathematical objects—the set of all real numbers, the set of solutions of a given differential equation, the set of vectors parallel to a given vector, the orthogonal trajectory of a family of curves, and so on. In many applications of mathematics, especially in those of probability theory, it is convenient to deal with sets in which nothing is assumed about the nature of the individual objects in the collection. Abstract set theory has been developed to deal with such collections of arbitrary objects, and from this generality the theory derives its power.

1.3 Notations for designating sets

Sets usually are denoted by capital letters: $A, B, C, \ldots, X, Y, Z$; elements are designated by lower-case letters: $a, b, c, \ldots, x, y, z$. We use the special notation

$$x \in S$$

to mean that "x is an element of S" or "x belongs to S." If x does not belong to S we write $x \notin S$. When convenient, we shall designate sets by displaying the elements in braces; for example, the set of positive even integers less than 10 is denoted by the symbol $\{2, 4, 6, 8\}$ whereas the set of *all* positive integers is displayed as $\{1, 2, 3, \ldots\}$; the three dots take the place of "and so on." The dots are used only when the meaning of "and so on" is clear. The method of listing the members of a set within braces is often referred to as the *roster notation.*

The first basic concept that relates one set to another is the *equality* of sets:

DEFINITION OF SET EQUALITY. Two sets A and B are said to be equal (or identical) if they consist of exactly the same elements, in which case we write $A = B$. If one of the sets contains an element not in the other, we say the sets are unequal and we write $A \neq B$.

Example 1. According to this definition, the two sets $\{2, 4, 6, 8\}$ and $\{2, 8, 6, 4\}$ are equal, since they both consist of the four integers 2, 4, 6, and 8. Thus, when we use the

---

† George Boole (1815–1864) was an English mathematician and logician. His book, *An Investigation of the Laws of Thought,* published in 1854, marked the creation of the first workable system of symbolic logic. Georg F. L. P. Cantor (1845–1918) and his school created the modern theory of sets during the period 1874–1895.

roster notation to describe a set, the order in which the elements appear is irrelevant.

Example 2. The sets {2, 4, 6, 8} and {2, 2, 4, 4, 6, 8} are equal, even though in the second set each of the elements 2 and 4 is listed twice. Both sets contain the four elements 2, 4, 6, 8 and no others, so the definition requires that we call these sets equal. This example shows that we do not insist that the objects listed in the roster notation be distinct. A similar example is the set of letters in the word "*Mississippi*," which is identical to the set {*M, i, s, p*} consisting of the four distinct letters *M*, *i*, *s*, and *p*.

From a given set we may form new sets, called *subsets* of the given set. For example, the set consisting of those positive integers less than 10 which are divisible by 4 (the set {4, 8}) is a subset of the set of all even integers less than 10. In general, we have the following definition:

DEFINITION OF A SUBSET. A set *A* is said to be a subset of a set *B*, and we write

$$A \subseteq B,$$

whenever every element of *A* also belongs to *B*. We also say that *A* is included in *B* or that *B* includes *A*. The relation $\subseteq$ is referred to as set inclusion.

The statement $A \subseteq B$ does not rule out the possibility that $B \subseteq A$. In fact, we may have both $A \subseteq B$ and $B \subseteq A$, but this happens only if *A* and *B* have the same elements. In other words,

$$A = B \qquad \textit{if and only if} \quad A \subseteq B \text{ and } B \subseteq A.$$

This theorem is an immediate consequence of the foregoing definitions of equality and inclusion. If $A \subseteq B$ but $A \neq B$, then we say that *A* is a *proper subset* of *B*; we indicate this by writing $A \subset B$.

As will be the case in all our applications of set theory (especially in the applications to probability theory) we shall have a fixed set *S* given in advance, and we shall be concerned only with subsets of this given set. The underlying set *S* may vary from one application to another; it will be referred to as the *universal set* of each particular discourse. The notation

(1.1) $\{x \mid x \mathrel{\varepsilon} S \text{ and } x \text{ satisfies } P\}$

will designate the set of all elements *x* in *S* which satisfy the property *P*. When the universal set to which we are referring is understood, we omit the reference to *S* and abbreviate the notation in (1.1) by writing $\{x \mid x \text{ satisfies } P\}$. This is read "the set of all *x* such that *x* satisfies *P*." Sets designated in this way are said to be described by a *defining property*. For example, the closed interval [*a, b*] could be designated as $\{x \mid a \leq x \leq b\}$; the universal set *S* in this case is obviously the set of all real numbers. Similarly, the set of all positive integers {1, 2, 3, . . .} can be designated as $\{x \mid x \text{ is a positive integer}\}$. Of course, the letter "*x*" is a dummy and may be replaced by any other convenient symbol. Thus, we may write

$$\{x \mid a \leq x \leq b\} = \{y \mid a \leq y \leq b\} = \{t \mid a \leq t \leq b\},$$

and so on.

It is possible for a set to contain no elements whatever. This set is called the *empty set* or the *void set*, and will be denoted by the symbol ϕ. We will consider ϕ to be a subset

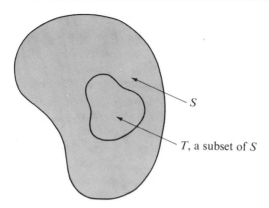

S

T, a subset of *S*

FIGURE 1.1   *Venn diagram illustrating subsets.*

of every set. Some people find it helpful to think of a set as analogous to a container (such as a bag or a box) containing certain objects, its elements. The empty set is then analogous to an empty container.

To avoid logical difficulties, we must distinguish between the *element* x and the *set* {x} whose only element is x. (A bag with a cat in it is conceptually distinct from the cat itself.) In particular, the empty set ϕ is not the same as the set {ϕ}. In fact, the empty set ϕ contains no elements, whereas the set {ϕ} has one element, ϕ. (A bag which contains an empty bag is not empty.) Sets consisting of exactly one element are sometimes called *one-element sets* or *singletons*.

Diagrams often help us visualize relations between sets. For example, we may think of the universal set *S* as a region in the plane, and each of its elements as a geometric point. Subsets of *S* may then be thought of as collections of points within *S*, as illustrated in Figure 1.1. Visual aids of this type, called *Venn diagrams*, are useful for testing the validity of theorems in set theory or for suggesting methods to prove them. Of course, the proofs themselves must rely only on the definitions of the concepts and not on the diagrams.

1.4   Exercises

1. Use the roster notation to designate the following sets of real numbers:

$$A = \{x \mid x^2 - 2x + 1 = 0\}, \qquad D = \{x \mid x + 8 = 9\},$$
$$B = \{x \mid x > 0 \text{ and } \sin \pi x = 0\}, \qquad E = \{x \mid (x + 8)^2 = 9^2\},$$
$$C = \{x \mid x > 0 \text{ and } \cos \pi x = 1\}, \qquad F = \{x \mid (x^2 + 16x)^2 = 17^2\}.$$

2. For the sets in Exercise 1, note that $C \subseteq B$. List all the inclusion relations that hold among the sets *A*, *B*, *C*, *D*, *E*, *F*.

3. Identify the following sets of real numbers with a sketch:

(a) $\{x \mid 0 < x < 1\}$.

(b) $\{x \mid 0 < x^2 < 2\}$.

(c) $\{x \mid x^2 > 2\}$.

(d) $\{x \mid x > 0 \text{ and } x^2 > 2\}$.

(e) $\{x \mid (x - 1)(x - 2)(x - 3) = 0\}$.

(f) $\{x \mid (x - 1)(x - 2)(x - 3) > 0\}$.

(g) $\{x \mid |x - 2| < 5\}$.

(h) $\{x \mid |x + 2| \geq 5\}$.

4. Identify (with a sketch) the following sets of points in the xy-plane:

   (a) $\{(x, y) \mid x^2 + y^2 = 1\}$. (d) $\{(x, y) \mid x^2 + x = y^2 + y\}$.
   (b) $\{(x, y) \mid x^2 + y^2 < 1\}$. (e) $\{(x, y) \mid x < |y|\}$.
   (c) $\{(x, y) \mid x < y\}$. (f) $\{(x, y) \mid x^2 + y^2 < 0\}$.

5. (a) If $A \subset B$ and $B \subset C$, prove that $A \subset C$.
   (b) If $A \subseteq B$ and $B \subseteq C$, prove that $A \subseteq C$.
   (c) What can you conclude if $A \subset B$ and $B \subseteq C$?
   (d) If $x \in A$ and $A \subseteq B$, is it necessarily true that $x \in B$?
   (e) If $x \in A$ and $A \in B$, is it necessarily true that $x \in B$?

6. Prove the following properties of set equality:

   (a) $\{a, a\} = \{a\}$.
   (b) $\{a, b\} = \{b, a\}$.
   (c) $\{a\} = \{b, c\}$ if, and only if, $a = b = c$.

7. Let $A = \{1\}$ and let $B = \{\{1\}, 1\}$. Discuss the validity of the following statements (prove the ones that are true and explain why the others are not true):

   (a) $A = B$. (d) $1 \subset A$.
   (b) $A \in B$. (e) $1 \in A$.
   (c) $A \subseteq B$. (f) $1 \subseteq B$.

8. Given the set $S = \{1, 2, 3, 4\}$. Display all subsets of S. (There are 16 altogether, counting ϕ and S. Remember to count the singletons $\{1\}$, $\{2\}$, $\{3\}$, and $\{4\}$.)

9. If a finite set S consists of n elements, prove that there are exactly 2^n subsets of S.

10. Given the following four sets:

$$A = \{1, 2\}, \quad B = \{\{1\}, \{2\}\}, \quad C = \{\{1\}, \{1, 2\}\}, \quad D = \{\{1\}, \{2\}, \{1, 2\}\}.$$

Discuss the validity of each of the following statements (prove the ones that are true and explain why the others are not true):

   (a) $A = B$. (f) $A \subset D$.
   (b) $A \subseteq B$. (g) $A \in D$.
   (c) $A \subset B$. (h) $B \subset C$.
   (d) $A \subset C$. (i) $B \subset D$.
   (e) $A \in C$. (j) $B \in D$.

1.5 Unions, intersections, and complements. Set algebra

From two given sets A and B, we can always form a new set called the *union* of A and B. This new set is denoted by the symbol

$$A \cup B \text{ (read: ``A union B'')}$$

and is defined to be the set of those elements which are in A, in B, or in both. That is to say, $A \cup B$ is the set of all elements which belong to at least one of the sets A, B. An example is illustrated in Figure 1.2 (a), where the shaded portion represents $A \cup B$.

Similarly, the *intersection* of A and B, denoted by

$$A \cap B \text{ (read: ``A intersection B'')}$$

is defined to be the set of those elements common to *both* A and B. This is illustrated by the shaded portion of Figure 1.2 (b). In Figure 1.2 (c) the two sets A and B have no

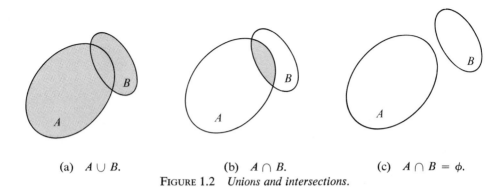

(a) $A \cup B$.   (b) $A \cap B$.   (c) $A \cap B = \phi$.

FIGURE 1.2   *Unions and intersections.*

elements in common; in this case their intersection is the empty set ϕ. Two sets A and B are said to be *disjoint* if $A \cap B = \phi$.

If A and B are given sets, the *difference* $A - B$ (also called the *complement of B relative to A*) is defined to be the set of all elements of A which are not in B. Thus, by definition,

$$A - B = \{x \mid x \,\varepsilon\, A \text{ and } x \notin B\} .$$

In Figure 1.3, A is the set of points lying within or on the boundary of the rectangle shown, and B is the set of points within or on the boundary of the triangle. The shaded region represents $A - B$ and consists of everything in the rectangle which is outside the triangle.

If S is the universal set of a particular discussion, and if $T \subseteq S$, then the difference $S - T$ is also denoted by the symbol T' and is called, simply, the *complement* of T. For example, in the real-number system, the complement of the set of rational numbers is the set of irrational numbers. For any two subsets A and B of a universal set S, we have the identity

$$A - B = A \cap B' .$$

This follows at once from the definition of $A - B$.

The operations of union and intersection have many formal similarities to (as well as differences from) ordinary addition and multiplication of real numbers. For example, since there is no question of order involved in the definitions of union and intersection, it follows that $A \cup B = B \cup A$ and that $A \cap B = B \cap A$. That is to say, union and

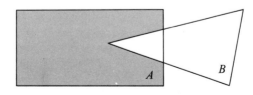

FIGURE 1.3   *Complements. The shaded region denotes* $A - B$.

intersection are *commutative* operations. The definitions are also phrased in such a way that the operations are *associative*:

$$(A \cup B) \cup C = A \cup (B \cup C) \quad \text{and} \quad (A \cap B) \cap C = A \cap (B \cap C).$$

These and other theorems related to the "algebra of sets" are listed as Exercises in Section 1.6. One of the best ways for the reader to become familiar with the terminology and notations introduced above is to carry out the proofs of each of these laws. A sample of the type of argument that is needed appears immediately after the Exercises.

The operations of union and intersection can be extended to finite or infinite collections of sets as follows: Let $\mathcal{F}$ be a nonempty class† of sets. The *union* of all the sets in $\mathcal{F}$ is defined as the set of those elements which belong to at least one of the sets in $\mathcal{F}$, and is denoted by the symbol

$$\bigcup_{A \varepsilon \mathcal{F}} A.$$

If $\mathcal{F}$ is a finite collection of sets, say $\mathcal{F} = \{A_1, A_2, \ldots, A_n\}$, we write

$$\bigcup_{A \varepsilon \mathcal{F}} A = \bigcup_{k=1}^{n} A_k = A_1 \cup A_2 \cup \cdots \cup A_n.$$

Similarly, the intersection of all the sets in $\mathcal{F}$ is defined to be the set of those elements which belong to every one of the sets in $\mathcal{F}$; it is denoted by the symbol

$$\bigcap_{A \varepsilon \mathcal{F}} A.$$

For finite collections (as above) we write

$$\bigcap_{A \varepsilon \mathcal{F}} A = \bigcap_{k=1}^{n} A_k = A_1 \cap A_2 \cap \cdots \cap A_n.$$

Unions and intersections have been defined in such a way that associative laws for these operations are automatically satisfied. Hence there is no ambiguity when we write $A_1 \cup A_2 \cup \cdots \cup A_n$ or $A_1 \cap A_2 \cap \cdots \cap A_n$.

1.6 Exercises

Prove the set relations in Exercises 1 through 17.
  1. *Commutative laws:*
    $$A \cup B = B \cup A, \quad A \cap B = B \cap A.$$
  2. *Associative laws:*
    $$A \cup (B \cup C) = (A \cup B) \cup C, \quad A \cap (B \cap C) = (A \cap B) \cap C.$$
  3. *Distributive laws:*
    $$A \cap (B \cup C) = (A \cap B) \cup (A \cap C), \quad A \cup (B \cap C) = (A \cup B) \cap (A \cup C).$$

† To help simplify the language, we call a collection of sets a *class*. Capital script letters $\mathcal{A}$, $\mathcal{B}$, $\mathcal{C}$, ... are used to denote classes. The usual terminology and notation of set theory applies, of course, to classes. Thus, for example, $A \varepsilon \mathcal{F}$ means that A is one of the sets in the class $\mathcal{F}$. $\mathcal{A} \subseteq \mathcal{B}$ means that every set in $\mathcal{A}$ is also in $\mathcal{B}$, and so forth.

4. *Idempotent laws:*

$A \cup A = A,$ $A \cap A = A.$

5. $A \subseteq A \cup B,$ $A \cap B \subseteq A.$

6. $A \cup \phi = A,$ $A \cap \phi = \phi.$

7. $A \cup (A \cap B) = A,$ $A \cap (A \cup B) = A.$

8. If $A \subseteq C$ and $B \subseteq C$, then $A \cup B \subseteq C.$

9. If $C \subseteq A$ and $C \subseteq B$, then $C \subseteq A \cap B.$

In Exercises 10 through 17, complements denoted by A', B', etc., are understood to be relative to a common universal set S.

10. If $A \subseteq B$, then $B' \subseteq A'.$

11. *Involution law:*

$(A')' = A.$

12. *DeMorgan's laws:*

$(A \cup B)' = A' \cap B',$ $(A \cap B)' = A' \cup B'.$

13. $A \cup A' = S,$ $A \cap A' = \phi.$

14. $S' = \phi,$ $\phi' = S.$

15. $A - B = (A' \cup B)'.$

16. $A - (B \cap C) = (A - B) \cup (A - C).$

17. *Generalized DeMorgan's laws:*
Let $\mathcal{F}$ be a class of sets. Then

$$ B - \bigcup_{A \in \mathcal{F}} A = \bigcap_{A \in \mathcal{F}} (B - A) \quad \text{and} \quad B - \bigcap_{A \in \mathcal{F}} A = \bigcup_{A \in \mathcal{F}} (B - A). $$

18. Three circular regions X, Y, and Z are shown in Figure 1.4. The set C is $X \cap Z$. In a similar way, express each of the sets A, B, D, E, and F in terms of unions and intersections of X, Y, Z and their complements X', Y', Z', the complements being relative to the whole plane.

19. (a) Prove that one of the following two formulas is always right and the other one is sometimes wrong:

(i) $A - (B - C) = (A - B) \cup C,$
(ii) $A - (B \cup C) = (A - B) - C.$

(b) State an additional necessary and sufficient condition for the formula which is sometimes incorrect to be always right.

20. Certain subsets of a given set S are called A-sets and others are called B-sets. Suppose that these subsets are chosen in such a way that the following properties are satisfied:

(a) The union of any collection of A-sets is an A-set.
(b) The intersection of any finite number of A-sets is an A-set.
(c) The complement of an A-set is a B-set and the complement of a B-set is an A-set.

Prove that we have:

(d) The intersection of any collection of B-sets is a B-set.
(e) The union of any finite number of B-sets is a B-set.

21. Let $S = \{1, 2, 3\}$ and let us refer to the following subsets as A-sets:

$$ \phi, \{1\}, \{2\}, \{1, 2\}, S. $$

Choose a collection of B-sets so that the five properties listed in Exercise 20 are satisfied. Is the collection of B-sets uniquely determined by these properties?

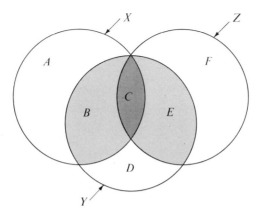

FIGURE 1.4   *Exercise 18.*

22. Among the subsets of a given set S, choose some (which we call A-sets) that satisfy properties (a) and (b) of Exercise 20.

(a) Show that a collection of B-sets can always be chosen so that all five properties (a) through (e) of Exercise 20 are satisfied. Is the collection of B-sets uniquely determined?

(b) If $S = \{1, 2, 3\}$ and the A-sets are ϕ, $\{1\}$, find a corresponding collection of B-sets.

Proof of DeMorgan's laws (*Exercise 12*). We shall prove first that

(1.2) $$(A \cup B)' = A' \cap B' .$$

Let us denote the set on the left of (1.2) by X and the set on the right by Y. We shall prove that $X = Y$ by proving the two statements $X \subseteq Y$ and $Y \subseteq X$. To prove that $X \subseteq Y$, suppose $x \, \varepsilon \, X$. This means that x is not in the union $A \cup B$; in other words, x is in neither A nor B. But this implies that $x \, \varepsilon \, A'$ and $x \, \varepsilon \, B'$. Hence $x \, \varepsilon \, A' \cap B'$, which is equivalent to $x \, \varepsilon \, Y$. Therefore, if $x \, \varepsilon \, X$, then $x \, \varepsilon \, Y$, so that $X \subseteq Y$. The proof that $Y \subseteq X$ is entirely similar. The two statements $X \subseteq Y$ and $Y \subseteq X$ together prove (1.2).

The other DeMorgan law, $(A \cap B)' = A' \cup B'$, may now be deduced from (1.2) as follows: First we use (1.2) with A and B replaced by their complements A' and B'. This gives us

(1.3) $$(A' \cup B')' = A \cap B ,$$

because of the involution law $(A')' = A$ (Exercise 11). If, now, we take the complement of each side of Equation (1.3) and use the involution law again, we obtain the relation $A' \cup B' = (A \cap B)'$ which we set out to prove.

1.7 Finitely additive set functions

When a mathematician attempts to develop a general abstract theory encompassing many different concepts, he tries to isolate common properties which seem to be basic in each of the particular situations in question. He then uses these properties as the fundamental building blocks of his theory. To illustrate this process we shall consider features common to the notions of area, length, and mass; stated abstractly in the language of set theory, they lead to a general concept known as a *finitely additive set function*.

When we assign an area to a region, a length to a curve, or a mass to a system of particles, we are associating a number with a set. For example, a curve is a set of points, and the length of the curve is a number associated with this set. From a purely mathematical viewpoint this means that we have a function f which assigns a real number, $f(A)$, to each set A in some given class of sets. Thus, the class of curves which can be assigned a length is the collection of all rectifiable curves. A function of this kind, whose domain of definition is a class of sets and whose function values are real numbers, is called a *set function*.

If a curve is cut into two pieces, its length is the sum of the lengths of the individual pieces. This property, which also applies to area and mass, is known as *finite additivity*; it can be defined for arbitrary set functions as follows:

DEFINITION OF A FINITELY ADDITIVE SET FUNCTION. A set function f is said to be finitely additive on a class $\mathcal{A}$ of sets if

$$f(A \cup B) = f(A) + f(B)$$

whenever A and B are disjoint sets in $\mathcal{A}$ such that $A \cup B$ is also in $\mathcal{A}$.

The set functions which represent area, length, and mass have further properties in common. For example, they are all *nonnegative* set functions. That is,

(1.4) $$f(A) \geq 0$$

for each set A in the class under consideration.

Another property shared by area, length, and mass may be described as follows:

(1.5) $$f(A) \leq f(B) \qquad \text{whenever} \quad A \subseteq B.$$

In other words, the measure of part of a set cannot exceed that of the whole set. Set functions with this property† are said to be *monotone*.

Example. Let $S = \{a_1, a_2, \ldots, a_n\}$ be a set consisting of n (distinct) elements, and let $\mathcal{A}$ denote the class of all subsets of S. For each A in $\mathcal{A}$, let $\nu(A)$ denote the number of distinct elements in A (ν is the Greek letter "nu"). It is easy to verify that this function is finitely additive on $\mathcal{A}$. In fact, if A has k elements and if B has m elements, $\nu(A) = k$ and $\nu(B) = m$. If A and B are disjoint it is clear that the union $A \cup B$ is a subset of S with $k + m$ elements, so

$$\nu(A \cup B) = k + m = \nu(A) + \nu(B).$$

This particular set function is also nonnegative and monotone.

1.8 Exercises

1. Let f be a finitely additive set function defined on a class $\mathcal{A}$ of sets. Let $A_1, \ldots, A_n$ be n sets

---

† Properties (1.4) and (1.5) are not completely independent of one another. In fact, if we restrict the class of sets under consideration, we can prove that (1.4) and (1.5) are logically equivalent. These restricted classes, which are discussed in more detail in Section 1.9, are called *Boolean rings* (or simply *rings*).

in α such that $A_i \cap A_j = \phi$ if $i \neq j$. (Such a collection is called a *disjoint collection* of sets.) If the union $\bigcup\limits_{k=1}^{m} A_k$ is in class α for all $m \leq n$, use induction to prove that

$$f(\bigcup_{k=1}^{n} A_k) = \sum_{k=1}^{n} f(A_k).$$

2. Let $\mathcal{F}$ denote the class of all *finite* sets. That is to say, a set A belongs to $\mathcal{F}$ if and only if A contains a finite number of elements. (The empty set is also considered to be a finite set.) For each A in $\mathcal{F}$, let $\nu(A)$ denote the number of distinct elements in A.

(a) Show that $A \cup B$ and $A \cap B$ are in $\mathcal{F}$ whenever A and B are in $\mathcal{F}$.

(b) Prove that $\nu(A \cup B) = \nu(A) + \nu(B)$ if A and B are disjoint.

(c) If A and B have elements in common, then each such element contributes 2 to the sum $\nu(A) + \nu(B)$, but only 1 to the number $\nu(A \cup B)$, so the formula in part (b) cannot hold if $A \cap B$ is nonempty. Prove that, instead, we have the more general formula

$$\nu(A \cup B) = \nu(A) + \nu(B) - \nu(A \cap B)$$

for any two sets in $\mathcal{F}$. In Exercises 3 and 4 below we outline a method for extending this formula to more general finitely additive set functions.

(d) Show that $B - A \, \mathcal{E} \, \mathcal{F}$ whenever A and B are in $\mathcal{F}$.

(e) Prove that $\nu(B - A) = \nu(B) - \nu(A)$ whenever $A \subseteq B$. This implies, in particular, that $\nu(\phi) = 0$. (Why?)

(f) Show, by means of counterexamples, that the equation in part (e) is not necessarily true if A is not a subset of B.

3. Let α denote the class of all subsets of a given universal set and let A and B be arbitrary sets in α. Prove that:

(a) $A \cap B'$ and B are disjoint.

(b) $A \cup B = (A \cap B') \cup B$. (This formula expresses $A \cup B$ as the union of two disjoint sets.)

(c) $A \cap B$ and $A \cap B'$ are disjoint.

(d) $(A \cap B) \cup (A \cap B') = A$. (This formula expresses A as a union of two disjoint sets.)

4. Let f be a finitely additive set function defined on class α of Exercise 3. Prove that, for arbitrary sets A and B in α, we have

(a) $f(A \cap B') = f(A \cup B) - f(B)$.

(b) $f(A \cap B') = f(A) - f(A \cap B)$.

(c) $f(A \cup B) = f(A) + f(B) - f(A \cap B)$. [*Hint.* Use (a) and (b).]

(d) $f(A \cup B) \leq f(A) + f(B)$ when f is nonnegative.

5. Exercise 3(b) shows how to express the union of two sets as the union of two *disjoint* sets. Express in a similar way the union of three sets $A_1 \cup A_2 \cup A_3$ and, more generally, of n sets $A_1 \cup A_2 \cup \cdots \cup A_n$. Illustrate with a Venn diagram when $n = 3$.

6. A study of a set S consisting of 1000 college graduates ten years after graduation revealed that the "successes" formed a subset A of 400 members, the Caltech graduates formed a subset B of 300 members, and the intersection $A \cap B$ consisted of 200 members.

(a) For each of the following properties, use set notation to describe, in terms of unions and intersections of A, B, and their complements A' and B' relative to S, the subsets consisting of those persons in S that have the property:

(i) Neither a "success" nor a Caltech graduate.

(ii) A "success" but not a Caltech graduate.

(iii) A "success" or a Caltech graduate, or both.

(iv) Either a "success" or a Caltech graduate, but not both.

(v) Belongs to not more than one of A or B.

(b) Determine the exact number of individuals in each of the five subsets of part (a).

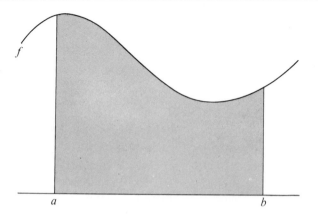

FIGURE 1.5   *The ordinate set of f over [a, b].*

7. If f is a real-valued nonnegative function defined on a set T of real numbers, the set of points $\{(x, y) \mid x \in T, 0 \leq y \leq f(x)\}$ is called the *ordinate set* of f over T. The shaded region in Figure 1.5 illustrates an example in which T is a closed interval $[a, b]$. Let us restrict our considerations to functions f that are bounded and integrable on finite intervals and let $\mathcal{O}$ denote the class of all ordinate sets over half-open intervals of the form $[a, b)$ (closed on the left and open on the right). If S is such an ordinate set, let

$$\alpha(S) = \int_a^b f(x) \, dx \,.$$

This equation defines a set function α on class $\mathcal{O}$. Properties of the integral may be translated into properties of the set function α.

Note. We use the half-open intervals $[a, b)$ so that we can obtain ordinate sets as disjoint unions of other ordinate sets. Thus, for example, if S is the ordinate set of f over $[a, b)$ and if R is the ordinate set of g over $[b, c)$, the union $S \cup R$ is the ordinate set of h over $[a, c)$, where $h(x) = f(x)$ if $a \leq x < b$ and $h(x) = g(x)$ if $b \leq x < c$.

(a) Prove that α has the following properties:
     (i) α is finitely additive on $\mathcal{O}$.
     (ii) α is monotone.
     (iii) α is nonnegative.
     (iv) $\alpha(R) = c(b - a)$ if R is the ordinate set of a function that has the constant value c on the open interval (a, b).

(b) Let β denote *any* set function, defined on $\mathcal{O}$, that has the four properties listed in part (a). From these properties alone, deduce the formula

(1.6) $$\beta(S) = \int_a^b f(x) \, dx$$

if S is the ordinate set of f over $[a, b)$. This proves that the integral is the *only* set function that has the four properties mentioned. [*Hint.* Given S, let s and t be arbitrary step functions such that $s(x) \leq f(x) \leq t(x)$ for each x in $[a, b]$. Prove that

$$\int_a^b s(x) \, dx \leq \beta(S) \leq \int_a^b t(x) \, dx \,.$$

Use the integrability of f to deduce (1.6).]

1.9 Boolean rings and Boolean algebras of sets

To discuss further properties of finitely additive set functions it is convenient to introduce the concept of a ring of sets.

DEFINITION OF A BOOLEAN RING. *A nonempty class $\Re$ of sets is said to be a Boolean ring if $A \cup B$ and $A - B$ are in $\Re$ whenever A and B are in $\Re$.*

If a set A is in a ring $\Re$, $A - A$ must also be in the ring. This proves that the empty set belongs to every ring of sets. A standard example of a Boolean ring is the class of all subsets of a given universal set S. This class is obviously a ring because $A \cup B$ and $A - B$ are subsets of S whenever A and B are.

DEFINITION OF A FINITELY ADDITIVE MEASURE. *A nonnegative set function f that is finitely additive on a ring $\Re$ of sets is called a finitely additive measure (or simply a measure) on $\Re$.*

In other words, a measure is a set function that satisfies the following two properties for all sets A and B in a ring $\Re$:

$$(1.7) \quad f(A) \geq 0, \quad \text{and} \quad f(A \cup B) = f(A) + f(B) \quad \text{whenever} \quad A \cap B = \phi.$$

In particular, if we take $A = B = \phi$ we find $f(\phi) = 0$, so measures always assign the value 0 to the empty set.

For the purpose of this definition $\Re$ need not necessarily be a ring because no statement is made about the difference $A - B$. The ring properties are needed when we derive further properties of measures. First of all, we can prove that every measure satisfies the equation

$$(1.8) \quad f(B - A) = f(B) - f(A) \quad \text{whenever} \quad A \subseteq B.$$

In fact, if $A \subseteq B$, then A and $B - A$ are disjoint sets whose union is B; hence the additive property gives us $f(B) = f(A) + f(B - A)$, which is equivalent to Equation (1.8). The ring property is used here to guarantee that $B - A$ is in $\Re$. Since $f(B - A) \geq 0$, it follows from Equation (1.8) that $f(A) \leq f(B)$ whenever $A \subseteq B$; therefore *every measure is monotone*.

An example of a measure defined on a Boolean ring may be constructed as follows:

Example 1. A *triangular region* will designate a set of points lying inside a triangle, along with some, none, or all the boundary points. The empty set, line segments, and isolated points are to be thought of as degenerate triangular regions. Two triangular regions are said to be nonoverlapping if they have no interior points in common. (They may have boundary points in common.) By a *polygonal set* we shall understand any set of points in the plane which can be expressed as the union of a finite number of nonoverlapping triangular regions. Let $\Re$ denote the collection of all polygonal sets. The union $A \cup B$ and the difference $A - B$ of two polygonal sets A and B is again a polygonal set, so $\Re$ is a Boolean ring. For example, if A and B are two adjacent triangular regions (each including its complete boundary), as shown in Figure 1.6, then the union $A \cup B$ is a rectangular region with its complete boundary, but the difference $A - B$ is the triangular region A with one of its edges missing. It is easy to imagine examples in which

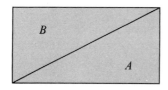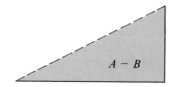

FIGURE 1.6 *Polygonal sets.*

$A - B$ is a degenerate triangular region, and we have included these among the polygonal sets to guarantee that $A - B$ is in $\mathcal{R}$ whenever A and B are in $\mathcal{R}$.

If $A \, \varepsilon \, \mathcal{R}$, we let $f(A)$ denote the sum of the areas of the individual triangles whose union is A. (Degenerate triangular regions are assigned zero area.) Although a given polygonal set A can be decomposed in more than one way as a union of nonoverlapping triangular regions, it can be shown that the sum of the areas of the triangular regions is always the same, this sum being the area of A. Therefore the number $f(A)$ is well defined. This set function (area) is a finitely additive measure defined on the Boolean ring of polygonal sets.

Example 2. Another example may be formed by considering the class $\mathcal{R}$ of those polygonal sets which are subsets of a given polygonal set S. Again, with the agreements described in the foregoing example, $\mathcal{R}$ is a Boolean ring and area is a measure defined on this ring.

One property of Example 2 not shared by the ring in Example 1 is that for each A in $\mathcal{R}$ the complement A' is again in $\mathcal{R}$. (In Example 1 the universal set is the whole plane and the complement of a polygonal set is not a polygonal set.) Boolean rings with this property are called *Boolean algebras*. Because of its fundamental importance in probability theory, we shall state a formal definition of a Boolean algebra:

DEFINITION OF A BOOLEAN ALGEBRA OF SETS. Let $\mathcal{B}$ denote a nonempty class of sets and let S denote the universal set under consideration. (Elements of $\mathcal{B}$ are subsets of S.) Then $\mathcal{B}$ is called a Boolean algebra if for every A and B in $\mathcal{B}$ we have

$$A \cup B \, \varepsilon \, \mathcal{B} \qquad \text{and} \qquad A' \, \varepsilon \, \mathcal{B} \, .$$

The complement A' is, of course, $S - A$.

Notice that every Boolean algebra is automatically a Boolean ring because of the identity

$$A - B = A \cap B' = (A' \cup B)' \, .$$

On the other hand, Example 1 above shows that every Boolean ring is not necessarily a Boolean algebra. The logical distinction between the two is that a Boolean algebra is a Boolean ring which also contains the universal set S under consideration. The presence of the universal set S in a Boolean algebra $\mathcal{B}$ follows from the fact that $\phi \, \varepsilon \, \mathcal{B}$ (since $\mathcal{B}$ is a Boolean ring); hence S, the complement of ϕ, must also belong to $\mathcal{B}$.

Many Boolean algebras can be formed from the subsets of a given universal set S. The smallest such algebra is the class $\mathcal{B}_0 = \{\phi, S\}$, which consists of only two special subsets: ϕ and S. At the other extreme is the class $\mathcal{B}_1$, which consists of *all* subsets of S.

Every Boolean algebra $\mathcal{B}$ consisting of subsets of S must satisfy the inclusion relation $\mathcal{B}_0 \subseteq \mathcal{B} \subseteq \mathcal{B}_1$.

1.10 Exercises

In the following exercises, S denotes a finite set consisting of n (distinct) elements, say $S = \{a_1, a_2, \ldots, a_n\}$.

1. Let $A_1 = \{a_1\}$, the subset consisting of a_1 alone.

(a) Show that the class $\mathcal{R} = \{\phi, A_1\}$ is the smallest Boolean ring containing A_1. That is to say, $\mathcal{R}$ is a Boolean ring containing A_1, and every Boolean ring which contains A_1 must include $\mathcal{R}$ as a subclass.

(b) Show that the class $\mathcal{B} = \{\phi, A_1, A_1', S\}$ is the smallest Boolean algebra containing A_1.

2. Let $A_1 = \{a_1\}$, $A_2 = \{a_2\}$. Describe, in a manner similar to that used in Exercise 1, the smallest Boolean ring $\mathcal{R}$ containing both A_1 and A_2 and the smallest Boolean algebra $\mathcal{B}$ containing both A_1 and A_2.

3. Do the same as in Exercise 2 for the subsets $A_1 = \{a_1\}$, $A_2 = \{a_2\}$, and $A_3 = \{a_3\}$.

4. If $\mathcal{B}_k$ denotes the smallest Boolean algebra which contains the k subsets $A_1 = \{a_1\}$, $A_2 = \{a_2\}$, $\ldots$, $A_k = \{a_k\}$, show that $\mathcal{B}_k$ contains 2^{k+1} subsets of S if $k < n$ and 2^n subsets if $k = n$.

Part II. Elementary Probability Theory

1.11 Historical introduction to probability theory

A gambler's dispute in 1654 led to the creation of the theory of probability by two famous French mathematicians, Blaise Pascal and Pierre de Fermat. Antoine Gombaud, Chevalier de Méré, a French nobleman with an interest in gaming and gambling questions, called Pascal's attention to an apparent contradiction concerning a popular dice game. The game consisted in throwing a pair of dice 24 times; the problem was to decide whether or not to bet even money on the occurrence of at least one "double six" during the 24 throws. A seemingly well-established gambling rule led de Méré to believe that betting on a double six in 24 throws would be profitable, but his own calculations indicated just the opposite.

This problem and others posed by de Méré led to an exchange of letters between Pascal and Fermat in which the fundamental principles of probability theory were formulated for the first time. Although a few special problems on games of chance had been solved by some Italian mathematicians in the 15th and 16th centuries, no general theory was developed before this famous correspondence.

The Dutch scientist Christian Huygens, a teacher of Leibniz, learned of this correspondence and shortly thereafter (in 1657) published the first book on probability; entitled *De Ratiociniis in Ludo Aleae*, it was a treatise on problems associated with gambling. Because of the inherent appeal of games of chance, probability theory soon became popular, and the subject developed rapidly during the 18th century. The major contributors during this period were Jakob Bernoulli† (1654–1705) and Abraham de Moivre (1667–1754).

† Sometimes referred to as James Bernoulli.

In 1812 Pierre de Laplace (1749–1827) introduced a host of new ideas and mathematical techniques in his book, *Theorie analytique des probabilities*. Before Laplace, probability theory was solely concerned with developing a mathematical analysis of games of chance. Laplace showed that the theory could also be applied to many scientific and practical problems. The *theory of errors, actuarial mathematics,* and *statistical mechanics* are examples of some of the important applications of probability theory developed in the 19th century.

Like so many other branches of mathematics, the development of probability theory has been stimulated by the variety of its applications. Conversely, each advance in the theory has enlarged the scope of its influence. Mathematical statistics is one important branch of applied probability; other applications occur in such widely different fields as genetics, psychology, economics, and engineering. Many workers have contributed to the theory since Laplace's time; among the most important are Chebyshev, Markov, von Mises, and Kolmogorov.

An understanding of contemporary probability theory in its purest form requires a substantial background in the theory of measure and integration. Nevertheless, by restricting the theory to relatively simple situations, it is possible to give an elementary treatment of the subject which illustrates the true flavor of its methods and techniques. The remainder of this chapter presents the basic notions of modern *elementary* probability theory, with some applications, primarily to games of chance such as coin tossing, dice, and card games. This brief account is intended to demonstrate the logical structure of the subject as a deductive science and to give the reader a feeling for and an interest in probabilistic thinking.

Many mathematical questions, especially those that arise in the applications of probability theory, may be reduced to problems on counting the number of elements in a finite set. Systematic methods for studying such problems form part of a mathematical discipline known as *combinatorial analysis.* A knowledge of some of the simplest counting techniques is needed to understand how the principles of probability theory are applied in practice. Therefore, before we begin the study of probability theory itself, we shall digress briefly to discuss some basic ideas in combinatorial analysis that are useful in analyzing some of the problems in probability theory that will be encountered in the later sections.

1.12 Some basic principles of combinatorial analysis

If all the elements of a finite set are displayed before us, there is usually no difficulty in counting their total number. More often than not, however, a set is described in a way that makes it impossible or undesirable to display all its elements. For example, we might ask for the total number of distinct bridge hands that can be dealt. Each player is dealt 13 cards from a 52-card deck. The number of possible distinct hands is the same as the number of different subsets of 13 elements that can be formed from a set of 52 elements. Since this number exceeds 635 billion, a direct enumeration of all the possibilities is clearly not the best way to attack this problem; however, it can readily be solved by combinatorial analysis.

This problem is a special case of the more general problem of counting the number of distinct subsets of k elements that may be formed from a set of n elements,† where $n \geq k$.

† When we say that a set has n elements, we mean that it has n *distinct* elements. Such a set is sometimes called an n-element set.

Let us denote this number by $f(n, k)$. It has long been known that

(1.9) $$f(n, k) = \binom{n}{k},$$

where, as usual, $\binom{n}{k}$ denotes the binomial coefficient,

$$\binom{n}{k} = \frac{n!}{k!(n-k)!}.$$

In the problem of bridge hands we have $f(52, 13) = \binom{52}{13} = 635{,}013{,}559{,}600$ different hands that a player can be dealt.

There are many methods known for proving (1.9). A straightforward approach is to form each subset of k elements by choosing the elements one at a time. There are n possibilities for the first choice, $n - 1$ possibilities for the second choice, and $n - (k - 1)$ possibilities for the kth choice. If we make all possible choices in this manner we obtain a total of

$$n(n-1)\cdots(n-k+1) = \frac{n!}{(n-k)!}$$

subsets of k elements. Of course, these subsets are not all distinct. For example, if $k = 3$ the six subsets

(1.10) $$\{a, b, c\}, \{b, c, a\}, \{c, a, b\}, \{a, c, b\}, \{c, b, a\}, \{b, a, c\}$$

are all equal. In general, this method of enumeration counts each k-element subset exactly $k!$ times.† Therefore we must divide the number $n!/(n - k)!$ by $k!$ to obtain $f(n, k)$. This gives us $f(n, k) = \binom{n}{k}$, as asserted.

This line of argument is more or less typical of the combinatorial analysis required in the later sections. Hence it seems worthwhile to digress briefly to discuss the fundamental principles on which this analysis is based. For this purpose it is convenient to introduce the concept of an *ordered n-tuple*.

In the definition of set equality no mention is made of the order in which elements appear; this is why the six sets listed in (1.10) are all equal. Sometimes the order *is* important in forming finite sets. For example, in plane analytic geometry the coordinates (x, y) of a point represent an *ordered pair* of numbers. The point with coordinates $(2, 5)$ is not the same as the point with coordinates $(5, 2)$, although the *sets* $\{2, 5\}$ and $\{5, 2\}$ *are* equal. In the same way, if we have a pair of objects a and b (not necessarily distinct) and if we wish to distinguish one of the objects, say a, as the *first* object and the other, b, as the *second*, we enclose the objects in parentheses, (a, b). We refer to this as an ordered pair. We agree that two ordered pairs (a, b) and (c, d) are to be considered equal if and only if their first objects are the same and their second objects are the same. That is to say,

† The reason for this will become clear in Example 3 on p. 20, where we give a more rigorous derivation of (1.9).

(1.11) $\qquad (a, b) = (c, d) \qquad$ *if and only if* $\qquad a = c$ *and* $b = d$.

Note. It is possible to give a definition of an ordered pair purely in terms of set theory. This can be done by indicating the two objects in the pair and specifying which of the two is to be considered the first object. Therefore, we may describe the ordered pair (a, b) by specifying the set $\{a, b\}$ which determines the objects, and the set $\{a\}$ which identifies a as the first object. This suggests the following definition of an ordered pair:

(1.12) $\qquad\qquad\qquad (a, b) = \{\{a, b\}, \{a\}\}$.

An interesting exercise involving the definition of set equality is to deduce the property in (1.11) from the definition in (1.12). (See Exercise 12 of Section 1.13 for hints.)

The concept of an *ordered triple* (a, b, c) and, more generally, an ordered n-tuple $(x_1, x_2, \ldots, x_n)$ can be defined by induction in terms of ordered pairs. Thus, we define

(1.13) $\qquad\qquad\qquad (a, b, c) = ((a, b), c)$.

That is, the ordered triple (a, b, c) is an ordered pair whose first element is the ordered pair (a, b) and whose second element is c. In the same way, the ordered n-tuple $(x_1, x_2, \ldots, x_n)$ is defined recursively as follows:

(1.14) $\qquad\qquad (x_1, x_2, \ldots, x_n) = ((x_1, x_2, \ldots, x_{n-1}), x_n)$.

From this definition it can be proved (by induction) that two ordered n-tuples are equal if and only if the objects in corresponding positions are the same. That is, from (1.12) and (1.14) it follows that

$\qquad (x_1, x_2, \ldots, x_n) = (y_1, y_2, \ldots, y_n) \qquad$ if and only if $\qquad x_1 = y_1, \ldots, x_n = y_n$.

Examples of ordered n-tuples of real numbers were encountered in Volume I when we studied properties of vectors in n-space. Of course, the x's which appear in the n-tuple defined in (1.14) are not necessarily real numbers—they may be arbitrary objects of any kind. Sometimes it is convenient to adopt vector terminology and refer to the element x_1 which appears in the first position of an n-tuple as the *first component* of the n-tuple, the element x_2 in the second position as the *second component*, and so on.

In later applications we shall wish to construct sets of ordered pairs (a, b) in which the first components are chosen from a set A and the second components are chosen from a set B. The set of all such pairs (a, b) is called the *Cartesian product* of the two sets A and B and is denoted by the symbol $A \times B$, defined as follows:

$$A \times B = \{(a, b) \mid a \mathcal{E} A, b \mathcal{E} B\} .$$

Figure 1.7 illustrates an example in which $A = \{1, 2, 4, 5\}$ and $B = \{1, 3\}$. The Cartesian product $A \times B$ is represented geometrically by the points (a, b) obtained by letting a take the values 1, 2, 4, and 5, and b the values 1 and 3. The concept of Cartesian product occurs also in plane analytic geometry, where the set of all points in the xy-plane may be thought of as the Cartesian product of the two coordinate axes.

More generally, the Cartesian product of n sets $A_1, A_2, \ldots, A_n$ is denoted by the symbol $A_1 \times A_2 \times \cdots \times A_n$ and is defined to be the set

$$A_1 \times A_2 \times \cdots \times A_n = \{(a_1, a_2, \ldots, a_n) \mid a_1 \mathcal{E} A_1, a_2 \mathcal{E} A_2, \ldots, a_n \mathcal{E} A_n\} .$$

In solid analytic geometry, xyz-space is the Cartesian product of the three coordinate axes.

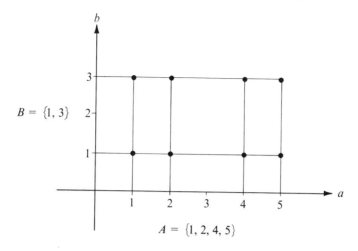

FIGURE 1.7 *An example illustrating the Cartesian product of two sets. The plotted points represent*
A × B.

Suppose that sets A and B are finite sets, where A consists of n elements and B consists of m elements. It is clear that the Cartesian product $A \times B$ consists of nm elements. Once we know this we may use mathematical induction to count the number of elements in the Cartesian product of n finite sets $A_1 \times \cdots \times A_n$. (See Exercise 14 in Section 1.13.) In fact, if A_r consists of k_r elements, the Cartesian product in question consists of $k_1 \cdots k_n$ elements.

To express these results in the language of set functions, let $\mathcal{F}$ denote the class of all finite sets and let ν be the set function defined on $\mathcal{F}$ as follows: If $A \varepsilon \mathcal{F}$, $\nu(A)$ is the number of distinct elements in A. (For the empty set we define $\nu(\phi) = 0$.) Then it is easy to verify that ν is a finitely additive set function, so we may write

$$(1.15) \qquad \nu(\bigcup_{i=1}^{n} S_i) = \sum_{i=1}^{n} \nu(S_i)$$

if $\{S_1, S_2, \ldots, S_n\}$ is a disjoint collection of finite sets (that is, if $S_i \cap S_j = \phi$ whenever $i \neq j$). The number of elements in a Cartesian product may be expressed in terms of ν as follows:

$$(1.16) \qquad \nu(A_1 \times A_2 \times \cdots \times A_n) = \nu(A_1) \nu(A_2) \cdots \nu(A_n).$$

A similar formula tells us how to count the number of elements in any set T of n-tuples if we know the number of possible choices for each of the successive components. For example, suppose there are k_1 possible choices for the first component x_1. Let k_2 be the number of possible choices for the second component x_2, once x_1 is known. Similarly, let k_r be the number of possible choices for the rth component x_r, once $x_1, x_2, \ldots, x_{r-1}$ are known. Then the number of n-tuples that can be formed with these choices is

$$\nu(T) = k_1 k_2 \cdots k_n.$$

This formula is often referred to as the *principle of sequential counting*. It can be proved by induction on n. In many applications the set of choices for x_r may not be easy to describe since it may not be determined until after the choices of the earlier components have been made. (This was the case when we used the principle to count bridge hands.) Fortunately, to apply the principle of sequential counting we do not need to know the actual set of choices for x_r, but only the *number* of possible choices for x_r.

The additive property in formula (1.15) and the principle of sequential counting provide the key to the solution of many counting problems. The following examples show how they can be applied.

Example 1: Sampling with replacement. Given a set S consisting of n elements. If $k \geq 1$, how many ordered k-tuples can be formed if each component may be an arbitrary element of S?

Note. It may be helpful to think of S as an urn containing n balls labeled $1, 2, \ldots, n$. We select a ball and record its label as the first component of our k-tuple. Replacing the ball in the urn, we again select a ball and use its label as the second component, and so on, until we have made k selections. Since we replace each ball after it is drawn, the same label may appear in different components of our k-tuple.

Solution. Each k-tuple is an element of the Cartesian product

$$T = S_1 \times \cdots \times S_k \,,$$

where each $S_i = S$. Conversely, each element of T is one of the k-tuples in question. Hence the number of k-tuples formed in this way is

$$\nu(T) = \nu(S_1) \cdots \nu(S_k) = n^k \,.$$

Example 2: Sampling without replacement. Given a set S consisting of n elements. If $k \leq n$, how many ordered k-tuples can be formed if the components are chosen from S *without* replacement, that is to say, if no element of S may be used twice in any given k-tuple?

Solution. Consider any k-tuple $(x_1, x_2, \ldots, x_k)$ formed from the elements of S without replacement. For the first component x_1 there are n choices (the n elements of S). When x_1 is chosen there remain $n - 1$ ways to choose x_2. With x_2 chosen, there remain $n - 2$ ways to choose x_3, and so on, there being $n - k + 1$ ways to choose x_k. Therefore, by the principle of sequential counting, the total number of k-tuples so formed is

$$n(n - 1)(n - 2) \cdots (n - k + 1) = \frac{n!}{(n - k)!} \,.$$

In particular, when $k = n$ this result tells us that $n!$ distinct n-tuples may be formed from a given set S of n elements, with no two components of any n-tuple being equal.

Example 3: The number of k-element subsets of an n-element set. If $k \leq n$, how many distinct subsets of k elements can be formed from a set S consisting of n elements?

Solution. Let r denote the number of subsets in question and let us denote these subsets as

$$A_1, A_2, \ldots, A_r \,.$$

These sets are distinct but need not be disjoint. We shall compute r in terms of n and k by an indirect method. For this purpose, let B_i denote the collection of k-tuples that can be formed by choosing the components from the elements of A_i without replacement. The sets $B_1, B_2, \ldots, B_r$ *are* disjoint. Moreover, if we apply the result of Example 2 with $n = k$ we have

$$\nu(B_i) = k! \qquad \text{for each} \quad i = 1, 2, \ldots, r.$$

Now let

$$T = B_1 \cup B_2 \cup \cdots \cup B_r.$$

Then T consists of all k-tuples that can be formed by choosing the components from S without replacement. From Example 2 we have

$$\nu(T) = n!/(n - k)!$$

and by additivity we also have

$$\nu(T) = \sum_{i=1}^{r} \nu(B_i) = k!r.$$

Equating the two expressions for $\nu(T)$ we obtain

$$r = \frac{n!}{k!(n - k)!} = \binom{n}{k}.$$

This proves formula (1.9) stated earlier in this section.

If we use the result of Example 3 to count the total number of subsets of a set S consisting of n elements, we obtain

$$\sum_{k=0}^{n} \binom{n}{k}.$$

Since this sum is also obtained when we expand $(1 + 1)^n$ by the binomial theorem, the number of subsets of S is 2^n.

1.13 Exercises

1. Let $A = \{1, 2, 3\}$. Display in roster notation the set of ordered pairs (a, b) obtained by choosing the first component from A and the second component from the *remaining* elements of A. Can this set of pairs be expressed as a Cartesian product?

2. A two-card hand can be dealt from a deck of 52 cards in $52 \cdot 51 = 2652$ ways. Determine the number of *distinct* hands, and explain your reasoning.

3. A senate committee consisting of six Democrats and four Republicans is to choose a chairman and a vice-chairman. In how many ways can this pair of officers be chosen if the chairman must be a Democrat?

4. An experiment consists of tossing a coin twice and then rolling a die. Display each outcome of this experiment as an ordered triple (a, b, c), where each of a and b is either H (heads) or T (tails) and c is the number of points on the upturned face of the die. For example, $(H, H, 3)$ means that heads came up on both tosses and 3 appeared on the die. Express the set of all possible outcomes as a Cartesian product and determine the number of possible outcomes.

5. In how many ways can a bridge deck of 52 cards be dealt into four hands, each containing 13 cards? Explain your reasoning.

6. Two dice, one red and one white, are tossed. Represent the outcome as an ordered pair (a, b), where a denotes the number of points on the red die, b the number on the white die. How many ordered pairs (a, b) are possible? How many are there for which the sum $a + b$ is:
(a) even?   (b) divisible by 3?   (c) either even or divisible by 3?

7. A poker hand contains five cards dealt from a deck of 52. How many distinct poker hands can be dealt containing:

    (a) two pairs (for example, 2 kings, 2 aces, and a 3)?

    (b) a flush (five cards in a given suit)?

    (c) a straight flush (any five in sequence in a given suit, but not including ten, jack, queen, king, ace)?

    (d) a royal flush (ten, jack, queen, king, ace in a single suit)?

8. How many committees of 50 senators can be formed that contain:

    (a) exactly one senator from Alaska?

    (b) both senators from Alaska?

9. A code group consists of four symbols in a row, each symbol being either a dot or a dash. How many distinct code groups can be formed?

10. How many k-letter words can be formed with an alphabet containing n letters?

11. Show that:

(a) $\dbinom{n}{0} + \dbinom{n}{2} + \dbinom{n}{4} + \cdots = \dbinom{n}{1} + \dbinom{n}{3} + \dbinom{n}{5} + \cdots = 2^{n-1}$.

(b) $\dbinom{n}{0}^2 + \dbinom{n}{1}^2 + \cdots + \dbinom{n}{n}^2 = \dbinom{2n}{n}$.

12. Deduce Equation (1.11) on page 18 from the definition of an ordered pair given in (1.12). [*Hint.* If $(a, b) = (c, d)$, then $\{\{a, b\}, \{a\}\} = \{\{c, d\}, \{c\}\}$. The definition of set equality means that either (i) $\{a, b\} = \{c, d\}$ and $\{a\} = \{c\}$ or (ii) $\{a, b\} = \{c\}$ and $\{a\} = \{c, d\}$. In each case, show that $a = c$ and $b = d$.]

13. Prove, by induction on n, that two ordered n-tuples are equal if and only if their corresponding components are equal.

14. Suppose a set of ordered pairs (a, b) is constructed by choosing the first component from a set of k elements, say from the set $\{a_1, \ldots, a_k\}$, and the second component from a set of m elements, say from $\{b_1, \ldots, b_m\}$. There are a total of m pairs with first component a_1, namely, (a_1, b_1), $\ldots, (a_1, b_m)$. Similarly, there are m pairs $(a_i, b_1), \ldots, (a_i, b_m)$ with first component a_i. Therefore the total number of ordered pairs (a, b) is $m + m + \cdots + m$ (k summands). This sum equals km, which proves the principle of sequential counting for sets of ordered pairs. Use induction to prove the principle for sets of ordered n-tuples.

1.14 Countable and uncountable sets

To count the members of an n-element set we match the set, element by element, with the set of integers $\{1, 2, \ldots, n\}$. Comparing the sizes of two sets by matching them element by element takes the place of counting when we deal with infinite sets. The process of "matching" can be given a neat mathematical formulation by employing the function concept:

DEFINITION. *Two sets A and B are said to be in one-to-one correspondence if a function f exists with the following properties:*

    (a) *The domain of f is A and the range of f is B.*

(b) If x and y are distinct elements of A, then $f(x)$ and $f(y)$ are distinct elements of B. That is, for all x and y in A,

(1.17) $$x \neq y \quad \text{implies} \quad f(x) \neq f(y).$$

A function satisfying property (1.17) is said to be *one-to-one* on A. Two sets A and B in one-to-one correspondence are also said to be *equivalent*, and we indicate this by writing $A \sim B$. It is clear that every set A is equivalent to itself, since we may let $f(x) = x$ for each x in A.

A set can be equivalent to a proper subset of itself. For example, the set $P = \{1, 2, 3, \ldots\}$, consisting of all the positive integers, is equivalent to the proper subset $Q = \{2, 4, 6, \ldots\}$ consisting of the even integers. In this case a one-to-one function which makes them equivalent is given by $f(x) = 2x$ for x in P.

If $A \sim B$ we can easily show that $B \sim A$. In fact, if f is one-to-one on A and if the range of f is B, then for each b in B there is exactly one a in A such that $f(a) = b$. Therefore we can define an inverse function g on B as follows: If $b \in B$, $g(b) = a$, where a is the unique element of A such that $f(a) = b$. This g is one-to-one on B and its range is A; hence $B \sim A$. This property of equivalence is known as *symmetry*:

(1.18) $$A \sim B \quad \text{implies} \quad B \sim A.$$

It is also easy to show that equivalence has the following property, known as *transitivity*:

(1.19) $$A \sim B \text{ and } B \sim C \quad \text{implies} \quad A \sim C.$$

A proof of the transitive property is requested in Exercise 2 of Section 1.15.

A set S is called *finite* and is said to contain n elements if

$$S \sim \{1, 2, \ldots, n\}.$$

The empty set is also considered to be finite. Sets which are not finite are called *infinite sets*. A set S is said to be *countably infinite* if it is equivalent to the set of all positive integers, that is, if

(1.20) $$S \sim \{1, 2, 3, \ldots\}.$$

In this case there is a function f which establishes a one-to-one correspondence between the positive integers and the elements of S; hence the set S can be displayed in roster notation as follows:

$$S = \{f(1), f(2), f(3), \ldots\}.$$

Often we use subscripts and denote $f(k)$ by a_k (or by a similar notation) and we write $S = \{a_1, a_2, a_3, \ldots\}$. The important thing here is that the correspondence in (1.20) enables us to use the positive integers as "labels" for the elements of S.

A set is said to be *countable* if it is finite or countably infinite. A set which is not countable is called *uncountable*.† (Examples will be given presently.) Many set operations when performed on countable sets produce countable sets. For example, we have the following properties:

(a) Every subset of a countable set is countable.

---

† The words *denumerable* and *nondenumerable* are sometimes used as synonyms for *countable* and *uncountable*, respectively.

(b) The intersection of any collection of countable sets is countable.

(c) The union of a countable collection of countable sets is countable.

(d) The Cartesian product of a finite number of countable sets is countable.

Since we shall do very little with countably infinite sets in this book, detailed proofs of these properties will not be given.† Instead, we shall give a number of examples to show how these properties may be used to construct new countable sets from given ones.

Example 1. The set S of all integers (positive, negative, or zero) is countable.

Proof. If $n \in S$, let $f(n) = 2n$ if n is positive, and let $f(n) = 2|n| + 1$ if n is negative or zero. The domain of f is S and its range is the set of positive integers. Since f is one-to-one on S, this shows that S is countable.

Example 2. The set R of all rational numbers is countable.

Proof. For each fixed integer $n \geq 1$, let S_n denote the set of rational numbers of the form x/n, where x belongs to the set S of Example 1. Each set S_n is equivalent to S [take $f(t) = nt$ if $t \in S_n$] and hence each S_n is countable. Since R is the union of all the S_n, property (c) implies that R is countable.

Note. If $\mathfrak{F} = \{A_1, A_2, A_3, \ldots\}$ is a countable collection of sets, the union of all sets in the family $\mathfrak{F}$ is denoted by the symbols

$$\bigcup_{k=1}^{\infty} A_k \quad \text{or} \quad A_1 \cup A_2 \cup A_3 \cup \cdots .$$

Example 3. Let A be a countably infinite set, say $A = \{a_1, a_2, a_3, \ldots\}$. For each integer $n \geq 1$, let $\mathfrak{F}_n$ denote the family of n-element subsets of A. That is, let

$$\mathfrak{F}_n = \{S | \ S \subset A \text{ and } S \text{ has } n \text{ elements}\} .$$

Then each $\mathfrak{F}_n$ is countable.

Proof. If S is an n-element subset of A, we may write

$$S = \{a_{k_1}, a_{k_2}, \ldots, a_{k_n}\} ,$$

where $k_1 < k_2 < \cdots < k_n$. Let $f(S) = (a_{k_1}, a_{k_2}, \ldots, a_{k_n})$. That is, f is the function which associates with S the ordered n-tuple $(a_{k_1}, a_{k_2}, \ldots, a_{k_n})$. The domain of f is $\mathfrak{F}_n$ and its range, which we denote by T_n, is a subset of the Cartesian product $C_n = A \times A \times \cdots \times A$ (n factors). Since A is countable, so is C_n [by property (d)] and hence T_n is also [by property (a)]. But $T_n \sim \mathfrak{F}_n$ because f is one-to-one. This shows that $\mathfrak{F}_n$ is countable.

Example 4. The collection of all finite subsets of a countable set is countable.

Proof. The result is obvious if the given set is finite. Assume, then, that the given set (call it A) is countably infinite, and let $\mathfrak{F}$ denote the class of all finite subsets of A:

$$\mathfrak{F} = \{S | \ S \subset A \text{ and } S \text{ is finite}\} .$$

Then $\mathfrak{F}$ is the union of all the families $\mathfrak{F}_n$ of Example 3; hence, by property (c), $\mathfrak{F}$ is countable.

† Proofs are outlined in Exercises 3 through 8 of Section 1.15.

Example 5. The collection of *all* subsets of a countably infinite set is uncountable.

Proof. Let A denote the given countable set and let $\mathcal{Q}$ denote the family of all subsets of A. We shall assume that $\mathcal{Q}$ is countable and arrive at a contradiction. If $\mathcal{Q}$ is countable, then $\mathcal{Q} \sim A$ and hence there exists a one-to-one function f whose domain is A and whose range is $\mathcal{Q}$. Thus for each a in A, the function value $f(a)$ is a subset of A. This subset may or may not contain the element a. We denote by B the set of elements a such that $a \notin f(a)$. Thus,

$$B = \{a \mid a \in A \text{ but } a \notin f(a)\} \, .$$

This B, being a subset of A, must belong to the family $\mathcal{Q}$. This means that $B = f(b)$ for some b in A. Now there are only two possibilities: (i) $b \in B$, or (ii) $b \notin B$. If $b \in B$, then by the definition of B we have $b \notin f(b)$, which is a contradiction since $f(b) = B$. Therefore (i) is impossible. In case (ii), $b \notin B$, which means $b \notin f(b)$. This contradicts the definition of B, so case (ii) is also impossible. Therefore the assumption that $\mathcal{Q}$ is countable leads to a contradiction and we must conclude that $\mathcal{Q}$ is uncountable.

We give next an example of an uncountable set that is easier to visualize than that in Example 5.

Example 6. The set of real x satisfying $0 < x < 1$ is uncountable.

Proof. Again, we assume the set is countable and arrive at a contradiction. If the set is countable we may display its elements as follows: $\{x_1, x_2, x_3, \ldots \}$. Now we shall construct a real number y satisfying $0 < y < 1$ which is not in this list. For this purpose we write each element x_n as a decimal:

$$x_n = 0.a_{n,1} \, a_{n,2} \, a_{n,3} \ldots \, ,$$

where each $a_{n,i}$ is one of the integers in the set $\{0, 1, 2, \ldots , 9\}$. Let y be the real number which has the decimal expansion

$$y = 0.y_1 \, y_2 \, y_3 \ldots \, ,$$

where

$$y_n = \begin{cases} 1 & \text{if} \quad a_{n,n} \neq 1 \, , \\ 2 & \text{if} \quad a_{n,n} = 1 \, . \end{cases}$$

Then no element of the set $\{x_1, x_2, x_3, \ldots \}$ can be equal to y, because y differs from x_1 in the first decimal place, differs from x_2 in the second decimal place, and in general, y differs from x_k in the kth decimal place. (A situation like $x_n = 0.249999 \cdots$ and $y = 0.250000 \cdots$ cannot occur here because of the way the y_n are chosen.) Since this y satisfies $0 < y < 1$, we have a contradiction, and hence the set of real numbers in the open interval $(0,1)$ is uncountable.

1.15   Exercises

1. Let $P = \{1, 2, 3, \ldots\}$ denote the set of positive integers. For each of the following sets, exhibit a one-to-one function f whose domain is P and whose range is the set in question:

    (a) $A = \{2, 4, 6, \ldots\}$, the set of even positive integers.

    (b) $B = \{3, 3^2, 3^3, \ldots\}$, the set of powers of 3.

(c) $C = \{2, 3, 5, 7, 11, 13, \ldots\}$, the set of primes. [*Note.* Part of the proof consists in showing that C is an infinite set.]

(d) $P \times P$, the Cartesian product of P with itself.

(e) The set of integers of the form $2^m 3^n$, where m and n are positive integers.

2. Prove the transitive property of set equivalence:

$$\text{If } A \sim B \text{ and } B \sim C, \text{ then } A \sim C.$$

[*Hint.* If f makes A equivalent to B and if g makes B equivalent to C, show that the composite function $h = g \circ f$ makes A equivalent to C.]

Exercises 3 through 8 are devoted to providing proofs of the four properties (a), (b), (c), (d) of countable sets listed in Section 1.14.

3. Prove that every subset of a countable set is countable. [*Hint.* Suppose S is a countably infinite set, say $S = \{x_1, x_2, x_3, \ldots\}$, and let A be an infinite subset of S. Let $k(1)$ be the smallest positive integer m such that $x_m \in A$. Assuming $k(1), k(2), \ldots, k(n-1)$ have been defined, let $k(n)$ be the smallest positive integer $m > k(n-1)$ such that $x_m \in A$. Let $f(n) = x_{k(n)}$. Show that f is a one-to-one function whose domain is the set of positive integers and whose range is A. This proves the result when S is countably infinite. Construct a separate proof for a finite S.]

4. Show that the intersection of any collection of countable sets is countable. [*Hint.* Use the result of Exercise 3.]

5. Let $P = \{1, 2, 3, \ldots\}$ denote the set of positive integers.

(a) Prove that the Cartesian product $P \times P$ is countable. [*Hint.* Let Q denote the set of positive integers of the form $2^m 3^n$, where m and n are positive integers. Then $Q \subset P$, so Q is countable (by Exercise 3). If $(m, n) \in P \times P$, let $f(m, n) = 2^m 3^n$ and use this function to show that $P \times P \sim Q$.]

(b) Deduce from part (a) that the Cartesian product of two countable sets is countable. Then use induction to extend the result to n countable sets.

6. Let $\mathfrak{B} = \{B_1, B_2, B_3, \ldots\}$ be a countable collection of *disjoint* sets $(B_i \cap B_j = \phi$ when $i \neq j)$ such that each B_n is countable. Show that the union $\bigcup_{k=1}^{\infty} B_k$ is also countable. [*Hint.* Let $B_n = \{b_{1,n}, b_{2,n}, b_{3,n}, \ldots\}$ and $S = \bigcup_{k=1}^{\infty} B_k$. If $x \in S$, then $x = b_{m,n}$ for some unique pair (m, n) and we can define $f(x) = (m, n)$. Use this f to show that S is equivalent to a subset of $P \times P$ and deduce (by Exercise 5) that S is countable.]

7. Let $\mathfrak{A} = \{A_1, A_2, A_3, \ldots\}$ be a countable collection of sets, and let $\mathfrak{B} = \{B_1, B_2, B_3, \ldots\}$ be defined as follows: $B_1 = A_1$ and, for $n > 1$,

$$B_n = A_n - \bigcup_{k=1}^{n-1} A_k.$$

That is, B_n consists of those points in A_n which are not in any of the earlier sets $A_1, \ldots, A_{n-1}$. Prove that $\mathfrak{B}$ is a collection of disjoint sets $(B_i \cap B_j = \phi$ when $i \neq j)$ and that

$$\bigcup_{k=1}^{\infty} A_k = \bigcup_{k=1}^{\infty} B_k.$$

This enables us to express the union of any countable collection of sets as the union of a countable collection of *disjoint* sets.

8. If $\mathfrak{F}$ is a countable collection of countable sets, prove that the union of all sets in $\mathfrak{F}$ is countable. [*Hint.* Use Exercises 6 and 7.]

9. Show that the following sets are countable:

(a) The set of all intervals on the real axis with rational end points.

(b) The set of all circles in the plane with rational radii and centers having rational coordinates.

(c) Any set of disjoint intervals of positive length.

10. Show that the following sets are uncountable:
    (a) The set of irrational numbers in the interval (0, 1).
    (b) The set of all intervals of positive length.
    (c) The set of all sequences whose terms are the integers 0 and 1. (Recall that a sequence is a function whose domain is the set of positive integers.)

1.16   The definition of probability

In the language of set functions, probability is a specific kind of measure (to be denoted here by P) defined on a specific type of Boolean algebra of sets. We recall that the elements of a Boolean algebra $\mathcal{B}$ are subsets of a universal set S; $\mathcal{B}$ is a Boolean algebra if, for every pair of subsets A and B in $\mathcal{B}$, the union $A \cup B$ and the complement $A' = S - A$ also belong to $\mathcal{B}$. In probability theory the universal set S is called the *sample space*.

Two properties distinguish probability measures from other measures. First, the sample space is assigned the measure 1; that is, $P(S) = 1$. Second, the additive property $P(A \cup B) = P(A) + P(B)$, which all measures satisfy for any two disjoint sets A and B (and hence for any *finite* union of disjoint sets), is also assumed to hold for all countably infinite unions. That is, for every countably infinite collection $\{A_1, A_2, \ldots\}$ of elements of $\mathcal{B}$, we have

$$(1.21) \qquad P(\bigcup_{k=1}^{\infty} A_k) = \sum_{k=1}^{\infty} P(A_k) \qquad \text{if} \quad A_i \cap A_j = \phi \qquad \text{whenever} \quad i \neq j.$$

Finitely additive set functions which satisfy (1.21) are said to be *countably additive* (or *completely additive*). Of course, this property requires assuming also that the countable union $A_1 \cup A_2 \cup A_3 \cup \cdots$ is in $\mathcal{B}$ whenever each A_k is in $\mathcal{B}$. Not all Boolean algebras have this property. Those which do are called Boolean σ-algebras.

For most of the applications of probability in which we shall be interested, the sample space S will be *finite* and only finite additivity of P will be required. In this case, the definition of probability may be stated formally as follows:

DEFINITION OF PROBABILITY FOR FINITE SAMPLE SPACES. *Let $\mathcal{B}$ denote a Boolean algebra whose elements are subsets of a given finite set S. A set function P defined on $\mathcal{B}$ is called a probability measure if it satisfies the following three conditions:*
    (a) $P(A) \geq 0$ *for each A in $\mathcal{B}$.*
    (b) $P(S) = 1$.
    (c) *P is finitely additive on $\mathcal{B}$.*

Note: In both theory and practice the sample space is often countably infinite, and finite additivity alone is inadequate to define probability. (See Example 6 in Section 1.19.) In such cases, countable additivity is necessary for a satisfactory treatment and the definition of probability must be modified accordingly—the algebra $\mathcal{B}$ of subsets of S must be a Boolean σ-algebra, and condition (c) must be replaced by the assumption that P is countably additive on $\mathcal{B}$. The same definition of probability applies to uncountable sample spaces, except that special restrictions must be placed on S and its subsets. These are discussed in Chapter 3.

It is important to realize that for a complete description of a probability measure three things must be specified: the sample space S, the Boolean algebra $\mathcal{B}$ formed from certain subsets of S, and the set function P. The triple $(S, \mathfrak{B}, P)$ is often called a *probability space*. In most of the elementary applications S is finite and the Boolean algebra $\mathfrak{B}$ is taken to be the collection of *all* subsets of S.

An illustration of applied probability theory is found in the experiment of tossing a coin once. For a sample space S we take the set of all conceivable outcomes of the experiment. In this case, each outcome is either "heads" or "tails," which we label by the symbols h and t. Thus, the sample space S is $\{h, t\}$, the set consisting of h and t. For the Boolean algebra we take the collection of all subsets of S; there are four, ϕ, S, H, and T, where $H = \{h\}$ and $T = \{t\}$. Next, we assign probabilities to each of these subsets. For the subsets ϕ and S we have no choice in the assignment of values. Property (b) requires that $P(S) = 1$, and, since P is a nonnegative measure, $P(\phi) = 0$. However, there is some freedom in assigning probabilities to the other two subsets, H and T. Since H and T are disjoint sets whose union is S, the additive property requires that

$$P(H) + P(T) = P(S) = 1 .$$

We are free to assign any nonnegative values whatever to $P(H)$ and $P(T)$ so long as their sum is 1. If we feel that the coin is unbiased so that there is no *a priori* reason to prefer heads or tails, it seems natural to assign the values

$$P(H) = P(T) = \tfrac{1}{2} .$$

If, however, the coin is "loaded," we may wish to assign different values to these two probabilities. For example, the values $P(H) = \tfrac{1}{3}$ and $P(T) = \tfrac{2}{3}$ are just as acceptable as $P(H) = P(T) = \tfrac{1}{2}$. In fact, for any real p in the interval $0 \le p \le 1$ we may define $P(H) = p$ and $P(T) = 1 - p$, and the resulting function P will satisfy all the conditions for a probability measure.

For a given coin, there is no mathematical way to determine what the probability p "really" is. If we choose $p = \tfrac{1}{2}$ we can deduce logical consequences on the assumption that the coin is fair or unbiased. The theory for unbiased coins can then be used to test the fairness of an actual coin by performing a large number of experiments with the coin and comparing the results with the predictions based on the theory. The testing of agreement between theory and empirical evidence belongs to that branch of applied probability known as *statistical inference*, and will not be discussed in this book.

The foregoing example is a typical application of the concepts of probability theory. Probability questions often arise in situations referred to as "experiments." We shall not attempt to define an experiment; instead, we shall merely mention some familiar examples: tossing one or more coins, rolling a pair of dice, dealing a bridge hand, drawing a ball from an urn, counting the number of female students at the California Institute of Technology, selecting a number from a telephone directory, recording the radiation count of a Geiger counter.

To discuss probability questions that arise in connection with such experiments, our first task is to construct a sample space S that can be used to represent all conceivable outcomes of the experiment, as we did for coin tossing. Each element of S should represent an outcome of the experiment and each outcome should correspond to one and only one element of S. Next, we choose a Boolean algebra $\mathfrak{B}$ of subsets of S (usually *all* subsets of S) and then define a probability measure P on $\mathfrak{B}$. The choice of the set S, the choice of $\mathfrak{B}$, and the choice of P will depend on the information known about the details of the experiment and on the questions we wish to answer. The purpose of probability theory is not to discuss whether the probability space $(S, \mathfrak{B}, P)$ has been properly chosen. This motivation belongs to the science or gambling game from which the experiment emanates, and only experience can suggest whether or not the choices were well made. *Probability theory is the study of logical consequences that can be derived once the probability space is given.* Making a good choice of the probability space is, strictly speaking, not probability theory—it is not even mathematics; instead, it is part of the art of applying probability theory to the real world. We shall elaborate further on these remarks as we deal with specific examples in the later sections.

When the sample space S is *finite*, say $S = \{a_1, a_2, \ldots, a_n\}$, the probability function P is completely determined if we know its values on the singletons:

$$P(\{a_1\}), P(\{a_2\}), \ldots, P(\{a_n\}).$$

In fact, every subset A of S is a disjoint union of singletons, and $P(A)$ is determined by the additive property. For example, when

$$A = \{a_1\} \cup \{a_2\} \cup \cdots \cup \{a_k\},$$

the additive property requires that

$$P(A) = \sum_{i=1}^{k} P(\{a_i\}).$$

To simplify the notation and the terminology, we write $P(a_i)$ instead of $P(\{a_i\})$. This number is also called the *probability of the point* a_i. Therefore, the assignment of the point probabilities $P(x)$ for each element x in a finite set S amounts to a complete description of the probability function P.

The same is true, of course, when S is a countable set. In this case, every subset A of S is either finite or countably infinite and the probability of the event A is computed by adding the point probabilities of all elements in A. This may be indicated symbolically as

$$P(A) = \sum_{x \in A} P(x).$$

The sum on the right is either a finite sum or an absolutely convergent infinite series.

1.17 Special terminology peculiar to probability theory

In discussions involving probability, one often sees phrases from everyday language such as "two events are equally likely," "an event is impossible," or "an event is certain to occur." Expressions of this sort have intuitive appeal and it is both pleasant and helpful to be able to employ such colorful language in mathematical discussions. Before we can do so, however, it is necessary to explain the meaning of this language in terms of the fundamental concepts of our theory.

Because of the way probability is used in practice, it is convenient to imagine that each probability space $(S, \mathfrak{B}, P)$ is associated with a real or conceptual experiment. The universal set S may then be thought of as the collection of all conceivable outcomes of the experiment, as in the example of coin tossing discussed in the foregoing section. Each element of S is called an *outcome* or a *sample* and the subsets of S that occur in the Boolean algebra $\mathfrak{B}$ are called *events*. The reasons for this terminology will become more apparent when we treat some examples.

Assume we have a probability space $(S, \mathcal{B}, P)$ associated with an experiment. Let A be an event, and suppose the experiment is performed and that its outcome is x. (In other words, let x be a point of S.) This outcome x may or may not belong to the set A. If it does, we say *that the event A has occurred*. Otherwise, we say that *the event A has not occurred*, in which case $x \, \mathcal{E} \, A'$, so the complementary event A' has occurred. An event A is called *impossible* if $A = \phi$, because in this case no outcome of the experiment can be an element of A. The event A is said to be *certain* if $A = S$, because then every outcome is automatically an element of A.

Each event A has a probability $P(A)$ assigned to it by the probability function P. [The actual value of $P(A)$ or the manner in which $P(A)$ is assigned does not concern us at present.] The number $P(A)$ is also called *the probability that an outcome of the experiment is one of the elements of A*. We also say that $P(A)$ is *the probability that the event A occurs* when the experiment is performed.

The impossible event ϕ must be assigned probability zero because P is a finitely additive measure. However, there may be events with probability zero that are not impossible. In other words, some of the nonempty subsets of S may be assigned probability zero. The certain event S must be assigned probability 1 by the very definition of probability, but there may be other subsets as well that are assigned probability 1. In Example 1 of Section 1.19 there are nonempty subsets with probability zero and proper subsets of S that have probability 1.

Two events A and B are said to be *equally likely* if $P(A) = P(B)$. The event A is called *more likely* than B if $P(A) > P(B)$, and *at least as likely* as B if $P(A) \geq P(B)$. Table 1.1 provides a glossary of further everyday language that is often used in probability discussions. The letters A and B represent events, and x represents an outcome of an experiment associated with the sample space S. Each entry in the left-hand column is a statement about the events A and B, and the corresponding entry in the right-hand column defines the statement in terms of set theory.

TABLE 1.1   Glossary of Probability Terms

Statement	*Meaning in set theory*
At least one of A or B occurs	$x \, \mathcal{E} \, A \cup B$
Both events A and B occur	$x \, \mathcal{E} \, A \cap B$
Neither A nor B occurs	$x \, \mathcal{E} \, A' \cap B'$
A occurs and B does not occur	$x \, \mathcal{E} \, A \cap B'$
Exactly one of A or B occurs	$x \, \mathcal{E} \, (A \cap B') \cup (A' \cap B)$
Not more than one of A or B occurs	$x \, \mathcal{E} \, (A \cap B') \cup (A' \cap B) \cup (A' \cap B')$
If A occurs, so does B (A implies B)	$A \subseteq B$
A and B are mutually exclusive	$A \cap B = \phi$
Event A or event B	$A \cup B$
Event A and event B	$A \cap B$

1.18 Exercises

Let S be a given sample space and let A, B, and C denote arbitrary events (that is, subsets of S in the corresponding Boolean algebra $\mathcal{B}$). Each of the statements in Exercises 1 through 12 is described verbally in terms of A, B, C. Express these statements in terms of unions and intersections of A, B, C and their complements.

1. If A occurs, then B does not occur.
2. None of the events A, B, C occurs.
3. Only A occurs.
4. At least one of A, B, C occurs.
5. Exactly one of A, B, C occurs.
6. Not more than one occurs.
7. At least two of A, B, C occur.
8. Exactly two occur.
9. Not more than two occur.
10. A and C occur but not B.
11. All three events occur.
12. Not more than three occur.

13. Let A denote the event of throwing an odd total with two dice, and let B denote the event of throwing at least one 6. Give a verbal description of each of the following events:

   (a) $A \cup B$, (b) $A \cap B$, (c) $A \cap B'$, (d) $A' \cap B$, (e) $A' \cap B'$, (f) $A' \cup B$.

14. Let A and B denote events. Show that

$$P(A \cap B) \leq P(A) \leq P(A \cup B) \leq P(A) + P(B) .$$

15. Let A and B denote events and let $a = P(A)$, $b = P(B)$, $c = P(A \cap B)$. Compute, in terms of a, b, and c, the probabilities of the following events:

   (a) A'
   (b) B'
   (c) $A \cup B$
   (d) $A' \cup B'$
   (e) $A' \cup B$
   (f) $A \cap B'$.

16. Given three events A, B, C. Prove that

$$P(A \cup B \cup C) = P(A) + P(B) + P(C) - P(A \cap B) - P(A \cap C) - P(B \cap C) + P(A \cap B \cap C) .$$

1.19 Worked examples

We shall illustrate how some of the concepts of the foregoing sections may be used to answer specific questions involving probabilities.

Example 1. What is the probability that at least one "head" will occur in two throws of a coin?

First Solution. The experiment in this case consists of tossing a coin twice; the set S of all possible outcomes may be denoted as follows:

$$S = \{hh, ht, th, tt\} .$$

If we feel that these outcomes are equally likely, we assign the point probabilities $P(x) = \frac{1}{4}$ for each x in S. The event "at least one head occurs" may be described by the subset

$$A = \{hh, ht, th\} .$$

The probability of this event is the sum of the point probabilities of its elements. Hence, $P(A) = \frac{1}{4} + \frac{1}{4} + \frac{1}{4} = \frac{3}{4}$.

Second Solution. Suppose we use the same sample space but assign the point probabilities as follows:†

$$P(hh) = 1, \quad P(ht) = P(th) = P(tt) = 0 .$$

---

† Note that for this assignment of probabilities there are nonempty subsets of S with probability zero and proper subsets with probability 1.

Then the probability of the event "at least one head occurs" is

$$P(hh) + P(ht) + P(th) = 1 + 0 + 0 = 1.$$

The fact that we arrived at a different answer from that in the first solution should not alarm the reader. We began with a different set of premises. Psychological considerations might lead us to believe that the assignment of probabilities in the first solution is the more natural one. Indeed, most people would agree that this is so if the coin is unbiased. However, if the coin happens to be loaded so that heads always turns up, the assignment of probabilities in the second solution is more natural.

The foregoing example shows that we cannot expect a unique answer to the question asked. To answer such a question properly we must specify the choice of sample space and the assignment of point probabilities. Once the sample space and the point probabilities are known only one probability for a given event can be logically deduced. Different choices of the sample space or point probabilities may lead to different "correct" answers to the same question.

Sometimes the assignment of probabilities to the individual outcomes of an experiment is dictated by the language used to describe the experiment. For example, when an object is chosen "at random" from a finite set of n elements, this is intended to mean that each outcome is equally likely and should be assigned point probability $1/n$. Similarly, when we toss a coin or roll a die, if we have no *a priori* reason to feel that the coin or die is loaded, we assume that all outcomes are equally likely. This agreement will be adopted in all the exercises of this chapter.

Example 2. If one card is drawn at random from each of two decks, what is the probability that at least one is the ace of hearts?

Solution. The experiment consists in drawing two cards, a and b, one from each deck. Suppose we denote a typical outcome as an ordered pair (a, b). The number of possible outcomes, that is, the total number of distinct pairs (a, b) in the sample space S is 52^2. We assign the probability $1/52^2$ to each such pair. The event in which we are interested is the set A of pairs (a, b), where either a or b is the ace of hearts. There are $52 + 51$ elements in A. Hence, under these assumptions we deduce that

$$P(A) = \frac{52 + 51}{52^2} = \frac{1}{26} - \frac{1}{52^2}.$$

Example 3. If two cards are drawn at random from one deck, what is the probability that one of them is the ace of hearts?

Solution. As in Example 2 we use ordered pairs (a, b) as elements of the sample space. In this case the sample space has $52 \cdot 51$ elements and the event A under consideration has $51 + 51$ elements. If we assign the point probabilities $1/(52 \cdot 51)$ to each outcome, we obtain

$$P(A) = \frac{2 \cdot 51}{52 \cdot 51} = \frac{1}{26}.$$

Example 4. What is the probability of throwing 6 or less with three dice?

Solution. We denote each outcome of the experiment as a triple of integers (a, b, c) where a, b, and c may take any values from 1 to 6. Therefore the sample space consists of 6^3 elements and we assign the probability $1/6^3$ to each outcome. The event A in question is the set of all triples satisfying the inequality $3 \leq a + b + c \leq 6$. If A_n denotes the set of (a, b, c) for which $a + b + c = n$, we have

$$A = A_3 \cup A_4 \cup A_5 \cup A_6 .$$

The sets A_n, with $n = 3, 4, 5,$ and 6 contain $1, 3, 6,$ and 10 elements, respectively. Therefore A has 20 elements and

$$P(A) = \frac{20}{6^3} = \frac{5}{54} .$$

Example 5. A die is thrown once. What is the probability that the number of points is either even or a multiple of 3?

Solution. We choose the sample space $S = \{1, 2, 3, 4, 5, 6\}$, consisting of six elements, to each of which we assign the probability $\frac{1}{6}$. The event "even" is the set $A = \{2, 4, 6\}$, the event "a multiple of 3" is $B = \{3, 6\}$. We are interested in their union, which is the set $A \cup B = \{2, 3, 4, 6\}$. Since this set contains four elements we have $P(A \cup B) = 4/6$.

This example may be solved in another way, using the formula

$$P(A \cup B) = P(A) + P(B) - P(A \cap B) = \frac{3}{6} + \frac{2}{6} - \frac{1}{6} .$$

Example 6. In all the foregoing examples the sample space was *finite*. To construct an experiment in which the sample space is infinite, suppose we toss a coin repeatedly until heads appears twice in succession or until tails appears twice in succession. The set S of all possible outcomes is a countable collection which may be displayed as follows:

$$S = \{hh,\ tt,\ thh,\ htt,\ hthh,\ thtt,\ ththh,\ hthtt,\ \dots \} .$$

Suppose we label these outcomes as follows:

$$H_2 = hh,\ T_2 = tt,\ H_3 = thh,\ T_3 = htt,\ H_4 = hthh,\ T_4 = thtt ,$$

and so on, where H_n denotes the outcome that requires exactly n tosses to achieve heads twice in succession and T_n denotes the outcome that requires exactly n tosses to achieve tails twice in succession. If we consider the outcomes H_n and T_n to be equally likely and assign the point probability p_n to each of them, then the countably additive property requires that

(1.22) $$\sum_{x \varepsilon S} P(x) = 2 \sum_{n=2}^{\infty} p_n = 1 .$$

There are, of course, many ways to assign the point probabilities p_n and still satisfy (1.22). One such assignment of values of $p_n = 2^{-n}$. If we use these values for p_n and compute the probability that, say, the experiment ends before the fifth toss, the event in question is the subset

$$A = \{H_2, T_2, H_3, T_3, H_4, T_4\}$$

and its probability is

$$P(A) = 2p_2 + 2p_3 + 2p_4 = 2\left(\frac{1}{4} + \frac{1}{8} + \frac{1}{16}\right) = \frac{7}{8} .$$

Another permissible assignment of values is $p_n = 1/[n(n + 1)]$. With this choice of p_n the probability of the foregoing subset A is

$$P(A) = 2\left(\frac{1}{2 \cdot 3} + \frac{1}{3 \cdot 4} + \frac{1}{4 \cdot 5}\right) = 2\left(\frac{1}{2} - \frac{1}{3} + \frac{1}{3} - \frac{1}{4} + \frac{1}{4} - \frac{1}{5}\right) = 2\left(\frac{1}{2} - \frac{1}{5}\right) = \frac{3}{5}.$$

1.20 Exercises

1. Let S be a finite sample space consisting of n elements. Suppose we assign equal probabilities to each of the points in S. Let A be a subset of S consisting of k elements. Prove that $P(A) = k/n$.

For each of Exercises 2 through 8, describe your choice of sample space and state how you are assigning the point probabilities. In the questions associated with card games, assume all cards have the same probability of being dealt.

2. Five counterfeit coins are mixed with nine authentic coins.
   (a) A coin is selected at random. Compute the probability that a counterfeit coin is selected.
   If two coins are selected, compute the probability that:
   (b) one is good and one is counterfeit.
   (c) both are counterfeit.
   (d) both are good.

3. Compute the probabilities of each of the events described in Exercise 13 of Section 1.18. Assign equal probabilities to each of the 36 elements of the sample space.

4. What is the probability of throwing at least one of 7, 11, or 12 with two dice?

5. Compute the probability for a poker hand to be:
   (a) a flush (five cards in a given suit).
   (b) a straight flush (any five in sequence in a given suit).
   (c) a royal flush (ten, jack, queen, king, ace in a single suit).

6. A poker hand contains four hearts and one spade. The spade is discarded and one card is drawn from the remainder of the deck. Compute the probability of filling the flush—that is, of drawing a fifth heart.

7. In poker, a straight is a five-card sequence, not necessarily all of the same suit. If a poker hand contains four cards in sequence (but not A234 or JQKA) and one extra card not in the sequence, compute the probability of filling the straight. (The extra card is discarded and a new card is drawn from the remainder of the deck.)

8. A poker hand has four cards out of a five-card sequence with a gap in the middle (such as 5689), and one extra card not in the sequence. The extra card is discarded and a new one is drawn from the remainder of the deck. Compute the probability of filling the "inside straight."

9. Consider the experiment described in Example 6 of Section 1.19. Assume $p_n = 2^{-n}$ and compute the probability that an odd number of tosses is required to terminate the experiment.

10. Consider an experiment in which a player throws a die repeatedly until he rolls a 5. Choose a sample space S. Let A_n denote the event that the experiment ends on the nth roll. Describe the events

$$E = \bigcup_{n=1}^{\infty} A_n \quad \text{and} \quad E'.$$

11. Let P_n denote the probability that exactly n of the events A and B will occur, where n takes the values 0, 1, 2. Express each of P_0, P_1, P_2 in terms of $P(A)$, $P(B)$, and $P(A \cap B)$.

Odds. Some gambling games are described in terms of "odds" rather than in terms of probabilities. For example, if we roll a fair die, the probability of the event "rolling a three" is 1/6. Since there are six possible outcomes, one of which is favorable to the event "rolling a three" and five of which are unfavorable, this is often described by saying that the odds in favor of the event are 1 to 5, or the odds against it are 5 to 1. In this case the odds are related to the probability by the equation

$$\frac{1}{6} = \frac{1}{1+5}.$$

In general, if A is an event with probability $P(A)$ and if a and b are two real numbers such that

(1.23)
$$P(A) = \frac{a}{a+b},$$

we say the *odds in favor of A* are a to b, or the *odds against A* are b to a. Since $1 - a/(a+b) = b/(a+b)$, the odds against A are the same as the odds in favor of the complementary event A'. The following exercises are devoted to further properties of odds and their relation to probabilities.

12. If $P(A) = 1$, show that (1.23) can be satisfied only when $b = 0$ and $a \neq 0$. If $P(A) \neq 1$, show that there are infinitely many choices of a and b satisfying (1.23) but that all have the same ratio a/b.

13. Compute the odds in favor of each of the events described in Exercise 2.

14. Given two events A and B. If the odds against A are 2 to 1 and those in favor of $A \cup B$ are 3 to 1, show that

$$\frac{5}{12} \leq P(B) \leq \frac{3}{4}.$$

Give an example in which $P(B) = 5/12$ and one in which $P(B) = 3/4$.

1.21 Conditional probability

An unbiased die is thrown and the result is known to be an even number. What is the probability that this number is divisible by 3? What is the probability that a child is color blind, given that it is a boy? These questions can be put in the following form: Let A and B be events of a sample space S. If B occurs, what is the probability that A occurs? This is not necessarily the same as asking for the probability of the event $A \cap B$. In fact, when $A = B$ the question becomes: If A occurs, what is the probability that A occurs? The answer in this case should be 1 and this may or may not be the probability of $A \cap B$. To see how to treat such problems in general, we turn to the question pertaining to rolling a die.

When we ask probability questions about rolling an unbiased die, we ordinarily use for the sample space the set $S = \{1, 2, 3, 4, 5, 6\}$ and assign point probability $\frac{1}{6}$ to each element of S. The event "divisible by 3" is the subset $A = \{3, 6\}$ and the event "even" is the subset $B = \{2, 4, 6\}$. We want the probability that an element is in A, given that it is in B. Since we are concerned only with outcomes in which the number is even, we disregard the outcomes 1, 3, 5 and use, instead of S, the set $B = \{2, 4, 6\}$ as our sample space. The event in which we are now interested is simply the singleton $\{6\}$, this being the only outcome of the new sample space that is divisible by 3. If all outcomes of B are considered equally likely, we must assign probability $\frac{1}{3}$ to each of them; hence, in particular, the probability of $\{6\}$ is also $\frac{1}{3}$.

Note that we solved the foregoing problem by employing a very elementary idea. We simply changed the sample space from S to B and provided a new assignment of probabilities. This example suggests a way to proceed in general.

Let $(S, \mathcal{B}, P)$ be a given probability space. Suppose A and B are events and consider the question: "If B occurs, what is the probability that A occurs?" As in the example just treated, we can change the sample space from S to B and provide a new assignment of probabilities. We are at liberty to do this in any manner consistent with the definition of probability measures. For B itself we have no choice except to assign the probability 1. Since we are interested in those elements of A which lie in the new sample space B, the problem before us is to compute the probability of the event $A \cap B$ according to the new assignment of probabilities. That is, if P' denotes the probability function associated with the new sample space B, then we must compute $P'(A \cap B)$.

We shall show now that if $P(B) \neq 0$ we can always define a probability function P' and a Boolean algebra $\mathcal{B}'$ of subsets of B such that $(B, \mathcal{B}', P')$ is a probability space. For the Boolean algebra $\mathcal{B}'$ we take the collection of all sets $T \cap B$ where T is in the original Boolean algebra $\mathcal{B}$. It is easy to verify that $\mathcal{B}'$, so defined, is indeed a Boolean algebra. One way to define a probability function P' on $\mathcal{B}'$ is simply to divide each of the old probabilities by $P(B)$. That is, if $C \; \mathcal{E} \; \mathcal{B}'$ we let

$$P'(C) = \frac{P(C)}{P(B)}.$$

(This is where the assumption $P(B) \neq 0$ comes in.) We are only changing the scale, with all probabilities magnified by the factor $1/P(B)$. It is easy to check that this definition of P' gives us a *bona fide* probability measure. It is obviously nonnegative and it assigns probability 1 to B. The additive property follows at once from the corresponding additive property for P.

Since each C in $\mathcal{B}'$ is of the form $A \cap B$, where A is an event in the original sample space S, we may rewrite the definition of P' as follows:

$$P'(A \cap B) = \frac{P(A \cap B)}{P(B)}.$$

This discussion suggests that the quotient $P(A \cap B)/P(B)$ provides a reasonable measure of the probability that A occurs, given that B occurs. The following definition is made with this motivation in mind:

DEFINITION OF CONDITIONAL PROBABILITY. Let $(S, \mathcal{B}, P)$ be a probability space and let B be an event such that $P(B) \neq 0$. The conditional probability that an event A will occur, given that B has occurred, is denoted by the symbol $P(A|B)$ (read: "the probability of A, given B") and is defined by the equation

$$P(A|B) = \frac{P(A \cap B)}{P(B)}.$$

The conditional probability $P(A|B)$ is not defined if $P(B) = 0$.

The following examples illustrate the use of the concept of conditional probability.

Example 1. Let us consider once more the problem raised earlier in this section: A die is thrown and the result is known to be an even number. What is the probability that this number is divisible by 3? As a problem in conditional probabilities, we may take for the sample space the set $S = \{1, 2, 3, 4, 5, 6\}$ and assign point probabilities $\frac{1}{6}$ to each element of S. The event "even" is the set $B = \{2, 4, 6\}$ and the event "divisible by 3" is the set $A = \{3, 6\}$. Therefore we have

$$P(A|B) = \frac{P(A \cap B)}{P(B)} = \frac{1/6}{3/6} = \frac{1}{3}.$$

This agrees, of course, with the earlier solution in which we used B as the sample space and assigned probability $\frac{1}{3}$ to each element of B.

Example 2. This is a favorite example used by the Caltech Biology Department to warn against the fallacy of superficial statistics. To "prove" statistically that the population of the U.S. contains more boys than girls, each student is asked to list the number of boys and girls in his family. Invariably, the total number of boys exceeds the total number of girls. The statistics in this case are biased because all undergraduates at Caltech are males. Therefore, the question considered here is not concerned with the probability that a child is a boy; rather, it is concerned with the conditional probability that a child is a boy, given that he comes from a family with at least one boy.

To compute the probabilities in an example of this type consider a sample of $4n$ families, each with two children. Assume that n families have 2 boys, $2n$ families one boy and one girl, and n families 2 girls. Let the sample space S be the set of all $8n$ children in these families and assign the point probability $P(x) = 1/(8n)$ to each x in S. Let A denote the event "the child is a boy" and B the event "the child comes from a family with at least one boy." The probability $P(A)$ is obviously $\frac{1}{2}$. Similarly, $P(B) = \frac{3}{4}$ since $3n$ of the $4n$ families have at least one boy. Therefore the probability that a child is a boy, given that he comes from a family with at least one boy, is the conditional probability

$$P(A|B) = \frac{P(A \cap B)}{P(B)} = \frac{P(A)}{P(B)} = \frac{1/2}{3/4} = \frac{2}{3}.$$

1.22 Independence

An important idea related to conditional probability is the concept of *independence of events*, which may be defined as follows:

DEFINITION OF INDEPENDENCE. Two events A and B are called independent (or stochastically independent) if, and only if,

(1.24) $$P(A \cap B) = P(A) P(B).$$

If A and B are independent, then $P(A|B) = P(A)$ if $P(B) \neq 0$. That is, the conditional probability of A, given B, is the same as the "absolute" probability of A. This relation exhibits the significance of independence. The knowledge that B has occurred does not influence the probability that A will occur.

Example 1. One card is drawn from a 52-card deck. Each card has the same probability of being selected. Show that the two events "drawing an ace" and "drawing a heart" are independent.

Solution. We choose a sample space S consisting of 52 elements and assign the point probability 1/52 to each element. The event A, "drawing an ace," has the probability $P(A) = 4/52 = 1/13$. The event B, "drawing a heart," has the probability $P(B) = 13/52 = 1/4$. The event $A \cap B$ means "drawing the ace of hearts," which has probability 1/52. Since $P(A \cap B) = P(A) P(B)$, Equation (1.24) is satisfied and events A and B are independent.

Example 2. Three true dice are rolled independently, so that each combination is equally probable. Let A be the event that the sum of the digits shown is six and let B be the event that all three digits are different. Determine whether or not these two events are independent.

Solution. For a sample space S we take the set of all triples (a, b, c) with a, b, c ranging over the values 1, 2, 3, 4, 5, 6. There are 6^3 elements in S, and since they are equally probable we assign the point probability $1/6^3$ to each element. The event A is the set of all triples (a, b, c) for which $a + b + c = 6$. Direct enumeration shows that there are 10 such triples, namely:

$$(1, 2, 3), (1, 3, 2), (1, 1, 4), (1, 4, 1),$$
$$(2, 1, 3), (2, 3, 1), (2, 2, 2),$$
$$(3, 1, 2), (3, 2, 1),$$
$$(4, 1, 1).$$

The event B consists of all triples (a, b, c) for which $a \neq b$, $b \neq c$, and $a \neq c$. There are $6 \cdot 5 \cdot 4 = 120$ elements in B. Exactly six of these elements are in set A, so that $A \cap B$ has six elements. Therefore

$$P(A \cap B) = 6/6^3, \qquad P(A) = 10/6^3, \qquad \text{and} \qquad P(B) = 120/6^3 .$$

In this case $P(A \cap B) \neq P(A) P(B)$; therefore events A and B are not independent.

Independence for more than two events is defined as follows. A finite collection $\mathcal{Q}$ of n events is said to be independent if the events satisfy the multiplicative property

(1.25)
$$P\left(\bigcap_{k=1}^{m} A_k\right) = \prod_{k=1}^{m} P(A_k)$$

for *every* finite subcollection $\{A_1, A_2, \ldots, A_m\}$, where m may take the values $m = 2$, $3, \ldots, n$, the sets A_i being in $\mathcal{Q}$.

When $\mathcal{Q}$ consists of exactly three events A, B, and C, the condition of independence in (1.25) requires that

(1.26) $P(A \cap B) = P(A) P(B), \qquad P(A \cap C) = P(A) P(C), \qquad P(B \cap C) = P(B) P(C),$

and

(1.27) $P(A \cap B \cap C) = P(A) P(B) P(C) .$

It might be thought that the three equations in (1.26) suffice to imply (1.27) or, in other words, that independence of three events is a consequence of independence *in pairs*. This is not true, as one can see from the following example:

Four tickets labeled a, b, c, and abc, are placed in a box. A ticket is drawn at random, and the sample space is denoted by

$$S = \{a, b, c, abc\} .$$

Define the events A, B, and C as follows:

$$A = \{a, abc\}, \qquad B = \{b, abc\}, \qquad C = \{c, abc\} .$$

In other words, the event X means that the ticket drawn contains the letter x. It is easy to verify that each of the three equations in (1.26) is satisfied so that the events A, B, and C are independent in pairs. However, (1.27) is not satisfied and hence the *three* events are not independent. The calculations are simple and are left as an exercise for the reader.

1.23 Exercises

1. Let A and B be two events with $P(A) \neq 0$, $P(B) \neq 0$. Show that

$$(1.28) \qquad P(A \cap B) = P(B) \, P(A|B) = P(A) \, P(B|A) \,.$$

Sometimes it is easier to compute the probabilities $P(A)$ and $P(B|A)$ directly by enumeration of cases than it is to compute $P(A \cap B)$. When this is the case, Equation (1.28) gives a convenient way to calculate $P(A \cap B)$. The next exercise is an example.

2. An urn contains seven white and three black balls. A second urn contains five white and five black balls. A ball is selected at random from the first urn and placed in the second. Then a ball is selected at random from the second. Let A denote the event "black ball on first draw" and B the event "black ball on second draw."

(a) Compute the probabilities $P(A)$ and $P(B|A)$ directly by enumerating the possibilities. Use Equation (1.28) to compute $P(A \cap B)$.

(b) Compute $P(A \cap B)$ directly by enumerating all possible pairs of drawings.

3. (a) Let A_1, A_2, A_3 be three events such that $P(A_1 \cap A_2) \neq 0$. Show that

$$P(A_1 \cap A_2 \cap A_3) = P(A_1) \, P(A_2|A_1) \, P(A_3|A_1 \cap A_2) \,.$$

(b) Use induction to generalize this result as follows: If A_1, A_2, $\ldots$, A_n are n events ($n \geq 2$) such that $P(A_1 \cap A_2 \cap \cdots \cap A_{n-1}) \neq 0$, then

$$P(A_1 \cap A_2 \cap \cdots \cap A_n) = P(A_1) \, P(A_2|A_1) \, P(A_3|A_1 \cap A_2) \cdots P(A_n|A_1 \cap A_2 \cap \cdots \cap A_{n-1}) \,.$$

4. A committee of 50 senators is chosen at random. Find the probability that both senators from Alaska are included, given that at least one is.

5. An urn contains five gold and seven blue chips. Two chips are selected at random (without replacement). If the first chip is gold, compute the probability that the second is also gold.

6. A deck of cards is dealt into four hands containing 13 cards each. If one hand has exactly eight spades, what is the probability that a particular one of the other hands has (a) at least one spade? (b) at least two spades? (c) a complete suit?

7. Show that $P(A \cup B|C) = P(A|C) + P(B|C) - P(A \cap B|C)$.

8. Let A_1, A_2, $\ldots$, A_n be n disjoint events whose union is the entire sample space S. For every event E we have the equation

$$E = E \cap S = E \cap \bigcup_{i=1}^{n} A_i = \bigcup_{i=1}^{n} (E \cap A_i) \,.$$

This equation states that E can occur only in conjunction with some A_i. Show that

(a) $P(E) = \sum\limits_{i=1}^{n} P(E \cap A_i)$.

(b) $P(E) = \sum\limits_{i=1}^{n} P(E|A_i) \, P(A_i)$.

This formula is useful when the conditional probabilities $P(E|A_i)$ are easier to compute directly than $P(E)$.

9. An unbiased coin is tossed repeatedly. It comes up heads on the first six tosses. What is the probability that it will come up heads on the seventh toss?

10. Given independent events A and B whose probabilities are neither 0 nor 1. Prove that A' and B' are independent. Is the same true if either of A or B has probability 0 or 1?

11. Given independent events A and B. Prove or disprove in each case that:
    (a) A' and B are independent.
    (b) $A \cup B$ and $A \cap B$ are independent.
    (c) $P(A \cup B) = 1 - P(A') P(B')$.

12. If $A_1, A_2, \ldots, A_n$ are independent events, prove that

$$P(\bigcup_{i=1}^{n} A_i) + \prod_{i=1}^{n} P(A_i') = 1 .$$

13. If the three events A, B, and C are independent, prove that $A \cup B$ and C are independent. [*Hint*. Use the result of Exercise 7 to show that $P(A \cup B|C) = P(A \cup B)$.]

14. Let A and B be events, neither of which has probability 0. Prove or disprove the following statements:
    (a) If A and B are disjoint, A and B are independent.
    (b) If A and B are independent, A and B are disjoint.

15. A die is thrown twice, the sample space S consisting of the 36 possible pairs of outcomes (a, b) each assigned probability 1/36. Let A, B, and C denote the following events:

$$A = \{(a, b) \mid a \text{ is odd}\}, B = \{(a, b) \mid b \text{ is odd}\}, C = \{(a, b) \mid a + b \text{ is odd}\} .$$

    (a) Compute $P(A)$, $P(B)$, $P(C)$, $P(A \cap B)$, $P(A \cap C)$, $P(B \cap C)$, and $P(A \cap B \cap C)$.
    (b) Show that A, B, and C are independent in pairs.
    (c) Show that A, B, and C are not independent.

1.24 Compound experiments

In the language of probability theory, the dice game that interested the Chevalier de Méré (Section 1.11) is an example of a *repeated experiment*. The Chevalier's question—whether or not to bet even money on the occurrence of at least one "double six" in 24 throws of the dice—can be stated in a more general form: What is the probability of throwing a double six at least once in n throws of a pair of dice? Is this probability more than one-half or less than one-half when $n = 24$?

This game will be analyzed by using the notion of a *compound experiment* which may be introduced as follows: Consider first the experiment of tossing a pair of dice *just once*. The outcomes of this game can be described by ordered pairs (a, b) in which a and b range over the values 1, 2, 3, 4, 5, 6. The sample space, which we shall denote by S_1, consists of 36 such pairs; we label them $x_1, x_2, \ldots, x_{36}$. If the dice are fair we assign the probability 1/36 to each x_i in S_1. However, let us not make this assumption as yet. Instead, let us assign the probability p_i to x_i and, for the moment, assume nothing about the p_i except that they are nonnegative and that their sum is 1.

Suppose we repeat the experiment and roll the dice a second time. For the second experiment we may use the same sample space S_1 and the same assignment of probabilities as before. The *succession* of the two experiments is *one* "compound" experiment which we wish to describe mathematically. To do this we need a new sample space S and a corresponding probability function P. We may think of the outcomes of the new game as ordered pairs (x_i, x_j), where each of x_i and x_j are outcomes of the original sample space S_1; the outcome x_i is the result of the first toss and x_j is the result of the second toss. The set of all such pairs (x_i, x_j), where x_i and x_j each range over the 36 elements of S_1, is the Cartesian product $S_1 \times S_1$. It seems natural to use this as the new sample space S. The next task is to decide how to assign the point probabilities $P(x_i, x_j)$ to the elements of S. As usual, we may do this in any manner consistent with the definition of a probability measure. However, the circumstances in this particular situation suggest a "natural" assignment of probabilities. Consider the following two special events, A and B, in the new space S:

$$A = \{(x_1, x_1), (x_1, x_2), \ldots, (x_1, x_{36})\}$$

and

$$B = \{(x_1, x_2), (x_2, x_2), \ldots, (x_{36}, x_2)\} \,.$$

That is, A is the set of all pairs in $S_1 \times S_1$ whose first element is x_1, and B is the set of all pairs whose second element is x_2. The intersection of the two sets A and B is the singleton $\{(x_1, x_2)\}$. If we feel that the first outcome x_1 should have no influence on the second outcome x_2 it seems reasonable to require events A and B to be independent. This means we would like to define the new probability function P in such a way that we have

(1.29) $$P(A \cap B) = P(A)\, P(B) \,.$$

If we decide how to assign the probabilities $P(A)$ and $P(B)$, Equation (1.29) will tell us how to assign the probability $P(A \cap B)$, that is, the probability $P(x_1, x_2)$. Event A occurs if and only if the outcome of the first experiment is x_1. Since p_1 is its probability, it seems natural to assign the value p_1 to $P(A)$ as well. Similarly, we assign the value p_2 to $P(B)$. Equation (1.29) then gives us

$$P(x_1, x_2) = p_1 p_2 \,.$$

The same kind of reasoning applied to x_i and x_j instead of to x_1 and x_2 leads to the formula

(1.30) $$P(x_i, x_j) = p_i p_j \,.$$

All this, of course, is merely heuristic. The only way to decide whether or not (1.30) is a permissible assignment for the point probabilities of $S_1 \times S_1$ is to check the fundamental properties of probability measures. Each number $P(x_i, x_j)$ is clearly nonnegative and the sum of all the point probabilities is equal to 1, since we have

$$\sum_{(x_i, x_j) \,\varepsilon\, S} P(x_i, x_j) = \sum_{i=1}^{36} \sum_{j=1}^{36} p_i p_j = \sum_{i=1}^{36} p_i \sum_{j=1}^{36} p_j = 1 \cdot 1 = 1 \,.$$

If the experiment is repeated n times instead of twice, we may think of the n repetitions as consisting of one compound experiment whose sample space is the set of all n-tuples $(x_{i_1}, x_{i_2}, \ldots, x_{i_n})$, where each x_{i_k} runs through the 36 points of S_1. That is, the new sample space is the Cartesian product $S_1 \times S_1 \times \cdots \times S_1$ (n factors). The corresponding probability function P is defined as follows:

(1.31) $$P(x_{i_1}, x_{i_2}, \ldots, x_{i_n}) = p_{i_1} p_{i_2} \cdots p_{i_n} \,.$$

This definition may be motivated by the same kind of argument used for the case $n = 2$, and it is an acceptable assignment of probabilities because the sum of all the point probabilities is 1. Of course, for each subset C of $S_1 \times S_1 \times \cdots \times S_1$ we must define $P(C)$ as the sum of the point probabilities of all elements of C.

If we specialize and assume that each $p_i = 1/36$, we may ask for the probability of the event "at least one double six in n throws." Denote this event by E. Actually, in this case it is easier to compute the probability of the complementary event E', which means "no double six in n throws." Each element of E' is an n-tuple $(y_1, y_2, \ldots, y_n)$ where each component y_i is an ordered pair (a_i, b_i) from the original sample space S_1. Each y_i can be any element of S_1 except $(6, 6)$, so there are 35 possible values for each y_i and hence $(35)^n$ elements altogether in E'. Because of (1.31), each element in E' has probability $(1/36)^n$; therefore the sum of all the point probabilities in E' is $(35/36)^n$. This gives us

$$P(E) = 1 - P(E') = 1 - (35/36)^n .$$

To answer de Méré's question we must decide whether $P(E)$ is more than one-half or less than one-half when $n = 24$. The inequality $P(E) \geq \frac{1}{2}$ is equivalent to $1 - (35/36)^n \geq \frac{1}{2}$, or $(35/36)^n \leq \frac{1}{2}$. Taking logarithms we find

$$n \log 35 - n \log 36 \leq - \log 2, \quad \text{or} \quad n \geq \frac{\log 2}{\log 36 - \log 35} = 24.6+ .$$

Therefore $P(E) < \frac{1}{2}$ when $n = 24$ and $P(E) > \frac{1}{2}$ when $n \geq 25$.

This discussion suggests a general procedure for dealing with successive experiments. If an experiment is repeated two or more times, the result can be considered one compound experiment. More generally, a compound experiment may be the result of performing two or more distinct experiments successively. The individual experiments may be related to each other or they may be stochastically independent, in the sense that the probability of the outcome of any one of them is unrelated to the results of the others. For the sake of simplicity, we shall discuss how one may combine *two* independent experiments into one compound experiment. The generalization to more than two experiments will be evident.

To associate a *bona fide* probability space with a compound experiment we must explain how to define the new sample space S, the corresponding Boolean algebra $\mathcal{B}$ of subsets of S, and the probability measure P defined on $\mathcal{B}$. As in the above example, we use the concept of *Cartesian product*.

Suppose we have two probability spaces, say $(S_1, \mathcal{B}_1, P_1)$ and $(S_2, \mathcal{B}_2, P_2)$. These spaces may be thought of as associated with two experiments E_1 and E_2. By the compound experiment E we mean the one for which the sample space S is the Cartesian product $S_1 \times S_2$. An outcome of E is a pair (x, y) in S, with the first component x an outcome of E_1 and the second component y an outcome of E_2. If S_1 has n elements and S_2 m elements, then $S_1 \times S_2$ has nm elements. Although the definition of $S_1 \times S_2$ makes sense if either S_1 or S_2 is an infinite set (countable or not), we shall restrict ourselves to sample spaces S_1 and S_2 which are either *finite* or *countably infinite*.

For the new Boolean algebra $\mathcal{B}$ we take the collection of all subsets of S. Next we define the probability function P. Since S is finite or countable, we may define $P(x, y)$ for each point (x, y) in S and then use additivity to define P for subsets of S. The point probabilities $P(x, y)$ may be assigned in many ways. However, if the two experiments E_1 and E_2 are stochastically *independent*, then an argument similar to that given in the analysis of de Méré's problem suggests that we should define P as follows:

(1.32) $\qquad\qquad P(x, y) = P_1(x)\, P_2(y) \qquad \text{for each } (x, y) \text{ in } S .$

This is an acceptable definition of probability because we have

$$(1.33) \qquad \sum_{(x,y)\,\varepsilon\,S} P(x,\,y) = \sum_{x\,\varepsilon\,S_1} P_1(x) \cdot \sum_{y\,\varepsilon\,S_2} P_2(y) = 1 \cdot 1 = 1\,.$$

The sums in (1.33) are either finite sums or absolutely convergent infinite series.

When we say that a compound experiment E is determined by two stochastically independent experiments E_1 and E_2, we mean that the probability space $(S,\,\mathcal{B},\,P)$ is defined in the manner just described, "independence" being reflected in the fact that $P(x,\,y)$ is the product $P_1(x)\,P_2(y)$. It can be shown that the assignment of probabilities in (1.32) implies the formula

$$(1.34) \qquad P(U \times V) = P_1(U)\,P_2(V)$$

for every pair of subsets U in $\mathcal{B}_1$ and V in $\mathcal{B}_2$. (See Exercise 14 in Section 1.26 for an outline of the proof.) We shall deduce some important consequences of this formula.

Let A be an event (in the compound experiment E) of the form

$$A = C_1 \times S_2\,,$$

where $C_1\,\varepsilon\,\mathcal{B}_1$. Each outcome in A is an ordered pair $(x,\,y)$ where x is restricted to be an outcome of C_1 (in the first experiment E_1) but y can be any outcome of S_2 (in the second experiment E_2). If we apply (1.34) we find

$$P(A) = P(C_1 \times S_2) = P_1(C_1)\,P_2(S_2) = P_1(C_1)\,,$$

since $P_2(S_2) = 1$. Thus the definition of P assigns the same probability to A that P_1 assigns to C_1. For this reason, such an event A is said to be *determined by the first experiment* E_1. Similarly, if B is an event of E of the form

$$B = S_1 \times C_2\,,$$

where $C_2\,\varepsilon\,\mathcal{B}_2$, we have

$$P(B) = P(S_1 \times C_2) = P_1(S_1)\,P_2(C_2) = P_2(C_2)$$

and B is said to be *determined by the second experiment* E_2. We shall now show, using (1.34), that two such events A and B are *independent*. That is, we have

$$(1.35) \qquad P(A \cap B) = P(A)\,P(B)\,.$$

First we note that

$$\begin{aligned} A \cap B &= \{(x,\,y)\mid (x,\,y)\,\varepsilon\,C_1 \times S_2 \text{ and } (x,\,y)\,\varepsilon\,S_1 \times C_2\} \\ &= \{(x,\,y)\mid x\,\varepsilon\,C_1 \text{ and } y\,\varepsilon\,C_2\} \\ &= C_1 \times C_2\,. \end{aligned}$$

Hence, by (1.34), we have

$$(1.36) \qquad P(A \cap B) = P(C_1 \times C_2) = P_1(C_1)P_2(C_2)\,.$$

Since $P_1(C_1) = P(A)$ and $P_2(C_2) = P(B)$ we obtain (1.35). Note that Equation (1.36) also shows that we can compute the probability $P(A \cap B)$ as a product of probabilities in the individual sample spaces S_1 and S_2; hence no calculations with probabilities in the compound experiment are needed.

The generalization to compound experiments determined by n experiments E_1, E_2, $\ldots$, E_n is carried out in the same way. The points in the new sample space are n-tuples

$(x_1, x_2, \ldots, x_n)$ and the point probabilities are defined as the product of the probabilities of the separate outcomes,

$$(1.37) \qquad P(x_1, x_2, \ldots, x_n) = P_1(x_1)\, P_2(x_2) \cdots P_n(x_n)\,.$$

When this definition of P is used we say that E is determined by n *independent experiments* $E_1, E_2, \ldots, E_n$. In the special case in which all the experiments are associated with the same probability space, the compound experiment E is said to be an example of *independent repeated trials under identical conditions*. Such an example is considered in the next section.

1.25 Bernoulli trials

An important example of a compound experiment was studied extensively by Jakob Bernoulli and is now known as a *Bernoullian sequence of trials*. This is a sequence of repeated trials executed under the same conditions, each result being stochastically independent of all the others. The experiment being repeated has just two possible outcomes, usually called "success" and "failure"; the probability of success is denoted by p and that of failure by q. Of course, $q = 1 - p$. The main result associated with Bernoullian sequences is the following theorem:

1– 1   THEOREM. *Bernoulli's formula.* The probability of exactly k successes in n Bernoullian trials is

$$(1.38) \qquad \binom{n}{k} p^k\, q^{n-k}\,,$$

where $\binom{n}{k}$ denotes the binomial coefficient, $\binom{n}{k} = \dfrac{n!}{k!\,(n-k)!}\,.$

Proof. Denote "success" by S and "failure" by F and consider a particular sequence of n results. This may be represented by an n-tuple

$$(x_1, x_2, \ldots, x_n)\,,$$

where each x_i is either an S or an F. The event A in which we are interested is the collection of all n-tuples that contain exactly k S's and $n - k$ F's. Let us compute the point probability of a particular n-tuple in A. The probability of each S is p, and that of each F is q. Hence, by (1.37), the probability of each particular n-tuple in A is the product of k factors equal to p with $n - k$ factors equal to q. That is,

$$P(x_1, x_2, \ldots, x_n) = p^k\, q^{n-k} \qquad \text{if} \quad (x_1, x_2, \ldots, x_n)\, \varepsilon\, A\,.$$

Therefore, to compute $P(A)$ we need only count the number of elements in A and multiply this number by $p^k\, q^{n-k}$. But the number of elements in A is simply the number of ways of putting exactly k S's into the n possible positions of the n-tuple. This is the same as the number of subsets of k elements that can be formed from a set consisting of n elements; we have already seen that this number is $\binom{n}{k}$. Therefore, if we add the point probabilities for all points in A we obtain

$$P(A) = \binom{n}{k} p^k\, q^{n-k}\,.$$

Example 1. An unbiased coin is tossed 50 times. Compute the probability of exactly 25 heads.

Solution. We interpret this experiment as a sequence of 50 Bernoulli trials, in which "success" means "heads" and "failure" means "tails." Since the coin is unbiased we assign the probabilities $p = q = \frac{1}{2}$, and formula (1.38) gives us $\binom{50}{k}\left(\frac{1}{2}\right)^{50}$ for the probability of exactly k heads in 50 tosses. In particular, when $k = 25$ we obtain

$$\binom{50}{25}\left(\frac{1}{2}\right)^{50} = \frac{50!}{25!\,25!}\left(\frac{1}{2}\right)^{50}.$$

To express this number as a decimal it is best to use logarithms, since tables of logarithms of factorials are readily available. If we denote the number in question by P, a table of common logarithms (base 10) gives us

$$\begin{aligned}
\log P &= \log 50! - 2\log 25! - 50\log 2 \\
&= 64.483 - 50.381 - 15.052 = -0.950 = 0.05 - 1.00 \\
&= \log 1.12 - \log 10 = \log 0.112,
\end{aligned}$$

so $P = 0.112$.

Example 2. What is the probability of at least r successes in n Bernoullian trials?

Solution. Let A_k denote the event "exactly k successes in n trials." Then the event E in which we are interested is the union

$$E = A_r \cup A_{r+1} \cup \cdots \cup A_n.$$

Since the A_k are disjoint, we find

$$P(E) = \sum_{k=r}^{n} P(A_k) = \sum_{k=r}^{n} \binom{n}{k} p^k q^{n-k}.$$

Since

$$\sum_{k=0}^{n} \binom{n}{k} p^k q^{n-k} = (p + q)^n = 1,$$

the probability of the complementary event E' may be computed as follows:

$$P(E') = 1 - P(E) = \sum_{k=0}^{r-1} \binom{n}{k} p^k q^{n-k}.$$

This last sum gives us the probability of at most $r - 1$ successes in n trials.

1.26 Exercises

1. A coin is tossed twice, the probability of heads on the first toss being p_1 and that on the second toss p_2. Consider this a compound experiment determined by two stochastically independent experiments, and let the sample space be

$$S = \{(H, H), (H, T), (T, H), (T, T)\}.$$

(a) Compute the probability of each element of S.
(b) Can p_1 and p_2 be assigned so that

$$P(H, H) = \frac{1}{9},\ P(H, T) = P(T, H) = \frac{2}{9},\ P(T, T) = \frac{4}{9}?$$

(c) Can p_1 and p_2 be assigned so that

$$P(H, H) = P(T, T) = \frac{1}{3}, P(H, T) = P(T, H) = \frac{1}{6}?$$

(d) Consider the following four events (subsets of S):

H_1: heads on the first toss,
H_2: heads on the second toss,
T_1: tails on the first toss,
T_2: tails on the second toss.

Determine which pairs of these four events are independent.

In each of Exercises 2 through 12 describe your sample space, your assignment of probabilities, and the event whose probability you are computing.

2. A student takes a true-false examination consisting of 10 questions. He is completely unprepared so he plans to guess each answer. The guesses are to be made at random. For example, he may toss a fair coin and use the outcome to determine his guess.

(a) Compute the probability that he guesses correctly at least five times.

(b) Compute the probability that he guesses correctly at least nine times.

(c) What is the smallest n such that the probability of guessing at least n correct answers is less than $\frac{1}{2}$?

3. Ten fair dice are tossed together. What is the probability that exactly three sixes occur?

4. A fair coin is tossed five times. What is the probability of getting (a) exactly three heads? (b) at least three heads? (c) at most one head?

5. A man claims to have a divining rod which locates hidden sources of oil. The Caltech Geology Department conducts the following experiment to test his claim. He is taken into a room in which there are 10 sealed barrels. He is told that five of them contain oil and five contain water. His task is to decide which of the five contain oil and which do not.

(a) What is the probability that he locates the five oil barrels correctly just by chance?

(b) What is the probability that he locates at least three of the oil barrels correctly by chance?

6. A little old lady from Pasadena claims that by tasting a cup of tea made with milk she can tell whether the milk or the tea was added first to the cup. The lady's claim is tested by requiring her to taste and classify 10 pairs of cups of tea, each pair containing one cup of tea made by each of the two methods under consideration. Let p denote her "true" probability of classifying a pair of cups correctly. (If she is skillful, p is substantially greater than $\frac{1}{2}$; if not, $p \leq \frac{1}{2}$.) Assume the 10 pairs of cups are classified under independent and identical conditions.

(a) Compute, in terms of p, the probability that she classifies correctly at least eight of the 10 pairs of cups.

(b) Evaluate this probability explicitly when $p = \frac{1}{2}$.

7. (Another problem of Chevalier de Méré.) Determine whether or not it is advantageous to bet even money on at least one 6 appearing in four throws of an unbiased die. [*Hint.* Show that the probability of at least one 6 in n throws is $1 - (5/6)^n$.]

8. An urn contains w white balls and b black balls. If $k \leq n$, compute the probability of drawing k white balls in n drawings, if each ball is replaced before the next one is drawn.

9. Two dice are thrown eight times. Compute the probability that the sum is 11 exactly three times.

10. Throw a coin 10 times or 10 coins once and count the number of heads. Find the probability of obtaining at least six heads.

11. After a long series of tests on a certain kind of rocket engine it has been determined that in approximately 5% of the trials there will be a malfunction that will cause the rocket to misfire. Compute the probability that in 10 trials there will be at least one failure.

12. A coin is tossed repeatedly. Compute the probability that the total number of heads will be at least 6 before the total number of tails reaches 5.

13. Exercise 12 may be generalized as follows: Show that the probability of at least m successes before n failures in a sequence of Bernoullian trials is

$$\sum_{k=m}^{m+n-1} \binom{m+n-1}{k} p^k q^{m+n-k-1}.$$

14. Suppose a compound experiment $(S, \mathcal{B}, P)$ is determined by two stochastically independent experiments $(S_1, \mathcal{B}_1, P_1)$ and $(S_2, \mathcal{B}_2, P_2)$, where $S = S_1 \times S_2$ and

$$P(x, y) = P_1(x) P_2(y)$$

for each (x, y) in S. The purpose of this exercise is to establish the formula

(1.39) $$P(U \times V) = P_1(U) P_2(V)$$

for every pair of subsets U in $\mathcal{B}_1$ and V in $\mathcal{B}_2$. The sample spaces S_1 and S_2 are assumed to be finite or countably infinite.

(a) Verify that Equation (1.39) is true when U and V are singletons, and also when at least one of U or V is empty.

Suppose now that

$$U = \{u_1, u_2, \ldots, u_k\} \qquad \text{and} \qquad V = \{v_1, v_2, \ldots, v_m\}.$$

Then $U \times V$ consists of the km pairs (u_i, v_j). For each $i = 1, 2, \ldots, k$ let A_i denote the set of m pairs in $U \times V$ whose first component is u_i.

(b) Show that the A_i are disjoint sets whose union is $U \times V$.

(c) Show that

$$P(A_i) = \sum_{j=1}^{m} P(u_i, v_j) = P_1(u_i) P_2(V).$$

(d) From (b) and (c) deduce that

$$P(U \times V) = \sum_{i=1}^{k} P(A_i) = P_1(U) P_2(V).$$

This proves (1.39) in the finite case.

(e) Modify the argument as necessary for the countably infinite case.

1.27 Miscellaneous exercises on probability

1. What is the probability of rolling a seven with two unbiased dice?

2. Ten men and their wives are seated at random at a banquet. Compute the probability that a particular man sits next to his wife if (a) they are seated at a round table; (b) they are seated in a row.

3. A box has two drawers. Drawer number 1 contains four gold coins and two silver coins. Drawer number 2 contains three gold coins and three silver coins. A drawer is opened at random and a coin selected at random from the open drawer. Compute the probability of each of the following events:

(a) Drawer number 2 was opened and a silver coin was selected.

(b) A gold coin was selected from the opened drawer.

4. Two cards are picked in succession from a deck of 52 cards, each card having the same probability of being drawn.

(a) What is the probability that at least one is a spade?

The two cards are placed in a sack unexamined. One card is drawn from the sack and examined and found not to be a spade. (Each card has the same probability of being drawn.)

(b) What is the probability now of having at least one spade?

The card previously drawn is replaced in the sack and the cards mixed. Again a card is drawn and examined. No comparison is made to see if it is the same card previously drawn. The card is again replaced in the sack and the cards mixed. This is done a total of three times, including that of part (b), and each time the card examined is not a spade.

(c) What is a sample space and a probability function for this experiment? What is the probability that one of the two original cards is a spade?

5. Three horses A, B, and C are in a horse race. The event "A beats B" will be denoted symbolically by writing AB. The event "A beats B who beats C" will be denoted by ABC, etc. Suppose it is known that

$$P(AB) = 2/3, \qquad P(AC) = 2/3, \qquad P(BC) = 1/2,$$

and that

$$P(ABC) = P(ACB), \qquad P(BAC) = P(BCA), \qquad P(CAB) = P(CBA).$$

(a) Compute the probability that A wins.
(b) Compute the probability that B wins.
(c) Compute the probability that C wins.
(d) Are the events AB, AC, and CB independent?

6. The final step in a long computation requires the addition of three integers a_1, a_2, a_3. Assume that (a) the computations of a_1, a_2, and a_3 are stochastically independent; (b) in the computation of each a_i there is a common probability p that it is correct and that the probability of making an error of $+1$ is equal to the probability of making an error of -1; (c) no error larger than $+1$ or less than -1 can occur. Remember the possibility of compensating errors, and compute the probability that the sum $a_1 + a_2 + a_3$ is correct.

7. *The game of "odd man out."* Suppose n persons toss identical coins simultaneously and independently, where $n \geq 3$. Assume there is a probability p of obtaining heads with each coin. Compute the probability that in a given toss there will be an "odd man," that is, a person whose coin does not have the same outcome as that of any other member of the group.

8. Suppose n persons play the game "odd man out" with fair coins (as described in Exercise 7). For a given integer m compute the probability that it will take exactly m plays to conclude the game (the mth play is the first time there is an "odd man").

2

MULTIPLE INTEGRATION

2.1 Introduction

In the first chapter of Volume I we discussed the concept of the integral $\int_a^b f(x)\,dx$ for functions that were defined and bounded on finite intervals $[a, b]$. Chapter 9 extended the ideas to unbounded functions and infinite intervals. Here we shall generalize the notion of the integral in another direction. The one-dimensional interval $[a, b]$ will be replaced by a two-dimensional region to be referred to as the *region of integration*. First we shall consider rectangular regions of integration; later we shall consider more general regions with curved boundaries. The integrand will be replaced by a function of two variables, defined and bounded on the region of integration. The resulting integral (which will be defined in Section 2.6) is called a *double integral*, and is denoted by the symbol

$$\iint_R f, \qquad \text{or by} \qquad \iint_R f(x, y)\,dx\,dy\,,$$

where R stands for the region of integration and $f(x, y)$ denotes the function value of the integrand at the point (x, y) in R. As in the case of the one-dimensional integral, the symbols (x, y), dx, and dy play no role in the definition of the double integral; however, they are useful in computations and manipulations with integrals.

Our approach to one-dimensional integration theory was based on the search for a definition of the concept of area. For double integrals the motivation arises from the concept of volume.

2.2 Volume as a set function

Volume can be thought of as a set function V defined on some class $\mathcal{C}$ of sets in 3-space. We shall call these sets *solids*. To each solid S in $\mathcal{C}$ the set function V assigns a number $V(S)$, which we call the volume of S. Before we define volume we shall list a number of properties we feel volume should have. Later we shall find that for a large class of solids there is only one set function with these properties. Finally, we shall express this set function as a double integral and use this integral, in turn, to give a definition of volume.

Property 1. $V(S) \geq 0$ for every solid S in $\mathcal{C}$.
Property 2. If a solid in $\mathcal{C}$ is cut by a plane into a union of two solids S and T in $\mathcal{C}$, then

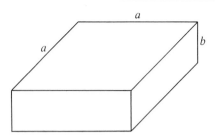

FIGURE 2.1   *A square prism with altitude b.*

$$V(S \cup T) = V(S) + V(T).$$

Property 3. V is a monotone set function. That is, if S and T are in $\mathcal{C}$, then

$$V(S) \leq V(T) \qquad \text{whenever} \quad S \subseteq T.$$

Property 4. If S is a square prism in $\mathcal{C}$, with a square base having edge a and with altitude b, then $V(S) = a^2b$. (A square prism is a rectangular parallelepiped with a square base. An example is shown in Figure 2.1.)

Property 5. If S and T are solids in $\mathcal{C}$ and if T is congruent† to S, then $V(T) = V(S)$.

Property 1 simply states that the volume of a solid is either a positive number or zero. Property 2 is a condition of finite additivity. When a solid is cut into two pieces, the volume of the whole should be the sum of the volumes of the individual pieces. Property 3 states that a solid which is part of another solid cannot have a larger volume. A special case of Property 4 states that the volume of a square prism of unit altitude is a^2; when the altitude is multiplied by a factor b the volume is also multiplied by b. Finally, Property 5 states that solids of the same size and shape have equal volumes.

It is important to realize that for a complete description of volume, two things must be specified—the class of solids for which volume is defined, and a rule for assigning the volume to each solid in this class. If the class $\mathcal{C}$ does not contain any square prisms we can define the volume of each solid in $\mathcal{C}$ to be zero, and all five properties are trivially satisfied. If class $\mathcal{C}$ contains square prisms, Property 4 assigns nonzero volume to these prisms. An ideal definition of volume would be applicable to *all* bounded sets‡ in 3-space. If class $\mathcal{C}$ contains all bounded sets it can be shown that *no* set function V satisfies all five properties of volume. The reason is that certain sets exist to which volume cannot be assigned in any way consistent with the foregoing properties. Such sets must be excluded from consideration. In the language of modern integration theory, they are called *nonmeasurable sets*. Although they are important in advanced theoretical work,

---

† Congruence is used here in the same sense as in elementary Euclidean geometry. Two sets are said to be congruent if their points can be put in one-to-one correspondence in such a way that distances are preserved. That is, if two points p and q in one set correspond to p' and q' in the other, the distance from p to q must be equal to the distance from p' to q'; this must be true for all choices of p and q.

‡ A set in 3-space is called *bounded* if it can be enclosed in a sphere about the origin.

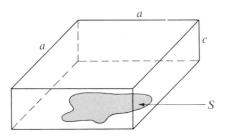

FIGURE 2.2   *A bounded plane set S enclosed in a square prism.*

nonmeasurable sets do not occur in ordinary applications concerned with volume. The solids for which volume *can* be defined are called *measurable sets*. We shall not attempt to describe the class of measurable sets here. Instead, we merely mention that this class is comprehensive enough to include all simple solids that occur in practice.

The class of measurable sets includes, among others, (a) the empty set ϕ, (b) sets consisting of a single point, (c) line segments, (d) bounded sets which lie in a plane, and (e) finite unions of sets of types (b), (c), and (d). It is easy to prove that the volume of each of these sets must be zero. In fact, since the sets in (a), (b), and (c) are all of type (d), it suffices to prove that $V(S) = 0$ for every bounded plane set S, and to use finite additivity to deduce the result for sets of type (e).

A bounded plane set S may be enclosed within a square in the plane of the set. Let us denote the edge of this square by a and consider a prism of altitude c having this square as its base, as shown in Figure 2.2. Then, by Property 3, $V(S) \leq a^2c$. Suppose now that $V(S) > 0$ and choose c so that $c < V(S)/a^2$. This contradicts the inequality $V(S) \leq a^2c$, hence $V(S)$ cannot be positive. Therefore $V(S) = 0$, as asserted.

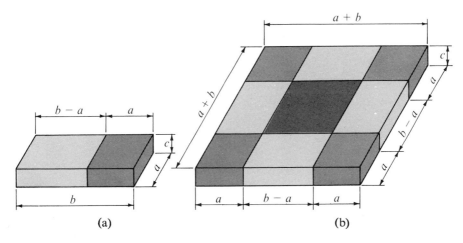

(a)   (b)

FIGURE 2.3   *Proof that $V(S) = abc$ when S is a rectangular box.*

If class $\mathcal{C}$ contains all rectangular parallelepipeds we can prove, from the five properties listed above, that the volume of a rectangular parallelepiped (a box) is the product of its three edges. For this purpose, consider a rectangular box S with edges a, b, and c, where $a < b$. We wish to prove that $V(S) = abc$. Figure 2.3(a) shows such a solid cut into two parts, one having a square base of edge a, and the other a rectangular base whose sides are a and $b - a$. Both parts have altitude c. If we denote the latter part by T, the additive property tells us that

(2.1) $V(S) = a^2c + V(T)$.

By Property 4, a square prism whose base has edge $a + b$ and whose altitude is c has volume $(a + b)^2c$. In Figure 2.3(b) such a prism is shown cut by planes into nine pieces. Each of the four corners is a square prism with volume a^2c and the center piece is a square prism with volume $(b - a)^2c$. By Property 5, each of the remaining four pieces has volume $V(T)$. Therefore, by repeated application of the additive property, we have

$$(b + a)^2c = 4a^2c + 4V(T) + (b - a)^2c = 4V(S) + (b - a)^2c ,$$

where we have used Equation (2.1) to obtain the last equality. Solving for $V(S)$ we find

$$V(S) = \frac{(b + a)^2c - (b - a)^2c}{4} = abc .$$

This proves that S has volume abc, as asserted.

2.3   An example of a set function satisfying the properties of volume

In Section 1.44 of Volume I we defined volume for certain special solids. Each of these solids S had cross sections of known area perpendicular to a given line; the volume $V(S)$ was defined to be the integral of the cross-sectional area. To verify that this definition of volume gives us a set function satisfying all the properties listed above, we must describe the collection $\mathcal{C}$ that is to be referred to as the class of solids, and then check that V has the desired properties for the sets of $\mathcal{C}$. For the sake of simplicity we shall consider only a very special class of solids and verify that V has the properties for this particular class. These solids are like rectangular prisms, except that one face is replaced by a curved surface.

Specifically, let f be a function that is defined and bounded on a rectangle R in the xy-plane, as shown in Figure 2.4(a). This rectangle is the set of all points (x, y) such that $a \le x \le b$ and $c \le y \le d$. When we say that f is *bounded* on R we mean that there exists a constant $M > 0$ such that

$$|f(x, y)| \le M \qquad \text{for all} \quad (x, y) \text{ in } R .$$

If f is *nonnegative*, the set of points (x, y, z) in 3-space with (x, y) in R and $0 \le z \le f(x, y)$ is called the *ordinate set* of f over R. It consists of those points between the rectangle R and the surface $z = f(x, y)$. Let S denote such an ordinate set. For each t in the interval $[c, d]$, the intersection of S with the plane $y = t$ is a plane region $S(t)$, as shown by the example in Figure 2.4(b). The plane set $S(t)$ is itself the ordinate set of a function of one variable, namely, the function f_t defined on the interval $[a, b]$ by the equation

$$f_t(x) = f(x, t) \qquad \text{if} \quad a \le x \le b .$$

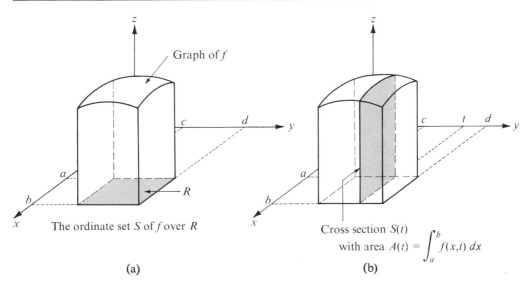

FIGURE 2.4 *The volume of S is the integral of the cross-sectional area:* $V(S) = \int_c^d A(t)\, dt.$

We assume that the function f_t is integrable on $[a, b]$. Then the area of $S(t)$, which we denote by $A(t)$, is given by the formula

$$A(t) = \int_a^b f_t(x)\, dx = \int_a^b f(x, t)\, dx\,.$$

We assume further that the function A so defined is integrable on $[c, d]$, and we define the volume of S to be the integral of the cross-sectional area:

$$V(S) = \int_c^d A(t)\, dt\,.$$

For the class $\mathcal{C}$ of solids we shall take all ordinate sets S of all such nonnegative functions defined and bounded over rectangles with sides parallel to the x- and y-axes. Each $V(S)$ is clearly nonnegative, so Property 1 is satisfied. To check Property 2, we begin with an ordinate set U over a rectangle R and decompose it into a union of two ordinate sets S and T over two adjacent rectangles R_S and R_T whose union is R.† The rectangles R_S and R_T have a common edge which is either parallel to the y-axis, as shown in Figure 2.5(a), or parallel to the x-axis, as shown in Figure 2.5(b). In the first case, suppose the common edge lies on the line $x = a'$, and denote by A_S, A_T, and A_U the cross-sectional areas for S, T, and U, respectively. Then we have

$$A_S(y) = \int_a^{a'} f(x, y)\, dx, \quad A_T(y) = \int_{a'}^b f(x, y)\, dx, \quad A_U(y) = \int_a^b f(x, y)\, dx\,.$$

† To cut U into a union of two solids in class $\mathcal{C}$, we must have the cutting plane perpendicular to the xy-plane and parallel to the x- or y-axis. Other planes cut U into two pieces, but the pieces are not in class $\mathcal{C}$.

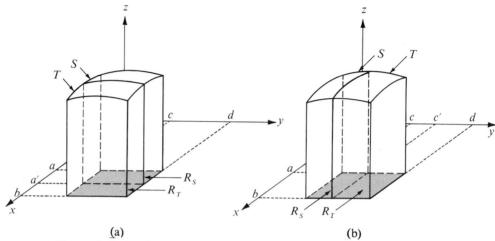

(a)   (b)

FIGURE 2.5   *Verification of the additive property* $V(S \cup T) = V(S) + V(T)$.

Next we note that $A_U(y) = A_S(y) + A_T(y)$ because of the additive property of one-dimensional integrals. Therefore

$$V(S) + V(T) = \int_c^d A_S(y)\, dy + \int_c^d A_T(y)\, dy = \int_c^d [A_S(y) + A_T(y)]\, dy$$

$$= \int_c^d A_U(y)\, dy = V(U) = V(S \cup T).$$

This verifies the additive property $V(S \cup T) = V(S) + V(T)$ for the case shown in Figure 2.5(a). In the second case, shown in Figure 2.5(b), the argument is similar, except that we use the additivity of the one-dimensional integral over the interval $[c, d]$.

Property 3 follows easily from the comparison theorem for integrals, and from the fact that the integral of a nonnegative function over an interval I cannot be less than the integral of the same function over any subinterval of I. To verify Property 4 we simply note that when f is constant over R, say $f(x, y) = k$, we have

$$A(t) = \int_a^b k\, dx = k(b - a) \qquad \text{and} \qquad V(S) = \int_c^d A(t)\, dt = k(b - a)(d - c).$$

This clearly implies Property 4.

To verify Property 5 it would be necessary to describe the collection of all ordinate sets congruent to a given one, and then to show that all these ordinate sets are assigned equal volumes. We shall not attempt to do this here. Instead, we merely mention that when two congruent ordinate sets S and T in $\mathbb{Q}$ differ only by a translation parallel to the x-axis, a translation parallel to the y-axis, or a succession of two such translations, the equation $V(S) = V(T)$ follows easily from the fact that one-dimensional integrals are invariant under translations of the interval of integration.

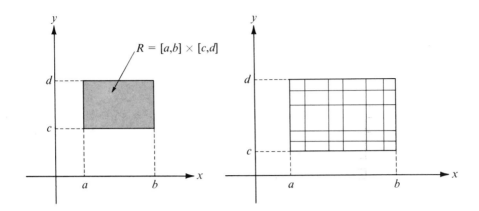

FIGURE 2.6   *A rectangle R, the Cartesian product of two intervals.*   FIGURE 2.7   *A partition of a rectangle R.*

2.4   Partitions of rectangles. Step functions

Double integrals will be treated here in much the same way as one-dimensional integrals were treated in Volume I. The theory will be developed first for step functions, and then for more general functions.

Let the region of integration be a rectangle R, as shown in Figure 2.6. This rectangle may be thought of as the Cartesian product† of two closed intervals $[a, b]$ and $[c, d]$, one on the x-axis, the other on the y-axis. That is,

$$R = [a, b] \times [c, d] = \{(x, y) \mid x \in [a, b] \text{ and } y \in [c, d]\} .$$

Now consider two partitions P_1 and P_2 of $[a, b]$ and $[c, d]$, respectively, say

$$P_1 = \{x_0, x_1, \ldots, x_{n-1}, x_n\} \qquad \text{and} \qquad P_2 = \{y_0, y_1, \ldots, y_{m-1}, y_m\} ,$$

where $x_0 = a$, $x_n = b$, $y_0 = c$, $y_m = d$. The Cartesian product $P_1 \times P_2$ is said to be a partition of R. Since P_1 decomposes $[a, b]$ into n subintervals and P_2 decomposes $[c, d]$ into m subintervals, the partition $P = P_1 \times P_2$ decomposes R into mn subrectangles. Figure 2.7 illustrates an example of a partition of R into 30 subrectangles. A partition P' of R is said to be finer than P if $P \subseteq P'$, that is, if every point in P is also in P'.

The Cartesian product of two *open* subintervals of P_1 and P_2 is a subrectangle with its edges missing. This is called an *open subrectangle* of P. A function f defined on R is said to be a *step function* if a partition P of R exists such that f is constant on each of the open subrectangles of P. The graph of an example, consisting largely of horizontal rectangular patches, is shown in Figure 2.8. Of course, the function must also have a well-defined value at each of the boundary points of the subrectangles, but the actual values at these points are not relevant to integration theory. The double integral of such

† The Cartesian product $A \times B$ of two sets A and B is the set of all ordered pairs (a, b) in which the first element a comes from A and the second element b comes from B. (See Section 1.12 for a further discussion of Cartesian products.)

a step function will be so defined that when f is nonnegative (as in the example shown in Figure 2.8), the value of the integral will be the volume of the set lying above the xy-plane and beneath the rectangular patches.

2.5   The double integral of a step function

Let $P = P_1 \times P_2$ be a partition of a rectangle R into mn subrectangles and let f be a step function that is constant on the open subrectangles of P. Let the subrectangle determined by $[x_{i-1}, x_i]$ and $[y_{j-1}, y_j]$ be denoted by R_{ij} and let c_{ij} denote the constant

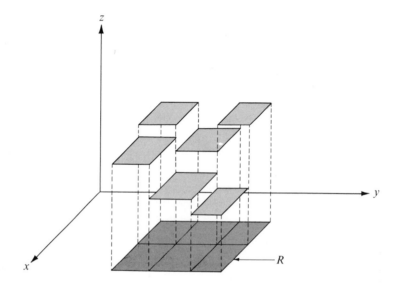

FIGURE 2.8   *The graph of a step function defined over a rectangle R.*

value that f takes on at the interior points of R_{ij}. If f is positive, the volume of the rectangular box with base R_{ij} and altitude c_{ij} is the product

$$c_{ij} \cdot (x_i - x_{i-1})(y_j - y_{j-1}) \, .$$

For any step function f, positive or not, the sum of all these products is defined to be the double integral of f over R. Thus, by definition, we have

$$(2.2) \qquad \iint_R f = \sum_{i=1}^{n} \sum_{j=1}^{m} c_{ij} \cdot (x_i - x_{i-1})(y_j - y_{j-1}) \, .$$

As in the one-dimensional case, the value of the integral does not change if the partition P is replaced by any finer partition P'. Thus, the value of the integral is independent of the choice of P so long as f is constant on the open subrectangles of P. For brevity, we sometimes write Δx_i instead of $(x_i - x_{i-1})$ and Δy_j instead of $(y_j - y_{j-1})$, and the sum in (2.2) becomes

$$\sum_{i=1}^{n} \sum_{j=1}^{m} c_{ij} \, \Delta x_i \, \Delta y_j \, .$$

To remind ourselves how this sum is formed, we may write the symbol for the integral as

$$\iint_R f(x, y) \, dx \, dy \, .$$

This symbol is merely an alternative notation for $\iint_R f$.

Note that if f is constant on the interior of R, say $f(x, y) = k$ when $a < x < b$ and $c < y < d$, we have

(2.3)
$$\iint_R f = k(b - a)(d - c) \, ,$$

regardless of the values of f on the edges of R. Since we have

$$b - a = \int_a^b dx \qquad \text{and} \qquad d - c = \int_c^d dy \, ,$$

formula (2.3) may also be written as

(2.4)
$$\iint_R f = \int_c^d \left[\int_a^b f(x, y) \, dx \right] dy = \int_a^b \left[\int_c^d f(x, y) \, dy \right] dx \, .$$

The integrals which appear on the right are one-dimensional integrals, and the formula is said to provide an evaluation of the double integral by *repeated* or *iterated* integration. In particular, if we apply this formula when f is a step function of the type described above, we may write

$$\iint_{R_{ij}} f = \int_{y_{j-1}}^{y_j} \left[\int_{x_{i-1}}^{x_i} f(x, y) \, dx \right] dy = \int_{x_{i-1}}^{x_i} \left[\int_{y_{j-1}}^{y_j} f(x, y) \, dy \right] dx \, .$$

Summing on i and j and using (2.2), we find that (2.4) holds for step functions.

The following further properties of the double integral of a step function are generalizations of the corresponding one-dimensional theorems. They may be proved as direct consequences of the definition in (2.2) or by use of formula (2.4) and the companion theorems for one-dimensional integrals. In the following theorems the symbols s and t denote step functions defined on a rectangle R. To avoid trivial special cases we assume that R is a nondegenerate rectangle; in other words, that R is not merely a single point or a line segment.

2– 1   THEOREM. *Linearity property.* For every real c_1 and c_2 we have

$$\iint_R [c_1 s(x, y) + c_2 t(x, y)] \, dx \, dy = c_1 \iint_R s(x, y) \, dx \, dy + c_2 \iint_R t(x, y) \, dx \, dy \, .$$

2– 2   THEOREM. *Additive property.* If R is subdivided into two rectangles R_1 and R_2, then

$$\iint_R s(x, y) \, dx \, dy = \iint_{R_1} s(x, y) \, dx \, dy + \iint_{R_2} s(x, y) \, dx \, dy \, .$$

2–3   THEOREM.   *Comparison theorem. If $s(x, y) < t(x, y)$ for every (x, y) in R, we have*

$$\iint\limits_{R} s(x, y)\, dx\, dy < \iint\limits_{R} t(x, y)\, dx\, dy\,.$$

In particular, if $t(x, y) > 0$ for every (x, y) in R, then

$$\iint\limits_{R} t(x, y)\, dx\, dy > 0\,.$$

The proofs of these theorems are left as exercises. For the linearity property it should be noted that $c_1 s + c_2 t$ is actually a step function. In fact, if P_1 and P_2 are partitions of R such that s is constant on the open subrectangles of P_1 and t is constant on the open subrectangles of P_2, then $c_1 s + c_2 t$ is constant on the open subrectangles of the union $P_1 \cup P_2$ (which we may call the *common* refinement of P_1 and P_2).

2.6   The definition of the double integral of a function defined and bounded on a rectangle

Let f be a function that is defined and bounded on a rectangle R; specifically, suppose that

$$|f(x, y)| \le M \qquad \text{if} \quad (x, y)\, \varepsilon\, R\,.$$

Then f may be surrounded from above and from below by two constant step functions s and t, where $s(x, y) = -M$ and $t(x, y) = M$ for all (x, y) in R. Now consider *any* two step functions s and t, defined on R, such that

(2.5) $s(x, y) \le f(x, y) \le t(x, y)$ for every point (x, y) in R .

If there is one and only one number I such that

$$\iint\limits_{R} s \le I \le \iint\limits_{R} t$$

for *every* pair of step functions satisfying the inequalities in (2.5), this number I is called the double integral of f over R and is denoted by the symbol

$$\iint\limits_{R} f \qquad \text{or} \qquad \iint\limits_{R} f(x, y)\, dx\, dy\,.$$

When such an I exists the function f is said to be *integrable* on R.

This definition is entirely analogous to the one-dimensional case. Therefore it is not surprising to learn that the linearity property, the additive property, and the comparison theorem, as stated for step functions in Section 2.5, also hold for double integrals in general. The proofs of these statements may be deduced from the corresponding properties of integrals of step functions. The details of the proofs are analogous to those in the one-dimensional case.

2.7   Geometric interpretation of the double integral as a volume

Let f be a nonnegative function that is integrable on a rectangle R and let S denote the ordinate set of f over R. [An example is shown in Figure 2.4(a).] The double integral of f over R can be used to define a set function ϕ which assigns to S the value

(2.6)
$$\phi(S) = \iint\limits_R f.$$

If we let $\mathcal{O}$ denote the class of all ordinate sets of nonnegative integrable functions defined on rectangles with edges parallel to the x- and y-axes we can show that the set function ϕ has all the properties of volume described in Section 2.2.

From the comparison theorem (Theorem 2–3) it follows that ϕ is nonnegative, so Property 1 is satisfied. To check Property 2, let us suppose an ordinate set over a rectangle R is cut by a plane into two ordinate sets S and T over rectangles R_1 and R_2, respectively. Then the additive property of double integrals (Theorem 2–2) tells us that

$$\phi(S \cup T) = \phi(S) + \phi(T),$$

so ϕ satisfies the additivity required in Property 2. To verify that ϕ is monotone (Property 3) we use both the comparison theorem and the additive property for double integrals. Next, Equation (2.3) tells us that $\phi(S) = a^2 b$ when S is a square prism with a square base of edge a and altitude b, so Property 4 is satisfied. It can also be shown that $\phi(S) = \phi(T)$ whenever S and T are congruent ordinate sets, but we shall not discuss the proof here. According to the criteria set forth in Section 2.2, the function ϕ defined by the double integral in Equation (2.6) is an acceptable definition for the volume of the ordinate set of f over R.

We shall prove next that the double integral is the *only* set function which has the five properties of volume on class $\mathcal{O}$. In fact, let V be any set function satisfying Properties 1 through 4 (Property 5 will not be required in this argument), and take for the measurable sets the class $\mathcal{O}$ consisting of ordinate sets of nonnegative integrable functions defined on rectangles in the xy-plane with their sides parallel to the coordinate axes. Let S be the ordinate set of an arbitrary f that is nonnegative and integrable over a rectangle R. We shall prove that

$$V(S) = \iint\limits_R f.$$

To do this, let us consider an arbitrary pair of step functions s and t satisfying the inequalities

(2.7) $\qquad 0 \le s(x, y) \le f(x, y) \le t(x, y) \qquad$ for each $\quad (x, y)$ in R.

Let P be a partition of R such that s and t are constant on the open subrectangles of P and denote the constant values in the subrectangle R_{ij} by s_{ij} and t_{ij}, respectively, where $i = 1, 2, \ldots, n$ and $j = 1, 2, \ldots, m$. If A and B are the ordinate sets corresponding to s and t, we have

$$A \subseteq S \subseteq B.$$

Hence, since V is monotone, we also have

(2.8) $\qquad\qquad\qquad V(A) \le V(S) \le V(B).$

But the ordinate sets A and B are finite unions of rectangular prisms; therefore, by additivity, we must have

(2.9) $\qquad V(A) = \sum_{i=1}^{n} \sum_{j=1}^{m} s_{ij} \, \Delta x_i \, \Delta y_j \qquad$ and $\qquad V(B) = \sum_{i=1}^{n} \sum_{j=1}^{m} t_{ij} \, \Delta x_i \, \Delta y_j.$

The sums in (2.9) are the double integrals of s and t over R. Therefore, if we combine (2.9) with (2.8), we find

$$\iint\limits_R s \leq V(S) \leq \iint\limits_R t \,.$$

In other words, $V(S)$ is a number which lies between $\iint\limits_R s$ and $\iint\limits_R t$ for every pair of step functions satisfying (2.7). But since f is integrable, there is only one number which has this property, so $V(S) = \iint\limits_R f$, as asserted. This proves that the double integral is the only set function, defined on class $\mathcal{O}$, which satisfies the properties ascribed to volume. For this reason, it is natural to call $V(S)$ the volume of S.

2.8   Evaluation of a double integral by repeated one-dimensional integration

In one-dimensional integration theory, the second fundamental theorem of calculus provides a method for calculating integrals without requiring the definition of the integral in each case. The next theorem accomplishes the same result in the two-dimensional theory; it enables us to evaluate certain double integrals by means of two successive one-dimensional integrations. The result is an extension of formula (2.4), which we have already proved for step functions.

2–4   THEOREM. *Let f be defined and bounded on the rectangle R in the xy-plane given by $R = [a, b] \times [c, d]$, and assume that f is integrable on R. For each fixed y in $[c, d]$ assume that the one-dimensional integral $\int_a^b f(x, y)\, dx$ exists, and denote the value of this integral by $A(y)$. Then the integral $\int_c^d A(y)\, dy$ exists and is equal to the double integral $\iint\limits_R f$. In other words, we have the formula*

(2.10) $$\iint\limits_R f(x, y)\, dx\, dy = \int_c^d \left[\int_a^b f(x, y)\, dx \right] dy \,.$$

Formula (2.10) is said to provide an evaluation of the double integral by *repeated* or *iterated* integration. The process is described by saying that first we integrate f with respect to x from a to b (holding y fixed), and then we integrate the result with respect to y from c to d. If we interchange the order of integration, we have a similar formula, namely,

(2.11) $$\iint\limits_R f(x, y)\, dx\, dy = \int_a^b \left[\int_c^d f(x, y)\, dy \right] dx \,,$$

which holds if we assume that $\int_c^d f(x, y)\, dy$ exists for each fixed x in $[a, b]$.

A proof of this theorem for a special class of integrands will be given in Section 2.10. The remainder of this section gives a geometric argument indicating why the theorem should be true, and illustrates the use of the theorem through some numerical examples.

Geometric motivation. Let us restrict ourselves to nonnegative integrands and interpret both sides of Equation (2.10) in terms of the volume of the ordinate set S of f over R.

For each fixed y the one-dimensional integral

$$A(y) = \int_a^b f(x, y)\, dx$$

represents the area of the cross section of S cut by a plane perpendicular to the y-axis, as shown in Figure 2.4(b). As we have already seen in Section 2.3, the integral of the cross-sectional area has the properties we ascribed to the volume of such ordinate sets, so the volume of S [call it $V(S)$] is given by the formula

$$V(S) = \int_c^d A(y)\, dy = \int_c^d \left[\int_a^b f(x, y)\, dx \right] dy .$$

On the other hand, we just proved that the double integral $\iint_R f$ is the *only* set function having the properties ascribed to volume, so $V(S)$ must necessarily be equal to $\iint_R f$. This argument shows why we should expect Equation (2.10) to hold. The same kind of argument applies to (2.11); the only difference is that the cross sections are cut by planes perpendicular to the x-axis. Actually, the argument provides a rigorous proof of the theorem for nonnegative integrands, except for the statement that the cross-sectional area A is an integrable function.

Note. If it is known that the integral $\int_c^d A(y)\, dy$ exists, the proof of formula (2.10) is simple. We choose two step functions s and t satisfying $s(x, y) \leq f(x, y) \leq t(x, y)$ for all (x, y) in R. Integrating with respect to x we find

$$\int_a^b s(x, y)\, dx \leq A(y) \leq \int_a^b t(x, y)\, dx .$$

If the integral $\int_c^d A(y)\, dy$ is known to exist, we may integrate both these inequalities with respect to y and use Equation (2.4) to obtain

$$\iint_R s \leq \int_c^d A(y)\, dy \leq \iint_R t .$$

Therefore $\int_c^d A(y)\, dy$ is a number which lies between $\iint_R s$ and $\iint_R t$ for all step functions s and t approximating f from below and from above, respectively. Since f is integrable on R, the only number with this property is the double integral of f over R. Therefore $\int_c^d A(y)\, dy = \iint_R f$, which is the same as Equation (2.10).

In Section 2.10 we shall give a complete proof of the theorem for a special but important class of integrands known as *piecewise monotonic functions*. First, however, we apply the theorem in two numerical examples.

Example 1. If $R = [-1, 1] \times [0, \pi/2]$, evaluate $\iint_R (x \sin y - ye^x)\, dx\, dy$, given that the integral exists. The region of integration is shown in Figure 2.9.

Solution. Integrating first with respect to x and calling the result $A(y)$, we have

$$A(y) = \int_{-1}^1 (x \sin y - ye^x)\, dx = \left(\frac{x^2}{2} \sin y - ye^x \right) \Bigg|_{x=-1}^{x=1} = -ey + y/e .$$

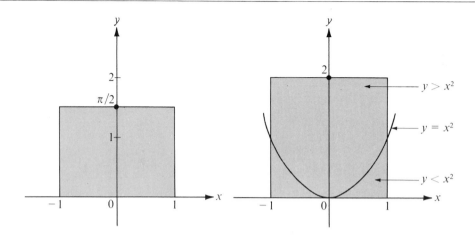

FIGURE 2.9   *The region of integration for*   FIGURE 2.10   *The region of integration for*
Example 1.   *Example 2.*

Applying Theorem 2–4 we find

$$\iint_R (x \sin y - ye^x)\, dx\, dy = \int_0^{\pi/2} A(y)\, dy = \int_0^{\pi/2} (-ey + y/e)\, dy$$

$$= (1/e - e) \int_0^{\pi/2} y\, dy = (1/e - e)\, \pi^2/8 .$$

As a check on the calculations we may integrate first with respect to y:

$$\iint_R (x \sin y - ye^x)\, dx\, dy = \int_{-1}^1 \left[\int_0^{\pi/2} (x \sin y - ye^x)\, dy \right] dx$$

$$= \int_{-1}^1 (-x \cos y - \tfrac{1}{2}y^2 e^x) \Bigg|_{y=0}^{y=\pi/2} dx$$

$$= \int_{-1}^1 (-\pi^2 e^x/8 + x)\, dx = (1/e - e)\, \pi^2/8 .$$

Example 2. If $R = [-1, 1] \times [0, 2]$, evaluate the double integral $\iint_R \sqrt{|y - x^2|}\, dx\, dy$, given that it exists.

Solution. If we integrate first with respect to y and call the result $H(x)$, we have $H(x) = \int_0^2 \sqrt{|y - x^2|}\, dy$. The region of integration is the rectangle shown in Figure 2.10. The parabola $y = x^2$ is also shown because of the presence of $|y - x^2|$ in the integrand. Above this parabola we have $y > x^2$ and below it we have $y < x^2$. This suggests that we split the integral for $H(x)$ as follows:

$$H(x) = \int_0^2 \sqrt{|y - x^2|}\, dy = \int_0^{x^2} \sqrt{x^2 - y}\, dy + \int_{x^2}^2 \sqrt{y - x^2}\, dy .$$

We remember that x is treated as a constant in each of these integrals. In the first integral we make the change of variable $t = x^2 - y$ and in the second we put $t = y - x^2$. This gives us

$$H(x) = \int_0^2 \sqrt{|y - x^2|}\, dy = -\int_{x^2}^0 \sqrt{t}\, dt + \int_0^{2-x^2} \sqrt{t}\, dt = \tfrac{2}{3} x^3 + \tfrac{2}{3}(2 - x^2)^{3/2}\,.$$

Applying Theorem 2–4 we find

$$\iint\limits_R \sqrt{|y - x^2|}\, dx\, dy = \int_{-1}^1 \left[\frac{2}{3} x^3 + \frac{2}{3}(2 - x^2)^{3/2}\right] dx = \frac{4}{3} \int_0^1 (2 - x^2)^{3/2}\, dx$$

$$= \frac{1}{3}\left[x(2 - x^2)^{3/2} + 3x \sqrt{2 - x^2} + 6 \arcsin\left(\frac{x}{\sqrt{2}}\right)\right]\Bigg|_0^1 = \frac{4}{3} + \frac{\pi}{2}\,.$$

The same result may be obtained by integrating first with respect to x, but the calculations are more complicated.

2.9 Exercises

Evaluate the double integrals in Exercises 1 through 6 by repeated integration, given that each integral exists.

1. $\displaystyle\iint\limits_R xy(x + y)\, dx\, dy$, where $R = [0, 1] \times [0, 1]$.

2. $\displaystyle\iint\limits_R (\sqrt{y} + x - 3xy^2)\, dx\, dy$, where $R = [0, 1] \times [1, 3]$.

3. $\displaystyle\iint\limits_R \sin^2 x \sin^2 y\, dx\, dy$, where $R = [0, \pi] \times [0, \pi]$.

4. $\displaystyle\iint\limits_R |\cos(x + y)|\, dx\, dy$, where $R = [0, \pi] \times [0, \pi]$.

5. $\displaystyle\iint\limits_R f(x + y)\, dx\, dy$, where $R = [0, 2] \times [0, 2]$, and $f(t)$ denotes the greatest integer $\leq t$.

6. $\displaystyle\iint\limits_R y^{-3} e^{tx/y}\, dx\, dy$, where $R = [0, t] \times [1, t]$, $t > 0$.

7. If R is a rectangle, show that a double integral of the form $\iint\limits_R f(x)\, g(y)\, dx\, dy$ is equal to the product of two one-dimensional integrals. State the assumptions about existence that you are using.

8. Let f be defined on the rectangle $R = [0, 1] \times [0, 1]$ as follows:

$$f(x, y) = \begin{cases} 1 - x - y & \text{if } x + y \leq 1\,, \\ 0 & \text{otherwise}\,. \end{cases}$$

Make a sketch of the ordinate set of f over R and compute the volume of this ordinate set by double integration. (Assume the integral exists.)

9. Do the same as in Exercise 8 when $R = [-1, 1] \times [-1, 1]$ and

$$f(x, y) = \begin{cases} x^2 + y^2 & \text{if } x^2 + y^2 \leq 1\,, \\ 0 & \text{otherwise}\,. \end{cases}$$

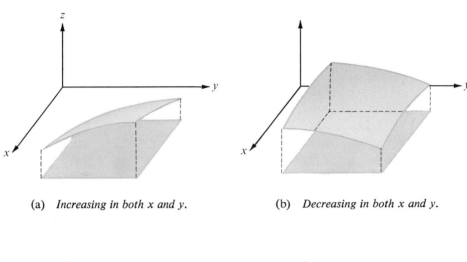

(a) *Increasing in both x and y.*   (b) *Decreasing in both x and y.*

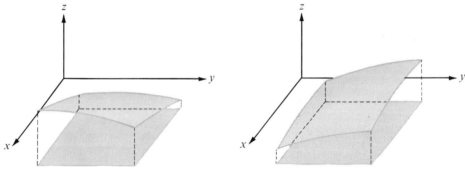

(c) *Increasing in x, decreasing in y.*   (d) *Decreasing in x, increasing in y.*

FIGURE 2.11   *Functions monotonic on a rectangle.*

10. Let f be defined on the rectangle $R = [1, 2] \times [1, 4]$ as follows:

$$f(x, y) = \begin{cases} (x + y)^{-2} & \text{if } x \le y \le 2x, \\ 0 & \text{otherwise}. \end{cases}$$

Indicate, by means of a sketch, the portion of R in which f is nonzero and compute the value of the double integral $\iint\limits_{R} f$, given that the integral exists.

2.10 Integrability of piecewise monotonic functions

In order to apply Theorem 2–4 to evaluate a double integral by repeated integration we must know in advance that f is integrable on R. As in the case of one-dimensional integration theory, further restrictions must be placed on a function defined and bounded on a rectangle to guarantee the existence of its integral. To settle this problem completely we need a *necessary and sufficient condition* for integrability. Such a condition is known and will be described in the next section. In this section we shall discuss a useful *sufficient* condition. As in the one-dimensional case we introduce a broad class of functions, known as *piecewise monotonic functions*, and prove that they are always integrable. Although this class does not include *all* integrable functions it does include many common examples.

A function f of two variables will be called piecewise monotonic if the intersection of the surface $z = f(x, y)$ with every plane $x = $ constant and every plane $y = $ constant is a piecewise monotonic plane curve. To describe this concept in analytic terms we introduce the following definitions.

Let f be defined and bounded on a rectangle $R = [a, b] \times [c, d]$. Let x_1 and x_2 denote arbitrary points in $[a, b]$, and let y_1 and y_2 denote arbitrary points in $[c, d]$. We say that f is *increasing in* x if

$$f(x_1, y_1) \le f(x_2, y_1) \qquad \text{whenever} \quad x_1 \le x_2 \,.$$

If, on the other hand, we have the opposite inequality

$$f(x_1, y_1) \ge f(x_2, y_1) \qquad \text{whenever} \quad x_1 \le x_2 \,,$$

we say that f is *decreasing in* x. The function f is said to be *monotonic in* x if it is increasing in x or decreasing in x. In a similar manner, we can define the expressions f is *increasing in* y, *decreasing in* y, or *monotonic in* y. For example, we say that f is increasing in y if

$$f(x_1, y_1) \le f(x_1, y_2) \qquad \text{whenever} \quad y_1 \le y_2 \,,$$

and so on. In each case it is to be understood that the inequalities are to hold for all choices of x_1, x_2 in $[a, b]$ and all choices of y_1, y_2 in $[c, d]$.

A function f is called *monotonic on* R if it is monotonic in both x and y. The various possibilities are illustrated in Figure 2.11. For example, in Figure 2.11(a), f is increasing in both x and y. In this case we have

$$f(x_1, y_1) \le f(x_2, y_2) \qquad \text{whenever} \quad x_1 \le x_2 \qquad \text{and} \qquad y_1 \le y_2 \,.$$

In Figure 2.11(c), f is increasing in x and decreasing in y, so we have

$$f(x_1, y_1) \le f(x_2, y_2) \qquad \text{whenever} \quad x_1 \le x_2 \qquad \text{and} \qquad y_1 \ge y_2 \,.$$

Sometimes we wish to consider functions monotonic on the open rectangle $(a, b) \times (c, d)$. In this case the above inequalities need hold only for x_1, x_2 in (a, b) and y_1, y_2 in (c, d).

A function f is said to be *piecewise monotonic on* R if there is a partition P of R such that f is monotonic on each of the open subrectangles of P. Geometrically, this means that the graph of f consists of monotonic pieces. In particular, all step functions are piecewise monotonic. Another example of a piecewise monotonic function is shown in Figure 2.12. Here $f(x, y) = e^{-x^2 - y^2}$ for $|x| \le 1$ and $|y| \le 1$.

We shall now prove the following important theorem concerning the integrability of monotonic functions.

2– 5   THEOREM.   Let f be defined and bounded on a rectangle R. If f is monotonic on R the double integral $\iint\limits_{R} f$ exists. Moreover, the value of the integral may be obtained by iterated integration. That is, if $R = [a, b] \times [c, d]$, we have

(2.12)
$$\iint\limits_{R} f = \int_c^d \left[\int_a^b f(x, y)\, dx \right] dy = \int_a^b \left[\int_c^d f(x, y)\, dy \right] dx .$$

Note. The existence of all the one-dimensional integrals in (2.12) will be demonstrated in the course of the proof.

Proof. Let us consider the case in which f is increasing in both x and y. First we shall prove that the double integral exists and then we shall prove formula (2.12).

Let P_1 be a partition of $[a, b]$ into n *equal* subintervals $[x_{i-1}, x_i]$, each of length $(b - a)/n$, and let P_2 be a partition of $[c, d]$ into n subintervals $[y_{j-1}, y_j]$ of length $(d - c)/n$. Then

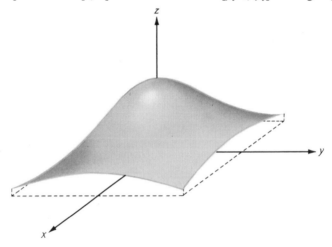

FIGURE 2.12   *A piecewise monotonic function:* $f(x, y) = e^{-x^2-y^2}$, $|x| \le 1$, $|y| \le 1$.

$P = P_1 \times P_2$ is a partition of R into n^2 subrectangles $R_{ij} = [x_{i-1}, x_i] \times [y_{j-1}, y_j]$. In R_{ij} the function f takes its largest value at the vertex (x_i, y_j) and its smallest value at the opposite vertex (x_{i-1}, y_{j-1}). Define two special step functions s and t as follows:

$$s(x, y) = f(x_{i-1}, y_{j-1}) \qquad \text{and} \qquad t(x, y) = f(x_i, y_j)$$

if (x, y) is in the open subrectangle $(x_{i-1}, x_i) \times (y_{j-1}, y_j)$. We automatically have

(2.13) $$s(x, y) \le f(x, y) \le t(x, y)$$

for all (x, y) in the open subrectangles. At the boundary points† of R_{ij} define s and t so

---

† For example, on the lower half-open edge of R_{ij} we have $x_{i-1} \le x < x_i$ and $y = y_{j-1}$, and we can define $s(x, y) = f(x_{i-1}, y_{j-1})$ and $t(x, y) = f(x_i, y_j)$. The same values can be assigned on the leftmost half-open edge, where $x = x_{i-1}$ and $y_{j-1} \le y < y_j$. Then we put $s(x, d) = f(a, d)$, $t(x, d) = f(b, d)$ for $a \le x \le b$, and $s(b, y) = f(b, c)$, $t(b, y) = f(b, d)$ for $c \le y \le d$.

as to preserve these inequalities. In a moment we shall prove that the integrals of these two step functions satisfy the inequality

(2.14)
$$\iint_R t - \iint_R s \le \frac{A}{n},$$

where $A = 2(b - a)(d - c)[f(b, d) - f(a, c)]$. Once we know this, it will be easy to prove that the double integral $\iint_R f$ exists. First we show how this inequality implies the existence of the double integral of f, and then we return to the proof of (2.14).

Suppose (2.14) holds. We shall assume that f is *not* integrable on R and arrive at a contradiction. If f is not integrable there are at least two numbers I_1 and I_2, say, with $I_1 < I_2$, such that

$$\iint_R s \le I_1 \le \iint_R t \quad \text{and} \quad \iint_R s \le I_2 \le \iint_R t$$

for *all* step functions s and t satisfying (2.13) on R. In particular, this must be true for the two special step functions just constructed. Combining these inequalities and using (2.14), we obtain

$$0 < I_2 - I_1 \le \iint_R t - \iint_R s \le \frac{A}{n}.$$

In other words, we have $0 < I_2 - I_1 \le A/n$ for every integer $n \ge 1$. But this is a contradiction because we can obviously take n large enough so that $A/n < I_2 - I_1$. Thus, the assumption that f is *not* integrable leads to a contradiction. Therefore the inequality (2.14) implies that f is integrable.

Next we prove (2.14). Using the definition of the double integral for step functions we have

$$\iint_R t - \iint_R s = \sum_{i=1}^{n} \sum_{j=1}^{n} [f(x_i, y_j) - f(x_{i-1}, y_{j-1})] (x_i - x_{i-1})(y_j - y_{j-1})$$

$$= \frac{(b - a)(d - c)}{n^2} \sum_{i=1}^{n} \sum_{j=1}^{n} [f(x_i, y_j) - f(x_{i-1}, y_{j-1})].$$

In the summand we add and subtract the term $f(x_i, y_{j-1})$ to obtain

$$\iint_R t - \iint_R s = \frac{(b - a)(d - c)}{n^2} \left\{ \sum_{i=1}^{n} \sum_{j=1}^{n} [f(x_i, y_j) - f(x_i, y_{j-1})] \right.$$

$$\left. + \sum_{j=1}^{n} \sum_{i=1}^{n} [f(x_i, y_{j-1}) - f(x_{i-1}, y_{j-1})] \right\}.$$

Each of the inner sums on the right telescopes, giving us

$$\iint_R t - \iint_R s = \frac{(b - a)(d - c)}{n^2} \left\{ \sum_{i=1}^{n} [f(x_i, y_n) - f(x_i, y_0)] \right.$$

$$\left. + \sum_{i=1}^{n} [f(x_n, y_{j-1}) - f(x_0, y_{j-1})] \right\}.$$

Since f is increasing in both x and y, each of the summands appearing on the right is no larger than $f(b, d) - f(a, c)$. If we replace each sum by $n[f(b, d) - f(a, c)]$ we obtain (2.14) at once. This completes the proof that f is integrable.

To prove that the double integral is equal to the iterated integrals in (2.12) we argue as follows: For each fixed y in $[c, d]$ the one-dimensional integral $\int_a^b f(x, y)\,dx$ exists (since f is increasing in x). Let $A(y)$ denote the value of this integral. Then, since f is increasing in y, we have

$$A(y_1) = \int_a^b f(x, y_1)\,dx \leq \int_a^b f(x, y_2)\,dx = A(y_2) \qquad \text{whenever} \quad y_1 \leq y_2 ,$$

so A is increasing on $[c, d]$. Therefore the one-dimensional integral $\int_c^d A(y)\,dy$ exists. Now choose arbitrary step functions s and t satisfying the inequalities (2.13) for all (x, y) in R. Integrating these inequalities with respect to x we find

$$\int_a^b s(x, y)\,dx \leq \int_a^b f(x, y)\,dx \leq \int_a^b t(x, y)\,dx .$$

Integrating again with respect to y over $[c, d]$ and using (2.4) we obtain

$$\iint_R s \leq \int_c^d \left[\int_a^b f(x, y)\,dx \right] dy \leq \iint_R t .$$

Since this is true for *arbitrary* step functions s and t satisfying (2.13), the iterated integral must be equal to the double integral $\iint_R f$. The same is true, of course, when the iteration is taken in reverse order; this proves (2.12).

For functions increasing in both x and y the proof of Theorem 2–5 is now complete. Call this case (1). There are three more cases to consider: (2) f decreasing in both x and y; (3) f increasing in x and decreasing in y; (4) f decreasing in x and increasing in y. The proof in case (2) may be obtained by applying case (1) to the function $-f$. The proof in case (3) is entirely analogous to that of case (1). Finally, case (4) can be deduced from case (3) by considering $-f$.

Although Theorem 2–5 refers to functions monotonic on a closed rectangle R, a slight modification of the proof shows that the conclusion also holds if f is bounded on R and monotonic only on the open rectangle $(a, b) \times (c, d)$. This verification is left as an exercise for the reader. It then follows from the additive property of double integrals that Theorem 2–5 may be extended as follows:

2– 6   THEOREM. Let f be defined and bounded on a rectangle R. If f is piecewise monotonic on R, the double integral $\iint_R f$ exists and is equal to both the iterated integrals in formula (2.12).

2.11 Continuity of functions of two variables

The concept of continuity for functions of two variables is a direct generalization of the one-dimensional case. Roughly speaking, a function f of two variables is called continuous at a point (x_0, y_0) if at all nearby points (x, y) the function values $f(x, y)$

differ only slightly from $f(x_0, y_0)$. To translate this idea into a precise mathematical statement we introduce the concept of a *neighborhood* of a point (x_0, y_0).

If $r > 0$, the set of points (x, y) satisfying $(x - x_0)^2 + (y - y_0)^2 < r^2$ is called a neighborhood of (x_0, y_0) of radius r. That is, a neighborhood of (x_0, y_0) is simply a circular disk with center at (x_0, y_0). When we speak of a function being continuous at (x_0, y_0) we always assume that f is defined at (x_0, y_0) and that every neighborhood of (x_0, y_0) contains at least one point (x, y) other than (x_0, y_0) at which f is defined. This ensures that there actually exist points (x, y) arbitrarily close to (x_0, y_0). Under these conditions, the definition of continuity takes the following form:

DEFINITION OF CONTINUITY. *A function f is said to be continuous at (x_0, y_0) if for every $\epsilon > 0$ there is a neighborhood of (x_0, y_0) such that for every point (x, y) in this neighborhood at which f is defined we have the inequality*

$$|f(x, y) - f(x_0, y_0)| < \epsilon .$$

If f is continuous at all points of a set S, we say that f is *continuous on S*. Most of the properties of continuous functions of one variable have direct extensions in the two-dimensional case. For example, if f and g are both continuous at a point (x_0, y_0), so are the sum $f + g$, the difference $f - g$, the product $f \cdot g$, and the quotient f/g. For the quotient we need the extra condition that $g(x_0, y_0) \neq 0$. The sum, difference, product, and quotient are, of course, those functions whose values at (x, y) are given by the respective formulas

$$f(x, y) + g(x, y), \ f(x, y) - g(x, y), \ f(x, y) \cdot g(x, y), \ \text{and} \ f(x, y)/g(x, y) .$$

The proofs of these properties are entirely analogous to those in the one-dimensional case and need not be discussed here. Instead, we mention a few examples and make some informal remarks about continuous functions of two variables.

The simplest examples are polynomials in two variables. These are functions f defined by formulas of the form

$$f(x, y) = \sum_{i=0}^{n} \sum_{j=0}^{m} c_{ij} x^i y^j ,$$

where the coefficients c_{ij} are constants. Polynomials are continuous at all points in the xy-plane. Familiar special cases are *linear functions,*

$$f(x, y) = Ax + By + C ,$$

whose graphs are planes, and *quadratic functions,*

$$f(x, y) = Ax^2 + Bxy + Cy^2 + Dx + Ey + F ,$$

whose graphs are quadric surfaces (or portions of quadric surfaces).

New examples may be constructed by employing the following theorem on continuity of composite functions: If X and Y are functions of two variables, both continuous at a point (x_0, y_0), and if f is another function of two variables continuous at the point (a, b), where $a = X(x_0, y_0)$ and $b = Y(x_0, y_0)$, the composite function g defined by the equation

$$g(x, y) = f[X(x, y), Y(x, y)]$$

is continuous at the point (x_0, y_0).

This theorem implies the continuity of g when $g(x, y)$ is given by formulas such as

$$\sin(x^2y), \quad \log(x^2 + y^2), \quad \frac{e^{x+y}}{x + y}, \quad \log[\cos(x^2 + y^2)].$$

These examples are continuous at all points at which the functions are defined. The first is continuous at all points in the plane, and the second at all points except the origin. The third is continuous at all points (x, y) at which $x + y \neq 0$, and the fourth at all points at which $x^2 + y^2$ is not an odd multiple of $\pi/2$. [The set of (x, y) such that $x^2 + y^2 = n\pi/2$, $n = 1, 3, 5, \ldots$, is a family of concentric circles centered at the origin.] These examples show that the discontinuities of a function of two variables may consist of isolated points, entire curves, or families of curves.

A function of two variables may be continuous in each variable separately and yet be discontinuous as a function of the two variables together. This is illustrated by the following example:

$$f(x, y) = \frac{xy}{x^2 + y^2} \quad \text{if} \quad (x, y) \neq (0, 0), \, f(0, 0) = 0.$$

For points (x, y) on the x-axis we have $y = 0$ and $f(x, y) = f(x, 0) = 0$, so the function has the constant value 0 everywhere on the x-axis. Therefore, if we put $y = 0$ and think of f as a function of x alone, f is continuous at $x = 0$. Similarly, f has the constant value 0 at all points on the y-axis, so if we put $x = 0$ and think of f as a function of y alone, f is continuous at $y = 0$. However, as a function of *two* variables, f is not continuous at the origin. In fact, at each point of the line $y = x$ (except at the origin) the function has the constant value $\frac{1}{2}$ because $f(x, x) = x^2/(2x^2) = \frac{1}{2}$; since there are points on this line arbitrarily close to the origin and since $f(0, 0) \neq \frac{1}{2}$, the function is not continuous at $(0, 0)$.

Continuity of functions of two variables will be examined in more detail in Chapter 4. At this stage we merely mention that an important theorem in the theory of integration states that the double integral $\iint\limits_R f$ always exists if f is continuous everywhere on a rectangle R. As a matter of fact, the integral also exists if there are only a finite number of discontinuities of f in R. More generally, if the set of discontinuities consists of a finite number of rectifiable curves, the double integral will still exist. Actually, the set of discontinuities of an integrable function can be more complicated than this. The definitive theorem in this connection was discovered by Lebesgue† and makes use of sets of measure zero, a concept that may be described as follows: A plane set S is said to have *measure zero* if for every $\epsilon > 0$ a finite or countably infinite collection of rectangles exists whose union contains S and whose total area is less than ϵ. In other words, a plane set of measure zero is one that can be enclosed in a union of rectangles whose total area is arbitrarily small. Isolated points and line segments are obviously sets of measure zero. It is easy to prove that every piecewise monotonic plane curve (the graph of a piecewise monotonic function) is of measure zero. Also, finite or countably infinite unions of sets of measure zero are again of measure zero. The reader may find it instructive to supply proofs of these statements. The last statement implies that the set of all points in the plane with rational coordinates has measure zero, since this set is a countable collection of points.

† Henri Lebesgue (1875–1941) was one of the creators of the modern theory of measure and integration. Lebesgue's theory of integration, introduced in 1902, is considered one of the outstanding contributions to 20th century mathematics.

This particular set is of interest because it has infinitely many points in every open rectangle, no matter how small.

Lebesgue's theorem may now be stated as follows:

2–7 THEOREM. *Let f be defined and bounded on a rectangle R. Then the double integral $\iint_R f$ exists if and only if the set of discontinuities of f on R forms a set of measure zero.*

Note. A function with this property is said to be *continuous almost everywhere* on R.

The proof of Lebesgue's theorem is lengthy and intricate and will not be discussed here.† We shall feel free to use the theorem to establish the existence of double integrals, although for most of the examples in this book integrability can be deduced directly from Theorem 2–6.

Lebesgue's theorem is not restricted to the two-dimensional theory. If S is a subset of the real line, then S is said to be a set of (one-dimensional) measure zero if, for every $\epsilon > 0$, S can be enclosed in a finite or countably infinite union of intervals, the sum of whose lengths is less than ϵ. Lebesgue's theorem for one-dimensional integrals states that if f is defined and bounded on a finite interval $[a, b]$, then the integral $\int_a^b f(x)\, dx$ exists if and only if the set of discontinuities of f on $[a, b]$ forms a set of measure zero. (Such a function is said to be continuous almost everywhere on $[a, b]$.)

In Section 2.32 of Volume I we proved that a one-dimensional integral $\int_a^b f(x)\, dx$ always exists if f is continuous on a finite interval $[a, b]$. The ideas employed in this proof can be extended to prove a corresponding theorem for functions continuous on a rectangle. These theorems and the theorems on integrability of piecewise monotonic functions provide *sufficient* conditions for integrability. The theorems of Lebesgue provide *necessary and sufficient* conditions.

2.12 Double integrals extended over more general regions

Up to this point the double integral has been defined only for rectangular regions of integration. However, it is not difficult to extend the concept to more general regions. We shall be interested here only in the simplest types of regions. First, we consider sets of points S in the xy-plane described as follows:

$$S = \{(x, y) \mid a \le x \le b \text{ and } \phi_1(x) \le y \le \phi_2(x)\}\,,$$

where ϕ_1 and ϕ_2 are continuous functions defined on a closed interval $[a, b]$. An example of such a region, to which we shall refer as a region of Type I, is shown in Figure 2.13. In a region of Type I, for each point c in $[a, b]$ the vertical line $x = c$ intersects S in a line segment joining the curve $y = \phi_1(x)$ to $y = \phi_2(x)$.

Another type of region T (Type II) may be described as follows:

$$T = \{(x, y) \mid c \le y \le d, \psi_1(y) \le x \le \psi_2(y)\}\,,$$

where ψ_1 and ψ_2 are continuous on the interval $[c, d]$. An example is shown in Figure 2.14. In this case horizontal lines intersect T in line segments. Most of the regions in

† A proof is given in Chapter 10 of the author's *Mathematical Analysis*, Addison-Wesley, Reading, Mass., 1957.

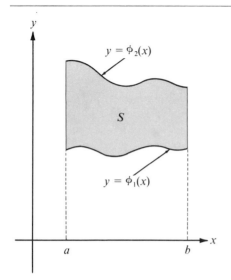

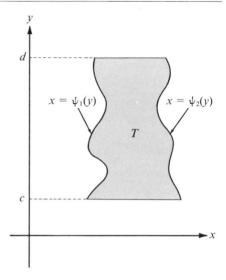

FIGURE 2.13   *A region S of Type I.*   FIGURE 2.14   *A region T of Type II.*

which we shall be interested here are either of one of these two types or they can be split into a finite number of pieces, each of which is of one of these two types. (See Figure 2.15.) Such regions will be called *standard regions*. The double integral over a standard region is defined to be the sum of the integrals over the individual pieces of the two types described.† Therefore, it remains to define the double integral over regions of Type I and of Type II. Since the two are entirely analogous, only regions of Type I need be treated.

First enclose the region S in a rectangle R. This is always possible because the functions ϕ_1 and ϕ_2 are continuous and hence *bounded* on $[a, b]$. Let f be the integrand in question; that is, suppose f is a function that is defined and bounded on S. Define a new function $\tilde{f}$ on the whole rectangle R as follows:

$$\tilde{f}(x, y) = \begin{cases} f(x, y) & \text{if } (x, y) \in S \\ 0 & \text{if } (x, y) \in R - S. \end{cases}$$

In other words, extend the definition of f to the whole rectangle R by making the function values equal to 0 outside S. Now ask whether or not the extended function $\tilde{f}$ is integrable on R. If so, we say that f is integrable on S and that, *by definition*,

$$\iint\limits_{S} f = \iint\limits_{R} \tilde{f}.$$

The discontinuities of $\tilde{f}$ in R will consist of the discontinuities of f in S plus those points on the boundary of S at which f is nonzero. In all the examples in this book, f

† It can be shown that two different decompositions of the region lead to the same value for the double integral, so the definition is not ambiguous.

will be continuous almost everywhere in S and the boundary of S will be a finite union of monotonic curves (and hence a set of measure zero), so the set of discontinuities of $\tilde{f}$ will also be a set of measure zero. The existence of $\iint_R \tilde{f}$ (and hence of $\iint_S f$) then follows by Lebesgue's theorem. In many cases $\tilde{f}$ is piecewise monotonic on R and the integrability of f follows also from Theorem 2–6.

When f is nonnegative, the set A of points (x, y, z) in 3-space such that $0 \le z \le f(x, y)$ and $(x, y) \,\varepsilon\, S$ is called the *ordinate set of f over S*. An example is shown in Figure 2.16. The volume $V(A)$ of such a set is defined by the equation

$$V(A) = \iint_S f.$$

It can be shown that the set function V so defined has all the properties of volume listed in Section 2.2. In fact, when f is continuous on S or when $\tilde{f}$ is piecewise monotonic on R, the properties of V follow at once from the results of Section 2.7.

If the hypotheses of Theorem 2–4 are satisfied by the function $\tilde{f}$ on the rectangle R, the double integral of f over S may be evaluated by repeated integration, the first integration being performed with respect to y:

$$\iint_S f(x, y)\, dx\, dy = \int_a^b \left[\int_{\phi_1(x)}^{\phi_2(x)} f(x, y)\, dy \right] dx.$$

In particular, if $f(x, y) = 1$ for each point (x, y) in S, we obtain

$$\iint_S dx\, dy = \int_a^b \left[\int_{\phi_1(x)}^{\phi_2(x)} dy \right] dx = \int_a^b [\phi_2(x) - \phi_1(x)]\, dx,$$

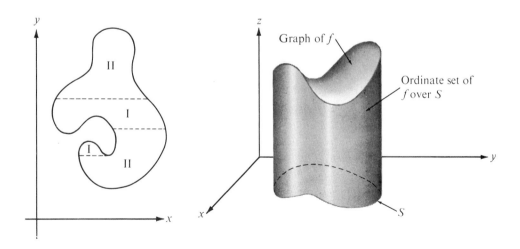

FIGURE 2.15 *A region decomposable into a finite union of regions of Types I and II.*

FIGURE 2.16 *The volume of the ordinate set of f over S is the double integral $\iint_S f$.*

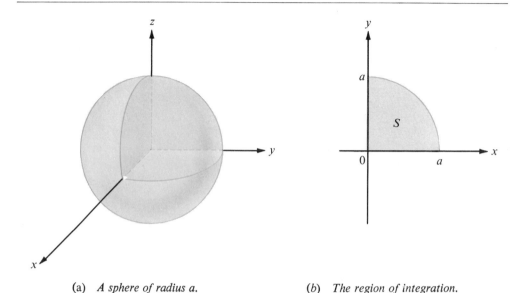

(a) *A sphere of radius a.*   (b) *The region of integration.*

FIGURE 2.17 *Computation of the volume of a sphere by double integration.*

which is equal to the *area* of S. Thus, the double integral may be used to compute areas as well as volumes; the area of S, which we denote by $A(S)$, is given by the formula

$$A(S) = \iint\limits_{S} dx\, dy \, .$$

When f is a positive constant, say $f(x, y) = k$ for each (x, y) in S, the ordinate set is a solid cylinder whose base is S and whose altitude is k. Its volume is equal to

$$\iint\limits_{S} k\, dx\, dy = k \iint\limits_{S} dx\, dy = k \cdot A(S) \, .$$

For sets of Type II the procedure is entirely analogous, and the formula for repeated integration is

$$\iint\limits_{T} f(x, y)\, dx\, dy = \int_{c}^{d} \left[\int_{\psi_1(y)}^{\psi_2(y)} f(x, y)\, dx \right] dy \, .$$

Of course, a region may be of both Type I and Type II. (The regions bounded by circles or ellipses are examples.) In this case the order of integration is immaterial and we may write

$$\int_{a}^{b} \left[\int_{\phi_1(x)}^{\phi_2(x)} f(x, y)\, dy \right] dx = \int_{c}^{d} \left[\int_{\psi_1(y)}^{\psi_2(y)} f(x, y)\, dx \right] dy \, .$$

In some cases one of these integrals may be much easier to compute than the other; it is usually worthwhile to examine both before attempting the actual evaluation of a double integral.

The following examples are more or less typical of the kinds of manipulations encountered in connection with the evaluation of double integrals.

Example 1. Compute the volume of a sphere of radius a.

Solution. We shall compute the volume V of one octant, that is, of that portion under the surface $x^2 + y^2 + z^2 = a^2$ for which x, y, and z are positive; then we shall multiply the result by 8. This volume is equal to the double integral

$$V = \iint\limits_{S} \sqrt{a^2 - x^2 - y^2} \, dx \, dy \,,$$

where S is the first quadrant of the circular disk $x^2 + y^2 \leq a^2$. (See Figure 2.17.) In this example the integral exists because the integrand is decreasing in both x and y. Because of the symmetry in x and y, it does not matter which integration we perform first. If we integrate first with respect to y we obtain

$$V = \int_0^a \left[\int_0^{\sqrt{a^2-x^2}} \sqrt{a^2 - x^2 - y^2} \, dy \right] dx \,.$$

Evaluation of the inner integral gives

$$\left(\frac{y}{2} \sqrt{a^2 - x^2 - y^2} + \frac{a^2 - x^2}{2} \arcsin \frac{y}{\sqrt{a^2 - x^2}} \right) \Bigg|_{y=0}^{y=\sqrt{a^2-x^2}} = \frac{\pi}{4}(a^2 - x^2) \,.$$

Hence

$$V = \frac{\pi}{4} \int_0^a (a^2 - x^2) \, dx = \frac{\pi a^3}{6} \,,$$

and the volume of the sphere, $8V$, is $\frac{4}{3}\pi a^3$.

Example 2. The double integral of a positive function f, $\iint\limits_{S} f(x, y) \, dx \, dy$, reduces to the repeated integral

$$\int_0^1 \left[\int_{x^2}^x f(x, y) \, dy \right] dx \,.$$

Determine the region S and interchange the order of integration.

Solution. For each fixed x between 0 and 1, the integration with respect to y is over the interval from x^2 to x. This means that the region is of Type I and lies between the two curves $y = x^2$ and $y = x$. The region S is the set of points between these two curves and above the interval $[0, 1]$. (See Figure 2.18.) Since S is also of Type II we may interchange the order of integration to obtain

$$\int_0^1 \left[\int_y^{\sqrt{y}} f(x, y) \, dx \right] dy \,.$$

Example 3. A double integral of a positive function f, $\iint\limits_{S} f(x, y) \, dx \, dy$, reduces to the repeated integral:

$$\int_0^3 \left[\int_{4y/3}^{\sqrt{25-y^2}} f(x, y) \, dx \right] dy \,.$$

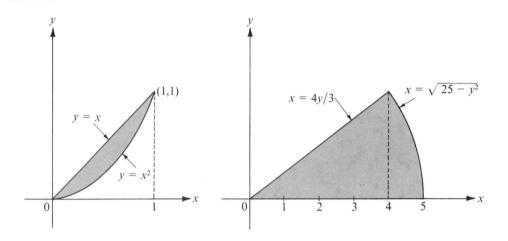

FIGURE 2.18   *Example 2.*   FIGURE 2.19   *Example 3.*

Determine the region S and interchange the order of integration.

Solution. For each fixed y between 0 and 3, the integration with respect to x is over the interval from $4y/3$ to $\sqrt{25 - y^2}$. Therefore region S is of Type II and lies between the two curves $x = 4y/3$ and $x = \sqrt{25 - y^2}$. This region, shown in Figure 2.19, is a sector of a circle. When the order of integration is reversed the region must be split into two regions of Type I; the result is the sum of two integrals:

$$\int_0^4 \left[\int_0^{3x/4} f(x, y) \, dy \right] dx + \int_4^5 \left[\int_0^{\sqrt{25 - x^2}} f(x, y) \, dy \right] dx \,.$$

2.13   Exercises

In all the exercises of this section you may assume the existence of all the double integrals encountered.

In Exercises 1 through 5, make a sketch of the region of integration and evaluate the double integral.

1. $\iint_S x \cos(x + y) \, dx \, dy$, where S is the triangular region whose vertices are $(0, 0), (\pi, 0), (\pi, \pi)$.

2. $\iint_S (1 + x) \sin y \, dx \, dy$, where S is the trapezoid with vertices $(0, 0), (1, 0), (1, 2), (0, 1)$.

3. $\iint_S e^{x+y} \, dx \, dy$, where $S = \{(x, y) \mid |x| + |y| \le 1\}$.

4. $\iint_S x^2 y^2 \, dx \, dy$, where S is the bounded portion of the first quadrant lying between the two hyperbolas $xy = 1$ and $xy = 2$ and the two straight lines $y = x$ and $y = 4x$.

5. $\iint_S (x^2 - y^2) \, dx \, dy$, where S is the region bounded by the curve $y = \sin x$ and the interval $[0, \pi]$.

6. A pyramid is bounded by the three coordinate planes and the plane $x + 2y + 3z = 6$. Make a sketch of the solid and compute its volume by double integration.

7. A solid is bounded by the surface $z = x^2 - y^2$, the xy-plane, and the planes $x = 1$ and $x = 3$. Make a sketch of the solid and compute its volume by double integration.

8. Compute, by double integration, the volume of the ordinate set of f over S if:

(a) $f(x, y) = x^2 + y^2$ and $S = \{(x, y) \mid |x| \leq 1, |y| \leq 1\}$.
(b) $f(x, y) = 3x + y$ and $S = \{(x, y) \mid 4x^2 + 9y^2 \leq 36, x > 0, y > 0\}$.
(c) $f(x, y) = y + 2x + 20$ and $S = \{(x, y) \mid x^2 + y^2 \leq 16\}$.

In Exercises 9 through 18 assume that the double integral of a positive function f extended over a region S reduces to the given repeated integral. In each case, make a sketch of the region S and interchange the order of integration.

9. $\displaystyle\int_0^1 \left[\int_0^y f(x, y)\, dx \right] dy.$

14. $\displaystyle\int_1^e \left[\int_0^{\log x} f(x, y)\, dy \right] dx.$

10. $\displaystyle\int_0^2 \left[\int_{y^2}^{2y} f(x, y)\, dx \right] dy.$

15. $\displaystyle\int_{-1}^1 \left[\int_{-\sqrt{1-x^2}}^{1-x^2} f(x, y)\, dy \right] dx.$

11. $\displaystyle\int_1^4 \left[\int_{\sqrt{x}}^2 f(x, y)\, dy \right] dx.$

16. $\displaystyle\int_0^1 \left[\int_{x^3}^{x^2} f(x, y)\, dy \right] dx.$

12. $\displaystyle\int_1^2 \left[\int_{2-x}^{\sqrt{2x-x^2}} f(x, y)\, dy \right] dx.$

17. $\displaystyle\int_0^\pi \left[\int_{-\sin\frac{x}{2}}^{\sin x} f(x, y)\, dy \right] dx.$

13. $\displaystyle\int_{-6}^2 \left[\int_{(x^2-4)/4}^{2-x} f(x, y)\, dy \right] dx.$

18. $\displaystyle\int_0^4 \left[\int_{-\sqrt{4-y}}^{(y-4)/2} f(x, y)\, dx \right] dy.$

19. When a double integral was set up for the volume V under the paraboloid $z = x^2 + y^2$ and above a region S of the xy-plane, the following sum of iterated integrals was obtained:

$$V = \int_0^1 \left[\int_0^y (x^2 + y^2)\, dx \right] dy + \int_1^2 \left[\int_0^{2-y} (x^2 + y^2)\, dx \right] dy.$$

Sketch the region S and express V as an iterated integral in which the order of integration is reversed. Also, carry out the integration and compute V.

20. When a double integral was set up for the volume V under the surface $z = f(x, y)$ and above a region S of the xy-plane, the following sum of iterated integrals was obtained:

$$V = \int_0^{a\sin c} \left[\int_{\sqrt{a^2-y^2}}^{\sqrt{b^2-y^2}} f(x, y)\, dx \right] dy + \int_{a\sin c}^{b\sin c} \left[\int_{y\cot c}^{\sqrt{b^2-y^2}} f(x, y)\, dx \right] dy.$$

Given that $0 < a < b$ and $0 < c < \pi/2$, sketch the region S, giving the equations of all curves which form its boundary.

21. When a double integral was set up for the volume V under the surface $z = f(x, y)$ and above a region S of the xy-plane, the following sum of iterated integrals was obtained:

$$V = \int_1^2 \left[\int_x^{x^3} f(x, y)\, dy \right] dx + \int_2^8 \left[\int_x^8 f(x, y)\, dy \right] dx.$$

(a) Sketch the region S and express V as an iterated integral in which the order of integration is reversed.

(b) Carry out the integration and compute V when $f(x, y) = e^y(x/y)^{1/2}$.

22. Let $A = \int_0^1 e^{-t^2}\, dt$ and $B = \int_0^{1/2} e^{-t^2}\, dt$. Evaluate the iterated integral

$$I = 2 \int_{-1/2}^1 \left[\int_0^x e^{-y^2}\, dy \right] dx$$

in terms of A and B. There are positive integers m and n such that

$$I = mA - nB + e^{-1} - e^{-1/4}.$$

Use this fact to check your answer.

23. A solid cone is obtained by connecting every point of a plane region S with a vertex not in the plane of S. Let A denote the area of S, and let h denote the altitude of the cone. Prove that:

(a) The cross-sectional area cut by a plane parallel to the base and at a distance t from the vertex is $(t/h)^2 A$, if $0 \le t \le h$.

(b) The volume of the cone is $\frac{1}{3}Ah$.

24. Reverse the order of integration to derive the formula

$$\int_0^a \left[\int_0^y e^{m(a-x)} f(x)\, dx \right] dy = \int_0^a (a - x)\, e^{m(a-x)} f(x)\, dx ,$$

where a and m are constants, $a > 0$.

2.14 Further applications of double integrals

We have already seen that the double integral may be used to compute volumes of solids and areas of plane regions. Many other concepts such as mass, center of mass, and moment of inertia can be defined and computed with the aid of double integrals. This section contains a brief discussion of these topics. They are of special importance in physics and engineering.

Let $\vec{P}$ denote the vector from an origin 0 to an arbitrary point P in 3-space. If n positive masses $m_1, m_2, \ldots, m_n$ are located at points $P_1, P_2, \ldots, P_n$, respectively, the *center of mass* of the system is defined to be the point C determined by the vector

$$\vec{C} = \frac{\sum\limits_{k=1}^{n} m_k \vec{P}_k}{\sum\limits_{k=1}^{n} m_k}.$$

The denominator, $\sum m_k$, is called the *total mass* of the system.

If each mass m_k is translated by a given vector $\vec{A}$ to a new point Q_k where $\vec{Q}_k = \vec{P}_k + \vec{A}$, the center of mass is also translated by $\vec{A}$, since we have

$$\frac{\sum m_k \vec{Q}_k}{\sum m_k} = \frac{\sum m_k (\vec{P}_k + \vec{A})}{\sum m_k} = \frac{\sum m_k \vec{P}_k}{\sum m_k} + \vec{A} = \vec{C} + \vec{A}.$$

This may also be described by saying that the location of the center of mass depends only on the points $P_1, P_2, \ldots, P_n$ and the masses, and not on the origin. The center of mass is a theoretically computed quantity which represents, so to speak, a fictitious "balance point" of the system.

If the masses lie in a plane at points with coordinates $(x_1, y_1), \ldots, (x_n, y_n)$, and if the center of mass has coordinates $(\bar{x}, \bar{y})$, the vector relation which defines $\vec{C}$ can be expressed as two scalar equations,

$$\bar{x} = \frac{\sum m_k x_k}{\sum m_k}, \qquad \text{and} \qquad \bar{y} = \frac{\sum m_k y_k}{\sum m_k}.$$

In the numerator of the quotient defining $\bar{x}$, the kth term of the sum, $m_k x_k$, is called the *moment* of the mass m_k about the y-axis. If a mass M equal to the total mass of the system were placed at the center of mass, its moment about the *y*-axis would be equal to the moment of the system,

$$M\bar{x} = \sum_{k=1}^{n} m_k x_k .$$

When we deal with a system whose total mass is distributed throughout some region in the plane rather than at a finite number of discrete points, the concepts of mass, center of mass, and moment are defined by means of integrals rather than sums. For example, consider a "thin plate" having the shape of a plane region *S*. Assume that matter is distributed along this plate with a known density (mass per unit area). By this we mean that there is a nonnegative function *f* defined on *S* and that $f(x, y)$ represents the mass per unit area at the point (x, y). If the plate is made of a homogeneous material the density is constant. In this case the total mass of the plate is defined to be the product of the density and the area of the plate.

To define total mass when the density varies from point to point we begin with a plate having the shape of a rectangle $R = [a, b] \times [c, d]$. Suppose this rectangle is partitioned into *mn* subrectangles $R_{ij} = [x_{i-1}, x_i] \times [y_{j-1}, y_j]$, where $\{x_0, x_1, \ldots, x_n\}$ and $\{y_0, y_1, \ldots, y_m\}$ are partitions of $[a, b]$ and $[c, d]$, respectively. Assume that on each subrectangle R_{ij} the plate has a constant density c_{ij}. Then the total mass of R_{ij} is $c_{ij}(x_i - x_{i-1})(y_j - y_{j-1})$, the density times the area. We want mass to be an additive set function so we define the total mass of *R* to be the sum

$$\sum_{i=1}^{n} \sum_{j=1}^{m} c_{ij}(x_i - x_{i-1})(y_j - y_{j-1}) .$$

We recognize this sum as the double integral $\iint_R f$ of a step function *f* that has the constant value c_{ij} on the open subrectangles of the partition. Thus, when the density is a step function the mass is the double integral of the density. This suggests that we use the double integral of the density to define total mass in the general case. In other words, if a thin plate has the shape of a plane region *S* and if the density function *f* is integrable over *S*, we define the total mass *M* of the plate by the equation

$$M = \iint_S f(x, y) \, dx \, dy .$$

The quotient

$$\frac{\text{mass}}{\text{area}} = \frac{\iint_S f(x, y) \, dx \, dy}{\iint_S dx \, dy}$$

is called the *average density* of the plate. If *S* is thought of as a geometric configuration rather than as a thin plate, this quotient is called the *average* or *mean value* of the function *f* over the region *S*. In this case we do not require *f* to be nonnegative.

By analogy with the finite case, we define the *center of mass* of the plate to be the point $(\bar{x}, \bar{y})$ determined by the equations

$$(2.15) \qquad \bar{x} \, M = \iint_S x f(x, y) \, dx \, dy \qquad \text{and} \qquad \bar{y} \, M = \iint_S y f(x, y) \, dx \, dy .$$

The integrals on the right are called the moments of the plate about the y-axis and the x-axis, respectively. When the density is constant, say $f(x, y) = c$, a factor c cancels in each of Equations (2.15) and we obtain

$$\bar{x} A = \iint_S x \, dx \, dy \quad \text{and} \quad \bar{y} A = \iint_S y \, dx \, dy \, ,$$

where A is the area of S. In this case the point $(\bar{x}, \bar{y})$ is called the *centroid* of the plate (or of the region S).

If L is a line in the plane of the plate, let $\delta(x, y)$ denote the perpendicular distance from a point (x, y) in S to the line L. Then the number I_L defined by the equation

$$I_L = \iint_S \delta^2(x, y) f(x, y) \, dx \, dy$$

is called the *moment of inertia* of the plate about L. When $f(x, y) = 1$, I_L is called the moment of inertia or *second moment* of the region S about L. The moments of inertia about the x- and y-axes are denoted by I_x and I_y, respectively, and they are given by the integrals

$$I_x = \iint_S y^2 f(x, y) \, dx \, dy, \quad \text{and} \quad I_y = \iint_S x^2 f(x, y) \, dx \, dy \, .$$

The sum of these two integrals is called the *polar moment of inertia* I_0 about the origin:

$$I_0 = I_x + I_y = \iint_S (x^2 + y^2) f(x, y) \, dx \, dy \, .$$

Note. The mass and center of mass of a plate are properties of the body and are independent of the location of the origin and on the directions chosen for the coordinate axes. The polar moment of inertia depends on the location of the origin but not on the directions chosen for the axes. The moments and the moments of inertia about the x- and y-axes depend on the location of the origin and on the directions chosen for the axes. If a plate of constant density has an axis of symmetry, its centroid will lie on this axis. If there are two axes of symmetry, the centroid will lie on their intersection. These facts, which can be proven from the foregoing definitions, often help to simplify calculations involving center of mass and moment of inertia.

Example 1. A thin plate of constant density c is bounded by two concentric circles with radii a and b and center at the origin, where $0 < b < a$. Compute the polar moment of inertia.

Solution. The integral for I_0 is

$$I_0 = c \iint_S (x^2 + y^2) \, dx \, dy \, ,$$

where $S = \{(x, y) \mid b^2 \leq x^2 + y^2 \leq a^2\}$. To simplify the computations we note that this integral is an additive function of the region of integration (since the integrand is nonnegative), so we have

$$I_0 = c \iint_{S(a)} (x^2 + y^2) \, dx \, dy - c \iint_{S(b)} (x^2 + y^2) \, dx \, dy \, ,$$

where $S(a)$ and $S(b)$ are circular disks with radii a and b, respectively. We may use iterated integration to evaluate the integral over a, and we find

$$\iint\limits_{S(a)} (x^2 + y^2)\, dx\, dy = 4 \int_0^a \left[\int_0^{\sqrt{a^2 - x^2}} (x^2 + y^2)\, dy \right] dx = \frac{\pi a^4}{2}.$$

(We have omitted the details of the computation because this integral can be evaluated more easily with the use of polar coordinates, to be discussed in Section 2.17.) Therefore

$$I_0 = \frac{\pi c}{2}(a^4 - b^4) = \pi c(a^2 - b^2)\frac{(a^2 + b^2)}{2} = M\frac{a^2 + b^2}{2},$$

where $M = \pi c(a^2 - b^2)$, the mass of the plate.

Example 2: A theorem of Pappus.† Mass and moment of inertia are additive set functions because they are defined by integrals of nonnegative functions. In this example we describe a property of the center of mass that takes the place of additivity. Let A and B be two thin plates that are either disjoint or intersect along a set of measure zero. Let $M(A)$ and $M(B)$ denote their masses and let $\vec{C}_A$ and $\vec{C}_B$ denote vectors from an origin 0 to their respective centers of mass. Then the union $A \cup B$ has mass $M(A) + M(B)$, and its center of mass is determined by the vector $\vec{C}$, where

$$\vec{C} = \frac{M(A)\vec{C}_A + M(B)\,\vec{C}_B}{M(A) + M(B)}.$$

This is one of the theorems of Pappus. The quotient for $\vec{C}$ is a linear combination of the form $a\vec{C}_A + b\vec{C}_B$, where a and b are nonnegative scalars with sum 1. Therefore the tip of $\vec{C}$ lies on the line segment joining the tips of $\vec{C}_A$ and $\vec{C}_B$. The quotient for $\vec{C}$ is sometimes called a *convex combination* of $\vec{C}_A$ and $\vec{C}_B$.

Pappus' theorem follows at once from the definition of the center of mass given in (2.15). The theorem can be extended in an obvious way to the union of three or more regions. It is especially useful in practice when a plate of constant density is made up of several pieces, each of which has geometric symmetry. We determine the centroid of each piece and then form a suitable convex combination to find the centroid of the union.

2.15 Exercises

In the exercises of this section you may assume the existence of all the double integrals encountered.

In Exercises 1 through 8 a region S is bounded by one or more curves described by the given equations. In each case sketch the region S and determine the coordinates $\bar{x}$ and $\bar{y}$ of the centroid.

1. $y = x^2$, $x + y = 2$.
2. $y^2 = x + 3$, $y^2 = 5 - x$.
3. $x - 2y + 8 = 0$, $x + 3y + 5 = 0$, $x = -2$, $x = 4$.
4. $y = \sin x$, $y = 0$, $0 \le x \le \pi$.

† Pappus of Alexandria, who lived in the second half of the 3rd century, was one of the last geometers of the Alexandrian school of early Greek mathematics. He wrote a compendium of eight books summarizing much of the mathematical knowledge of his time. The last six and a part of the second are extant.

5. $y = \sin x$, $y = \cos x$, $0 \le x \le \dfrac{\pi}{4}$.

6. $y = \log x$, $y = 0$, $1 \le x \le a$.

7. $\sqrt{x} + \sqrt{y} = 1$, $x = 0$, $y = 0$.

8. $x^{2/3} + y^{2/3} = 1$, $x = 0$, $y = 0$, in first quadrant.

9. A thin plate is bounded by an arc of the parabola $y = 2x - x^2$ and the interval $0 \le x \le 2$. Determine its mass if the density at each point (x, y) is $(1 - y)/(1 + x)$.

10. Find the center of mass of a thin plate in the shape of a rectangle $ABCD$ if the density at any point is the product of the distances of the point from two adjacent sides AB and AD.

In Exercises 11 through 16, compute the moments of inertia I_x and I_y of a thin plate S in the xy-plane bounded by the one or more curves described by the given equations. In each case $f(x, y)$ denotes the density at an arbitrary point (x, y) of S.

11. $y = \sin^2 x$, $y = - \sin^2 x$, $-\pi \le x \le \pi$; $f(x, y) = 1$.

12. $\dfrac{x}{a} + \dfrac{y}{b} = 1$, $\dfrac{x}{c} + \dfrac{y}{b} = 1$, $y = 0$, $0 < c < a$, $b > 0$; $f(x, y) = 1$.

13. $(x - r)^2 + (y - r)^2 = r^2$, $x = 0$, $y = 0$, $0 \le x \le r$, $0 \le y \le r$; $f(x, y) = 1$.

14. $xy = 1$, $xy = 2$, $x = 2y$, $y = 2x$, $x > 0$, $y > 0$; $f(x, y) = 1$.

15. $y = e^x$, $y = 0$, $0 \le x \le a$; $f(x, y) = xy$.

16. $y = \sqrt{2x}$, $y = 0$, $0 \le x \le 2$; $f(x, y) = |x - y|$.

17. Let S be a thin plate of mass M, and let L_0 and L be two parallel lines in the plane of S, where L_0 passes through the center of mass of S. Prove the *parallel-axis theorem:*

$$I_L = I_{L_0} + Mh^2,$$

where h is the perpendicular distance between the two lines L and L_0. [*Hint.* A careful choice of coordinate axes will simplify the work.]

18. The boundary of a thin plate is an ellipse with semi-axes a and b. Let L denote a line in the plane of the plate passing through the center of the ellipse and making an angle α with the axis of length $2a$. If the density is constant and if the mass of the plate is M, show that the moment of inertia I_L is equal to $\frac{1}{4}M(a^2 \sin^2 \alpha + b^2 \cos^2 \alpha)$.

19. Find the average distance from one corner of a square of side h to points inside the square.

20. Let δ denote the distance from an arbitrary point P inside a circle of radius r to a fixed point P_0 whose distance from the center of the circle is h. Find the average of the function δ^2 over the region enclosed by the circle.

21. Let A, B, C denote the following rectangles in the xy-plane:

$$A = [0, 4] \times [0, 1], \qquad B = [2, 3] \times [1, 3], \qquad C = [2, 4] \times [3, 4].$$

Use the theorem of Pappus to determine the centroid of each of the following figures:

(a) $A \cup B$

(b) $A \cup C$

(c) $B \cup C$

(d) $A \cup B \cup C$.

22. An isosceles triangle T has base 1 and altitude h. The base of T coincides with one edge of a rectangle R of base 1 and altitude 2. Find a value of h so that the centroid of $R \cup T$ will lie on the edge common to R and T.

2.16 Change of variable in a double integral

In one-dimensional integration theory the method of substitution often enables us to evaluate complicated integrals by transforming them into simpler ones or into types that can be more easily recognized. The method is based on the formula

(2.16)
$$\int_a^b f(x) \, dx = \int_c^d f[g(t)] \, g'(t) \, dt \,,$$

where $a = g(c)$ and $b = g(d)$. We proved this formula (in Volume I) under the assumptions that g has a continuous derivative on an interval $[c, d]$ and that f is continuous on the set of values taken by $g(t)$ as t runs through the interval $[c, d]$.

There is a two-dimensional analog of (2.16) called the formula for making a change of variable in a double integral. It transforms an integral of the form $\iint_S f(x, y) \, dx \, dy$, extended over a region S in the xy-plane, into another double integral $\iint_T F(u, v) \, du \, dv$, extended over a new region T in the uv-plane. The exact relationship between the regions S and T and the integrands $f(x, y)$ and $F(u, v)$ will be discussed presently. The method of substitution for double integrals is more elaborate than in the one-dimensional case because there are two formal substitutions to be made, one for x and another for y. This means that instead of the one function g which appears in Equation (2.16), we now have two functions, say X and Y, which connect x, y with u, v as follows:

(2.17)
$$x = X(u, v), \qquad y = Y(u, v) \,.$$

Geometrically, the two equations in (2.17) can be thought of as defining a "mapping" which carries a point (u, v) in the uv-plane into an image point (x, y) in the xy-plane. A set T of points in the uv-plane is mapped onto another set S in the xy-plane, as suggested by Figure 2.20. The mapping can also be described by means of a vector-valued function. From the origin in the xy-plane we draw the radius vector $\vec{r}$ to a general point (x, y) of S, as shown in Figure 2.20. The vector $\vec{r}$ depends on both u and v and can be considered a vector-valued function of two variables defined by the equation

(2.18)
$$\vec{r}(u, v) = X(u, v)\vec{i} + Y(u, v)\vec{j} \qquad \text{if} \quad (u, v) \, \varepsilon \, T \,.$$

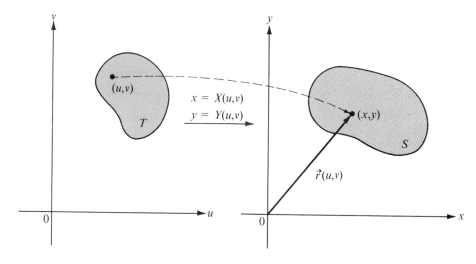

FIGURE 2.20 *The mapping defined by the vector equation* $\vec{r}(u, v) = X(u, v)\vec{i} + Y(u, v)\vec{j}$.

This equation is called the *vector equation* of the mapping. As (u, v) runs through the points of T the tip of $\vec{r}(u, v)$ traces out the points of S.

Sometimes the two equations in (2.17) can be solved for u and v in terms of x and y. When this is possible we may express the result in the form

$$u = U(x, y), \qquad v = V(x, y).$$

These equations define a mapping from the xy-plane to the uv-plane, called the *inverse mapping* of the one defined by (2.17), since it carries points of S back to T. The so-called *one-to-one mappings* are of special importance. These carry *distinct* points of T onto *distinct* points of S; in other words, no two distinct points of T are mapped onto the same point of S by a one-to-one mapping. Each such mapping establishes a one-to-one correspondence between the points in T and those in S and enables us (at least in theory) to go back from S to T by the inverse mapping (which, of course, is also one-to-one).

We shall consider mappings for which the functions X and Y are continuous and have continuous partial derivatives $\partial X/\partial u$, $\partial X/\partial v$, $\partial Y/\partial u$, and $\partial Y/\partial v$ on S. Similar assumptions are made for the functions U and V. These are not serious restrictions since they are satisfied by most functions encountered in practice.

The formula for transforming double integrals may be written as

$$(2.19) \qquad \iint_S f(x, y)\, dx\, dy = \iint_T f[X(u, v),\, Y(u, v)]\, |J(u, v)|\, du\, dv.$$

The factor $J(u, v)$ which appears in the integrand on the right plays the role of the factor $g'(t)$ which appears in the one-dimensional formula (2.16). This factor is called the *Jacobian* of the mapping defined by (2.17); it is equal to the determinant

$$J(u, v) = \begin{vmatrix} \dfrac{\partial X}{\partial u} & \dfrac{\partial Y}{\partial u} \\[2mm] \dfrac{\partial X}{\partial v} & \dfrac{\partial Y}{\partial v} \end{vmatrix}.$$

Sometimes the symbol $\partial(X, Y)/\partial(u, v)$ is used instead of $J(u, v)$ to represent the Jacobian.

We shall not discuss the most general conditions under which the transformation formula (2.19) is valid. It can be shown† that (2.19) holds if, in addition to the continuity assumptions on X, Y, U, and V mentioned above, we assume that the mapping from T to S is one-to-one and that the Jacobian $J(u, v)$ is never zero. The formula is also valid if the mapping fails to be one-to-one on a subset of T of measure zero or if the Jacobian vanishes on such a set.

In Section 2.21 we show how the transformation formula (2.19) may be derived as a consequence of one of its special cases, namely, the case in which S is a rectangle and the function f has the constant value 1 at each point of S. In this special case (2.19) becomes

$$(2.20) \qquad \iint_S dx\, dy = \iint_T |J(u, v)|\, du\, dv.$$

Even for this case a proof is not simple. In a later chapter a proof of (2.20) will be given with the aid of line integrals. The remainder of this section will present a simple geometric argument which explains why a formula like (2.20) should hold.

† See Theorem 10–30 of the author's *Mathematical Analysis, ibid.*

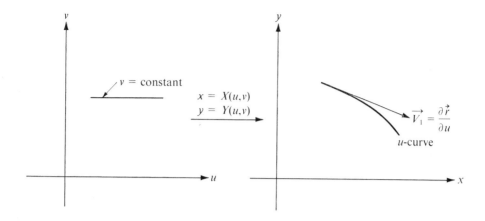

FIGURE 2.21   *A u-curve and a corresponding velocity vector.*

Geometric motivation for Equation (2.20): Take a region T in the uv-plane, as shown in Figure 2.20, and let S denote the set of points in the xy-plane onto which T is mapped by the vector function $\vec{r}$ given by (2.18). Now introduce two new vector-valued functions $\vec{V}_1$ and $\vec{V}_2$ which are obtained by taking the partial derivatives of the components of $\vec{r}$ with respect to u and v, respectively. That is, define

$$\vec{V}_1 = \frac{\partial \vec{r}}{\partial u} = \frac{\partial X}{\partial u}\,\vec{i} + \frac{\partial Y}{\partial u}\,\vec{j} \qquad \text{and} \qquad \vec{V}_2 = \frac{\partial \vec{r}}{\partial v} = \frac{\partial X}{\partial v}\,\vec{i} + \frac{\partial Y}{\partial v}\,\vec{j}.$$

These vectors may be interpreted geometrically as follows: Consider a horizontal line segment in the uv-plane (v is constant on such a segment). The vector function $\vec{r}$ maps this segment onto a curve (called a u-curve) in the xy-plane, as suggested in Figure 2.21. If we

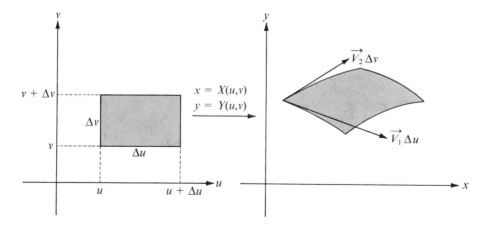

FIGURE 2.22   *The image of a rectangular region in the uv-plane is a curvilinear parallelogram in the xy-plane.*

think of u as a parameter representing "time," the vector $\vec{V}_1$ represents the velocity of the position $\vec{r}$ and is therefore tangent to the curve traced out by the tip of $\vec{r}$. In the same way, each vector $\vec{V}_2$ represents the velocity vector of a v-curve obtained by setting $u = $ constant. A u-curve and a v-curve pass through each point of the region S.

Consider now a small rectangle with dimensions Δu and Δv, as shown in Figure 2.22. If Δu is the length of a small time interval, then in time Δu a point of a u-curve moves along the curve a distance approximately equal to the product $|\vec{V}_1|\,\Delta u$ (since $|\vec{V}_1|$ represents the speed and Δu the time). Similarly, in time Δv a point on a v-curve moves a distance nearly equal to $|\vec{V}_2|\,\Delta v$. Hence the rectangular region with dimensions Δu and Δv in the uv-plane is traced onto a portion of the xy-plane that is nearly a parallelogram, whose sides are the vectors $\vec{V}_1\,\Delta u$ and $\vec{V}_2\,\Delta v$, as suggested by Figure 2.22. The area of this parallelogram is the magnitude of the cross product of the two vectors $\vec{V}_1\,\Delta u$ and $\vec{V}_2\,\Delta v$; this is equal to

$$|(\vec{V}_1\,\Delta u) \times (\vec{V}_2\,\Delta v)| = |\vec{V}_1 \times \vec{V}_2|\,\Delta u\,\Delta v .$$

If we compute the cross product $\vec{V}_1 \times \vec{V}_2$ in terms of the components of $\vec{V}_1$ and $\vec{V}_2$ we find

$$\vec{V}_1 \times \vec{V}_2 = \begin{vmatrix} \vec{i} & \vec{j} & \vec{k} \\ \dfrac{\partial X}{\partial u} & \dfrac{\partial Y}{\partial u} & 0 \\ \dfrac{\partial X}{\partial v} & \dfrac{\partial Y}{\partial v} & 0 \end{vmatrix} = \begin{vmatrix} \dfrac{\partial X}{\partial u} & \dfrac{\partial Y}{\partial u} \\ \dfrac{\partial X}{\partial v} & \dfrac{\partial Y}{\partial v} \end{vmatrix} \vec{k} = J(u,\,v)\,\vec{k} .$$

Therefore the magnitude of $\vec{V}_1 \times \vec{V}_2$ is exactly $|J(u,\,v)|$ and the area of the curvilinear parallelogram in Figure 2.22 is nearly equal to $|J(u,\,v)|\,\Delta u\,\Delta v$.

If $J(u,\,v) = 1$ for all points in T, then the "parallelogram" has the same area as the rectangle and the mapping preserves areas. Otherwise, to obtain the area of the parallelogram we must multiply the area of the rectangle by $|J(u,\,v)|$. This suggests that the Jacobian may be thought of as a "magnification factor" for areas.

Now let P be a partition of a large rectangle R enclosing the entire region T and consider a typical subrectangle of P of, say, dimensions Δu and Δv. If Δu and Δv are small, the function J is nearly constant on the subrectangle and hence J acts somewhat like a step function on R. (We define J to be zero outside T.) If we think of J as an actual step function, then the double integral of $|J|$ over R (and hence over T) is a sum of products of the form $|J(u,\,v)|\,\Delta u\,\Delta v$ and the above remarks suggest that this sum is nearly equal to the area of S, which we know to be the double integral $\iint_S dx\,dy$. This geometric discussion, which merely suggests why we might expect an equation like (2.20) to hold, can be made the basis of a rigorous proof but the details are lengthy and rather intricate. As mentioned above, a proof of (2.20), based on an entirely different approach, will be given in a later chapter.

If $J(u,\,v) = 0$ at a particular point $(u,\,v)$, the two vectors $\vec{V}_1$ and $\vec{V}_2$ are parallel (since their cross product is the zero vector) and the parallelogram degenerates into a portion of a curve. Such points are called *singular points* of the mapping. As we have already mentioned, transformation formula (2.19) is also valid whenever there are only a finite number of such singular points or, more generally, when the singular points form a set of measure zero. This is the case for all the mappings we shall use. In the next section we illustrate the use of formula (2.19) in two important examples.

2.17 Special cases of the transformation formula

Example 1: Polar coordinates. In this case we write r and θ instead of u and v and describe the mapping by the two equations:

$$x = r \cos \theta, \qquad y = r \sin \theta .$$

That is, $X(r, \theta) = r \cos \theta$ and $Y(r, \theta) = r \sin \theta$. To obtain a one-to-one mapping we keep $r > 0$ and restrict θ to lie in an interval of the form $\theta_0 \leq \theta < \theta_0 + 2\pi$. For example, the mapping is one-to-one on any subset of the rectangle $(0, a] \times [0, 2\pi)$ in the $r\theta$-plane. The Jacobian of this mapping is

$$J(r, \theta) = \begin{vmatrix} \dfrac{\partial X}{\partial r} & \dfrac{\partial Y}{\partial r} \\[2mm] \dfrac{\partial X}{\partial \theta} & \dfrac{\partial Y}{\partial \theta} \end{vmatrix} = \begin{vmatrix} \cos \theta & \sin \theta \\ -r \sin \theta & r \cos \theta \end{vmatrix} = r(\cos^2 \theta + \sin^2 \theta) = r .$$

Hence the transformation formula in (2.19) becomes

$$\iint_S f(x, y) \, dx \, dy = \iint_T f(r \cos \theta, r \sin \theta) \, r \, dr \, d\theta .$$

The r-curves are straight lines through the origin and the θ-curves are circles concentric with the origin. The image of a rectangle in the $r\theta$-plane is a "parallelogram" in the xy-plane bounded by two radial lines and two circular arcs, as shown in Figure 2.23.

Since $\vec{V}_1 = \cos \theta \, \vec{i} + \sin \theta \, \vec{j}$, we have $|\vec{V}_1| = 1$, so there is no distortion of distances along the r-curves. On the other hand, we have

$$\vec{V}_2 = -r \sin \theta \, \vec{i} + r \cos \theta \, \vec{j}, \qquad |\vec{V}_2| = r ,$$

so distances along the θ-curves are multiplied by the factor r.

Polar coordinates are particularly suitable when the region of integration has bounda-

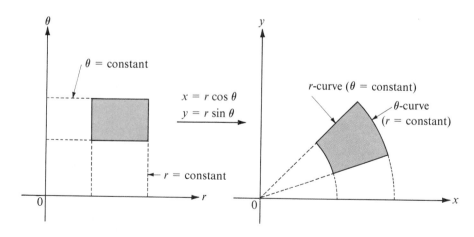

FIGURE 2.23 *Transformation by polar coordinates.*

ries along which r or θ is constant. For example, consider the integral for the volume of one octant of a sphere of radius a,

$$\iint_S \sqrt{a^2 - x^2 - y^2} \, dx \, dy ,$$

where the region S is the first quadrant of the circular disk $x^2 + y^2 \le a^2$, shown in Figure 2.17. We calculated this integral in rectangular coordinates in Section 2.12. In polar coordinates the integral becomes

$$\iint_T \sqrt{a^2 - r^2} \, r \, dr \, d\theta ,$$

where the region of integration T is now a rectangle $[0, a] \times [0, \tfrac{1}{2}\pi]$. Integrating first with respect to θ and then with respect to r we obtain

$$\iint_T \sqrt{a^2 - r^2} \, r \, dr \, d\theta = \frac{\pi}{2} \int_0^a r \sqrt{a^2 - r^2} \, dr = \frac{\pi}{2} \cdot \frac{(a^2 - r^2)^{3/2}}{-3} \Big|_0^a = \frac{\pi a^3}{6} .$$

This is the same result obtained previously, but the use of polar coordinates has shortened the work considerably.

Example 2: Linear transformations. A linear transformation is a mapping defined by a pair of equations of the form

(2.21) $x = Au + Bv , \qquad y = Cu + Dv ,$

where A, B, C, D are given constants. The Jacobian is

$$J(u, v) = AD - BC ,$$

and in order to have an inverse we assume that $AD - BC \neq 0$. This assures us that the two linear equations in (2.21) may be solved for u and v in terms of x and y.

Linear transformations carry straight lines into straight lines. Therefore the image of a rectangle in the uv-plane is a quadrilateral in the xy-plane, and its area is that of the rectangle multiplied by the factor $|J(u, v)| = |AD - BC|$. Transformation formula (2.19) becomes

$$\iint_S f(x, y) \, dx \, dy = |AD - BC| \iint_T f(Au + Bv, Cu + Dv) \, du \, dv .$$

To illustrate an example in which a linear change of variable is useful, let us consider the integral

$$\iint_S e^{(y-x)/(y+x)} \, dx \, dy ,$$

where S is the triangle bounded by the line $x + y = 2$ and the two coordinate axes. (See Figure 2.24.) The presence of $y - x$ and $y + x$ in the integrand suggests the change of variable

$$u = y - x , \qquad v = y + x .$$

Solving for x and y we find

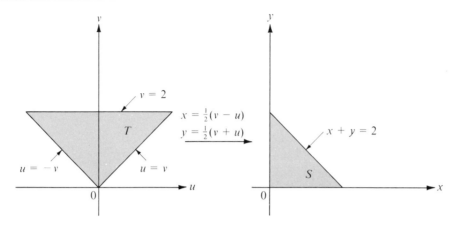

FIGURE 2.24   *Mapping by a linear transformation.*

$$x = \frac{v - u}{2} \quad \text{and} \quad y = \frac{v + u}{2}.$$

The Jacobian is $J(u, v) = -\frac{1}{2} \cdot \frac{1}{2} - \frac{1}{2} \cdot \frac{1}{2} = -\frac{1}{2}$. To find the image T of S in the uv-plane we note that the lines $x = 0$ and $y = 0$ map onto the lines $u = v$ and $u = -v$, respectively; the line $x + y = 2$ maps onto the line $v = 2$. Points inside S satisfy $0 < x + y < 2$ and these are carried into points of T satisfying $0 < v < 2$. Therefore the new region of integration T is a triangular region, as shown in Figure 2.24. The double integral in question becomes

$$\iint\limits_{S} e^{(y-x)/(y+x)} \, dx \, dy = \tfrac{1}{2} \iint\limits_{T} e^{u/v} \, du \, dv .$$

Integrating first with respect to u we find

$$\frac{1}{2} \iint\limits_{T} e^{u/v} \, du \, dv = \frac{1}{2} \int_0^2 \left[\int_{-v}^{v} e^{u/v} \, du \right] dv = \frac{1}{2} \int_0^2 v \left(e - \frac{1}{e} \right) dv = e - \frac{1}{e} .$$

2.18   Exercises

In each of Exercises 1 through 5, make a sketch of the region S and express the double integral $\iint\limits_{S} f(x, y) \, dx \, dy$ as an iterated integral in polar coordinates.

1. $S = \{(x, y) \mid x^2 + y^2 \le a^2\}$,   where $a > 0$.
2. $S = \{(x, y) \mid x^2 + y^2 \le 2x\}$.
3. $S = \{(x, y) \mid a^2 \le x^2 + y^2 \le b^2\}$,   where $0 < a < b$.
4. $S = \{(x, y) \mid 0 \le y \le 1 - x, 0 \le x \le 1\}$.
5. $S = \{(x, y) \mid x^2 \le y \le 1, -1 \le x \le 1\}$.

In each of Exercises 6 through 9, transform the integral to polar coordinates and compute its value. (The letter a denotes a positive constant.)

6. $\int_0^{2a} \left[\int_0^{\sqrt{2ax-x^2}} (x^2 + y^2) \, dy \right] dx.$

8. $\int_0^1 \left[\int_{x^2}^x (x^2 + y^2)^{-1/2} \, dy \right] dx.$

7. $\int_0^a \left[\int_0^x \sqrt{x^2 + y^2} \, dy \right] dx.$

9. $\int_0^a \left[\int_0^{\sqrt{a^2-y^2}} (x^2 + y^2) \, dx \right] dy.$

In Exercises 10 through 13, transform each of the given integrals to one or more iterated integrals in polar coordinates.

10. $\int_0^1 \left[\int_0^1 f(x, y) \, dy \right] dx.$

12. $\int_0^1 \left[\int_{1-x}^{\sqrt{1-x^2}} f(x, y) \, dy \right] dx.$

11. $\int_0^2 \left[\int_x^{x\sqrt{3}} f(\sqrt{x^2 + y^2}) \, dy \right] dx.$

13. $\int_0^1 \left[\int_0^{x^2} f(x, y) \, dy \right] dx.$

14. Use a suitable linear transformation to evaluate the double integral

$$\iint_S (x - y)^2 \sin^2(x + y) \, dx \, dy$$

where S is the parallelogram with vertices $(\pi, 0)$, $(2\pi, \pi)$, $(\pi, 2\pi)$, $(0, \pi)$.

15. Consider the mapping defined by the equations

$$x = u + v, \qquad y = v - u^2.$$

(a) Compute the Jacobian $J(u, v)$.

(b) A triangle T in the uv-plane has vertices $(0, 0)$, $(2, 0)$, $(0, 2)$. Describe, by means of a sketch, its image S in the xy-plane.

(c) Calculate the area of S by a double integral extended over S and also by a double integral extended over T.

(d) Evaluate $\iint_S (x - y + 1)^{-2} \, dx \, dy$.

16. Consider the mapping defined by the two equations

$$x = u^2 - v^2, \qquad y = 2uv.$$

(a) Compute the Jacobian $J(u, v)$.

(b) Let T denote the rectangle in the uv-plane with vertices $(1, 1)$, $(2, 1)$, $(2, 3)$, $(1, 3)$. Describe, by means of a sketch, the image S in the xy-plane.

(c) Evaluate the double integral $\iint_C xy \, dx \, dy$ by making the change of variable $x = u^2 - v^2$, $y = 2uv$, where $C = \{(x, y) \mid x^2 + y^2 \leq 1\}$.

17. Evaluate the double integral

$$I(p, r) = \iint_R \frac{dx \, dy}{(p^2 + x^2 + y^2)^p}$$

over the circular disk $R = \{(x, y) \mid x^2 + y^2 \leq r^2\}$. Determine those values of p for which $I(p, r)$ tends to a limit as $r \to +\infty$.

In Exercises 18 through 20, establish the given equations by introducing a suitable change of variable in each case.

18. $\iint_S f(x + y) \, dx \, dy = \int_{-1}^1 f(u) \, du$, where $S = \{(x, y) \mid |x| + |y| \leq 1\}$.

19. $\iint_S f(ax + by + c) \, dx \, dy = 2 \int_{-1}^1 \sqrt{1 - u^2} \, f(u\sqrt{a^2 + b^2} + c) \, du$,

where $S = \{(x, y) \mid x^2 + y^2 \leq 1\}$, and $a^2 + b^2 \neq 0$.

20. $\iint\limits_{S} f(xy)\, dx\, dy = \log 2 \int_{1}^{2} f(u)\, du$, where S is the region in the first quadrant bounded by

the curves $xy = 1$, $xy = 2$, $y = x$, $y = 4x$.

2.19 Triple integrals

After the transition has been made from one-dimensional integrals to double integrals, it is not difficult to go one step further and introduce the concept of a triple integral. The region of integration is now a solid in 3-space and the integrand is a function f of three variables defined and bounded on this solid. The resulting integral is denoted by the symbol

$$\iiint\limits_{S} f, \qquad \text{or} \qquad \iiint\limits_{S} f(x, y, z)\, dx\, dy\, dz\,,$$

where S stands for the region of integration.

Since the development of the theory of triple integrals is entirely analogous to that of double integrals and involves no new ideas, we shall merely sketch the principal results. First we assume that the region of integration is a rectangular parallelepiped (the Cartesian product of three one-dimensional intervals), which we refer to as a *cell*. A cell R is called *open* or *closed* according to whether R is the Cartesian product of three open intervals or of three closed intervals. If a cell R is the Cartesian product of three closed intervals, say

$$R = [a_1, b_1] \times [a_2, b_2] \times [a_3, b_3]\,,$$

and if P_1, P_2, P_3 are partitions of these intervals, the Cartesian product $P = P_1 \times P_2 \times P_3$ is called a partition of R. If

$$P_1 = \{x_0, x_1, \ldots, x_n\}\,, \qquad P_2 = \{y_0, y_1, \ldots, y_m\}\,, \qquad P_3 = \{z_0, z_1, \ldots, z_p\}\,,$$

the cells $[x_{i-1}, x_i] \times [y_{j-1}, y_j] \times [z_{k-1}, z_k]$ are called *subcells* of P. A function f defined on a cell R is called a step function if it is constant on each of the open subcells determined by some partition P. The integral of such a step function may be defined by the formula

$$\iiint\limits_{R} f = \sum_{i=1}^{n} \sum_{j=1}^{m} \sum_{k=1}^{p} c_{ijk} \cdot (x_i - x_{i-1})(y_j - y_{j-1})(z_k - z_{k-1})\,,$$

where c_{ijk} is the constant value taken by f on the open subcell $(x_{i-1}, x_i) \times (y_{j-1}, y_j) \times (z_{k-1}, z_k)$. The value of the integral is independent of the choice of P so long as f is constant on the open subcells of P.

Having defined the integral for step functions, we define the integral for more general bounded functions defined on cells, following the usual procedure. The problem of existence of triple integrals is settled by an extension of Lebesgue's theorem. To state this theorem we need to know the meaning of continuity for functions of three variables. As in the two-dimensional case we define continuity in terms of neighborhoods.

In 3-space, a neighborhood of a point (x_0, y_0, z_0) is the set of points (x, y, z) satisfying $(x - x_0)^2 + (y - y_0)^2 + (z - z_0)^2 < r^2$, where $r > 0$. Thus, a neighborhood of (x_0, y_0, z_0) is a spherical solid with center at (x_0, y_0, z_0). When we speak of f being continuous at (x_0, y_0, z_0) we assume that f is defined at (x_0, y_0, z_0) and at other points in every neighbor-

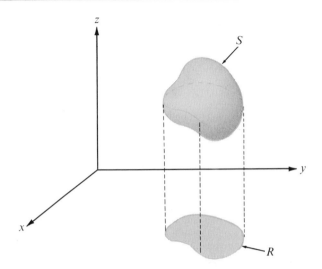

FIGURE 2.25   *A solid S and its projection R in the xy-plane.*

hood of (x_0, y_0, z_0). The definition of continuity is entirely analogous to the two-dimensional case.

DEFINITION OF CONTINUITY. A function f is said to be continuous at (x_0, y_0, z_0) if, for every $\epsilon > 0$, there is a neighborhood of (x_0, y_0, z_0) such that for every point (x, y, z) in this neighborhood at which f is defined we have the inequality

$$|f(x, y, z) - f(x_0, y_0, z_0)| < \epsilon .$$

If f is continuous at all points of a set S, we say that f is *continuous on S.*

In three dimensions, a set of measure zero is one that can be enclosed in a union of cells whose volume is arbitrarily small. More precisely, a set S is said to be of three-dimensional measure zero if, for every $\epsilon > 0$, S can be enclosed in a finite or countably infinite collection of cells, the sum of whose volumes is less than ϵ. In particular, isolated points, line segments, plane sets, and, in general, all sets with zero volume are examples of sets having three-dimensional measure zero. Lebesgue's theorem† for triple integrals may now be stated as follows:

2– 8   THEOREM.   If f is defined and bounded on a cell R, then the triple integral $\iiint\limits_{R} f$ exists if and only if the set of discontinuities of f on R is a set of three-dimensional measure zero.

More general regions of integration may now be introduced. The most important of these are solids S in 3-space described as follows:

† A proof of Lebesgue's theorem for triple integrals may be found in Chapter 10 of the author's *Mathematical Analysis, ibid.*

(2.23) $S = \{(x, y, z) \mid (x, y) \; \varepsilon \; R \text{ and } \phi_1(x, y) \leq z \leq \phi_2(x, y)\}$,

where R is a two-dimensional region, called the projection of S on the xy-plane. (An example is shown in Figure 2.25.) Sets of this type are bounded by two surfaces whose equations are $z = \phi_1(x, y)$ and $z = \phi_2(x, y)$ and (perhaps) a portion of the cylinder generated by a line moving parallel to the z-axis along the boundary of R. Lines parallel to the z-axis intersect this solid in line segments joining the lower surface to the upper one. The definition of the triple integral of f over S is given by extending f to a new function $\tilde{f}$ which agrees with f on S and has the value zero outside S; the integral of f over S is defined to be the integral of $\tilde{f}$ over a cell containing S.

The first important result concerning triple integrals is the generalization of Theorem 2–4, which reduces the calculation of a triple integral to iterated integrals of lower dimension. For a set S of the type described in (2.23) the iteration formula may be written as

(2.24) $$\iiint_S f(x, y, z)\, dx\, dy\, dz = \iint_R \left[\int_{\phi_1(x, y)}^{\phi_2(x, y)} f(x, y, z)\, dz \right] dx\, dy \, .$$

That is, for fixed x and y, the first integration is performed with respect to z from the lower boundary surface to the upper one. This reduces the calculation to a double integral over the projection R, which may be treated by the methods discussed in the foregoing sections.

There are two more types of sets analogous to those described by (2.23) in which the x- and y-axes play the role of the z-axis, with the projections taken in the yz- or xz-planes, respectively. Triple integrals over such sets may be computed by iteration, with formulas analogous to (2.24). Most solids that we shall encounter are either of one of the three types just mentioned or they can be split into a finite number of pieces, each of which is of one of these types.

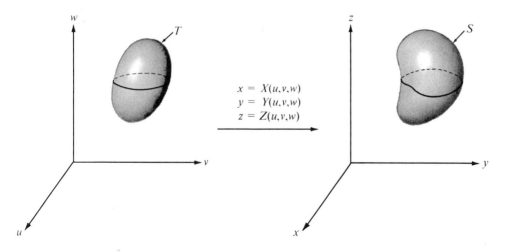

$$x = X(u, v, w)$$
$$y = Y(u, v, w)$$
$$z = Z(u, v, w)$$

FIGURE 2.26   *A mapping from uvw-space to xyz-space.*

Another important theorem in the theory of triple integration is the formula for making a change of variables. Suppose we introduce new variables u, v, w related to x, y, z by three equations of the form

$$(2.25) \qquad x = X(u, v, w), \qquad y = Y(u, v, w), \qquad z = Z(u, v, w).$$

If the three functions X, Y, Z are defined on a set T in uvw-space the three equations in (2.25) define a mapping of T onto a set S in xyz-space, as suggested in Figure 2.26. We consider one-to-one mappings for which the functions X, Y, Z are continuous and have continuous partial derivatives on T.

The transformation formula for triple integrals assumes the form

$$(2.26) \quad \iiint\limits_{S} f(x, y, z) \, dx \, dy \, dz = \iiint\limits_{T} f[X(u, v, w), Y(u, v, w), Z(u, v, w)] \, |J(u, v, w)| \, du \, dv \, dw,$$

where $J(u, v, w)$ is the Jacobian of the mapping, defined by the determinant

$$J(u, v, w) = \begin{vmatrix} \dfrac{\partial X}{\partial u} & \dfrac{\partial Y}{\partial u} & \dfrac{\partial Z}{\partial u} \\[2mm] \dfrac{\partial X}{\partial v} & \dfrac{\partial Y}{\partial v} & \dfrac{\partial Z}{\partial v} \\[2mm] \dfrac{\partial X}{\partial w} & \dfrac{\partial Y}{\partial w} & \dfrac{\partial Z}{\partial w} \end{vmatrix}.$$

In 3-space the Jacobian may be thought of as a magnification factor for *volumes*. In fact, if we introduce the vector-valued function $\vec{r}$ defined by the equation

$$\vec{r}(u, v, w) = X(u, v, w) \, \vec{i} + Y(u, v, w) \, \vec{j} + Z(u, v, w) \, \vec{k}$$

and the vectors

$$\vec{V}_1 = \frac{\partial \vec{r}}{\partial u} = \frac{\partial X}{\partial u} \vec{i} + \frac{\partial Y}{\partial u} \vec{j} + \frac{\partial Z}{\partial u} \vec{k}$$

$$\vec{V}_2 = \frac{\partial \vec{r}}{\partial v} = \frac{\partial X}{\partial v} \vec{i} + \frac{\partial Y}{\partial v} \vec{j} + \frac{\partial Z}{\partial v} \vec{k}$$

$$\vec{V}_3 = \frac{\partial \vec{r}}{\partial w} = \frac{\partial X}{\partial w} \vec{i} + \frac{\partial Y}{\partial w} \vec{j} + \frac{\partial Z}{\partial w} \vec{k},$$

an argument similar to that given in Section 2.16 suggests that a rectangular parallelepiped of dimensions Δu, Δv, Δw in uvw-space is carried into a solid which is nearly a curvilinear "parallelepiped" in xyz-space determined by the three vectors $\vec{V}_1 \Delta u$, $\vec{V}_2 \Delta v$, and $\vec{V}_3 \Delta w$. The boundaries of this solid are surfaces obtained by setting $u = $ constant, $v = $ constant, and $w = $ constant, respectively. The volume of a parallelepiped is equal to the absolute value of the scalar triple product of the three vectors which determine it, so the volume of the curvilinear parallelepiped is nearly equal to

$$|(\vec{V}_1 \Delta u) \cdot (\vec{V}_2 \Delta v) \times (\vec{V}_3 \Delta w)| = |\vec{V}_1 \cdot \vec{V}_2 \times \vec{V}_3| \, \Delta u \, \Delta v \, \Delta w = |J(u, v, w)| \, \Delta u \, \Delta v \, \Delta w.$$

As in the two-dimensional case, the transformation formula (2.26) is valid if the mapping (2.25) is one-to-one on T and if the Jacobian $J(u, v, w)$ is never zero on T. It

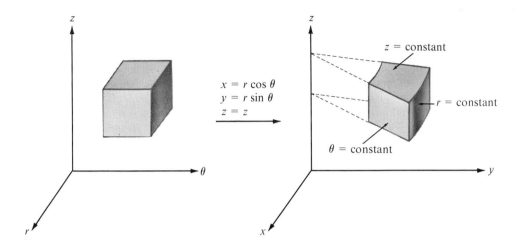

FIGURE 2.27 *Transformation by cylindrical coordinates.*

is also valid if the mapping fails to be one-to-one on a subset of T having three-dimensional measure zero, or if the Jacobian vanishes on such a subset.

Two important special cases of (2.26) are discussed in the next two examples.

Example 1: Cylindrical coordinates. Here we write r, θ, z for u, v, w and define the mapping by the equations

(2.27) $$x = r \cos \theta, \qquad y = r \sin \theta, \qquad z = z.$$

In other words, we replace x and y by their polar coordinates in the xy-plane and leave z unchanged. Again, to get a one-to-one mapping we must keep $r > 0$ and restrict θ to be in an interval of the form $\theta_0 \leq \theta < \theta_0 + 2\pi$. Figure 2.27 shows what happens to a rectangular parallelepiped in the $r\theta z$-space.

The Jacobian of the mapping in (2.27) is

$$J(r, \theta, z) = \begin{vmatrix} \cos \theta & \sin \theta & 0 \\ -r \sin \theta & r \cos \theta & 0 \\ 0 & 0 & 1 \end{vmatrix} = r(\cos^2 \theta + \sin^2 \theta) = r,$$

and therefore the transformation formula in (2.26) becomes

$$\iiint_S f(x, y, z)\, dx\, dy\, dz = \iiint_T f(r \cos \theta, r \sin \theta, z)\, r\, dr\, d\theta\, dz.$$

Example 2: Spherical coordinates. In this case the symbols ρ, θ, ϕ are used instead of u, v, w and the mapping is defined by the equations

$$x = \rho \cos \theta \sin \phi, \qquad y = \rho \sin \theta \sin \phi, \qquad z = \rho \cos \phi.$$

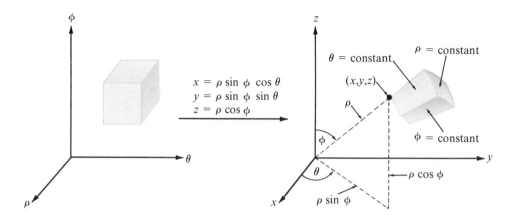

FIGURE 2.28   *Transformation by spherical coordinates.*

The geometric meanings of ρ, θ, and ϕ are shown in Figure 2.28. To get a one-to-one mapping we keep $\rho > 0$, $0 \leq \theta < 2\pi$, and $0 \leq \phi < \pi$. The surfaces $\rho = $ constant are spheres concentric with the origin, the surfaces $\theta = $ constant are planes passing through the z-axis, and the surfaces $\phi = $ constant are circular cones with their axes along the z-axis. Therefore a rectangular box in $\rho\theta\phi$-space is mapped onto a solid of the type shown in Figure 2.28.

The Jacobian of the mapping is

$$J(\rho, \theta, \phi) = \begin{vmatrix} \cos\theta \sin\phi & \sin\theta \sin\phi & \cos\phi \\ -\rho \sin\theta \sin\phi & \rho \cos\theta \sin\phi & 0 \\ \rho \cos\theta \cos\phi & \rho \sin\theta \cos\phi & -\rho \sin\phi \end{vmatrix} = -\rho^2 \sin\phi \, .$$

Since $\sin\phi \geq 0$ if $0 \leq \phi < \pi$, we have $|J(\rho, \theta, \phi)| = \rho^2 \sin\phi$ and the formula for transforming triple integrals becomes

$$\iiint_S f(x, y, z) \, dx \, dy \, dz = \iiint_T F(\rho, \theta, \phi) \, \rho^2 \sin\phi \, d\rho \, d\theta \, d\phi \, ,$$

where $F(\rho, \theta, \phi) = f(\rho \cos\theta \sin\phi, \rho \sin\theta \sin\phi, \rho \cos\phi)$.

2.20   Exercises

Evaluate each of the triple integrals in Exercises 1 through 5. Make a sketch of the region of integration in each case. You may assume the existence of all the integrals encountered.

1. $\iiint_S xy^2 z^3 \, dx \, dy \, dz$,   where S is the solid bounded by the surface $z = xy$ and the planes $y = x$, $x = 1$, and $z = 0$.

2. $\iiint_S (1 + x + y + z)^{-3} \, dx \, dy \, dz$,   where S is the solid bounded by the three coordinate planes and the plane $x + y + z = 1$.

3. $\iiint_S xyz \, dx \, dy \, dz$,   where $S = \{(x, y, z) \mid x^2 + y^2 + z^2 \leq 1, x \geq 0, y \geq 0, z \geq 0\}$.

4. $\iiint\limits_{S} \left(\dfrac{x^2}{a^2} + \dfrac{y^2}{b^2} + \dfrac{z^2}{c^2} \right) dx\,dy\,dz,$ where S is the solid bounded by the ellipsoid $\dfrac{x^2}{a^2} + \dfrac{y^2}{b^2} + \dfrac{z^2}{c^2} = 1.$

5. $\iiint\limits_{S} \sqrt{x^2 + y^2}\, dx\,dy\,dz,$ where S is the solid formed by the upper nappe of the cone $z^2 = x^2 + y^2$ and the plane $z = 1.$

In Exercises 6, 7, and 8, a triple integral $\iiint\limits_{S} f(x, y, z)\,dx\,dy\,dz$ of a positive function reduces to the iterated integral given. In each case describe the region of integration S by means of a sketch, showing its projection on the xy-plane. Then express the triple integral as one or more iterated integrals in which the first integration is with respect to y.

6. $\displaystyle\int_0^1 \left(\int_0^{1-x} \left[\int_0^{x+y} f(x, y, z)\, dz \right] dy \right) dx.$

7. $\displaystyle\int_{-1}^{1} \left(\int_{-\sqrt{1-x^2}}^{\sqrt{1-x^2}} \left[\int_{\sqrt{x^2+y^2}}^{1} f(x, y, z)\, dz \right] dy \right) dx.$

8. $\displaystyle\int_0^1 \left(\int_0^1 \left[\int_0^{x^2+y^2} f(x, y, z)\, dz \right] dy \right) dx.$

9. Show that:

$$\int_0^x \left(\int_0^v \left[\int_0^u f(t)\, dt \right] du \right) dv = \tfrac{1}{2} \int_0^x (x - t)^2 f(t)\, dt\,.$$

Evaluate the integrals in Exercises 10, 11, and 12 by transforming to cylindrical coordinates. You may assume the existence of all integrals encountered.

10. $\iiint\limits_{S} (x^2 + y^2)\,dx\,dy\,dz,$ where S is the solid bounded by the surface $x^2 + y^2 = 2z$ and the plane $z = 2.$

11. $\iiint\limits_{S} dx\,dy\,dz,$ where S is the solid bounded by the three coordinate planes, the surface $z = x^2 + y^2,$ and the plane $x + y = 1.$

12. $\iiint\limits_{S} (y^2 + z^2)\,dx\,dy\,dz,$ where S is a right circular cone of altitude h with its base, of radius a, in the xy-plane and its axis along the z-axis.

Evaluate the integrals in Exercises 13, 14, and 15 by transforming to spherical coordinates.

13. $\iiint\limits_{S} dx\,dy\,dz,$ where S is a solid sphere of radius a and center at the origin.

14. $\iiint\limits_{S} dx\,dy\,dz,$ where S is the solid bounded by two concentric spheres of radii a and b, where $0 < a < b,$ and the center is at the origin.

15. $\iiint\limits_{S} [(x - a)^2 + (y - b)^2 + (z - c)^2]^{-1/2}\, dx\,dy\,dz,$ where S is a solid sphere of radius R and center at the origin, and (a, b, c) is a fixed point outside this sphere.

16. Generalized spherical coordinates may be defined by the following mapping:

$$x = a\rho \cos^m \theta \sin^n \phi, \qquad y = b\rho \sin^m \theta \sin^n \phi, \qquad z = c\rho \cos^n \phi\,,$$

where $a, b, c, m,$ and n are positive constants. Show that the Jacobian is equal to

$$-abcmn\rho^2 \cos^{m-1} \theta \sin^{m-1} \theta \cos^{n-1} \phi \sin^{2n-1} \phi\,.$$

Triple integrals may be used to compute volume, mass, center of mass, moment of inertia, and other physical concepts associated with solids. If S is a solid, its volume V is given by the triple integral

$$V = \iiint\limits_S dx\, dy\, dz\,.$$

If the solid is assigned a density $f(x, y, z)$ at each of its points (x, y, z) (mass per unit volume), its mass M is defined to be

$$M = \iiint\limits_S f(x, y, z)\, dx\, dy\, dz\,,$$

and its center of mass the point $(\bar{x}, \bar{y}, \bar{z})$ with coordinates

$$\bar{x} = \frac{1}{M} \iiint\limits_S x\, f(x, y, z)\, dx\, dy\, dz\,,$$

and so on. The moment of inertia I_{xy} about the xy-plane is defined by the equation

$$I_{xy} = \iiint\limits_S z^2\, f(x, y, z)\, dx\, dy\, dz$$

and similar formulas are used to define I_{yz} and I_{zx}. The moment of inertia I_L about a line L is defined to be

$$I_L = \iiint\limits_S \delta^2(x, y, z)\, f(x, y, z)\, dx\, dy\, dz\,,$$

where $\delta(x, y, z)$ denotes the perpendicular distance from a general point (x, y, z) of S to the line L.

17. Show that the moments of inertia about the coordinate axes are

$$I_x = I_{xy} + I_{xz},\ I_y = I_{yx} + I_{yz},\ I_z = I_{zx} + I_{zy}\,.$$

18. Find the volume of the solid bounded above by the sphere $x^2 + y^2 + z^2 = 5$ and below by the paraboloid $x^2 + y^2 = 4z$.

19. Find the volume of the solid bounded by the xy-plane, the cylinder $x^2 + y^2 = 2x$, and the cone $z = \sqrt{x^2 + y^2}$.

20. Compute the mass of the solid lying between two concentric spheres of radii a and b, where $0 < a < b$, if the density at each point is equal to the square of the distance of this point from the center.

21. Determine the center of mass of a cone of altitude h if its density at each point is proportional to the distance of this point from the base.

22. Determine the center of mass of a cone of altitude h if its density at each point is proportional to the distance of this point from the axis of the cone.

23. A solid is bounded by two concentric hemispheres of radii a and b, where $0 < a < b$. If the density is constant, find the center of mass.

24. Find the center of mass of a cube of side h if its density at each point is proportional to the square of the distance of this point from one corner of the base. (Take the base in the xy-plane and place the edges on the coordinate axes.)

25. A right circular cone has altitude h, radius of base a, constant density, and mass M. Find its moment of inertia about an axis through the vertex parallel to the base.

26. Find the moment of inertia of a sphere of radius R and mass M about a diameter if the density is constant.

27. Find the moment of inertia of a cylinder of radius a and mass M if its density at each point is proportional to the distance of this point from the axis of the cylinder.

28. The stem of a mushroom is a right circular cylinder of diameter 1 and length 2, and its cap is a hemisphere of radius R. If the mushroom is a homogeneous solid with axial symmetry, and if its center of mass lies in the plane where the stem joins the cap, find R.

29. A new space satellite has a smooth unbroken skin made up of portions of two circular cylinders of equal diameters D whose axes meet at right angles. It is proposed to ship the satellite to Cape Canaveral in a cubical packing box of inner dimension D. Prove that one-third of the box will be waste space.

30. (a) Evaluate the double integral

$$\iint_{D} \frac{|xy|}{\sqrt{x^2 + y^2}} \, dx \, dy$$

over the disk D bounded by the ellipse $x^2/a^2 + y^2/b^2 = 1$.

(b) It can be shown that the corresponding triple integral

$$\iiint_{E} \frac{|xyz|}{\sqrt{x^2 + y^2 + z^2}} \, dx \, dy \, dz$$

over the solid E bounded by the ellipsoid $x^2/a^2 + y^2/b^2 + z^2/c^2 = 1$ has the value

$$\frac{8}{15} a^2 \, b^2 \, c^2 \, \frac{(bc + ca + ab)}{(b + c) \, (c + a) \, (a + b)} \,.$$

Verify that this formula is correct in the special case in which the ellipsoid is a sphere and check your answer in part (a) by a similar specialization.

⋆2.21 Further discussion of the transformation formula for double integrals

Suppose the equations

(2.28)
$$x = X(u, v), \qquad y = Y(u, v)$$

define a one-to-one mapping which carries a region T in the uv-plane onto a region S of the xy-plane and suppose the inverse mapping is given by the equations

(2.29)
$$u = U(x, y), \qquad v = V(x, y).$$

Let $J(u, v)$ denote the Jacobian of the mapping in (2.28). If f is integrable on S the transformation formula for double integrals states that

(2.30)
$$\iint_{S} f(x, y) \, dx \, dy = \iint_{T} f[X(u, v), Y(u, v)] \, |J(u, v)| \, du \, dv \,.$$

In the special case in which S is a rectangle R and $f(x, y) = 1$ for each point in this rectangle the formula simplifies to

(2.31)
$$\iint_{R} dx \, dy = \iint_{I(R)} |J(u, v)| \, du \, dv \,,$$

where R denotes a rectangle in the xy-plane and $I(R)$ denotes the image of R under the inverse mapping in (2.29). In this section we show how the general formula in (2.30) may be derived as a consequence of the special case in (2.31). We assume the existence of the integrals in (2.30) and in (2.31).

Suppose that (2.31) is valid whenever R is a rectangle. We shall prove that we have

$$(2.32) \qquad \iint\limits_R s(x, y) \, dx \, dy = \iint\limits_{I(R)} s[X(u, v), Y(u, v)] \, |J(u, v)| \, du \, dv \,,$$

where s is any step function defined on R. For this purpose, let P be a partition of R into mn subrectangles R_{ij} of dimensions Δx_i and Δy_j, and let c_{ij} be the constant value that s takes on the open subrectangle R_{ij}. To prove (2.32) we first prove

$$(2.33) \qquad \sum_{i=1}^{n} \sum_{j=1}^{m} c_{ij} \, \Delta x_i \, \Delta y_j = \sum_{i=1}^{n} \sum_{j=1}^{m} \iint\limits_{I(R_{ij})} s[X(u, v), Y(u, v)] \, |J(u, v)| \, du \, dv \,,$$

and then use the additive property of double integrals to deduce (2.32). Each integral on the right of (2.33) exists because of the assumptions we have made about (2.31).

Since s is a step function Equation (2.33) is the same as

$$(2.34) \qquad \sum_{i=1}^{n} \sum_{j=1}^{m} c_{ij} \, \Delta x_i \, \Delta y_j = \sum_{i=1}^{n} \sum_{j=1}^{m} c_{ij} \iint\limits_{I(R_{ij})} |J(u, v)| \, du \, dv \,.$$

But if we apply (2.31) to the rectangle R_{ij} we find

$$\Delta x_i \, \Delta y_j = \iint\limits_{R_{ij}} dx \, dy = \iint\limits_{I(R_{ij})} |J(u, v)| \, du \, dv \,.$$

Multiplying both sides by c_{ij} and summing on i and j we obtain (2.34). This argument shows that (2.32) is a consequence of (2.31).

Now we can easily show that the step function s in (2.32) may be replaced by an arbitrary integrable function f. Let f be integrable over a rectangle R and choose step functions s and t satisfying the inequalities

$$(2.35) \qquad s(x, y) \le f(x, y) \le t(x, y)$$

for all points (x, y) in R. Then we also have

$$(2.36) \qquad s[X(u, v), Y(u, v)] \le f[X(u, v), Y(u, v)] \le t[X(u, v), Y(u, v)]$$

for every point (u, v) in the image $I(R)$. For brevity, write $S(u, v)$ for $s[X(u, v), Y(u, v)]$ and define $F(u, v)$ and $T(u, v)$ similarly. Multiplying the inequalities in (2.36) by $|J(u, v)|$ and integrating over $I(R)$ we obtain

$$\iint\limits_{I(R)} S(u, v) \, |J(u, v)| \, du \, dv \le \iint\limits_{I(R)} F(u, v) \, |J(u, v)| \, du \, dv \le \iint\limits_{I(R)} T(u, v) \, |J(u, v)| \, du \, dv \,.$$

[At this stage we must assume the existence of the integral $\iint\limits_{I(R)} F(u, v) \, |J(u, v)| \, du \, dv$.] Because of (2.32), the foregoing inequalities are the same as

$$\iint\limits_R s(x, y) \, dx \, dy \le \iint\limits_{I(R)} F(u, v) \, |J(u, v)| \, du \, dv \le \iint\limits_R t(x, y) \, dx \, dy \,.$$

Therefore $\iint_{I(R)} F(u, v) |J(u, v)| \, du \, dv$ is a number which lies between the integrals $\iint_R s(x, y) \, dx \, dy$ and $\iint_R t(x, y) \, dx \, dy$ for *all* choices of step functions s and t satisfying (2.35). Since f is integrable, this implies that

$$\iint_R f(x, y) \, dx \, dy = \iint_{I(R)} F(u, v) |J(u, v)| \, du \, dv$$

and hence (2.30) is valid for integrable functions defined over rectangles.

Once we know that (2.30) is valid for rectangles we can easily extend it to more general regions S by the usual procedure of enclosing S in a rectangle R and extending the function f to a new function $\tilde{f}$ which agrees with f on S and has the value 0 outside S. Then we note that

$$\iint_S f = \iint_R \tilde{f} = \iint_{I(R)} \tilde{f}[X(u, v), Y(u, v)] |J(u, v)| \, du \, dv = \iint_{I(S)} F(u, v) |J(u, v)| \, du \, dv$$

and this proves that (2.30) is, indeed, a consequence of (2.31). Of course, we have not yet proved (2.31). As remarked earlier, a proof of (2.31) will be given in a later chapter, with the use of line integrals.

3

INTRODUCTION TO CALCULUS OF PROBABILITIES

3.1 Introduction

The basic concepts of probability theory were introduced in Chapter 1. We recall that probability is a countably additive measure P defined on a specific collection of subsets of a given universal set S (called the sample space) such that $P(S) = 1$. In all the examples discussed in Chapter 1 the sample space was either finite or countably infinite. In such cases the probability of an event A (that is, of a subset of S) can be computed by adding the point probabilities $P(x)$ for all x in A; thus, we have

$$P(A) = \sum_{x \in A} P(x),$$

where the sum on the right is either a finite sum or an absolutely convergent infinite series. Of course, the resulting sum, $P(A)$, is a number satisfying $0 \leq P(A) \leq 1$.

We wish now to consider situations in which the sample space S is infinite but not necessarily countable. Familiar uncountable sets are the set of all real numbers, the set of numbers in a given interval, the set of points in a rectangle, and the set of points in a circle.

It is easy to visualize experiments in which sets like these might occur as sample spaces. For example, consider a game of chance which consists of throwing a dart at a circular target. Assume the game is such that the dart is "unbiased," that is, assume it is just as likely to strike one point as any other. An outcome of the game is that point at which the dart strikes the target. The collection of all points on the target comprises the sample space S. Events are represented by subsets of S.

Let us assume that a probability measure P is defined on S. The statement that the dart is unbiased will be interpreted to mean that the point probabilities $P(x)$ are equal for all x in S. We can easily prove that all these point probabilities must be zero. In fact, suppose the probability $P(x)$ is positive for some x, say $P(x) = p > 0$. Choose an integer n such that $n > 1/p$ and let A be a subset of S consisting of n points, say $A = \{a_1, a_2, \ldots, a_n\}$. (This is possible because S is infinite.) Since $P(a_i) = p$ for all i, the additivity of P gives us

$$P(A) = \sum_{i=1}^{n} P(a_i) = np > 1,$$

which is a contradiction, since probabilities cannot exceed 1. This contradiction proves that $P(x) = 0$ for all x in S. Therefore, a knowledge of all the point probabilities is of no help in computing the probabilities of arbitrary events. For example, we cannot compute the probability that the dart lands in the first quadrant merely by adding point probabilities.

The foregoing example is more or less typical of uncountable sample spaces. In any infinite sample space the point probabilities must all be zero if they are all equal. If they are not necessarily equal it is easy to show that they can be nonzero only at points of some finite or countably infinite set.† Therefore, if the sample space is uncountable, most (if not all) the point probabilities are zero; new ideas are needed to compute probabilities of events in such cases.

Let us return to the foregoing dart game. Since there is no reason to favor one position of the target over any other, our intuition tells us that the probability that the dart lands in a region T should be a measure of the fraction of S occupied by T. This suggests that we interpret the statement "the dart is unbiased" to mean that the probability that the dart falls in a region T is proportional to the area of T. That is, we assume

$$P(T) = cA(T),$$

where $A(T)$ denotes the area of T, and c is a constant. When $T = S$ this gives us $P(S) = cA(S)$, so $c = P(S)/A(S) = 1/A(S)$, and hence

$$P(T) = \frac{A(T)}{A(S)}$$

for every region T. If T is the first quadrant we have $A(T) = A(S)/4$, so $P(T) = 1/4$ which agrees with our intuition. As this example shows, for uncountable sample spaces a knowledge of the point probabilities alone does not enable us to compute probabilities of arbitrary events; further information is required. In a general discussion this information is best described by introducing *random variables* and *distribution functions*. In the sections that follow we shall find that the introduction of these new concepts makes it possible to use integral calculus as an aid in the computation of probabilities in many cases in which the sample space is uncountable. Integration takes the place of summation in the computation of probabilities.

We shall not present a thorough and comprehensive treatment of the calculus of probabilities. Our aims here are to introduce some of the important basic concepts and to help the reader acquire a feeling for probabilistic thinking. Familiarity with the commonly used terminology and techniques described in this chapter should enable him to read some of the scientific literature that uses probabilistic ideas.

3.2 Random variables

In many experiments we are interested in *numbers* associated with the outcomes of the experiment. For example, n coins are tossed simultaneously and we ask for the number of heads. A pair of dice is rolled and we ask for the sum of the points on the upturned faces. A dart is thrown at a circular target and we ask for its distance from the center. Whenever we associate a real number with each outcome of an experiment we are dealing with a *function* whose domain is the set of possible outcomes and whose range is the set

---

† Given an integer $n \geq 2$, there are at most $n - 1$ points x for which $P(x) > 1/n$. From this it follows that the set of x for which $P(x) > 0$ is finite or countably infinite.

of real numbers in question. Such a function is called a *random variable*. A formal definition may be given as follows:

DEFINITION OF A RANDOM VARIABLE. Let S denote a sample space. A real-valued function
defined on S is called a one-dimensional random variable. If the function values are
ordered pairs of real numbers (that is, vectors in 2-space), the function is said to be a
two-dimensional random variable. More generally, an n-dimensional random variable is
simply a function whose domain is the given sample space S and whose range is a collection of n-tuples of real numbers (vectors in n-space).

Thus, a random variable is nothing but a vector-valued function defined on a set. The
term "random" is used merely to remind us that the set in question is a sample space.†
Because of the generality of the above definition, it is possible to have many random
variables associated with a given experiment. In any particular example the experimenter
must decide which random variables will be of interest and importance to him. In general,
we try to work with random variables whose function values reflect, as simply as possible,
the properties of the outcomes of the experiment which are really essential.

Notations. Capital letters such as X, Y, Z are ordinarily used to denote one-dimensional
random variables. A typical outcome of the experiment (that is, a typical element of the
sample space) is usually denoted by the Greek letter ω (omega). Thus, $X(\omega)$ denotes that
real number which the random variable X associates with the outcome ω.

The following are some simple examples of random variables.

Example 1. An experiment consists of rolling a die and reading the number of points
on the upturned face. The most "natural" random variable X to consider is the one
stamped on the die by the manufacturer, namely:

$$X(\omega) = \omega \qquad \text{for} \quad \omega = 1, 2, 3, 4, 5, 6.$$

If we are interested in whether the number of points is even or odd, then we can consider
instead the random variable Y, which is defined as follows:

$$Y(\omega) = 0 \qquad \text{if} \quad \omega \text{ is even},$$
$$Y(\omega) = 1 \qquad \text{if} \quad \omega \text{ is odd}.$$

The values 0 and 1 are not essential—any two distinct real numbers could be used instead.
However, 0 and 1 suggest "even" and "odd," respectively, because they represent the
remainder obtained when the outcome ω is divided by 2.

Example 2. A dart is thrown at a circular target. The set of all possible outcomes is
the set of all points ω on the target. If we imagine a coordinate system placed on the
target with the origin at the center, we can assign various random variables to this
experiment. A natural one is the two-dimensional random variable which assigns to the
point ω its rectangular coordinates (x, y). Another is that which assigns to ω its polar
coordinates (r, θ). Examples of one-dimensional random variables are those which assign

---

† The terms "stochastic variable" and "chance variable" are also used as synonyms for "random
variable." The word "stochastic" is derived from a Greek stem meaning "chance" and seems to
have been invented by Jakob Bernoulli. It is commonly used in the literature of probability theory.

to each ω just one of its coordinates, such as the x-coordinate or the r-coordinate (distance from the origin). In an experiment of this type we often want to know the probability that the dart will land in a particular region of the target, for example, the first quadrant. This event can be described most simply by the random variable which assigns to each point ω its polar coordinate angle θ, so that $X(\omega) = \theta$; the event "the dart lands in the first quadrant" is the set of ω such that $0 \leq X(\omega) \leq \frac{1}{2}\pi$.

The sample space S of Example 2 is an uncountable set. To be precise about such examples, we should say more about the Boolean algebra of subsets of S on which the probability measure P is defined. In a case like this, when the sample space is uncountable, we should not consider the Boolean algebra of *all* subsets of S. Instead, we should consider only those special subsets which, in the language of modern integration theory, are called *measurable* subsets of S. The reason for this distinction is that so-called *non-measurable* sets exist to which probabilities cannot be assigned in any reasonable way; these sets must be excluded from consideration. Although they are important in advanced theoretical work, nonmeasurable sets do not occur in the ordinary applications of probability. For finite or countable sample spaces, *all* subsets are measurable and no difficulties of this kind occur. To attempt to describe the exact meaning of a measurable set would take us too far afield; instead, we shall mention some of the properties possessed by the class of measurable sets.

First we consider subsets of the real line. Let R denote the set of all real numbers. Then the measurable subsets of R have the following properties:

(1) If A is measurable, so is $R - A$, the complement of A.

(2) If $\{A_1, A_2, A_3, \ldots\}$ is a countable collection of measurable sets, then the union $A_1 \cup A_2 \cup A_3 \cup \cdots$ is also measurable.

(3) Every interval (open, closed, half-open, finite, or infinite) is measurable.

Thus, the measurable sets in R form a Boolean σ-algebra which contains the intervals. A smallest Boolean σ-algebra exists which has this property; its members are called *Borel sets*, after the French mathematician Émile Borel (1871–1956). Similarly, in 2-space a smallest Boolean σ-algebra exists which contains all Cartesian products of pairs of intervals; its members are the two-dimensional Borel sets. Borel sets in n-space are defined in an analogous fashion.

Henceforth, whenever we use a set S of real numbers as a sample space, or, more generally, whenever we use a set S in n-space as a sample space, we shall assume that this set is a Borel set. The Borel subsets of S themselves form a Boolean σ-algebra; we shall assume our probability measures are defined on these Boolean algebras. These algebras of subsets are extensive enough to include all the events that occur in the ordinary applications of probability theory.

Abbreviations. We avoid cumbersome notation by using special abbreviations to describe certain types of events and their probabilities. For example, if t is a real number, the set of all ω in the sample space such that $X(\omega) = t$ is denoted briefly by writing

$$X = t .$$

The probability of this event is written $P(X = t)$ instead of the lengthier $P(\{\omega \mid X(\omega) = t\})$. Symbols such as $P(X = a$ or $X = b)$ and $P(a < X \leq b)$ are defined in a similar fashion. Thus, the event "$X = a$ or $X = b$" is the union of the two events "$X = a$" and "$X = b$"; the symbol $P(X = a$ or $X = b)$ denotes the probability of this union. The event "$a < X \leq b$" is the set of all points ω such that $X(\omega)$ lies in the half-open interval $(a, b]$, and the symbol $P(a < X \leq b)$ denotes the probability of this event.

3.3 Exercises

1. Let X be a one-dimensional random variable.
   (a) If $a < b$, show that the two events $a < X \leq b$ and $X \leq a$ are disjoint.
   (b) Determine the union of the two events in part (a).
   (c) Show that $P(a < X \leq b) = P(X \leq b) - P(X \leq a)$.

2. Let (X, Y) denote a two-dimensional random variable defined on a sample space S. This means that (X, Y) is a function which assigns to each ω in S a pair of real numbers $(X(\omega), Y(\omega))$. Of course, each of X and Y is a one-dimensional random variable defined on S. The notation

$$X \leq a, \; Y \leq b$$

stands for the set of all elements ω in S such that $X(\omega) \leq a$ and $Y(\omega) \leq b$.
   (a) If $a < b$ and $c < d$, describe, in terms of elements of S, the meaning of the following notation: $a < X \leq b, \; c < Y \leq d$.
   (b) Show that the two events "$X \leq a, \; Y \leq c$" and "$X \leq a, \; c < Y \leq d$" are disjoint. Interpret these events geometrically.
   (c) Determine the union of the two events in (b).
   (d) Generalize Exercise 1(c) to the two-dimensional case.

3. Two fair dice are rolled, each outcome being an ordered pair (a, b), where each of a and b is an integer from 1 to 6. Let X be the random variable which assigns the value $a + b$ to the outcome (a, b).
   (a) Describe, in roster notation, the events "$X = 7$," "$X = 11$," "$X = 7$ or $X = 11$."
   (b) Compute the probabilities of the events in part (a).

4. Consider an experiment in which four coins are tossed simultaneously (or one coin is tossed four times). For each coin define a random variable which assigns the value 1 to heads and the value 0 to tails, and denote these random variables by X_1, X_2, X_3, X_4. Assign the probabilities $P(X_i = 1) = P(X_i = 0) = \frac{1}{2}$ for each X_i. Consider a new random variable Y which assigns to each outcome the total number of heads among the four coins. Express Y in terms of X_1, X_2, X_3, X_4 and compute the probabilities $P(Y = 0)$, $P(Y = 1)$, and $P(Y \leq 1)$.

5. A small railroad company has facilities for transporting 100 passengers a day between two cities, at a fixed cost (to the company) of \$7 per passenger. If more than 100 passengers buy tickets in any one day the railroad is obligated to provide bus transportation for the excess at a cost of \$10 per passenger. Let X be the random variable which counts the number of passengers that buy tickets in a given day. The possible values of X are the integers 0, 1, 2, 3, ... up to a certain unknown maximum. Let Y denote the random variable which describes the total daily cost (in dollars) to the railroad for handling passengers. Express Y in terms of X.

6. A factory production line consists of two work stations A and B. At station A, X units per hour are assembled; they are immediately transported to station B, where they are inspected at the rate of Y units per hour, where $Y < X$. The possible values of X and Y are the integers 8, 9, and 10. Let Z denote the random variable which counts the number of units that come off the production line during the first hour of production.
   (a) Express Z in terms of X and Y, assuming each of X and Y is constant during this hour.
   (b) Describe, in a similar way, the random variable U which counts the number of units de-

livered in the first two consecutive hours of production. Each of X and Y is constant during each hour, but the constant values during the second hour need not be the same as those during the first.

3.4 Distribution functions

We turn now to the problem of computing the probabilities of events associated with a given random variable. Let X be a one-dimensional random variable defined on a sample space S, where S is a Borel set in n-space for some $n \geq 1$. Let P be a probability measure defined on the Borel subsets of S. For each ω in S, $X(\omega)$ is a real number, and as ω runs through the elements of S the numbers $X(\omega)$ run through a set of real numbers (the range of X). This set may be finite, countably infinite, or uncountable. For each real number t we consider the following special subset of S:

$$A(t) = \{\omega \mid X(\omega) \leq t\} \,.$$

If t is less than all the numbers in the range of X, the set $A(t)$ will be empty; otherwise, $A(t)$ will be a nonempty subset of S. We assume that for each t the set $A(t)$ is an *event*, that is, a Borel set. According to the convention discussed at the end of Section 3.2, we denote this event by the symbol $X \leq t$.

Suppose we know the probability $P(X \leq t)$ for every real t. We shall find in a moment that this knowledge enables us to compute the probabilities of many other events of interest. This is done by using the probabilities $P(X \leq t)$ as a basis for constructing a new function F, called the *distribution function* of X. It is defined as follows:

DEFINITION OF A DISTRIBUTION FUNCTION. Let X be a one-dimensional random variable. The function F defined for all real t by the equation

$$F(t) = P(X \leq t)$$

is called the distribution function of the random variable X.

Note. Sometimes the notation F_X is used to emphasize the fact that the distribution function is associated with the particular random variable X. The value of the function at t is then denoted by $F_X(t)$.

It is important to realize that the distribution function F is defined over the entire real axis, even though the range of X may be only a bounded portion of the real axis. In fact, if all numbers $X(\omega)$ lie in some finite interval $[a, b]$, then for $t < a$ the probability $P(X \leq t)$ is zero (since for $t < a$ the set $X \leq t$ is empty) and for $t > b$ the probability $P(X \leq t)$ is 1 (because in this case the set $X \leq t$ is the entire sample space). This means that for *bounded* random variables X whose range is within an interval $[a, b]$ we have $F(t) = 0$ for all $t < a$ and $F(t) = 1$ for all $t > b$.

We now proceed to derive a number of properties common to all distribution functions.

3–1   THEOREM.   Let F denote the distribution function of a one-dimensional random variable X. Then if $a < b$ we have

(3.1) $$P(a < X \leq b) = F(b) - F(a) \,.$$

In other words, the probability that the random variable X lies in the half-open interval $(a, b]$ is $F(b) - F(a)$.

Proof. The events "$a < X \le b$" and "$X \le a$" are disjoint. Their union is the event "$X \le b$." Using additivity we obtain

$$P(a < X \le b) + P(X \le a) = P(X \le b),$$

which can also be expressed as

$$P(a < X \le b) = P(X \le b) - P(X \le a) = F(b) - F(a).$$

This completes the proof.

The foregoing theorem tells us how to compute (in terms of F) the probability that X lies in a half-open interval of the form $(a, b]$. To compute the probability that X lies in the *closed* interval $[a, b]$ we use the additive property again to obtain

$$P(a \le X \le b) = P(X = a) + P(a < X \le b) = P(X = a) + F(b) - F(a).$$

When $P(X = a)$ is zero (which it may or may not be), this equation tells us that the two events $a < X \le b$ and $a \le X \le b$ have equal probabilities. Similarly, we find

$$P(a < X < b) = P(a < X \le b) - P(X = b) = F(b) - F(a) - P(X = b)$$

and

$$P(a \le X < b) = P(a < X < b) + P(X = a) = F(b) - F(a) + P(X = a) - P(X = b).$$

Thus, when $P(X = a)$ and $P(X = b)$ are both zero, all four events

$$a < X \le b, \quad a \le X \le b, \quad a < X < b, \quad \text{and} \quad a \le X < b$$

have equal probabilities.

As a corollary of Theorem 3–1 we can prove that all distributions are monotonically increasing functions whose values lie between 0 and 1. That is to say, we have:

3– 2   THEOREM. Let F be the distribution function of a one-dimensional random variable X. Then

(a) $0 \le F(x) \le 1$ for every real x;
(b) $F(x) \le F(y)$ whenever $x < y$.

Proof. Part (a) follows immediately from the definition of F, because probabilities always lie between 0 and 1. To prove part (b) we use Equation (3.1) to obtain

$$F(y) - F(x) = P(x < X \le y) \ge 0.$$

As we remarked earlier, when the random variable X is *bounded*, say $a \le X(\omega) \le b$ for all ω in the sample space, we must have

(3.2) $F(t) = 0$ for all $t < a$,   and $F(t) = 1$ for all $t > b$.

A simple example is shown in Figure 3.1. Here we have

$$F(t) = 0 \quad \text{for } t < 0, \quad F(t) = t \quad \text{for } 0 \le t \le 1, \quad F(t) = 1 \quad \text{for } t > 1.$$

This particular example, known as a *uniform distribution*, will be discussed further in Section 3.7.

Figure 3.2 shows an example of a distribution function corresponding to an *unbounded*

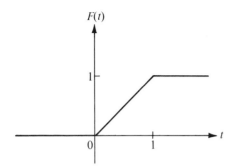

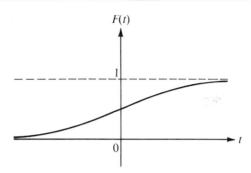

FIGURE 3.1   *A distribution for a bounded*
random variable.

FIGURE 3.2   *A distribution for an unbounded*
random variable.

random variable X. This example is known as the *Cauchy distribution* and its function values are given by the formula

$$F(t) = \frac{1}{2} + \frac{1}{\pi} \text{ arc tan } t .$$

(Experiments that lead to a Cauchy distribution will be discussed in Section 3.7.) Note that in this example we have

$$\lim_{t \to -\infty} F(t) = \frac{1}{2} + \frac{1}{\pi}\left(-\frac{\pi}{2}\right) = 0 \quad \text{and} \quad \lim_{t \to +\infty} F(t) = \frac{1}{2} + \frac{1}{\pi}\left(\frac{\pi}{2}\right) = 1 .$$

This property is shared by all random variables. That is, at the extremities of the real axis every distribution function F satisfies the two limit relations

(3.3) $$\lim_{t \to -\infty} F(t) = 0 \quad \text{and} \quad \lim_{t \to +\infty} F(t) = 1 .$$

[Because of (3.2), these equations hold trivially for distributions of bounded random variables.] The *existence* of the two limits in (3.3) and the fact that each of the two limits lies between 0 and 1 follow at once, since F is a monotonic function whose values lie between 0 and 1.

Let us denote the limits in (3.3) by L_1 and L_2, respectively. To prove that $L_1 = 0$ and that $L_2 = 1$ we shall use the countably additive property of probability. For this purpose we express the whole space S as a countable union of disjoint events:

$$S = \bigcup_{n=1}^{\infty} (-n < X \le -n + 1) \cup \bigcup_{n=0}^{\infty} (n < X \le n + 1) .$$

Then, using additivity, we get

$$P(S) = \sum_{n=1}^{\infty} P(-n < X \le -n + 1) + \sum_{n=0}^{\infty} P(n < X \le n + 1)$$

$$= \lim_{M \to \infty} \sum_{n=1}^{M} [F(-n + 1) - F(-n)] + \lim_{N \to \infty} \sum_{n=0}^{N} [F(n + 1) - F(n)] .$$

The sums on the right telescope, giving us

$$P(S) = \lim_{M \to \infty} [F(0) - F(-M)] + \lim_{N \to \infty} [F(N + 1) - F(0)]$$

$$= F(0) - L_1 + L_2 - F(0) = L_2 - L_1 .$$

Since $P(S) = 1$, this proves that $L_2 - L_1 = 1$ or $L_2 = 1 + L_1$. On the other hand, we also have $L_2 \leq 1$ and $L_1 \geq 0$. This implies that $L_1 = 0$ and $L_2 = 1$, as asserted.

With the foregoing argument we have proved the following theorem:

3–3   THEOREM.   Let F be the distribution function of a one-dimensional random variable X. Then we have

(3.4) $$\lim_{t \to -\infty} F(t) = 0 \quad \text{and} \quad \lim_{t \to +\infty} F(t) = 1 .$$

The two limits in (3.4) are often denoted by the symbols $F(-\infty)$ and $F(+\infty)$. This notation is consistent with the definition of F if we interpret the "event" $X \leq -\infty$ to be the empty set and the "event" $X \leq +\infty$ to be the entire sample space.

———————————

A physical interpretation of distributions often helps to illustrate the meaning of various definitions and theorems in probability theory. Imagine that we have an amount of *mass*, with the total quantity equal to 1, and that we are able to distribute this mass in any way we please along the real axis. At some points along the axis we may place no mass at all; at other points we may "smear" the mass along the axis with a uniform or perhaps a varying thickness, or we may place concentrated "lumps" of mass at certain points. If we denote by $F(t)$ the total amount of mass located from $-\infty$ to t (including the point t itself), the function F so defined has exactly the same mathematical properties as a distribution function. The amount of mass located in a half-open interval $(a, b]$ is $F(b) - F(a)$, just as though this were the probability that a random variable takes on a value in $(a, b]$.

With this interpretation of the example shown in Figure 3.1, we would say that no mass has been placed to the left of the origin or to the right of the point $t = 1$. The entire mass has been distributed along the interval $[0, 1]$. The graph of F is linear over this interval because the mass is smeared with a uniform thickness. In Figure 3.2 the mass has been smeared along the entire axis with a varying thickness.

When we put a concentrated lump of mass at a particular point, the distribution function F will have a discontinuity at that point, as shown in Figure 3.3. The discontinuities occur at points at which concentrated lumps of mass have been placed, with the jump in each case equal to the amount of mass concentrated at that particular point. The graph is horizontal above those intervals which carry no mass at all, and linear over those intervals which carry mass with a uniform thickness. The graph is curved over those intervals which carry mass with a varying thickness.

———————————

We conclude this section with an important theorem concerning the nature of the discontinuities of a distribution function.

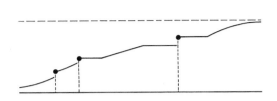

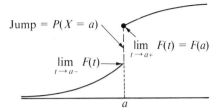

FIGURE 3.3   *A possible distribution function.*

FIGURE 3.4   *Illustrating a jump discontinuity of a distribution function.*

3– 4   THEOREM.   Let F be the distribution function of a one-dimensional random variable X. Then for each real a we have

(3.5)
$$\lim_{t \to a+} F(t) = F(a)$$

and

(3.6)
$$\lim_{t \to a-} F(t) = F(a) - P(X = a).$$

The limit relation in (3.5) tells us that F is *continuous from the right* at each point a, because $F(t) \to F(a)$ as $t \to a$ from the right. On the other hand, Equation (3.6) tells us that as $t \to a$ from the left, $F(t)$ will approach $F(a)$ if and only if the probability $P(X = a)$ is zero. When $P(X = a)$ is *not* zero, the graph of F has a jump discontinuity at a of the type shown in Figure 3.4.

Proof. The existence of the limits follows at once from the monotonicity and boundedness of F. We prove now that the limits have the values indicated. For this purpose we use Equation (3.1) of Theorem 3–1. If $t > a$ we write

(3.7)
$$F(t) = F(a) + P(a < X \le t);$$

if $t < a$ we write

(3.8)
$$F(t) = F(a) - P(t < X \le a).$$

Letting $t \to a+$ in (3.7) we find

$$\lim_{t \to a+} F(t) = F(a) + \lim_{t \to a+} P(a < X \le t),$$

whereas if $t \to a-$ in (3.8) we obtain

$$\lim_{t \to a-} F(t) = F(a) - \lim_{t \to a-} P(t < X \le a).$$

Therefore to prove (3.5) and (3.6) we must establish two equations:

(3.9)
$$\lim_{t \to a+} P(a < X \le t) = 0$$

and

(3.10)
$$\lim_{t \to a-} P(t < X \le a) = P(X = a).$$

These may be justified intuitively as follows: When $t \to a+$, the half-open interval $(a, t]$ shrinks to the empty set. That is, the intersection of all half-open intervals $(a, t]$, for $t > a$, is empty. On the other hand, when $t \to a-$ the half-open interval $(t, a]$ shrinks to the point a. (The intersection of all intervals $(t, a]$ for $t < a$ is the set $\{a\}$.) Therefore, if probability behaves in a continuous fashion, Equations (3.9) and (3.10) must be valid. To convert this argument into a rigorous proof we proceed as follows:

For each integer $n \geq 1$, let

$$(3.11) \qquad p_n = P\left(a < X \leq a + \frac{1}{n}\right).$$

To prove (3.9) it suffices to show that $p_n \to 0$ as $n \to \infty$. Let S_n denote the event

$$a + \frac{1}{n+1} < X \leq a + \frac{1}{n}.$$

The sets S_n are disjoint and their union $S_1 \cup S_2 \cup S_3 \cup \cdots$ is the event $a < X \leq a + 1$. By countable additivity we have

$$(3.12) \qquad \sum_{n=1}^{\infty} P(S_n) = P(a < X \leq a + 1) = p_1 .$$

On the other hand, Equation (3.11) implies that

$$p_n - p_{n+1} = P(S_n) ,$$

so from (3.12) we obtain the relation

$$(3.13) \qquad \sum_{n=1}^{\infty} (p_n - p_{n+1}) = p_1 .$$

The convergence of the series is a consequence of (3.12). But the series on the left of (3.13) is a telescoping series with sum

$$p_1 - \lim_{n \to \infty} p_n .$$

Therefore (3.13) implies that $\lim_{n \to \infty} p_n = 0$, and this proves (3.9).

A slight modification of this argument enables us to prove (3.10) as well. Since

$$P(t < X \leq a) = P(t < X < a) + P(X = a)$$

we need only prove that

$$\lim_{t \to a-} P(t < X < a) = 0 .$$

For this purpose we introduce the numbers

$$q_n = P\left(a - \frac{1}{n} < X < a\right)$$

and show that $q_n \to 0$ as $n \to \infty$. In this case we consider the events T_n given by

$$a - \frac{1}{n} < X \leq a - \frac{1}{n+1}$$

for $n = 1, 2, 3, \ldots$. These are disjoint and their union is the event $a - 1 < X < a$, so we have

$$\sum_{n=1}^{\infty} P(T_n) = P(a - 1 < X < a) = q_1 .$$

We now note that $q_n - q_{n+1} = P(T_n)$, and we complete the proof as above.

The most general type of distribution is any real-valued function F that has the following properties:

(a) F is monotonically increasing on the real axis,
(b) F is continuous from the right at each point,
(c) $\lim_{t \to -\infty} F(t) = 0$ and $\lim_{t \to +\infty} F(t) = 1$.

In fact, it can be shown that for each such function F there is a corresponding set function P, defined on the Borel sets of the real line, such that P is a probability measure which assigns the probability $F(b) - F(a)$ to each half-open interval $(a, b]$. For a proof of this statement, see H. Cramér, *Mathematical Methods of Statistics*, Princeton University Press, Princeton, N.J., 1946.

There are two special types of distributions, known as *discrete* and *continuous*, that are of particular importance in practice. In the discrete case the entire mass is concentrated at a finite or countably infinite number of points, whereas in the continuous case the mass is smeared, in uniform or varying thickness, along the entire axis. These two types of distributions will be treated in some detail in the next few sections.

3.5   Discrete distributions. Probability mass functions

Let X be a one-dimensional random variable and consider a new function p, called the *probability mass function* of X. Its values $p(t)$ are defined for every real number t by the equation

$$p(t) = P(X = t) .$$

That is, $p(t)$ is the probability that X takes the value t. When we want to emphasize that p is associated with X we write p_X instead of p and $p_X(t)$ instead of $p(t)$.

The set of real numbers t for which $p(t) > 0$ is either finite or countable. We denote this set by T; that is, we let

$$T = \{t \mid p(t) > 0\} .$$

The random variable X is said to be *discrete* if

$$\sum_{t \in T} p(t) = 1 .$$

In other words, X is discrete if a unit probability mass is distributed over the real line by concentrating a positive mass $p(t)$ at each point t of some finite or countably infinite set T and no mass at the remaining points. The points of T are called the *mass points* of X.

For discrete random variables a knowledge of the probability mass function enables

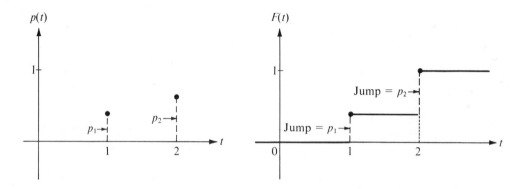

(a)　*The mass function p.*　　　　　　　　(b)　*The distribution function F.*

FIGURE 3.5　*The probability mass function and the distribution function of a discrete random variable with two mass points.*

us to compute probabilities of arbitrary events. In fact, if E is a set of real numbers we have

(3.14) $$P(X \mathrel{\varepsilon} E) = \sum_{x \mathrel{\varepsilon} E \cap T} p(x),$$

where $P(X \mathrel{\varepsilon} E)$ denotes the probability of the set of ω such that $X(\omega) \mathrel{\varepsilon} E.\dagger$ Since $p(x) = 0$ when $x \notin T$, the sum on the right of (3.14) may be written as $\sum_{x \mathrel{\varepsilon} E} p(x)$ without danger of its being misunderstood. When E is the set of all real numbers that do not exceed t the sum in (3.14) gives the value of the distribution function $F(t)$. Thus we have

(3.15) $$F(t) = P(X \le t) = \sum_{x \le t} p(x).$$

When a random variable X is discrete, the corresponding distribution function F is also called discrete.

For example, suppose that among the elements of a sample space S there are exactly two elements ω_1 and ω_2 that are assigned nonzero probabilities, say $P(\omega_1) = p_1$ and $P(\omega_2) = p_2$, where $p_1 + p_2 = 1$. Consider a random variable X such that

† Equation (3.14) is easily proved as follows: Let S denote the set of all real numbers. Since $E \cap T \subseteq E$ and $T - E \subseteq S - E$, we have the two inequalities

$$\sum_{x \mathrel{\varepsilon} E \cap T} p(x) \le P(X \mathrel{\varepsilon} E) \qquad \text{and} \qquad \sum_{x \mathrel{\varepsilon} T-E} p(x) \le P(X \notin E).$$

But $E \cap T$ and $T - E$ are disjoint sets whose union is T, so the second inequality is equivalent to

$$1 - \sum_{x \mathrel{\varepsilon} E \cap T} p(x) \le 1 - P(X \mathrel{\varepsilon} E), \qquad \text{or} \qquad \sum_{x \mathrel{\varepsilon} E \cap T} p(x) \ge P(X \mathrel{\varepsilon} E).$$

Combining this with the first inequality we obtain (3.14).

$$X(\omega_1) = 1 \qquad \text{and} \qquad X(\omega_2) = 2.$$

(The values of X at the remaining points of S are not relevant to this discussion.) The corresponding mass function p is given by the formulas

$$p(t) = \begin{cases} 0 & \text{if } t \neq 1 \text{ or } t \neq 2, \\ p_1 & \text{if } t = 1, \\ p_2 & \text{if } t = 2. \end{cases}$$

Since $p(t) = 0$ unless $t = 1$ or $t = 2$, the set T where $p(t) > 0$ consists of the two integers 1 and 2. The graph of p is shown in Figure 3.5(a). The corresponding distribution function F is given by the sum in Equation (3.15). When $t < 1$ there are no positive terms in this sum, so $F(t) = 0$. When $1 \leq t < 2$ there is exactly one value of $x \leq t$ with $p(x) > 0$, namely, $x = 1$, so that $F(t) = p(1) = p_1$. Similarly, when $t \geq 2$ there are two values of $x \leq t$ which give positive contributions to the sum, and we have $F(t) = p(1) + p(2) = p_1 + p_2$. Thus, we may write

$$F(t) = \begin{cases} 0 & \text{if } t < 1, \\ p_1 & \text{if } 1 \leq t < 2, \\ p_1 + p_2 = 1 & \text{if } t \geq 2. \end{cases}$$

The graph of F is shown in Figure 3.5(b). Note that there is a jump p_1 at the mass point $t = 1$ and another jump p_2 at the mass point $t = 2$.

If the random variable X had the values x_1 and x_2 instead of 1 and 2 at the points ω_1 and ω_2, the general shape of the graph of F would be like that in Figure 3.5(b), except that jumps p_1 and p_2 would occur at points x_1 and x_2.

The situation is similar if exactly three elements ω_1, ω_2, ω_3 of a sample space S have nonzero probabilities, say $P(\omega_1) = p_1$, $P(\omega_2) = p_2$, $P(\omega_3) = p_3$, where p_1, p_2, p_3 are positive numbers whose sum is 1. If we have a random variable X such that, for example, $X(\omega_k) = k$ for $k = 1, 2, 3$, the mass function p is given by the following formulas:

$$p(t) = \begin{cases} 0 & \text{if } t \neq 1, t \neq 2, \text{ or } t \neq 3, \\ p_1 & \text{if } t = 1, \\ p_2 & \text{if } t = 2, \\ p_3 & \text{if } t = 3. \end{cases}$$

The graph of p is shown in Figure 3.6(a). The corresponding distribution function F is given by

$$F(t) = \begin{cases} 0 & \text{if } t < 1, \\ p_1 & \text{if } 1 \leq t < 2, \\ p_1 + p_2 & \text{if } 2 \leq t < 3, \\ p_1 + p_2 + p_3 = 1 & \text{if } t \geq 3. \end{cases}$$

Its graph is like that shown in Figure 3.6(b).

Next we discuss an example in which the mass is concentrated at the points of a countably infinite set. Consider a sample space S for which the elements with nonzero probability are $\omega_1, \omega_2, \omega_3, \ldots$, and suppose that $P(\omega_k) = 2^{-k}$ for each $k \geq 1$. Consider a random variable X such that $X(\omega_k) = 2^{1-k}$ for $k = 1, 2, 3, \ldots$. Then $p(t) = 2^{-k}$ if $t = 2^{1-k}$ $(k = 1, 2, 3, \ldots)$ and $p(t) = 0$ otherwise. [Part of the graph of p is shown in

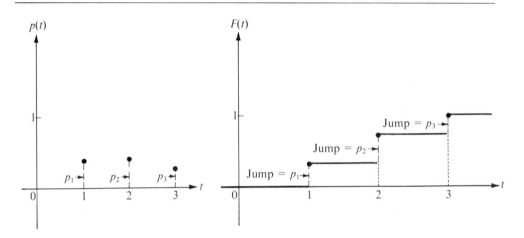

(a)   *The mass function p.*   (b)   *The distribution function F.*

FIGURE 3.6   *The probability mass function and the distribution function of a discrete random variable with three mass points.*

Figure 3.7 (a).] The corresponding distribution function F has the values $F(t) = 0$ for $t \leq 0$ and $F(t) = 1$ for $t \geq 1$. In the half-open intervals of the form $[2^{-k}, 2^{1-k})$, $k = 1$, $2, 3, \ldots$, the function value $F(t)$ is constant and equal to 2^{-k}, as indicated in Figure 3.7 (b).

   The foregoing examples illustrate some of the possible discrete distributions that can occur. More complicated examples can easily be constructed but we shall not discuss them here. Instead, we discuss briefly two discrete distributions that occur frequently in practice.

Example 1: Binomial distribution. Let p be a given real number satisfying $0 \leq p \leq 1$ and let $q = 1 - p$. Suppose a random variable X assumes the values $0, 1, 2, \ldots, n$, where n is a fixed positive integer, and suppose the probability $P(X = k)$ is given by the formula

$$P(X = k) = \binom{n}{k} p^k q^{n-k} \qquad \text{for} \quad k = 0, 1, 2, \ldots, n \,.$$

This assignment of probabilities is permissible because the sum of all the point probabilities is

$$\sum_{k=0}^{n} P(X = k) = \sum_{k=0}^{n} \binom{n}{k} p^k q^{n-k} = (p + q)^n = 1 \,.$$

The corresponding distribution function F_X is said to be a *binomial distribution* with parameters n and p. Its values may be computed by the summation formula

$$F_X(t) = \sum_{0 \leq k \leq t} \binom{n}{k} p^k q^{n-k} \,.$$

Binomial distributions arise naturally from a Bernoullian sequence of trials if p is the probability of "success" and q the probability of "failure." In fact, when the random variable X counts the number of successes in n trials, $P(X = k)$ is precisely $\binom{n}{k} p^k q^{n-k}$ because of Bernoulli's formula. (See Theorem 1-1 in Section 1.25.)

Example 2: Poisson distribution. Let λ be a positive real number and let a random variable X assume the values 0, 1, 2, 3, ... If the probability $P(X = k)$ is given by the formula

$$P(X = k) = \frac{e^{-\lambda} \lambda^k}{k!} \qquad \text{for} \quad k = 0, 1, 2, \ldots ,$$

the corresponding distribution function F_X is said to be a *Poisson distribution* with parameter λ. It is so named in honor of the French mathematician S. D. Poisson (1781–1840). This assignment of probabilities is permissible because

$$\sum_{k=0}^{\infty} P(X = k) = e^{-\lambda} \sum_{k=0}^{\infty} \frac{\lambda^k}{k!} = e^{-\lambda} e^{\lambda} = 1 .$$

The values of the distribution function are computed from the partial sums

$$F_X(t) = e^{-\lambda} \sum_{0 \le k \le t} \frac{\lambda^k}{k!} .$$

The Poisson distribution is applicable to many problems involving random events occurring in time, such as traffic accidents, connections to wrong numbers in a telephone exchange, and chromosome interchanges in cells induced by x-ray radiation. Some

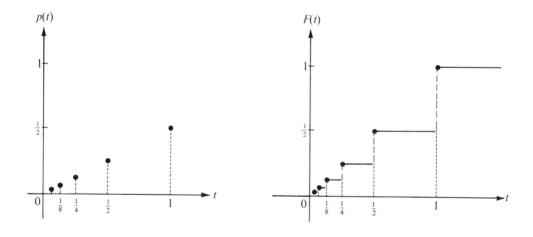

(a) *The mass function p.*   (b) *The distribution function F.*

FIGURE 3.7   *The probability mass function and the distribution function of a discrete random variable with a countable number of mass points.*

specific applications are discussed in the books by Feller and Parzen listed at the end of this chapter.

3.6   Exercises

1. A perfectly balanced die is rolled. For a random variable X we take the function which counts the number of points on the upturned face. Draw a graph of the corresponding distribution function F_X.

2. Two dice are rolled. Let X denote the random variable which counts the total number of points on the upturned faces. Construct a table giving the nonzero values of the probability mass function p_X and draw a graph of the corresponding distribution function F_X.

3. The distribution function F of a random variable X is given by the following formulas:

$$F(t) = \begin{cases} 0 & \text{if } t < -2, \\ \frac{1}{2} & \text{if } -2 \le t < 0, \\ \frac{3}{4} & \text{if } 0 \le t < 2, \\ 1 & \text{if } t \ge 2. \end{cases}$$

(a) Sketch the graph of F.

(b) Describe the probability mass function p and draw its graph.

(c) Compute the following probabilities: $P(X = 1)$, $P(X \le 1)$, $P(X < 1)$, $P(X = 2)$, $P(X \le 2)$, $P(0 < X < 2)$, $P(0 < X \le 2)$, $P(1 \le X \le 2)$.

4. Consider a random variable X whose possible values are all rational numbers of the form $\frac{n}{n+1}$ and $\frac{n+1}{n}$, where $n = 1, 2, 3, \ldots$. If

$$P\left(X = \frac{n}{n+1}\right) = P\left(X = \frac{n+1}{n}\right) = \frac{1}{2^{n+1}},$$

verify that this assignment of probabilities is permissible and sketch the general shape of the graph of the distribution function F_X.

5. The probability mass function p of a random variable X is zero except at points $t = 0$, 1, 2. At these points it has the values

$$p(0) = 3c^3, \quad p(1) = 4c - 10c^2, \quad p(2) = 5c - 1,$$

for some $c > 0$.

(a) Determine the value of c.

(b) Compute the following probabilities: $P(X < 1)$, $P(X < 2)$, $P(1 < X \le 2)$, $P(0 < X < 3)$.

(c) Describe the distribution function F and sketch its graph.

(d) Find the largest t such that $F(t) < \frac{1}{2}$.

(e) Find the smallest t such that $F(t) > \frac{1}{3}$.

6. A random variable X has a binomial distribution with parameters $n = 4$ and $p = \frac{1}{3}$.

(a) Describe the probability mass function p and sketch its graph.

(b) Describe the distribution function F and sketch its graph.

(c) Compute the probabilities $P(1 < X \le 2)$ and $P(1 \le X \le 2)$.

7. Assume that if a thumbtack is tossed on a table, it lands either with point up or in a stable position with point resting on the table. Assume there is a positive probability p that it lands with point up.

(a) Suppose two identical tacks are tossed simultaneously. Assuming stochastic independence, show that the probability that both land with point up is p^2.

(b) Continuing part (a), let X denote the random variable which counts the number of tacks which land with point up (the possible values of X are 0, 1, and 2). Compute the probabilities $P(X = 0)$ and $P(X = 1)$.

(c) Draw the graph of the distribution function F_X when $p = \frac{1}{3}$.

8. Given a random variable X whose possible values are 1, 2, ..., n. Assume that the probability $P(X = k)$ is proportional to k. Determine the constant of proportionality, the probability mass function p_X, and the distribution function F_X.

9. Given a random variable X whose possible values are 0, 1, 2, 3, ... Assume that $P(X = k)$ is proportional to $c^k/k!$, where c is a fixed real number. Determine the constant of proportionality and the probability mass function p.

10. (a) A fair die is rolled. The sample space is $S = \{1, 2, 3, 4, 5, 6\}$. If the number of points on the upturned face is odd a player receives one dollar; otherwise he must pay one dollar. Let X denote the random variable which measures his financial outcome (number of dollars) on each play of the game. (The possible values of X are $+1$ and -1.) Describe the probability mass function p_X and the distribution F_X. Sketch their graphs.

(b) A fair coin is tossed. The sample space $S = \{H, T\}$. If the outcome is heads a player receives one dollar; if it is tails he must pay one dollar. Let Y denote the random variable which measures his financial outcome (number of dollars) on each play of the game. Show that the mass function p_Y and the distribution F_Y are identical to those in part (a). This example shows that different random variables may have the same probability distribution function. Actually, there are infinitely many random variables having a given probability distribution F. (Why?) Such random variables are said to be *identically distributed*. Each theorem concerning a particular distribution function is applicable to any of an infinite collection of random variables having this distribution.

11. The number of minutes that one has to wait for a train at a certain subway station is known to be a random variable X with the following probability mass function:

$$p(t) = 0 \qquad \text{unless} \quad t = 3k/10 \qquad \text{for some} \quad k = 0, 1, 2, \ldots, 10 \, .$$

$$p(t) = \frac{1}{12} \qquad \text{if} \quad t = 0, 0.3, 0.6, 0.9, 2.1, 2.4, 2.7, 3.0 \, .$$

$$p(t) = \frac{1}{9} \qquad \text{if} \quad t = 1.2, 1.5, 1.8 \, .$$

Sketch the graph of the corresponding distribution function F. Let A be the event that one has to wait between 0 and 2 minutes (including 0 and 2), and let B be the event that one has to wait between 1 and 3 minutes (including 1 and 3). Compute the following probabilities: $P(A)$, $P(B)$, $P(A \cap B)$, $P(B|A)$, $P(A \cup B)$.

12. (a) If $0 < p < 1$ and $q = 1 - p$, show that

$$\binom{n}{k} p^k q^{n-k} = \frac{(np)^k}{k!} \left(1 - \frac{np}{n} \right)^n Q_n ,$$

where

$$Q_n = \frac{\displaystyle\prod_{r=2}^{k} \left(1 - \frac{r-1}{n} \right)}{(1-p)^k} \, .$$

(b) Given $\lambda > 0$, let $p = \lambda/n$ for $n > \lambda$. Show that $Q_n \to 1$ as $n \to \infty$ and that

$$\binom{n}{k} p^k q^{n-k} \to \frac{\lambda^k}{k!} e^{-\lambda} \qquad \text{as} \quad n \to \infty \, .$$

This result suggests that for large n and small p, the binomial distribution is approximately the same as the Poisson distribution, provided the product np is nearly constant; this constant is the parameter λ of the Poisson distribution.

3.7   Continuous distributions. Density functions

Let X be a one-dimensional random variable and let F be its distribution function, so that $F(t) = P(X \leq t)$ for every real t. If the probability $P(X = t)$ is zero for every t then, because of Theorem 3–4, F is continuous everywhere on the real axis. In this case F is called a *continuous distribution* and X is called a *continuous random variable*. If the derivative F' exists and is continuous on an interval $[a, t]$ we may use the second fundamental theorem of calculus to write

$$(3.16) \qquad F(t) - F(a) = \int_a^t f(u) \, du \, ,$$

where f is the derivative of F. The difference $F(t) - F(a)$ is, of course, the probability $P(a < X \leq t)$, and Equation (3.16) expresses this probability as an integral.

Sometimes the distribution function F can be expressed as an integral of the form (3.16), in which the integrand f is integrable but not necessarily continuous. Whenever an equation such as (3.16) holds for all intervals $[a, t]$, the integrand f is called the *probability density function* of the random variable X (or of the distribution F). When the distribution F has a derivative at a point, this derivative is the value of the density f at that point. But the density may exist at points at which the derivative F' does not exist. The density is always a nonnegative function. This follows from the monotonicity of F when f is the derivative of F, and it is postulated as a requirement otherwise. In other words, we have the following definition:

DEFINITION OF A PROBABILITY DENSITY FUNCTION. Let X be a continuous random variable with distribution function F. A nonnegative function f is called a probability density of X (or of F) if f is integrable on every interval $[a, t]$ and if

$$(3.17) \qquad F(t) - F(a) = \int_a^t f(u) \, du \, .$$

If we let $a \to -\infty$ in (3.17) then $F(a) \to 0$ and we obtain the important formula

$$(3.18) \qquad F(t) = P(X \leq t) = \int_{-\infty}^t f(u) \, du \, ,$$

valid for all real t. If we now let $t \to +\infty$ and remember that $F(t) \to 1$ we find that

$$(3.19) \qquad \int_{-\infty}^{+\infty} f(u) \, du = 1 \, .$$

For discrete random variables the sum of all the probabilities $P(X = t)$ is equal to 1. Formula (3.19) is the continuous analog of this statement. There is also a strong analogy between formulas (3.18) and (3.15). The density function f plays the same role for continuous distributions that the probability mass function p plays for discrete distributions— integration takes the place of summation in the computation of probabilities. There is one important difference, however. In the discrete case $p(t)$ is the probability that $X = t$, but in the continuous case $f(t)$ is *not* the probability that $P(X = t)$. In fact, this probability is zero because F is continuous for every t. Of course, this also means that for a continuous distribution we have

$$P(a \leq X \leq b) = P(a < X < b) = P(a < X \leq b) = P(a \leq X < b) \, .$$

If F has a density f each of these probabilities is equal to the integral $\int_a^b f(u) \, du$.

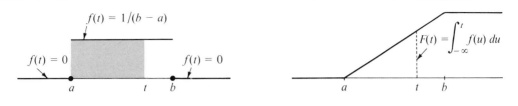

(a) *The density function f.*   (b) *The distribution function F.*

FIGURE 3.8   *A uniform distribution over an interval [a, b] and the corresponding density function.*

Since f is nonnegative, Equation (3.18) may be interpreted geometrically as the area of that portion of the ordinate set of f lying to the left of the line $x = t$. The area of the entire ordinate set is equal to 1. The area of the portion of the ordinate set above a given interval (whether it is open, closed, or half-open) is the probability that the random variable X takes on a value in that interval. Figure 3.8 shows an example of a continuous distribution function F and its density function f. The ordinate $F(t)$ in Figure 3.8 (b) is equal to the area of the shaded region in Figure 3.8 (a).

We conclude this section with a discussion of four important examples of continuous distributions and their density functions.

Example 1: Uniform distribution over an interval. A random variable X is said to have a uniform distribution function F over an interval $[a, b]$ if F is given by the following formulas:

$$F(t) = \begin{cases} 0 & \text{if } t \leq a \\ \dfrac{t - a}{b - a} & \text{if } a \leq t \leq b \\ 1 & \text{if } t \geq b. \end{cases}$$

This is a continuous distribution whose graph is shown in Figure 3.8 (b).

The derivative $F'(t)$ exists everywhere except at the points a and b, and we may write

$$F(t) = \int_{-\infty}^{t} f(u) \, du,$$

where f is the density function, defined as follows:

$$f(t) = \begin{cases} 1/(b - a) & \text{if } a < t < b, \\ 0 & \text{otherwise}. \end{cases}$$

The graph of f is shown in Figure 3.8 (a).

Let us consider an experiment that leads to a uniform distribution. Suppose two vertical lines, $x = a$ and $x = b$, are drawn in the xy-plane. A dart is dropped on the plane from so great a height that aiming is impossible. An outcome of the experiment is the point (x, y) at which the dart strikes the plane. However, the only outcomes counted are those that land in the vertical strip $a < x < b$. This strip may be considered the sample space

S. For the random variable *X* we take the *x*-coordinate of the point of contact. We now proceed to show that, under certain reasonable assumptions, the probability distribution *F* of this random variable is uniform over [*a*, *b*].

Since we cannot have $X \leq a$ or $X \geq b$, we assign the probabilities

$$P(X \leq t) = 0 \quad \text{if} \quad t \leq a \quad \text{and} \quad P(X \geq t) = 0 \quad \text{if} \quad t \geq b.$$

This gives us $F(t) = 0$ for each $t \leq a$. When $t \geq b$ we have

$$F(t) = P(X \leq t) = 1 - P(X > t) = 1.$$

We now determine the function *F* over the open interval (*a*, *b*) under the assumption that *F* has a continuous derivative *f* for each point in (*a*, *b*).

Consider any vertical strip of width *w* lying within the strip *S*, such as the event $x \leq X \leq x + w$. The statement that "aiming is impossible" means the probability of this event depends only on *w* and not on *x*. Therefore we have

(3.20) $F(x + w) - F(x) = P(x < X \leq x + w) = P(x \leq X \leq x + w).$

The two probabilities on the right are independent of *x*, provided, of course, that both *x* and *x* + *w* are in (*a*, *b*). If we differentiate both sides of (3.20) with respect to *x* we obtain

$$f(x + w) - f(x) = 0$$

if *x* and *x* + *w* are in (*a*, *b*). Since *w* is arbitrary, this means that *f* is constant on (*a*, *b*). Call this constant *C*. If we prove that $C = 1/(b - a)$ this will show that *F* is uniform over [*a*, *b*]. But this follows at once from the equation

$$1 = \int_{-\infty}^{+\infty} f(u)\, du = \int_a^b f(u)\, du = \int_a^b C\, du = C \cdot (b - a).$$

Example 2: Cauchy's distribution. A random variable *X* is said to have a Cauchy distribution *F* if

$$F(t) = \frac{1}{2} + \frac{1}{\pi} \text{ arc tan } t$$

for all real *t*. This function has a continuous derivative everywhere; the corresponding density function *f* is given by the formula

$$f(t) = \frac{1}{\pi(1 + t^2)}.$$

The graphs of *f* and *F* are shown in Figures 3.9 (a) and (b), respectively.

The following experiment leads to a Cauchy distribution. A pointer pivoted at the point (−1, 0) on the *x*-axis is spun and allowed to come to rest. An outcome of the experiment is *θ*, the angle of inclination from the *x*-axis made by a line drawn through the pointer; *θ* is measured so that $-\frac{1}{2}\pi < \theta \leq \frac{1}{2}\pi$. Reasoning similar to that in Example 1 shows that the random variable *X* defined by $X(\theta) = \theta$ has a uniform distribution over the interval $[-\frac{1}{2}\pi, \frac{1}{2}\pi]$ with density $f_X(t) = 1/\pi$ if $-\frac{1}{2}\pi < t < \frac{1}{2}\pi$. Consider now the random variable *Y* which measures the *y*-intercept of the line through the pointer. If *θ* is the angle described above, then

$$Y(\theta) = \tan \theta.$$

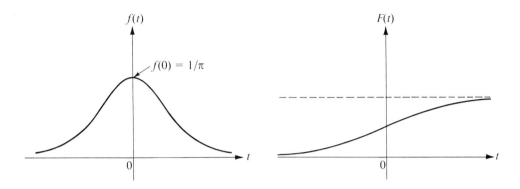

(a)   *The density function f.*   (b)   *The distribution function F.*

FIGURE 3.9   *Cauchy's distribution function and the corresponding density function.*

We shall prove now that Y has a Cauchy distribution F_Y if X has a uniform distribution. If $a < t$ let $\alpha = \text{arc tan } a$ and let $\theta = \text{arc tan } t$. Then we have

$$F_Y(t) - F_Y(a) = P(a < Y \leq t) = P(\alpha < X \leq \theta) = \int_\alpha^\theta f_X(u) \, du = \frac{\theta - \alpha}{\pi}.$$

Since $\alpha \rightarrow -\frac{1}{2}\pi$ as $a \rightarrow -\infty$ we find

$$F_Y(t) = \frac{\theta + \frac{1}{2}\pi}{\pi} = \frac{1}{\pi} \text{ arc tan } t + \frac{1}{2}.$$

This shows that Y has a Cauchy distribution, as asserted.

Example 3: Exponential distribution. Given a positive constant λ, a random variable X is said to have an exponential distribution with parameter λ if

$$F(t) = \begin{cases} 1 - e^{-\lambda t} & \text{for } t \geq 0, \\ 0 & \text{for } t < 0. \end{cases}$$

This is a monotonically increasing continuous function which approaches 0 as $t \rightarrow -\infty$ and which approaches 1 as $t \rightarrow +\infty$. The corresponding density f is given by the formulas

$$f(t) = \begin{cases} \lambda e^{-\lambda t} & \text{for } t \geq 0, \\ 0 & \text{for } t < 0. \end{cases}$$

The graphs of f and F are like those shown in Figures 3.10 (a) and (b), respectively.

Exponential distributions arise in problems of radioactive decay. If y denotes the amount of a radioactive substance present at time $t \geq 0$, and if the law of decay has the form of the differential equation

$$y' = -ky,$$

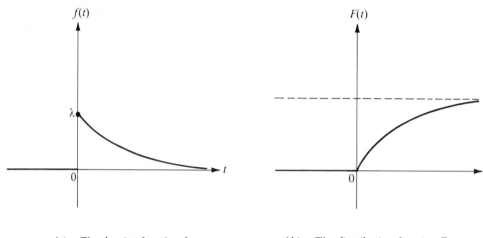

(a)   *The density function f.*   (b)   *The distribution function F.*

FIGURE 3.10   *An exponential distribution and the corresponding density function.*

where the decay constant k is positive, the general solution of this equation is given by the formula

(3.21) $y = y_0 \, e^{-kt} \, ,$

where y_0 is the initial amount present at time $t = 0$. To give this law a probabilistic interpretation we consider the disintegration of a single atom to be a random event and the decay of a sample of material to be the cumulative effect of a large number of random events. Each atom eventually disappears. The decay time will vary at random from atom to atom; it will be designated as a random variable X whose distribution we wish to determine. The problem is to assign a reasonable value to $P(X \le t)$, the probability that an atom disappears in time t. If $t < 0$ we assign probability zero to this event. If $t \ge 0$ we use (3.21) to write

(3.22) $\dfrac{y_0 - y}{y_0} = 1 - e^{-kt} \, .$

The quotient on the left of (3.22) measures the fraction of the original amount that disintegrates in time t. Since the right member depends only on t and is independent of the size of the sample, formula (3.22) suggests that we assign the value $1 - e^{-kt}$ as the probability of the event $X \le t$. This assignment of probabilities leads to an exponential distribution in which the parameter λ is the decay constant k. If $a < b$ the difference

$$F(b) - F(a) = e^{-ka} - e^{-kb}$$

represents the probability that an atom disappears during the time interval $[a, b]$.

   Suppose now we fix our attention on an atom that has *not* disappeared before time $t = a$, and ask for the probability that it disappears during the time interval $[a, b]$. This is a problem in conditional probabilities (Section 1.21). We wish to compute the conditional probability $P(B\,|\,A)$, where B denotes the event "the atom disappears during the time interval $[0,\, b]$" and A denotes the event "the atom does not disappear during the time interval $[0,\, a)$." By the definition of conditional probability we have

$$P(B\,|\,A) = \frac{P(A \cap B)}{P(A)}\,.$$

Since

$$P(A) = 1 - P(A') = 1 - [F(a) - F(0)] = 1 - (1 - e^{-ka}) = e^{-ka}$$

and

$$P(A \cap B) = F(b) - F(a) = e^{-ka} - e^{-kb},$$

we find

$$P(B\,|\,A) = \frac{e^{-ka} - e^{-kb}}{e^{-ka}} = 1 - e^{-k(b-a)}\,.$$

Note that $P(B\,|\,A)$ depends only on $b - a$, the *length* of the time interval $[a,\, b]$, and not on the time $t = a$ at which the interval begins. For example, if we pick an atom that has not disappeared before time $t = a$, the probability that it disappears during the interval $[a,\, a + 1]$ is $1 - e^{-k}$, a number independent of the age of the atom. On the other hand, if we pick an *arbitrary* atom, the probability that it disappears during the interval $[a,\, a + 1]$ is $F(a + 1) - F(a) = e^{-ka} - e^{-k(a+1)} = e^{-ka}(1 - e^{-k})$.

Example 4: Normal distribution. Let m and σ be fixed real numbers, with $\sigma > 0$. A random variable X is said to have a *normal distribution* with mean m and variance σ^2 if the density function f is given by the formula

$$f(t) = \frac{1}{\sigma\sqrt{2\pi}}\, e^{-\left(\frac{t-m}{\sigma}\right)^2/2}$$

for all real t. The corresponding distribution function F is, of course, the integral

$$F(t) = \frac{1}{\sigma\sqrt{2\pi}} \int_{-\infty}^{t} e^{-\left(\frac{u-m}{\sigma}\right)^2/2}\, du\,.$$

It is clear that this function F is monotonic increasing and continuous on the whole real axis, and that it tends to 0 as $t \to -\infty$. Also, it can be shown that $F(t) \to 1$ as $t \to +\infty$. (See Exercise 10 of Section 3.8.)

The special case $m = 0$, $\sigma = 1$ is called the *standard* normal distribution. In this case the function F is usually denoted by the letter Φ. Thus,

$$\Phi(t) = \frac{1}{\sqrt{2\pi}} \int_{-\infty}^{t} e^{-u^2/2}\, du\,.$$

The general case may be reduced to the standard case by introducing the change of variable $v = (u - m)/\sigma$ in the integral for F. This leads to the formula

$$F(t) = \Phi\!\left(\frac{t - m}{\sigma}\right).$$

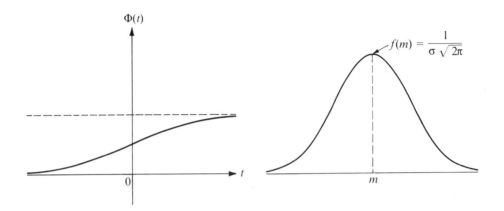

FIGURE 3.11   *The standard normal distribution*   FIGURE 3.12   *The density function of a normal*
function: $m = 0$, $\sigma = 1$.   *distribution with mean m and variance σ.*

Most mathematical handbooks contain tables of values of Φ. Its graph is shown in Figure 3.11. The graph of the density f is a famous "bell-shaped" curve, shown in Figure 3.12. The top of the bell is directly above the mean m. For large values of σ the curve tends to flatten out; for small σ it has a sharp peak, as in Figure 3.12.

Normal distributions are among the most important of all continuous distributions. Many random variables that occur in nature behave as though their distribution functions are normal or approximately normal. Examples include the measurement of the height of people in a large population, certain measurements on large populations of living organisms encountered in biology, and the errors of observation encountered when making large numbers of measurements. In physics, Maxwell's law of velocities implies that the distribution function of the velocity in any given direction of a molecule of mass M in a gas at absolute temperature T is normal with mean 0 and variance $M/(kT)$, where k is a constant (Boltzmann's constant).

The normal distribution is also of theoretical importance because it can be used to approximate the distributions of many random phenomena. One example is the binomial distribution with parameters n and p. If X is a random variable having a binomial distribution with parameters n and p, the probability $P(a \leq X \leq b)$ is given by the sum

$$\sum_{k=a}^{b} \binom{n}{k} p^k q^{n-k} \, ,$$

where $q = 1 - p$. For a large n, laborious computations are needed to evaluate this sum. In practice these computations are avoided by use of the approximate formula

$$(3.23) \qquad \sum_{k=a}^{b} \binom{n}{k} p^k q^{n-k} \sim \Phi\left(\frac{b - np + \frac{1}{2}}{\sqrt{npq}}\right) - \Phi\left(\frac{a - np - \frac{1}{2}}{\sqrt{npq}}\right),$$

where the symbol $\sim$ means that the two sides of (3.23) are asymptotically equal; that is, the ratio of the left member to the right member approaches the limit 1 as $n \to \infty$. The limit relation expressed in (3.23) is a special case of the so-called *central limit theorem* of the calculus of probabilities. This theorem (discussed in more detail in Section 3.18) explains the theoretical importance of normal distributions.

Figure 3.13 illustrates approximate formula (3.23) and shows that it can be accurate even for a relatively small value of *n*. The dotted lines are the ordinates of the probability mass function *p* of a binomial distribution with parameters $n = 10$ and $p = \frac{1}{5}$. These ordinates were computed from the formula

$$p(t) = P(X = t) = \binom{10}{t} \left(\frac{1}{5}\right)^t \left(\frac{4}{5}\right)^{10-t} \qquad \text{for} \quad t = 0, 1, 2, \ldots, 10 .$$

The ordinates for $t = 7, 8, 9$, and 10 are not shown because their numerical values are too near zero. For example, $p(10) = (1/5)^{10} = 2^{10}/10^{10} = 0.0000001024$. The smooth curve is the graph of the density function *f* of a normal distribution (with mean $m = np = 2$ and variance $\sigma^2 = npq = 1.6$). To compute the probability $P(a \leq t \leq b)$ from the mass function *p* we add the function values $p(t)$ at the mass points in the interval $a \leq t \leq b$. Each value $p(t)$ may be interpreted as the area of a rectangle of height $p(t)$ located over an interval of unit length centered about the mass point *t*. (An example, centered about $t = 3$, is shown in Figure 3.13.) The approximate formula in (3.23) is the result of replacing the areas of these rectangles by the area of the ordinate set of *f* over $[a, b]$.

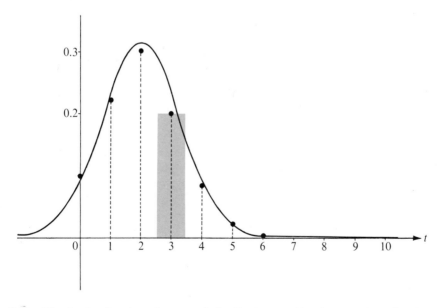

FIGURE 3.13   *The density function of a normal distribution considered as an approximation to the probability mass function of a binomial distribution.*

3.8   Exercises

1. A random variable X has a continuous distribution function F, where

$$F(t) = \begin{cases} 0 & \text{if } t \le 0, \\ ct & \text{if } 0 \le t \le 1, \\ 1 & \text{if } t > 1. \end{cases}$$

  (a) Determine the constant c and describe the density function f.
  (b) Compute the probabilities $P(X = \frac{1}{3})$, $P(X < \frac{1}{3})$, $P(|X| < \frac{1}{3})$.

2. Let $f(t) = c|\sin t|$ for $|t| < \pi/2$ and let $f(t) = 0$ otherwise. Determine the value of the constant c so that f will be the density of a continuous distribution function F. Also, describe F and sketch its graph.

3. A random variable X has a continuous distribution function F and a probability density f. The density has the following properties: $f(t) = 0$ if $t < \frac{1}{4}$, $f(\frac{1}{4}) = 1$, $f(t)$ is linear if $\frac{1}{4} \le t \le \frac{1}{2}$, $f(1 - t) = f(t)$ for all t.
  (a) Make a sketch of the graph of f.
  (b) Give a set of formulas for determining F and sketch its graph.
  (c) Compute the following probabilities: $P(X < 1)$, $P(X < \frac{3}{4})$, $P(X < \frac{1}{2})$, $P(X \le \frac{1}{4})$, $P(\frac{1}{2} < X < \frac{5}{8})$.

4. A random variable X has a uniform distribution over $[-3, 3]$.
  (a) Compute $P(X = 2)$, $P(X < 2)$, $P(|X| < 2)$, $P(|X - 2| < 2)$.
  (b) Find a t for which $P(X > t) = \frac{1}{3}$.

5. The Lethe Subway Company schedules a northbound train every 30 minutes at a certain station. A man enters the station at a random time. Let the random variable X count the number of minutes he has to wait for the next train. Assume X has a uniform distribution over the interval $[0, 30]$. (This is how we interpret the statement that he enters the station at "random time.")
  (a) For each $k = 5, 10, 15, 20, 25, 30$, compute the probability that he has to wait at least k minutes for the next train.
  (b) A competitor, the Styx Subway Company, is allowed to schedule a northbound train every 30 minutes at the same station, but at least 5 minutes must elapse between the arrivals of competitive trains. Assume the passengers come into the station at random times and always board the first train that arrives. Show that the Styx Company can arrange its schedule so that it receives five times as many passengers as its competitor.

6. A line segment is broken into two pieces, with the point of subdivision chosen at random. Let X denote the random variable which measures the ratio of the length of the left-hand segment to that of the right-hand segment. If $t > 0$, show that $P(X < t) = t/(1 + t)$.

7. Solve Exercise 6 when X measures the ratio of the length of the right-hand segment to that of the left-hand segment.

8. In Exercise 7, compute the probability that the longer segment is at least three times the length of the shorter segment. What is the probability that the longer segment is *exactly* three times longer?

9. Verify that the integral from $-\infty$ to $+\infty$ is 1 for the density of
  (a) the Cauchy distribution, (b) the exponential distribution.

10. If $r > 0$, let $I(r) = \int_{-r}^{r} e^{-u^2} \, du$.
  (a) Show that $I^2(r) = \iint_R e^{-(x^2+y^2)} \, dx \, dy$,   where R is the square $R = [-r, r] \times [-r, r]$

in the xy-plane.
  (b) If C_1 and C_2 are the circular disks inscribing and circumscribing R, show that

$$\iint\limits_{C_1} e^{-(x^2+y^2)}\,dx\,dy < I^2(r) < \iint\limits_{C_2} e^{-(x^2+y^2)}\,dx\,dy\,.$$

(c) Express the integrals over C_1 and C_2 in polar coordinates and use (b) to deduce that $I(r) \to \sqrt{\pi}$ as $r \to \infty$.

(d) Show that the integral from $-\infty$ to $+\infty$ is 1 for the density of any normal distribution.

11. A random variable X has a standard normal distribution Φ. Prove that
  (a) $P(|X| < k) = 2\,\Phi(k) - 1$, (b) $P(|X| > k) = 2(1 - \Phi(k))$.

12. Assume a random variable X has a standard normal distribution, and let $Y = X^2$.

(a) Show that $F_Y(t) = \dfrac{2}{\sqrt{2\pi}} \displaystyle\int_0^{\sqrt{t}} e^{-u^2/2}\,du$ \qquad if $t \geq 0$.

(b) Determine $F_Y(t)$ when $t < 0$ and describe the density function f_Y.

3.9 Remarks on more general distributions

In the foregoing sections we have discussed examples of discrete and continuous distributions. The values of a discrete distribution are computed by adding the values of the corresponding probability mass function. The values of a continuous distribution with a density are computed by integrating the density function. There are, of course, distributions that are neither discrete nor continuous. Among these are the so-called "mixed" types in which the mass distribution is partly discrete and partly continuous. (An example is shown in Figure 3.3.)

A distribution function F is called *mixed* if it can be expressed as a linear combination of the form

(3.24) $$F(t) = c_1\,F_1(t) + c_2\,F_2(t)\,,$$

where F_1 is discrete and F_2 is continuous. The constants c_1 and c_2 must satisfy the relations

$$0 < c_1 < 1\,, \quad 0 < c_2 < 1\,, \quad c_1 + c_2 = 1\,.$$

Properties of mixed distributions may be found by studying those that are discrete or continuous and then appealing to the linearity expressed in Equation (3.24).

A general kind of integral, known as the *Riemann-Stieltjes integral*, makes possible a simultaneous treatment of the discrete, continuous, and mixed cases.† Although this integral unifies the theoretical discussion of distribution functions, in any specific problem the computation of probabilities must be reduced to ordinary summation and integration. In this introductory account we shall not attempt to describe the Riemann-Stieltjes integral. Consequently, most of the topics we discuss come in pairs, one for the discrete case and one for the continuous case. However, we shall only give complete details for one case, leaving the untreated case for the reader to work out.

Even the Riemann-Stieltjes integral is inadequate for treating the *most general* distribution functions. But a more powerful concept, called the Lebesgue-Stieltjes integral,‡ does give a satisfactory treatment of all cases. The advanced theory of probability cannot be undertaken without a knowledge of the Lebesgue-Stieltjes integral.

---

† A discussion of the Riemann-Stieltjes integral may be found in Chapter 9 of the author's *Mathematical Analysis*, Addison-Wesley Publishing Company, Reading, Mass., 1957.

‡ See any book on measure theory.

3.10   Distributions of two-dimensional random variables

The concept of a distribution may be generalized to n-dimensional random variables in a straightforward way. The treatment of the case $n = 2$ will indicate how the extension takes place.

If X and Y are two one-dimensional random variables defined on a common sample space S, (X, Y) will denote the two-dimensional random variable whose value at a typical point ω of S is given by the pair of real numbers $(X(\omega), Y(\omega))$. The notation

$$X \leq a, Y \leq b$$

is an abbreviation for the set of all elements ω in S such that $X(\omega) \leq a$ and $Y(\omega) \leq b$; the probability of this event is denoted by

$$P(X \leq a, Y \leq b).$$

Notations such as $a < X \leq b, c < Y \leq d$, and $P(a < X \leq b, c < Y \leq d)$ are similarly defined.

The set of points (x, y) such that $x \leq a$ and $y \leq b$ is the Cartesian product $A \times B$ of the two one-dimensional infinite intervals $A = \{x \mid x \leq a\}$ and $B = \{y \mid y \leq b\}$. The set $A \times B$ is represented geometrically by the infinite rectangular region shown in Figure 3.14. The number $P(X \leq a, Y \leq b)$ represents the probability that a point $(X(\omega), Y(\omega))$ lies in this region. These probabilities are the two-dimensional analogs of the one-dimensional probabilities $P(X \leq a)$, and are used to define two-dimensional probability distributions.

DEFINITION. *The distribution function of the two-dimensional random variable (X, Y) is the real-valued function F defined for all real a and b by the equation*

$$F(a, b) = P(X \leq a, Y \leq b).$$

It is also known as the *joint distribution* of the two one-dimensional random variables X and Y.

To compute the probability that (X, Y) lies in a rectangle we use the following theorem, a generalization of Theorem 3–1:

3– 5   THEOREM.   *Let F be the distribution function of a two-dimensional random variable (X, Y). Then if $a < b$ and $c < d$ we have*

(3.25) $P(a < X \leq b, c < Y \leq d) = F(b, d) - F(a, d) - F(b, c) + F(a, c).$

Proof. The two events "$X \leq a, c < Y \leq d$" and "$X \leq a, Y \leq c$" are disjoint, and their union is "$X \leq a, Y \leq d$." Adding probabilities we obtain $P(X \leq a, c < Y \leq d) + P(X \leq a, Y \leq c) = P(X \leq a, Y \leq d)$; hence

$$P(X \leq a, c < Y \leq d) = F(a, d) - F(a, c).$$

Similarly, we have

$$P(a < X \leq b, Y \leq c) = F(b, c) - F(a, c).$$

Now the four events

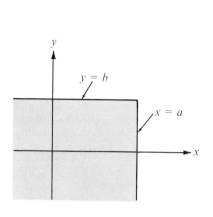

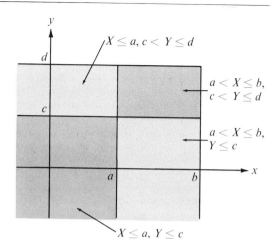

FIGURE 3.14   *An infinite rectangular region A $\times$ B, where A = $\{x \mid x \leq a\}$ and B = $\{y \mid y \leq b\}$.*

FIGURE 3.15   *The event "X $\leq$ b, Y $\leq$ d" expressed as the union of four disjoint events.*

"$X \leq a, Y \leq c$,"   "$X \leq a, c < Y \leq d$,"
         "$a < X \leq b, Y \leq c$,"   "$a < X \leq b, c < Y \leq d$"

are disjoint, and their union is "$X \leq b, Y \leq d$." (See Figure 3.15.) Adding the corresponding probabilities and using the two foregoing equations we obtain

$$F(a, c) + [F(a, d) - F(a, c)] + [F(b, c) - F(a, c)] + P(a < X \leq b, c < Y \leq d) = F(b, d),$$

which is equivalent to (3.25).

Formula (3.25) gives the probability that the random variable (X, Y) has a value in the rectangle $(a, b] \times (c, d]$. There are, of course, corresponding formulas for the rectangles, $[a, b] \times [c, d]$, $(a, b) \times (c, d)$, $[a, b) \times [c, d)$, and so forth.

If we keep y fixed we may study $F(x, y)$ as a function of x alone, by introducing

$$G_y(x) = F(x, y).$$

The function G_y is monotonic increasing on the entire x-axis. When $x \to -\infty$, $G_y(x) \to 0$, and when $x \to +\infty$, $G_y(x) \to P(Y \leq y)$. Similarly, if for each fixed x we define a new function H_x by the equation

$$H_x(y) = F(x, y),$$

then H_x is monotonic increasing, $H_x(y) \to 0$ as $y \to -\infty$, and $H_x(y) \to P(X \leq x)$ as $y \to +\infty$. It follows that we have

$$\lim_{y \to +\infty} [\lim_{x \to +\infty} F(x, y)] = \lim_{x \to +\infty} [\lim_{y \to +\infty} F(x, y)] = 1.$$

Note. The analogy with mass may be extended to the two-dimensional case. Here the total mass 1 is distributed over a plane. The probability $P(a < X \le b, c < Y \le d)$ represents the total amount of mass located in the rectangle $(a, b] \times (c, d]$. The number $F(a, b)$ represents the amount in the infinite rectangular region $X \le a, Y \le b$. As in the one-dimensional case, the two most important types of distributions are those known as *discrete* and *continuous*. In the discrete case the entire mass is located in lumps concentrated at a finite or countably infinite number of points. In the continuous case the mass is smeared all over the plane with a uniform or varying thickness.

If a random variable (X, Y) is given we may define a new function p, called the probability mass function of (X, Y), such that

$$p(x, y) = P(X = x, Y = y)$$

for every pair of real numbers (x, y). Let T denote the set of (x, y) for which $p(x, y) > 0$. It can be shown that T is either finite or countably infinite. If the sum of the $p(x, y)$ for all (x, y) in T is equal to 1, that is, if

$$(3.26) \qquad \sum_{(x, y) \varepsilon\, T} p(x, y) = 1 \,,$$

the random variable (X, Y) is said to be *discrete* (or *jointly discrete*). The points (x, y) in T are called the *mass points* of (X, Y).

Suppose that $x_1, x_2, x_3, \ldots$ and $y_1, y_2, y_3, \ldots$ are among the possible values of X and Y, respectively, and let

$$p_{ij} = P(X = x_i, Y = y_j) \,.$$

If each p_{ij} is positive and if the sum of all the p_{ij} is 1, then the probability of an event "$(X, Y) \varepsilon\, E$" is the sum of all the p_{ij} taken over all x_i and y_j for which $(x_i, y_j) \varepsilon\, E$. We indicate this by writing

$$P[(X, Y) \varepsilon\, E] = \sum_{\substack{x_i \\ (x_i, y_j)\, \varepsilon\, E}} \sum_{y_j} p_{ij} \,.$$

In particular, since $P(X \le x, Y \le y) = F(x, y)$, the joint distribution F (which is also called discrete) is given by the double sum

$$(3.27) \qquad F(x, y) = \sum_{x_i \le x} \sum_{y_j \le y} p_{ij} \,.$$

The numbers p_{ij} may also be used to reconstruct the probability mass functions p_X and p_Y of the one-dimensional random variables X and Y. In fact, if E_{ij} denotes the event "$X = x_i, Y = y_j$," the events $E_{i1}, E_{i2}, E_{i3}, \ldots$ are disjoint and their union is the event "$X = x_i$." Hence, by countable additivity, we obtain

$$(3.28) \qquad P(X = x_i) = \sum_{j=1}^{\infty} P(E_{ij}) = \sum_{j=1}^{\infty} p_{ij} \,.$$

Similarly, we have

$$(3.29) \qquad P(Y = y_j) = \sum_{i=1}^{\infty} P(E_{ij}) = \sum_{i=1}^{\infty} p_{ij} \,.$$

Therefore, the corresponding one-dimensional distributions F_X and F_Y may be computed from the formulas

$$F_X(t) = \sum_{x_i \le t} P(X = x_i) = \sum_{x_i \le t} \sum_{j=1}^{\infty} p_{ij}$$

and

$$F_Y(t) = \sum_{y_j \le t} P(Y = y_j) = \sum_{y_j \le t} \sum_{i=1}^{\infty} p_{ij} .$$

For finite sample spaces, of course, the infinite series must be replaced by finite sums.

As might be expected, *continuous distributions* are those that are continuous over the whole plane. For the majority of continuous distributions F that occur in practice there exists a nonnegative function f (called the *probability density* of F) such that the probabilities of most events of interest can be computed by double integration of the density. That is, the probability of an event "(X, Y) ε Q" is given by the integral formula

(3.30) $$P[(X, Y) \text{ ε } Q] = \iint_Q f .$$

When such an f exists it is also called the probability density of the random variable (X, Y), or the joint density of X and Y. We shall not attempt to describe the class of regions Q for which (3.30) is to hold, except to mention that this class should be extensive enough to include all regions that arise in the ordinary applications of probability. For example, if a joint density exists we always have

(3.31) $$P(a < X \le b, c < Y \le d) = \iint_R f(x, y) \, dx \, dy ,$$

where $R = [a, b] \times [c, d]$. The integrand f is usually sufficiently well behaved for the double integral to be evaluated by iterated one-dimensional integration, in which case (3.31) becomes

$$P(a < X \le b, c < Y \le d) = \int_c^d \left[\int_a^b f(x, y) \, dx \right] dy = \int_a^b \left[\int_c^d f(x, y) \, dy \right] dx .$$

In all the examples we shall consider, this formula is also valid in the limiting cases in which a and c are replaced by $-\infty$ and in which b and d are replaced by $+\infty$. Thus we have

(3.32) $$F(b, d) = \int_{-\infty}^d \left[\int_{-\infty}^b f(x, y) \, dx \right] dy = \int_{-\infty}^b \left[\int_{-\infty}^d f(x, y) \, dy \right] dx$$

for all b and d, and

(3.33) $$\int_{-\infty}^{+\infty} \left[\int_{-\infty}^{+\infty} f(x, y) \, dx \right] dy = \int_{-\infty}^{+\infty} \left[\int_{-\infty}^{+\infty} f(x, y) \, dy \right] dx = 1 .$$

Equations (3.32) and (3.33) are the continuous analogs of (3.27) and (3.26), respectively.

Example. Consider the function f that has the constant value 1 over the square $R = [0, 1] \times [0, 1]$, and the value 0 at all other points of the plane. A random variable (X, Y) having this density function is said to be *uniformly distributed* over R. The corresponding distribution function F is given by the following formulas:

$$F(x, y) = \begin{cases} xy & \text{if } (x, y) \in R, \\ x & \text{if } 0 < x < 1 \text{ and } y > 1, \\ y & \text{if } 0 < y < 1 \text{ and } x > 1, \\ 1 & \text{if } x \geq 1 \text{ and } y \geq 1, \\ 0 & \text{otherwise}. \end{cases}$$

The graph of F over R is part of the saddle-shaped surface $z = xy$. At all points (x, y) not on the boundary of R the mixed partial derivatives $D_{1,2}F(x, y)$ and $D_{2,1}F(x, y)$ exist and are equal to $f(x, y)$.

If a continuous distribution F has a density f, the partial derivatives $D_{1,2}F(x, y)$ and $D_{2,1}F(x, y)$ (if they exist) may be computed at the points of continuity of f by differentiation of the integrals which appear in (3.32). The result of this differentiation is the formula

$$D_{1,2}F(x, y) = D_{2,1}F(x, y) = f(x, y),$$

which is sometimes useful in obtaining the density from the distribution function.

As in the discrete case, the joint density f may be used to recover the one-dimensional densities f_X and f_Y. The formulas analogous to (3.28) and (3.29) are

$$f_X(x) = \int_{-\infty}^{+\infty} f(x, y) \, dy \qquad \text{and} \qquad f_Y(y) = \int_{-\infty}^{+\infty} f(x, y) \, dx.$$

The corresponding distributions $F_X(t)$ and $F_Y(t)$ are obtained, of course, by integrating the respective densities f_X and f_Y from $-\infty$ to t.

Further properties of two-dimensional distributions are developed in the following exercises. Applications are discussed in Section 3.12.

3.11   Exercises

1. Let X and Y be one-dimensional random variables with distribution functions F_X and F_Y, and let F be the joint distribution of X and Y. The random variables X and Y are called *independent* if, for all (x, y), $F(x, y)$ can be factored as follows:

$$F(x, y) = F_X(x) \, F_Y(y).$$

(a) Prove that X and Y are independent if, and only if, we have

$$P(a < X \leq b, c < Y \leq d) = P(a < X \leq b) \, P(c < Y \leq d)$$

for all a, b, c, d, with $a < b$ and $c < d$.

(b) Consider the discrete case. Assume $x_1, x_2, \ldots$ and $y_1, y_2, \ldots$ are the mass points of X and Y, respectively. Let $a_i = P(X = x_i)$ and $b_j = P(Y = y_j)$. If $p_{ij} = P(X = x_i, Y = y_j)$, show that X and Y are independent if $p_{ij} = a_i b_j$ for all i and j.

(c) Let X and Y have continuous distributions with corresponding densities f_X and f_Y and let f denote the density of the joint distribution. Assume the continuity of all three densities. Show that the condition of independence is equivalent to the statement $f(x, y) = f_X(x) f_Y(y)$ for all (x, y). [*Hint.* Express f as a derivative of the joint distribution F.]

2. Refer to Exercise 1. Suppose that $P(X = x_1, Y = y_1) = P(X = x_2, Y = y_2) = p/2$ and that $P(X = x_1, Y = y_2) = P(X = x_2, Y = y_1) = q/2$, where p and q are nonnegative with sum 1.

(a) Determine the one-dimensional probabilities $P(X = x_i)$ and $P(Y = y_j)$ for $i = 1, 2$ and $j = 1, 2$.

(b) For what value (or values) of p will X and Y be independent?

3. If $a < b$ and $c < d$, define f as follows:

$$f(x, y) = \begin{cases} \dfrac{1}{(b - a)(d - c)} & \text{if} \quad (x, y) \mathcal{E} [a, b] \times [c, d], \\ 0 & \text{otherwise}. \end{cases}$$

(a) Verify that this is the density of a continuous distribution F and determine F.

(b) Determine the one-dimensional distributions F_X and F_Y.

(c) Determine whether or not X and Y are independent.

4. If $P(Y \le b) \ne 0$, the conditional probability that $X \le a$, given that $Y \le b$, is denoted by $P(X \le a \mid Y \le b)$, and is defined by the equation

$$P(X \le a \mid Y \le b) = \frac{P(X \le a, Y \le b)}{P(Y \le b)}.$$

If $P(Y \le b) = 0$, we define $P(X \le a \mid Y \le b) = P(X \le a)$. Similarly, if $P(X \le a) \ne 0$, we define $P(Y \le b \mid X \le a) = P(X \le a, Y \le b)/P(X \le a)$. If $P(X \le a) = 0$, we define $P(Y \le b \mid X \le a) = P(Y \le b)$.

(a) Refer to Exercise 1 and describe the independence of X and Y in terms of conditional probabilities.

(b) Consider the discrete case. Assume $x_1, x_2, \dots$ and $y_1, y_2, \dots$ are the mass points of X and Y, respectively. Show that

$$P(X = x_i) = \sum_{j=1}^{\infty} P(Y = y_j) \, P(X = x_i \mid Y = y_j)$$

and

$$P(Y = y_j) = \sum_{i=1}^{\infty} P(X = x_i) \, P(Y = y_j \mid X = x_i).$$

5. A gambling house offers its clients the following game: A coin is tossed. If the result of the first throw is tails, the player loses and the game is over. If the first throw is heads, a second throw is allowed. If heads occurs the second time the player wins \$2, but if tails comes up the player wins \$1. Let X be the random variable which is equal to 1 or 0, according to whether heads or tails occurs on the first throw. Let Y be the random variable which counts the number of dollars won by the player. Use Exercise 4 (or some other method) to compute $P(Y = 0)$, $P(Y = 1)$, and $P(Y = 2)$.

6. Refer to Exercise 4. Derive the so-called Bayes' formulas:

$$P(X = x_k \mid Y = y_j) = \frac{P(X = x_k) \, P(Y = y_j \mid X = x_k)}{\sum_{i=1}^{\infty} P(X = x_i) \, P(Y = y_j \mid X = x_i)},$$

$$P(Y = y_k \mid X = x_i) = \frac{P(Y = y_k) \, P(X = x_i \mid Y = y_k)}{\sum_{j=1}^{\infty} P(Y = y_j) \, P(X = x_i \mid Y = y_j)}.$$

7. Given two urns A and B. Urn A contains one \$5 bill and two \$10 bills. Urn B contains three \$5 bills and one \$10 bill. Draw a bill from urn A and put it in urn B. Let Y be the random variable which counts the dollar value of the bill transferred. Now draw a bill from urn B and use the random variable X to count *its* dollar value. Compute the conditional probabilities

$$P(Y = 5 \mid X = 10) \quad \text{and} \quad P(Y = 10 \mid X = 10).$$

[*Hint.* Use Bayes' formulas of Exercise 6.]

8. Given three identical boxes, each containing two drawers. Box number 1 has one gold piece in one drawer and one silver piece in the other. Box 2 has one gold piece in each drawer and Box 3 has one silver piece in each drawer. One drawer is opened at random and a gold piece is found.

Compute the probability that the other drawer in the same box contains a silver piece.
[*Hint.* Use Bayes' formulas of Exercise 6.]

   9. Let Q be a plane region with area $A(Q)$. A continuous two-dimensional random variable (X, Y) is said to have a *uniform distribution* over Q if its density function f is given by the following formulas:

$$f(x, y) = \begin{cases} 1/A(Q) & \text{if } (x, y) \in Q, \\ 0 & \text{if } (x, y) \notin Q. \end{cases}$$

   (a) If E is a subregion of Q with area $A(E)$, show that $A(E)/A(Q)$ is the probability of the event $(X, Y) \in E$.
   (b) Raindrops fall at random on the square Q with vertices $(1, 0)$, $(0, 1)$, $(-1, 0)$, $(0, -1)$. An outcome is the point (x, y) in Q struck by a particular raindrop. Let $X(x, y) = x$ and $Y(x, y) = y$ and assume (X, Y) has a uniform distribution over Q. Determine the joint density function f and the one-dimensional densities f_X and f_Y. Are the random variables X and Y independent?

   10. A two-dimensional random variable (X, Y) has the joint distribution function F. Let $U = X - a$, $V = Y - b$, where a and b are constants. If G denotes the joint distribution of (U, V) show that

$$G(u, v) = F(u + a, v + b).$$

Derive a similar relation connecting the density function f of (X, Y) and g of (U, V) when f is continuous.

3.12   Distributions of functions of random variables

   If ϕ is a real-valued function whose domain includes the range of the random variable X, we can construct a new random variable Y by the equation

$$Y = \phi(X),$$

which means that $Y(\omega) = \phi[X(\omega)]$ for each ω in the sample space. If we know the distribution function F_X of X, how do we find the distribution F_Y of Y? We begin with an important special case. Suppose that ϕ is continuous and strictly increasing on the whole real axis and takes on every real value. In this case ϕ has a continuous strictly increasing inverse ψ such that, for all x and y,

$$y = \phi(x) \qquad \text{if and only if} \quad x = \psi(y).$$

By the definition of F_Y we have

$$F_Y(t) = P(Y \le t) = P[\phi(X) \le t].$$

Since ϕ is strictly increasing and continuous, the events "$\phi(X) \le t$" and "$X \le \psi(t)$" are identical. Therefore $P[\phi(X) \le t] = P[X \le \psi(t)] = F_X[\psi(t)]$. Hence the distributions F_Y and F_X are related by the equation

(3.34) $$F_Y(t) = F_X[\psi(t)].$$

When the distribution F_X and the function ϕ have derivatives we may differentiate both sides of (3.34), using the chain rule on the right, to obtain

$$F_Y'(t) = F_X'[\psi(t)] \cdot \psi'(t).$$

This gives us the following equation relating the densities:

$$f_Y(t) = f_X[\psi(t)] \cdot \psi'(t) \, .$$

Example 1: $Y = aX + b$, $a > 0$. In this case we have

$$\phi(x) = ax + b \, , \qquad \psi(y) = \frac{y - b}{a} \, , \qquad \psi'(y) = \frac{1}{a} \, .$$

Since ϕ is continuous and strictly increasing we may write

$$F_Y(t) = F_X\!\left(\frac{t - b}{a}\right) \qquad \text{and} \qquad f_Y(t) = \frac{1}{a} f_X\!\left(\frac{t - b}{a}\right) .$$

Example 2: $Y = X^2$. In this case $\phi(x) = x^2$ and the foregoing discussion is not directly applicable because ϕ is not strictly increasing. However, we can use the same method of reasoning to determine F_Y and f_Y. By the definition of F_Y we have

$$F_Y(t) = P(X^2 \leq t) \, .$$

If $t < 0$ the event "$X^2 \leq t$" is empty and hence $P(X^2 \leq t) = 0$. Therefore $F_Y(t) = 0$ for $t < 0$. If $t > 0$ we have

$$P(X^2 \leq t) = P(-\sqrt{t} \leq X \leq \sqrt{t}) = F_X(\sqrt{t}) - F_X(-\sqrt{t}) + P(X = -\sqrt{t}) \, .$$

For a continuous distribution F_X we have $P(X = -\sqrt{t}) = 0$ and we obtain the following relation between F_Y and F_X:

$$F_Y(t) = \begin{cases} 0 & \text{if } t < 0 \, , \\ F_X(\sqrt{t}) - F_X(-\sqrt{t}) & \text{if } t > 0 \, . \end{cases}$$

For all $t < 0$ and for those $t > 0$ such that F_X is differentiable at $\sqrt{t}$ and at $-\sqrt{t}$ we have the following equation relating the densities:

$$f_Y(t) = \begin{cases} 0 & \text{if } t < 0 \, , \\ \dfrac{f_X(\sqrt{t}) + f_X(-\sqrt{t})}{2\sqrt{t}} & \text{if } t > 0 \, . \end{cases}$$

    We turn now to a more general problem. If X and Y are one-dimensional random variables with known distributions, how do we find the distribution of new random variables such as $X + Y$, XY, or $X^2 + Y^2$? The remainder of this section describes a method that helps to answer questions like this. Two new random variables U and V are defined by equations of the form

$$U = M(X, Y) \, , \qquad V = N(X, Y) \, ,$$

where $M(X, Y)$ or $N(X, Y)$ is the particular combination in which we are interested. From a knowledge of the joint distribution f of the two-dimensional random variable (X, Y) we calculate the joint distribution g of (U, V). Once g is known, the individual distributions of U and V are easily found.

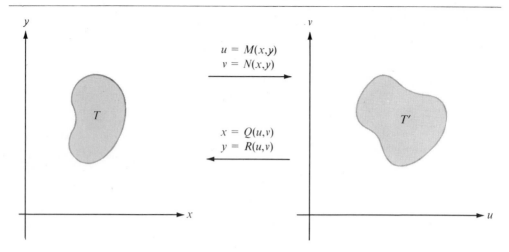

FIGURE 3.16 *A one-to-one mapping of a region T in the xy-plane onto a region T' in the uv-plane.*

To describe the method in detail, we consider a one-to-one mapping of the xy-plane onto the uv-plane defined by the pair of equations

$$u = M(x, y), \qquad v = N(x, y).$$

Let the inverse mapping be given by

$$x = Q(u, v), \qquad y = R(u, v),$$

and assume that Q and R have continuous partial derivatives. If T denotes a region in the xy-plane, let T' denote its image in the uv-plane, as suggested by Figure 3.16. Let X and Y be two one-dimensional continuous random variables having a continuous joint distribution and let f be the probability density function of (X, Y). Define new random variables U and V by writing $U = M(X, Y)$, $V = N(X, Y)$. To determine the probability density g of the random variable (U, V) we proceed as follows:

The random variables X and Y are associated with a sample space S. For each ω in S we have $U(\omega) = M[X(\omega), Y(\omega)]$ and $V(\omega) = N[X(\omega), Y(\omega)]$. Since the mapping is one-to-one, the two sets

$$\{\omega \mid (U(\omega), V(\omega)) \mathcal{E} T'\} \qquad \text{and} \qquad \{\omega \mid (X(\omega), Y(\omega)) \mathcal{E} T\}$$

are equal. Therefore we have

(3.35) $$P[(U, V) \mathcal{E} T'] = P[(X, Y) \mathcal{E} T].$$

Since f is the density function of (X, Y) we may write

(3.36) $$P[(X, Y) \mathcal{E} T] = \iint_T f(x, y)\, dx\, dy.$$

Using (3.35) and the formula for transforming a double integral we may rewrite (3.36) as follows:

$$P[(U, V) \, \varepsilon \, T'] = \iint\limits_{T'} f[Q(u, v), R(u, v)] \left| \frac{\partial(Q, R)}{\partial(u, v)} \right| du \, dv \, .$$

Since this is valid for every region T' in the uv-plane the density g of (U, V) is given by the integrand on the right; that is, we have

(3.37)
$$g(u, v) = f[Q(u, v), R(u, v)] \left| \frac{\partial(Q, R)}{\partial(u, v)} \right| .$$

The densities f_U and f_V may now be obtained by the integration formulas

$$f_U(u) = \int_{-\infty}^{\infty} g(u, v) \, dv, \qquad f_V(v) = \int_{-\infty}^{\infty} g(u, v) \, du \, .$$

To illustrate the method, let us find the probability density function of the random variable $(X + Y)/2$. We may take $U = (X + Y)/2$, $V = X$. Then the inverse mapping is given by $X = V$, $Y = 2U - V$. Therefore we may apply formula (3.37) with $Q(u, v) = v$ and $R(u, v) = 2u - v$. The Jacobian is

$$\frac{\partial(Q, R)}{\partial(u, v)} = \begin{vmatrix} \dfrac{\partial Q}{\partial u} & \dfrac{\partial Q}{\partial v} \\[2ex] \dfrac{\partial R}{\partial u} & \dfrac{\partial R}{\partial v} \end{vmatrix} = \begin{vmatrix} 0 & 1 \\ 2 & -1 \end{vmatrix} = -2 \, ,$$

and hence $g(u, v) = 2f(v, 2u - v)$. To obtain the density f_U of $(X + Y)/2$ we integrate with respect to v and we find

(3.38)
$$f_U(u) = 2 \int_{-\infty}^{+\infty} f(v, 2u - v) \, dv \, .$$

If we had taken $U = (X + Y)/2$ and $V = Y$ we would have arrived at the formula

$$f_U(u) = 2 \int_{-\infty}^{+\infty} f(2u - v, v) \, dv \, ,$$

which, of course, is equivalent to (3.38) by a change of variable. An important special case of (3.38) occurs when X and Y are independent. In this case the joint probability density factors into a product,

$$f(x, y) = f_X(x) f_Y(y) \, ,$$

and the integral in (3.38) becomes

$$f_U(u) = 2 \int_{-\infty}^{+\infty} f_X(v) f_Y(2u - v) \, dv \, .$$

Suppose now X and Y each have exponential distribution with parameters λ and μ, respectively. Then $f_X(t) = f_Y(t) = 0$ for $t < 0$, and

$$f_X(t) = \lambda e^{-\lambda t}, \quad f_Y(t) = \mu e^{-\mu t} \qquad \text{for} \quad t \geq 0 \, .$$

We shall determine the density of $U = (X + Y)/2$ when X and Y are independent. If $u < 0$ the integral for $f_U(u)$ gives 0. If $u \geq 0$ it becomes

$$f_U(u) = 2 \int_0^{2u} \lambda e^{-\lambda v} \cdot \mu e^{-\mu(2u - v)} \, dv = 2\lambda\mu e^{-2\mu u} \int_0^{2u} e^{(\mu - \lambda)v} \, dv \, .$$

To evaluate the integral we must consider two cases, $\mu = \lambda$ and $\mu \neq \lambda$. If $\mu = \lambda$ the integral has the value $2u$ and we find

$$f_U(u) = 4\lambda^2 u e^{-2\lambda u} \qquad \text{for} \quad u \geq 0.$$

If $\mu \neq \lambda$ we obtain

$$f_U(u) = 2\lambda\mu e^{-2\mu u} \frac{e^{(\mu-\lambda)2u} - 1}{\mu - \lambda} = 2\lambda\mu \frac{e^{-2\lambda u} - e^{-2\mu u}}{\mu - \lambda} \qquad \text{for} \quad u \geq 0.$$

3.13   Exercises

1. Assume X has a uniform distribution on the interval $[0, 1]$. Determine the distribution function F_Y and the probability density f_Y of the random variable Y if:

(a) $Y = 3X + 1$,   (d) $Y = \log |X|$,
(b) $Y = -3X + 1$,   (e) $Y = \log X^2$,
(c) $Y = X^2$,   (f) $Y = e^X$.

2. Let X be a random variable with a continuous distribution function F_X. If ϕ is continuous and strictly increasing on the whole real axis and if $\phi(x) \to a$ as $x \to -\infty$ and $\phi(x) \to b$ as $x \to +\infty$, determine the distribution function F_Y of the random variable $Y = \phi(X)$. Also, compute the density f_Y, assuming that F_X and ϕ are differentiable.

3. Assume X has a standard normal distribution. Determine the probability density function of the random variable Y when

(a) $Y = X^2$,   (c) $Y = e^X$,
(b) $Y = |X|^{1/2}$,   (d) $Y = \arctan X$.

4. Let X and Y be two independent continuous random variables, each with a uniform distribution over the interval $[0, 1]$.

(a) Determine the probability density function f of the two-dimensional random variable (X, Y).

(b) Let A denote the set of points in the xy-plane at which $f(x, y) > 0$. Draw a sketch of A and of its image A' under the mapping defined by

$$u = x + y, \qquad v = x - y.$$

(c) Let $U = X + Y$ and $V = X - Y$ be two new random variables and let g denote the probability density function of (U, V). Prove that

$$g(u, v) = \begin{cases} \frac{1}{2} & \text{if} \quad (u, v) \in A', \\ 0 & \text{otherwise}. \end{cases}$$

(d) If f_U denotes the probability density function of U, show that

$$f_U(u) = \begin{cases} u & \text{if} \quad 0 < u \leq 1, \\ 2 - u & \text{if} \quad 1 < u < 2, \\ 0 & \text{otherwise}. \end{cases}$$

(e) Describe, in a similar way, the probability density f_V of V.

(f) Determine whether or not U and V are independent.

5. Let X and Y be two independent random variables, each with the same probability density given by

$$f_X(t) = f_Y(t) = \begin{cases} e^{-t} & \text{if} \quad t > 0, \\ 0 & \text{if} \quad t \leq 0. \end{cases}$$

(a) Determine the probability density function f of the two-dimensional random variable (X, Y).

(b) Let A denote the set of points in the xy-plane at which $f(x, y) > 0$. Draw a sketch of A and of its image A' under the mapping defined by

$$u = x + y, \qquad v = \frac{x}{x + y}.$$

(c) Let $U = X + Y$ and $V = X/(X + Y)$ be two new random variables, and compute the probability density g of (U, V).

(d) Compute the probability density f_U.

(e) Compute the probability density f_V.

6. Let X and Y be two independent random variables, each with a standard normal distribution (mean $= 0$, variance $= 1$). Introduce new random variables U and V by the equations $U = X/Y$, $V = Y$. Let g denote the probability density function of (U, V).

(a) Show that $g(u, v) = -\dfrac{v}{2\pi} e^{-(1 + u^2)v^2/2}$ if $v < 0$.

(b) Find a similar formula for computing $g(u, v)$ when $v \geq 0$.

(c) Determine the probability density function of U.

7. Assume X has the density function given by

$$f_X(x) = \begin{cases} \dfrac{1}{\pi\sqrt{1 - x^2}} & \text{if } -1 < x < 1, \\ 0 & \text{if } |x| \geq 1. \end{cases}$$

If an independent random variable Y has density

$$f_Y(y) = \begin{cases} ye^{-y^2/2} & \text{if } y \geq 0, \\ 0 & \text{if } y < 0, \end{cases}$$

find the density function of $Z = XY$.

8. A random variable (X, Y) is said to have a *normal bivariate distribution* if its density function f is given by the formula

$$f(x, y) = \frac{\sqrt{D}}{2\pi} e^{-Q(x, y)/2},$$

where

$$Q(x, y) = A_{11}(x - x_0)^2 + 2A_{12}(x - x_0)(y - y_0) + A_{22}(y - y_0)^2.$$

Q is called a "quadratic form." The numbers A_{11}, A_{12}, A_{22} are constants with $A_{11} > 0$. The number $D = A_{11} A_{22} - A_{12}^2$ is called the *discriminant* of Q and is assumed to be positive. The numbers x_0 and y_0 are arbitrary.

(a) Show that $Q(x, y)$ can be expressed as a sum of squares as follows:

$$Q(x, y) = A_{11}\left(u + \frac{A_{12}}{A_{11}} v\right)^2 + \frac{D}{A_{11}} v^2, \qquad \text{where} \quad u = x - x_0, v = y - y_0.$$

(b) Define the "improper" double integral $\displaystyle\int\!\!\!\int_{-\infty}^{+\infty} f(x, y)\, dx\, dy$ to be the limit

$$\int\!\!\!\int_{-\infty}^{+\infty} f(x, y)\, dx\, dy = \lim_{t \to +\infty} \int\!\!\!\int_{R(t)} f(x, y)\, dx\, dy,$$

where $R(t)$ is the square $[-t, t] \times [-t, t]$. Show that

$$\iint\limits_{-\infty}^{+\infty} f(x, y) \, dx \, dy = 1 .$$

[*Hint.* Use part (a) to transform the double integral over $R(t)$ into a double integral in the uv-plane. Then perform a linear change of variables to simplify the integral and, finally, let $t \to +\infty$.]

9. If a two-dimensional random variable (X, Y) has a normal bivariate distribution as described in Exercise 8, show that X and Y themselves are normal one-dimensional random variables with means x_0 and y_0, respectively, and with variances $\sigma^2(X) = A_{22}/D$, $\sigma^2(Y) = A_{11}/D$.

10. If (X, Y) has a normal bivariate distribution as described in Exercise 8, show that the random variable $Z = X + Y$ has a one-dimensional normal distribution with mean $x_0 + y_0$ and variance $(A_{11} - 2A_{12} + A_{22})/D$.

3.14 Expectation and variance

The mass interpretation of probability distributions may be carried a step further by introducing the concepts of *expectation* and *variance*. These play the same role in probability theory that "center of mass" and "moment of inertia" play in mechanics. Without the Stieltjes integral we must give separate definitions for the discrete and continuous cases.

DEFINITIONS OF EXPECTATION AND VARIANCE. Let X be a one-dimensional random variable. The expectation of X and the variance of X are real numbers denoted by $E(X)$ and $\text{Var}(X)$ respectively, and are defined as follows:

(a) For a continuous random variable with density function f_X,

$$E(X) = \int_{-\infty}^{+\infty} t \, f_X(t) \, dt ,$$

$$\text{Var}(X) = \int_{-\infty}^{+\infty} [t - E(X)]^2 f_X(t) \, dt .$$

(b) For a discrete random variable with mass points $x_1, x_2, \ldots$ having probabilities $p_k = P(X = x_k)$, we define

$$E(X) = \sum_{k=1}^{\infty} x_k \, p_k ,$$

$$\text{Var}(X) = \sum_{k=1}^{\infty} [x_k - E(X)]^2 \, p_k .$$

Note. We say that $E(X)$ and $\text{Var}(X)$ *exist* only when the integral or series in question is *absolutely convergent*. It is understood that the series is a finite sum when the sample space is finite; in this case $E(X)$ and $\text{Var}(X)$ always exist. They also exist when f_X is 0 outside some finite interval.

The mathematical expectation $E(X)$ is a theoretically computed value associated with the random variable X. In some respects, the distribution acts as though its entire mass were concentrated at a single point, $E(X)$. The true significance of mathematical expectation in probability theory will be discussed in Section 3.17 in connection with the so-called "laws of large numbers."

In mechanics, a knowledge of the center of mass alone gives no indication of how the mass is spread or dispersed about its center. A measure of this dispersion is provided by the "second moment" or "moment of inertia." In probability theory, this second moment is the variance. It measures the tendency of a distribution to spread out from its expected value. In Section 3.16 we shall find that a small variance indicates that large deviations from the expected value are unlikely.

Although the expectation $E(X)$ may be positive or negative, the variance $\text{Var}(X)$ is always nonnegative. The symbol σ^2 is also used to denote the variance. Its positive square root is called the *standard deviation* and is denoted by σ. The standard deviation is a weighted average; in fact, σ is a weighted root mean square of the distance of each value of X from the expected value $E(X)$. The analogous concept in mechanics is the "radius of gyration."

Example 1: Uniform distribution. Let X have a uniform distribution over an interval $[a, b]$. Then $f(t) = 1/(b - a)$ if $a < t < b$, and $f(t) = 0$ otherwise. Therefore the expectation of X is given by

$$E(X) = \int_{-\infty}^{+\infty} t\, f(t)\, dt = \frac{1}{b - a} \int_a^b t\, dt = \frac{b^2 - a^2}{2(b - a)} = \frac{a + b}{2}.$$

Thus the mean is the mid-point of the interval. If we write m for $(a + b)/2$ and note that $m - a = b - m = (b - a)/2$ we find

$$\text{Var}(X) = \frac{1}{b - a} \int_a^b (t - m)^2\, dt = \frac{1}{b - a} \int_{a-m}^{b-m} u^2\, du = \frac{(b - a)^2}{12}.$$

Note that the variance depends only on the *length* of the interval.

Example 2: Binomial distribution. If X has a binomial distribution with parameters n and p we have

$$E(X) = \sum_{k=0}^{n} k \binom{n}{k} p^k\, q^{n-k},$$

where $q = 1 - p$. To evaluate this sum, let

$$f(x, y) = (x + y)^n = \sum_{k=0}^{n} \binom{n}{k} x^k\, y^{n-k}$$

and note that

$$\sum_{k=0}^{n} k \binom{n}{k} x^{k-1}\, y^{n-k} = \frac{\partial f(x, y)}{\partial x} = n(x + y)^{n-1}.$$

If we multiply both sides of this last equation by x and put $x = p$ and $y = q$, we obtain $E(X) = np$.

By a similar argument we may deduce the formula

$$\text{Var}(X) = \sum_{k=0}^{n} (k - np)^2 \binom{n}{k} p^k\, q^{n-k} = npq.$$

The proof of this formula is requested in Exercise 6 of Section 3.15.

Example 3: Normal distribution. The terms "mean" and "variance" have already been introduced in connection with our description of the normal distribution in Section 3.7. These terms are justified by the formulas

$$E(X) = \frac{1}{\sigma\sqrt{2\pi}} \int_{-\infty}^{+\infty} t \, e^{-\left(\frac{t-m}{\sigma}\right)^2/2} \, dt = m$$

and

$$\text{Var}(X) = \frac{1}{\sigma\sqrt{2\pi}} \int_{-\infty}^{+\infty} (t-m)^2 \, e^{-\left(\frac{t-m}{\sigma}\right)^2/2} \, dt = \sigma^2 \, .$$

Proofs of these formulas are requested in Exercise 7 of Section 3.15.

Gamblers often use the concept of expectation to decide whether a given game of chance is favorable or unfavorable. As an illustration we shall consider the game of betting on "red" or "black" in roulette.

Example 4: Roulette. A roulette wheel carries the numbers from 0 to 36. The number 0 appears on a gray background, half of the remaining 36 numbers on a red background, and the other half on a black background. The usual methods of betting are:

      (1) Bet \$1 on a color (red or black). Possible return: \$2.
      (2) Bet \$1 on a single number (0 excepted). Possible return: \$36.
      (3) Bet \$1 on any dozen numbers (0 excepted). Possible return: \$3.
If 0 is the winning number the house wins and all other players lose.

Let X be the random variable which measures the financial outcome of betting by method (1). The possible values of X are $x_1 = -1$ and $x_2 = +1$. The point probabilities are $P(X = x_1) = 19/37$, $P(X = x_2) = 18/37$. Therefore the expectation is

$$E(X) = (-1)\frac{19}{37} + (+1)\frac{18}{37} = -\frac{1}{37} \, ;$$

this is usually interpreted to mean that the game is unfavorable to those who play it. The mathematical justification for this interpretation is provided by one of the *laws of large numbers*, to be discussed in Section 3.17. The reader may verify that the expectation has the same value for methods (2) and (3) as well.

Example 5: A coin-tossing game. In a coin-tossing game there is a probability p that heads (H) will come up and a probability q that tails (T) will come up, where $0 \leq p \leq 1$ and $q = 1 - p$. The coin is tossed repeatedly until the first outcome occurs a second time; at this point the game ends. If the first outcome is H we are paid \$1 for each T that comes up until we get the next H. For example, $HTTTH$ pays \$3, but HH pays \$0. If the first outcome is T the same rules apply with H and T interchanged. The problem is to determine how much we should pay to play this game. For this purpose we shall consider the random variable which counts the number of dollars won and compute its expected value.

For the sample space we take the collection of all possible games that can be played in this manner. This set can be expressed as the union of two sets A and B, where

$A = \{TT, THT, THHT, THHHT, \dots\}$ and $B = \{HH, HTH, HTTH, HTTTH, \dots\}$.

We denote the elements of set A (in the order listed) as $a_0, a_1, a_2, a_3, \ldots$ and those of set B as $b_0, b_1, b_2, b_3, \ldots$. Next, we assign the point probabilities as follows:

$$P(a_n) = p^n q^2 \qquad \text{and} \qquad P(b_n) = q^n p^2 \,.$$

(When $p = 0$, we put $P(a_0) = 1$ and let $P(x) = 0$ for all other x in $A \cup B$. When $q = 0$ we put $P(b_0) = 1$ and let $P(x) = 0$ for all other x.) This is an acceptable assignment of probabilities because for $0 < p < 1$ we have

$$\sum_{n=0}^{\infty} P(a_n) + \sum_{n=0}^{\infty} P(b_n) = q^2 \sum_{n=0}^{\infty} p^n + p^2 \sum_{n=0}^{\infty} q^n = \frac{q^2}{1-p} + \frac{p^2}{1-q} = p + q = 1 \,.$$

The random variable X in which we are interested is defined on the sample space $A \cup B$ as follows:

$$X(a_n) = X(b_n) = n \qquad \text{for} \quad n = 0, 1, 2, \ldots .$$

The event "$X = n$" consists of the two games a_n and b_n, so we have

$$P(X = n) = p^n q^2 + q^n p^2 \,,$$

where p^0 and q^0 are to be interpreted as 1 when $p = 0$ or $q = 0$. The expectation of X is given by the sum

$$(3.39) \qquad E(X) = \sum_{n=0}^{\infty} n \, P(X = n) = q^2 \sum_{n=0}^{\infty} np^n + p^2 \sum_{n=0}^{\infty} nq^n \,.$$

If either $p = 0$ or $q = 0$, we obtain $E(X) = 0$. Otherwise we may compute the sums of the series in (3.39) by noting that for $0 < x < 1$ we have

$$\sum_{n=0}^{\infty} nx^n = x \frac{d}{dx} \sum_{n=0}^{\infty} x^n = x \frac{d}{dx} \left(\frac{1}{1-x} \right) = \frac{x}{(1-x)^2} \,.$$

Using this in (3.39) with $x = p$ and $x = q$ we obtain, for $0 < p < 1$,

$$E(X) = \frac{q^2 p}{(1-p)^2} + \frac{p^2 q}{(1-q)^2} = p + q = 1 \,.$$

We interpret this result by saying that the game is unfavorable to those who pay more than \$1 to play it.

This particular example is of special interest because the expectation $E(X)$ is independent of p when $0 < p < 1$. In other words, loading the coin in favor of heads or tails does not affect the expected value except in the extreme cases in which it is so loaded that it always falls heads or always falls tails. Note that, as a function of p, the expectation $E(X)$ is discontinuous at the points $p = 0$ and $p = 1$. Otherwise it has the constant value 1. This interesting example was suggested to the author by H. S. Zuckerman.

If a new random variable Y is related to a given one X by an equation of the form $Y = \phi(X)$, its expectation is given (in the continuous case) by the equation

$$(3.40) \qquad E(Y) = \int_{-\infty}^{+\infty} t \, f_Y(t) \, dt \,.$$

The expectation $E(Y)$ can be computed directly in terms of the density f_X without determining the density of Y. In fact, the following formula is equivalent to (3.40):

$$(3.41) \qquad E(Y) = \int_{-\infty}^{+\infty} \phi(t) f_X(t) \, dt \, .$$

A proof of (3.41) in the most general case is difficult and will not be attempted here. However, for many special cases of importance the proof is simple. In one such case, ϕ is differentiable and strictly increasing on the whole real axis, and takes on every real value. For a continuously distributed random variable X with density f_X we have the following formula for the density function f_Y (derived in Section 3.12):

$$f_Y(t) = f_X[\psi(t)] \cdot \psi'(t) \, ,$$

where ψ is the inverse of ϕ. If we use this in (3.40) and make the change of variable $u = \psi(t)$ [so that $t = \phi(u)$], we obtain

$$E(Y) = \int_{-\infty}^{+\infty} t \, f_Y(t) \, dt = \int_{-\infty}^{+\infty} t \, f_X[\psi(t)] \cdot \psi'(t) \, dt = \int_{-\infty}^{+\infty} \phi(u) \, f_X(u) \, du \, ,$$

which is the same as (3.41).

When Equation (3.41) is applied to $Y = (X - m)^2$, where $m = E(X)$, we obtain

$$E(Y) = \int_{-\infty}^{+\infty} (t - m)^2 f_X(t) \, dt = \mathrm{Var}(X) \, .$$

This shows that variance is itself an expectation. A formula analogous to (3.41) also holds, of course, in the discrete case. More generally, it can be shown that

$$E[\phi(X, Y)] = \int_{-\infty}^{+\infty} \int_{-\infty}^{+\infty} \phi(x, y) f(x, y) \, dx \, dy$$

if (X, Y) is a continuous random variable with joint density f.

Note. For two-dimensional random variables, expectation and variance may be defined in a manner similar to that used for the one-dimensional case, except that double integrals and double sums are employed. We shall not discuss this extension here.

3.15 Exercises

1. A die is rolled. Let X denote the number of points on the upturned face. Compute $E(X)$ and $\mathrm{Var}(X)$.

2. Assume that X is a continuous random variable with a probability density function. Let $Y = (X - m)/\sigma$, where $m = E(X)$ and $\sigma = \sqrt{\mathrm{Var}(X)}$. Show that $E(Y) = 0$ and $E(Y^2) = 1$.

3. Derive the following general properties of expectation and variance for either the discrete or the continuous case.
    (a) $E(cX) = c \, E(X)$,   where c is a constant.
    (b) $\mathrm{Var}(cX) = c^2 \, \mathrm{Var}(X)$,   where c is a constant.
    (c) $E(X + Y) = E(X) + E(Y)$.
    (d) $\mathrm{Var}(X) = E(X^2) - [E(X)]^2$.
    (e) $\mathrm{Var}(X + Y) = \mathrm{Var}(X) + \mathrm{Var}(Y) + 2 \, E[(X - E(X))(Y - E(Y))]$.
    (f) $E[\phi_1(X) + \phi_2(Y)] = E[\phi_1(X)] + E[\phi_2(Y)]$. [Part (c) is a special case.]

4. If X and Y are independent random variables, show that
    (a) $\mathrm{Var}(X + Y) = \mathrm{Var}(X) + \mathrm{Var}(Y)$.

(b) $E[\phi(X) \cdot \psi(Y)] = E[\phi(X)] \cdot E[\psi(Y)]$.

(c) If $X_1, X_2, \ldots, X_n$ are independent random variables with $E(X_k) = m_k$, show that

$$\mathrm{Var}\left[\sum_{k=1}^{n} (X_k - m_k)\right] = \sum_{k=1}^{n} \mathrm{Var}(X_k - m_k) = \sum_{k=1}^{n} \mathrm{Var}(X_k).$$

5. Let $X_1, X_2, X_3, \ldots, X_n$ be n independent random variables, each having the same expectation, $E(X_k) = m$, and the same variance, $\mathrm{Var}(X_k) = \sigma^2$. Let $\overline{X}$ denote the arithmetic mean, $\overline{X} = (1/n)\sum_{i=1}^{n} X_i$. Use Exercises 3 and 4 to prove that $E(\overline{X}) = m$ and $\mathrm{Var}(\overline{X}) = \sigma^2/n$.

6. (a) If $q = 1 - p$, prove the formula

$$\sum_{k=0}^{n} (k - np)^2 \binom{n}{k} p^k q^{n-k} = npq,$$

thereby showing that $\mathrm{Var}(X) = npq$ for a random variable X having a binomial distribution with parameters n and p. [*Hint*. $k^2 = k(k - 1) + k$.]

(b) If X has a binomial distribution with parameters n and p, show that X can be expressed as a sum of n independent random variables $X_1, X_2, \ldots, X_n$, each assuming the possible values 0 and 1 with probabilities p and q, respectively, and each having a binomial distribution. Use this result and Exercise 5 to show that $E(X) = np$ and $\mathrm{Var}(X) = npq$.

7. Determine the expectation and variance (whenever they exist) for a random variable X having

(a) a Poisson distribution with parameter λ.

(b) a Cauchy distribution.

(c) an exponential distribution with parameter λ.

(d) a normal distribution.

8. A random variable X has a probability density function given by

$$f(t) = \frac{C(r)}{|t|^r} \quad \text{if } |t| > 1, \qquad f(t) = 0 \quad \text{if } |t| \le 1,$$

where $r > 1$ and $C(r)$ is independent of t.

(a) Express $C(r)$ in terms of r and make a sketch to indicate the nature of the graph of f.

(b) Determine the corresponding distribution function F_X and make a sketch to indicate the nature of its graph.

(c) Compute $P(X < 5)$ and $P(5 < X < 10)$ in terms of r.

(d) For what values of r does X have a finite expectation? Compute $E(X)$ in terms of r when the expectation is finite.

(e) For what values of r does X have a finite variance? Compute $\mathrm{Var}(X)$ in terms of r when the variance is finite.

9. A gambler plays roulette according to the following "system." He plays in sets of three games. In the first and second games he always bets \$1 on red. For the third game he proceeds as follows:

(a) If he wins in the first and second games, he doesn't bet.

(b) If he wins in one of the first or second and loses in the other, he bets \$1 on the color opposite to the outcome of the second game.

(c) If he loses in both the first and second, he bets \$3 on red.

Let X, Y, and Z denote, respectively, the financial outcomes of the first, second, and third games. Compute $E(X)$, $E(Y)$, $E(Z)$, and $E(X + Y + Z)$.

10. (*Petersburg Problem*). A player tosses a coin and wins \$1 if his first toss is heads. If he tosses heads again he wins another dollar. If he succeeds in tossing heads a third time he gets another \$2 (for a total of \$4). As long as he tosses heads in succession n times, his accumulated winnings are 2^{n-1} dollars. The game terminates when he tosses tails. Let X denote the number of dollars won in

any particular game. Compute $E(X)$. In view of your result, how much would you be willing to pay Harold's Club in Reno for the privilege of playing this game?

11. (a) Assume X is a continuous random variable with probability density f_X. Let $Y = (X - m)/\sigma$, where $m = E(X)$ and $\sigma = \sqrt{\text{Var}(X)}$. Prove that

$$E(e^Y) = e^{-m/\sigma} \int_{-\infty}^{+\infty} e^{t/\sigma} f_X(t)\, dt \,.$$

(b) Let X be a discrete random variable having a Poisson distribution with parameter λ. Define Y as in part (a) and prove that

$$E(e^Y) = e^{-\lambda G(\lambda)}, \qquad \text{where} \quad G(\lambda) = 1 + \frac{1}{\sqrt{\lambda}} - e^{1/\sqrt{\lambda}} \,.$$

12. A random variable X has a standard normal distribution. Compute: (a) $E(|X|)$, (b) $E(e^X)$, (c) $\text{Var}(e^X)$, (d) $E(\sqrt{X^2 + Y^2})$. In part (d), Y also has a standard normal distribution but is independent of X.

3.16 Chebyshev's inequality

As mentioned earlier, a small value for the variance means that it is unlikely that a random variable X will deviate much from its expected value. To make this statement more precise we introduce the absolute value $|X - E(X)|$ which measures the actual distance between X and $E(X)$. How likely is it that this distance is more than a given amount? To answer this question we must determine the probability

(3.42) $P[|X - E(X)| > c]\,,$

where c is a given positive number. In the continuous case we have

$$P[|X - E(X)| > c] = 1 - P[|X - E(X)| \le c] = 1 - P[E(X) - c \le X \le E(X) + c]$$

$$= \int_{-\infty}^{+\infty} f_X(t)\, dt - \int_{E(X)-c}^{E(X)+c} f_X(t)\, dt$$

(3.43) $$= \int_{-\infty}^{E(X)-c} f_X(t)\, dt + \int_{E(X)+c}^{+\infty} f_X(t)\, dt \,;$$

therefore, the calculation of this probability can be accomplished once the density function f_X is known. Of course, if f_X is *unknown* this method gives no information. However, if the *variance* is known, we can obtain an upper bound for the probability in (3.42). This upper bound is provided by the following theorem of P. L. Chebyshev (1821–1894), a famous Russian mathematician who made many important contributions to probability theory and other branches of mathematics, especially the theory of numbers.

3– 6   THEOREM.   *Chebyshev's Inequality.* Let X be a one-dimensional random variable with finite expectation $E(X)$ and variance $\text{Var}(X)$. Then for every positive number c we have

(3.44) $$P[|X - E(X)| > c] \le \frac{\text{Var}(X)}{c^2} \,.$$

Proof. In the continuous case we have

$$\text{Var}(X) = \int_{-\infty}^{+\infty} [t - E(X)]^2 f_X(t)\, dt$$

$$\geq \int_{-\infty}^{E(X)-c} [t - E(X)]^2 f_X(t)\, dt + \int_{E(X)+c}^{+\infty} [t - E(X)]^2 f_X(t)\, dt$$

$$\geq c^2 \left(\int_{-\infty}^{E(X)-c} f_X(t)\, dt + \int_{E(X)+c}^{+\infty} f_X(t)\, dt \right).$$

Because of (3.43), the coefficient of c^2 on the right is $P[|X - E(X)| > c]$. Therefore, when we divide by c^2 we obtain (3.44). This completes the proof for the continuous case; the discrete case may be similarly treated.

Chebyshev's inequality tells us that the larger we make c the smaller the probability is that $|X - E(X)| > c$. In other words, it is unlikely that X will be very far from $E(X)$; it is even more unlikely if the variance $\text{Var}(X)$ is small.

If we replace c by $k\sigma$, where $k > 0$ and σ denotes the standard deviation $[\sigma = \sqrt{\text{Var}(X)}]$, Chebyshev's inequality becomes

$$P[|X - E(X)| > k\sigma] \leq \frac{1}{k^2}.$$

That is, the probability that X will differ from its expected value by more than k standard deviations does not exceed $1/k^2$. For example, when $k = 10$ this inequality tells us that the probability $P[|X - E(X)| > 10\sigma]$ does not exceed 0.010. In other words, the probability is no more than 0.010 that an observed value of X will differ from the expected value by more than ten standard deviations. Similarly, when $k = 3$ we find that the probability does not exceed 0.111 that an observed value will differ from the mean by more than three standard deviations.

Chebyshev's inequality is a general theorem that applies to all distributions. In many applications the inequality can be strengthened when more information is known about the particular distribution. For example, if X has a binomial distribution with parameters n and p it can be shown (by use of the normal approximation to the binomial distribution) that for large n the probability is nearly 0.003 that an observed value will differ from the mean by more than three standard deviations. (For this result, $n \geq 12$ suffices.) This is much smaller than the probability 0.111 provided by Chebyshev's inequality.

Example: Testing a coin for fairness. We want to decide whether or not a particular coin is fair by tossing it 10,000 times and recording the number of heads. For a fair coin the random variable X which counts the number of heads has a binomial distribution with parameters $n = 10,000$ and $p = \frac{1}{2}$. The mean of X is $np = 5,000$ and the standard deviation is $\sigma = \sqrt{npq} = 50$. (See Example 2 in Section 3.14.) As mentioned above, the probability for a binomially distributed random variable to differ from its expected value by more than 3σ is about 0.003. Therefore, let us agree to say that a coin is *not fair* if the number of heads in 10,000 tosses differs from the mean by more than 3σ. Since $E(X) = 5,000$ and $3\sigma = 150$, we would say the coin is unfair if the number of heads in 10,000 tosses is less than 4,850 or more than 5,150.

3.17 Laws of large numbers

In connection with coin-tossing problems, it is often said that the probability of tossing heads with a perfectly balanced coin is $\frac{1}{2}$. This does not mean that if a coin is tossed twice it will necessarily come up heads exactly once. Nor does it mean that in 1000 tosses heads will appear exactly 500 times. Let us denote by $h(n)$ the number of heads that occur in n tosses. Experience shows that even for very large n, the ratio $h(n)/n$ is not necessarily $\frac{1}{2}$. However, experience also shows that this ratio does seem to *approach* $\frac{1}{2}$ as n increases, although it may oscillate considerably above and below $\frac{1}{2}$ in the process. This suggests that it might be possible to prove that

$$(3.45) \qquad\qquad \lim_{n \to \infty} \frac{h(n)}{n} = \frac{1}{2}.$$

Unfortunately, this cannot be done. One difficulty is that the number $h(n)$ depends not only on n but also on the particular experiment being performed. We have no way of knowing in advance how $h(n)$ will vary from one experiment to another. But the real trouble is that it *is* possible (although not very likely) that in some particular experiment the ratio $h(n)/n$ may *not* tend to $\frac{1}{2}$ at all. For example, there is no reason to exclude the possibility of getting heads on *every* toss of the coin, in which case $h(n) = n$ and $h(n)/n \to 1$. Therefore, instead of trying to prove the formula in (3.45), we shall find it more reasonable (and more profitable) to ask how likely it is that $h(n)/n$ will differ from $\frac{1}{2}$ by a certain amount. In other words, given some positive number c, we seek the probability

$$P\left(\left| \frac{h(n)}{n} - \frac{1}{2} \right| > c \right).$$

By introducing a suitable random variable and using Chebyshev's inequality we can get a useful *upper bound* to this probability, a bound which does not require an explicit knowledge of $h(n)$. This leads to a new limit relation that serves as an appropriate substitute for (3.45).

No extra effort is required to treat the more general case of a Bernoullian sequence of trials, in which the probability of "success" is p and the probability of "failure" is q. (In coin tossing, "success" can mean "heads" and for p we may take $\frac{1}{2}$.) Let X denote the random variable which counts the number of successes in n independent trials. Then X has a binomial distribution with expectation $E(X) = np$ and variance $\mathrm{Var}(X) = npq$. Hence Chebyshev's inequality is applicable; it states that

$$(3.46) \qquad\qquad P(|X - np| > c) \le \frac{npq}{c^2}.$$

Since we are interested in the ratio X/n, which we may call the *relative frequency* of success, we divide the inequality $|X - np| > c$ by n and rewrite (3.46) as

$$(3.47) \qquad\qquad P\left(\left| \frac{X}{n} - p \right| > \frac{c}{n} \right) \le \frac{npq}{c^2}.$$

Since this is valid for every $c > 0$, we may let c depend on n and write $c = \epsilon n$, where ϵ is a fixed positive number. Then (3.47) becomes

$$P\left(\left| \frac{X}{n} - p \right| > \epsilon \right) \le \frac{pq}{n\epsilon^2}.$$

The appearance of n in the denominator on the right suggests that we let $n \to \infty$. This leads to the limit formula

$$(3.48) \qquad \lim_{n \to \infty} P\left(\left| \frac{X}{n} - p \right| > \epsilon \right) = 0 \qquad \text{for every fixed } \epsilon > 0 ,$$

called the *law of large numbers for the Bernoulli distribution*. It tells us that, given any $\epsilon > 0$ (no matter how small), the probability that the relative frequency of success differs from p by more than ϵ is a function of n which tends to 0 as $n \to \infty$. This limit relation gives a mathematical justification to the assignment of the probability $\frac{1}{2}$ for tossing heads with a perfectly balanced coin.

The limit relation in (3.48) is a special case of a more general result in which the "relative frequency" X/n is replaced by the arithmetic mean of n independent random variables having the same expectation and variance. This more general theorem is usually referred to as the *weak law of large numbers;* it may be stated as follows:

3– 7   THEOREM. *Weak law of large numbers.* Let $X_1, X_2, \ldots, X_n$ be n independent random variables, each having the same expectation and the same variance, say

$$E(X_k) = m \qquad \text{and} \qquad \text{Var}(X_k) = \sigma^2 \qquad \text{for} \quad k = 1, 2, \ldots, n .$$

Define a new random variable $\bar{X}$ (called the arithmetic mean of $X_1, X_2, \ldots, X_n$) by the equation

$$\bar{X} = \frac{1}{n} \sum_{k=1}^{n} X_k .$$

Then, for every fixed $\epsilon > 0$, we have

$$(3.49) \qquad \lim_{n \to \infty} P(|\bar{X} - m| > \epsilon) = 0 .$$

An equivalent statement is

$$(3.50) \qquad \lim_{n \to \infty} P(|\bar{X} - m| \leq \epsilon) = 1 .$$

Proof. We apply Chebyshev's inequality to $\bar{X}$. For this we need to know the expectation and variance of $\bar{X}$. These are

$$E(\bar{X}) = m \qquad \text{and} \qquad \text{Var}(\bar{X}) = \sigma^2/n .$$

(See Exercise 5 in Section 3.15.) Chebyshev's inequality becomes $P(|\bar{X} - m| > c) \leq \sigma^2/(nc^2)$. Letting $n \to \infty$ and replacing c by ϵ we obtain (3.49) and hence (3.50).

Note. To show that the limit relation in (3.48) is a special case of Theorem 3–7, we assume each X_k has the possible values 0 and 1, with probabilities $P(X_k = 1) = p$ and $P(X_k = 0) = 1 - p$. Then $\bar{X}$ is the relative frequency of success in n independent trials, $E(\bar{X}) = p$, and (3.49) reduces to (3.48).

Theorem 3–7 is called a *weak* law because there is also a *strong* law of large numbers which (under the same hypotheses) states that

$$(3.51) \qquad P\left(\lim_{n \to \infty} |\overline{X} - m| = 0\right) = 1 .$$

The principal difference between (3.51) and (3.50) is that the operations "limit" and "probability" are interchanged. It can be shown that the strong law implies the weak law, but not conversely.

Notice that the strong law in (3.51) seems to be closer to formula (3.45) than (3.50) is. In fact, (3.51) says that we have $\lim_{n \to \infty} \overline{X} = m$ "almost always," that is, with probability 1. When applied to coin tossing, in particular, it says that the failure of Equation (3.45) is less likely than the chance of tossing a fair coin repeatedly and always getting heads. The strong law really shows why probability theory corresponds to experience and to our intuitive feeling of what probability "should be."

The proof of the strong law is lengthy and will be omitted. Proofs appear in the books listed at the end of this chapter as References 1, 3, 8, and 10.

3.18   The central limit theorem of the calculus of probabilities

In many applications of probability theory, the random variables of interest are sums of other random variables. For example, the financial outcome after several plays of a game is the sum of the winnings at each play. A surprising thing happens when a large number of independent random variables are added together. Under general conditions (applicable in almost every situation that occurs in practice) the distribution of the sum tends to be normal, regardless of the distributions of the individual random variables that make up the sum. The precise statement of this remarkable fact is known as the *central limit theorem of the calculus of probabilities.* It accounts for the importance of the normal distribution in both theory and practice. A thorough discussion of this theorem belongs to the advanced study of probability theory. This section will merely describe what the theorem asserts.

Suppose we have an infinite sequence of random variables, say $X_1, X_2, \ldots$, with finite expectations and variances. Let

$$m_k = E(X_k) \qquad \text{and} \qquad \sigma_k^2 = \text{Var}(X_k), \qquad k = 1, 2, \ldots .$$

We form a new random variable S_n by adding the first n differences $X_k - m_k$:

$$(3.52) \qquad S_n = \sum_{k=1}^{n} (X_k - m_k) .$$

We add the *differences* rather than the X_k alone so that the sum S_n will have expected value 0. The problem here is to determine the limiting form, as $n \to \infty$, of the distribution function of S_n.

If $X_1, X_2, \ldots , X_n$ are *independent*, then [by Exercise 4(c) of Section 3.15] we have

$$\text{Var}(S_n) = \sum_{k=1}^{n} \text{Var}(X_k - m_k) = \sum_{k=1}^{n} \text{Var}(X_k) = \sum_{k=1}^{n} \sigma_k^2 .$$

Ordinarily, $\text{Var}(S_n)$ will be large even though the individual variances σ_k^2 may be small. Random variables with a large variance are not fruitful objects of study because their values tend to be widely dispersed from the expected value. For this reason, a new random variable T_n is introduced by the equation

(3.53) $$T_n = \frac{S_n}{\sqrt{\text{Var}(S_n)}} \, .$$

This new variable has expectation 0 and variance 1 and is called a *standardized* random variable. The standardized variable T_n is meaningful even if the random variables $X_1, X_2, \ldots, X_n$ are not independent.

We now introduce the following definition:

DEFINITION OF THE CENTRAL LIMIT PROPERTY. Let

(3.54) $$X_1, X_2, X_3, \ldots$$

be a sequence of random variables (not necessarily independent), where each X_k has a finite expectation m_k and a finite variance σ_k^2. Define S_n and T_n by (3.52) and (3.53). The sequence in (3.54) is said to satisfy the central limit property if, for all a and b with $a \leq b$, we have

(3.55) $$\lim_{n \to \infty} P(a \leq T_n \leq b) = \frac{1}{\sqrt{2\pi}} \int_a^b e^{-u^2/2} du \, .$$

In other words, the random variables in (3.54) satisfy the central limit property if the distribution of the standardized variable T_n approaches a standard normal distribution as $n \to \infty$. [Equation (3.55) is to hold also if $a = -\infty$ or $b = +\infty$.]

Laplace was the first to realize that this property is shared by many sequences of random variables, although a special case (random variables describing a Bernoullian sequence of trials) had been known earlier by DeMoivre. (Figure 3.13 shows a binomial distribution and a corresponding normal approximation.) Laplace stated a general central limit theorem which was first completely proved by the Russian mathematician A. Lyapunov in 1901. In 1922, J. W. Lindeberg generalized Laplace's result by showing that the property is satisfied if the random variables are independent and have a common distribution giving them the same expectations and variances, say $E(X_k) = m$ and $\text{Var}(X_k) = \sigma^2$ for all k. In this case the standardized variable becomes

$$T_n = \frac{\sum\limits_{k=1}^{n} X_k - nm}{\sigma \sqrt{n}} \, .$$

Lindeberg realized that independence alone is not sufficient to guarantee the central limit property, but he formulated another condition (now known as the *Lindeberg condition*) which, along with independence, *is* sufficient. In 1935, W. Feller showed that the Lindeberg condition is both necessary and sufficient for independent random variables to satisfy the central limit property. We shall not discuss the Lindeberg condition here except to mention that it implies

$$\text{Var}(S_n) \to \infty \qquad \text{as} \quad n \to \infty \, .$$

Fortunately, many independent random variables that occur in practice automatically satisfy the Lindeberg condition and therefore also have the central limit property. Up to now, the theory for *dependent* random variables is incomplete. Only a few special cases have been treated. Much of the contemporary research in probability theory centers about the search for general theorems dealing with dependent variables.

3.19   Exercises

1. Carry out the proof of Chebyshev's inequality in the discrete case.

2. If a is any real number, prove that

$$P(|X - a| > c\lambda) \leq \frac{1}{c^2}$$

for every $c > 0$, where $\lambda^2 = \int_{-\infty}^{+\infty} (t - a)^2 f_X(t)\, dt$. Chebyshev's inequality is the special case in which $a = E(X)$.

3. Let X denote the random variable which counts the number of successes in n independent trials of a Bernoullian sequence; the probability of success is p. Show that, for every $\epsilon > 0$,

$$P\left(\left|\frac{X}{n} - p\right| > \epsilon\right) \leq \frac{1}{4n\epsilon^2}.$$

4. A fair coin is tossed n times; the number of heads is denoted by X. Find the smallest n for which Chebyshev's inequality implies

$$P\left(0.4 < \frac{X}{n} < 0.6\right) > 0.90.$$

5. In a production line the number X of defective articles manufactured in any given hour is known to have a Poisson distribution with mean $E(X) = 100$. Use Chebyshev's inequality to compute a lower bound for the probability that in a given hour there will be between 90 and 110 defective articles produced.

6. Assume that a random variable X has a standard normal distribution (mean 0 and variance 1). Let p denote the probability that X differs from its expectation $E(X)$ by more than three times its standard deviation. Use Chebyshev's inequality to find an upper bound for p. Then use suitable tables of the normal distribution to show that there is an upper bound for p that is approximately one-fiftieth of that obtained by Chebyshev's inequality.

7. Given a sequence of independent random variables $X_1, X_2, \ldots$, each of which has a normal distribution. Let $m_k = E(X_k)$ and let $\sigma_k^2 = \text{Var}(X_k)$. Show that this sequence has the central limit property. [*Hint.* Refer to Exercise 10 in Section 3.13.]

8. Let $X_1, X_2, \ldots$ be independent random variables having the same binomial distribution. Assume each X_k takes the possible values 0 and 1 with probabilities $P(X_k = 1) = p$ and $P(X_k = 0) = q$, where $p + q = 1$. Let $Z_n = X_1 + \cdots + X_n$. The random variable Z_n counts the number of successes in n Bernoullian trials.

(a) Show that the central limit property takes the following form:

$$\lim_{n \to \infty} P\left(\frac{Z_n - np}{\sqrt{npq}} \leq t\right) = \frac{1}{\sqrt{2\pi}} \int_{-\infty}^{t} e^{-u^2/2}\, du.$$

(b) Use the approximation suggested by part (a) to estimate the probability of obtaining between 45 and 55 heads if a fair coin is tossed 100 times. Refer to tables of the normal distribution for the computation.

9. With the notation of Exercise 8, the central limit theorem for random variables describing a Bernoullian sequence of trials can be written in the form

$$\lim_{n \to \infty} \frac{P\left(t_1 \leq \dfrac{Z_n - np}{\sqrt{npq}} \leq t_2\right)}{\Phi(t_2) - \Phi(t_1)} = 1,$$

where Φ is the standard normal distribution. For this particular case it can be shown that the formula is also valid when t_1 and t_2 are functions of n given by $t_1 = (a - np)/\sqrt{npq}$ and $t_2 = (b - np)/\sqrt{npq}$, where a and b are fixed positive constants, $a < b$.

(a) Show that this relation implies the asymptotic formula

$$\sum_{k=a}^{b} \binom{n}{k} p^k q^{n-k} \sim \Phi\left(\frac{b - np + \frac{1}{2}}{\sqrt{npq}}\right) - \Phi\left(\frac{a - np - \frac{1}{2}}{\sqrt{npq}}\right) \quad \text{as} \quad n \to \infty .$$

(b) An unbiased die is tossed 180 times. Use the approximation suggested in part (a) to estimate the probability that the upturned face is a six exactly 30 times. Refer to tables of the normal distribution for the computation.

10. An unbiased die is tossed 100 times. Use the approximation suggested in Exercise 9(a) to estimate the probability that the upturned face is a six (a) exactly 25 times, (b) at least 25 times. Refer to tables of the normal distribution for the computation.

Suggested References

1. H. Cramér, *Elements of Probability Theory*, John Wiley, New York, 1955.

2. H. Cramér, *Mathematical Methods of Statistics*, Princeton Univ. Press, Princeton, N. J., 1946.

3. W. Feller, *An Introduction to Probability Theory and its Applications*, 2nd ed., John Wiley, New York, 1957.

4. B. V. Gnedenko and A. N. Kolmogorov, *Limit Distributions for Sums of Independent Random Variables*, Addison-Wesley, Reading, Mass., 1954.

5. S. Goldberg, *Probability, an Introduction*, Prentice-Hall, Englewood Cliffs, N. J., 1960.

6. H. Levy and L. Roth, *Elements of Probability*, Oxford Univ. Press, London and New York, 1936.

7. M. Loève, *Probability Theory: Foundations, Random Sequences*, Van Nostrand, New York, 1955.

8. M. E. Munroe, *Theory of Probability*, McGraw-Hill Book Co., Inc., New York, 1951.

9. J. Neyman, *First Course in Probability and Statistics*, Holt, Rinehart and Winston, New York, 1950.

10. E. Parzen, *Modern Probability Theory and its Applications*, John Wiley, New York, 1960.

11. I. Todhunter, *A History of the Mathematical Theory of Probability from the Time of Pascal to Laplace*, Chelsea Publishing Co., New York, 1949.

12. J. V. Uspensky, *Introduction to Mathematical Probability*, McGraw-Hill Book Co. Inc., New York, 1937.

4

DIFFERENTIAL CALCULUS OF SCALAR FIELDS

4.1 Scalar fields

Earlier we used the concept of a real-valued function of two real variables, that is, a real-valued function defined on some set in the xy-plane. If f is such a function, its value at a point (x, y) is a real number denoted by $f(x, y)$. It is often convenient to use vector notation and to write $f(\vec{X})$ instead of $f(x, y)$, where $\vec{X}$ stands for the vector from the origin to the point (x, y). When this is done, the function f is said to be a scalar-valued function of a vector variable or, more briefly, a *scalar field*. The same notation and terminology are used when the vector $\vec{X}$ is three-dimensional or, more generally, when $\vec{X}$ is n-dimensional. In the following discussion, the words "point" and "vector" are used interchangeably to refer to an ordered n-tuple of real numbers $(x_1, x_2, \ldots, x_n)$. In 2-space or 3-space, when we speak of the "point $\vec{X}$" we refer to the tip of the vector $\vec{X}$ when $\vec{X}$ is placed with its initial point at the origin.

If f is a scalar field defined at a point $\vec{X} = (x_1, \ldots, x_n)$ in n-space, the notations $f(\vec{X})$ and $f(x_1, \ldots, x_n)$ are both used to denote the value of f at that particular point. When the notation $f(x_1, \ldots, x_n)$ is used, the field f is said to be a function of the n real variables $x_1, \ldots, x_n$; when the notation $f(\vec{X})$ is used, f is said to be a function of the vector variable $\vec{X}$. We prefer the notation $f(\vec{X})$, not only because it is simpler and more compact than $f(x_1, \ldots, x_n)$, but also because it enables us to make some general statements about scalar fields without reference to the dimensionality of the space in which the vector $\vec{X}$ is assumed to lie.

This chapter extends some of the concepts of differential calculus to scalar fields. Since we use vector notation, no additional effort is required to develop many of the concepts for fields defined on sets in n-space for an arbitrary n. In most applications, however, n will be 2 or 3.

Scalar fields occur frequently in the applications of mathematics to science and engineering. For example, if at each point $\vec{X}$ of the atmosphere we assign a real number $T(\vec{X})$ which represents the temperature at $\vec{X}$, the function T so defined is a scalar field. On the other hand, if at each point of the atmosphere we assign a *vector* which represents the wind velocity at that point, we obtain an example of a vector-valued function of a vector variable. Such functions are called *vector fields*. Many examples will be given later in this chapter and in Chapter 5.

In physical problems dealing with either scalar or vector fields, it is important to know how the field changes as we move from one point to another. In the one-dimensional case, the derivative is the mathematical tool that enables us to study such changes. Partial derivatives can be used to describe the rate of change of a more general scalar field. When we form a partial derivative we treat the field as a function of one variable at a time, holding the other variables fixed. Therefore each partial derivative describes the rate of change of the field in the direction of a particular coordinate axis. It is more natural, however, to seek a broader concept of derivative, one which is not restricted to the special directions of the coordinate axes, but which deals with the rate of change in an *arbitrary* direction. The derivative introduced in Section 4.4 serves this purpose.

4.2 Neighborhoods and open sets

Derivative theory in the one-dimensional case deals with functions defined on *open intervals*. To extend the theory to higher dimensional spaces we must consider sets which are generalizations of open intervals. These sets are called *open sets*; they are of fundamental importance in analysis. Therefore, before we discuss derivatives, we digress briefly to describe the concept of an open set. First we extend the concept of a neighborhood to *n*-space; then we use neighborhoods, in turn, to describe open sets.

DEFINITION OF A NEIGHBORHOOD OF A POINT. Let $\vec{A}$ be a given point in *n*-space. If $r > 0$, the set of all points $\vec{X}$ in *n*-space such that

$$(4.1) \qquad\qquad |\vec{X} - \vec{A}| < r$$

is called a neighborhood of $\vec{A}$ with radius r and is denoted by the symbol $N(\vec{A})$ or $N(\vec{A}; r)$.

Thus, a neighborhood of $\vec{A}$ with radius r is the set of all points whose distance from $\vec{A}$ is less than r. In one-dimensional space this is simply an open interval with its center at point $\vec{A}$. In 2-space a neighborhood $N(\vec{A}; r)$ is a circular disk with center at $\vec{A}$ and radius r; in 3-space it is a spherical solid with center at $\vec{A}$ and radius r. (See Figure 4.1.) The

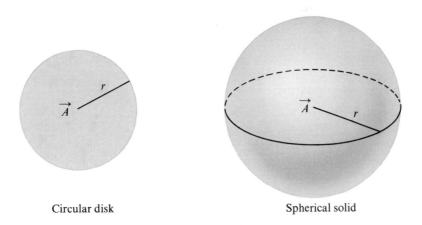

Circular disk   Spherical solid

FIGURE 4.1 *Neighborhoods in 2-space and in 3-space. The boundary points are not included.*

points $\vec{X}$ which satisfy $|\vec{X} - \vec{A}| = r$ are called *boundary points* of the neighborhood $N(\vec{A}; r)$. Because of the strict inequality in (4.1), *no* boundary points are included as part of the neighborhood. The definition of a neighborhood is meaningful for all values of n, although we do not attempt to draw a geometric picture of a neighborhood when the dimension n exceeds 3.

Having formulated the concept of a neighborhood, we turn now to the definition of an open set.

DEFINITION OF AN OPEN SET. *A set S of points in n-space is said to be open if for each point $\vec{A}$ in S there is a neighborhood $N(\vec{A})$, all of whose points lie in S. In other words, for every $\vec{A}$ in S there exists an $N(\vec{A})$ such that $N(\vec{A}) \subset S$.*

The simplest type of open set on the real line is an open interval. The union of two or more open intervals is also an open set. A closed interval, however, is not an open set because neither end point of the interval can be enclosed in a neighborhood which has all its points lying in the interval.

Some simple examples of open sets in the plane are: any two-dimensional neighborhood, the whole plane, the interior of a rectangle (the Cartesian product $(a, b) \times (c, d)$ of two open intervals), and the first quadrant (the set $\{(x, y) \mid x > 0, y > 0\}$). The reader should realize that an open interval on the real line is no longer an open set when it is considered a subset of the plane because a one-dimensional set cannot contain any two-dimensional neighborhoods.

To prove, for example, that the rectangle $R = (a, b) \times (c, d)$ is open we must show that for every point $\vec{A} = (a_1, a_2)$ in R there is a neighborhood $N(\vec{A})$ which lies completely within R. For this purpose, we choose a positive number r_1 such that the open interval $(a_1 - r_1, a_1 + r_1)$ lies within (a, b), and a positive number r_2 such that $(a_2 - r_2, a_2 + r_2)$ lies within (c, d). These choices of r_1 and r_2 are possible because (a, b) and (c, d) are open sets on the real line containing a_1 and a_2, respectively. If r denotes the smaller of r_1 and r_2 we can easily show that $N(\vec{A}; r) \subset R$. In fact, if $\vec{X} = (x_1, x_2)$ is any point in $N(\vec{A}; r)$, $|\vec{X} - \vec{A}| < r$, and hence $|x_1 - a_1| < r$ and $|x_2 - a_2| < r$. These inequalities imply that $|x_1 - a_1| < r_1$ and $|x_2 - a_2| < r_2$, so $x_1 \varepsilon (a, b)$ and $x_2 \varepsilon (c, d)$, which means that $\vec{X} \varepsilon R$. But since $\vec{X}$ is an arbitrary point of $N(\vec{A}; r)$ it follows that $N(\vec{A}; r) \subset R$, so R is open.

4.3 Exercises

1. Let f be a scalar field defined on a set S and let c be a given real number. The set of all points $\vec{X}$ in S such that $f(\vec{X}) = c$ is called a *level set* of f. (Geometric and physical problems dealing with level sets will be discussed later in this chapter.) For each of the following scalar fields, S is the whole space. Make a sketch to describe the level sets corresponding to the given values of c.

(a) $f(x, y) = x^2 + y^2,$ $c = 0, 1, 4, 9.$
(b) $f(x, y) = e^{xy},$ $c = e^{-2}, e^{-1}, 1, e, e^2, e^3.$
(c) $f(x, y) = \cos(x + y),$ $c = -1, 0, \frac{1}{2}, \frac{1}{2}\sqrt{2}, 1.$
(d) $f(x, y, z) = x + y + z,$ $c = -1, 0, 1.$
(e) $f(x, y, z) = x^2 + 2y^2 + 3z^2,$ $c = 0, 6, 12.$
(f) $f(x, y, z) = \sin(x^2 + y^2 + z^2),$ $c = -1, -\frac{1}{2}, 0, \frac{1}{2}\sqrt{2}, 1.$

2. In each of the following cases, let S be the set of all points (x, y) in the plane satisfying the given inequalities. Make a sketch showing the set S and explain, by a geometric argument, whether or not S is open.

(a) $x^2 + y^2 < 1$.

(b) $3x^2 + 2y^2 < 6$.

(c) $|x| < 1$ and $|y| < 1$.

(d) $x \geq 0$ and $y > 0$.

(e) $|x| \leq 1$ and $|y| \leq 1$.

(f) $x > 0$ and $y < 0$.

(g) $xy < 1$.

(h) $1 \leq x \leq 2$ and $3 < y < 4$.

(i) $1 < x < 2$ and $y > 0$.

(j) $x \geq y$.

(k) $x > y$.

(l) $y > x^2$ and $|x| < 2$.

(m) $(x^2 + y^2 - 1)(4 - x^2 - y^2) > 0$.

(n) $(2x - x^2 - y^2)(x^2 + y^2 - x) > 0$.

3. Solve Exercise 2 if S is the set of all points (x, y, z) in 3-space satisfying the following inequalities:

(a) $z^2 - x^2 - y^2 - 1 > 0$.

(b) $|x| < 1$, $|y| < 1$, and $|z| < 1$.

(c) $x + y + z < 1$.

(d) $|x| \leq 1$, $|y| < 1$, and $|z| < 1$.

(e) $x + y + z < 1$ and $x > 0$, $y > 0$, $z > 0$.

(f) $x^2 + 4y^2 + 4z^2 - 2x + 16y + 40z + 113 < 0$.

4. (a) If A is an open set in n-space and $x \, \& \, A$, show that the set $A - \{x\}$, obtained by removing the point x from A, is open.

(b) If A is an open interval on the real line and B is a closed subinterval of A, show that $A - B$ is open.

(c) If A and B are open intervals on the real line, show that $A \cup B$ and $A \cap B$ are open.

(d) If A is a closed interval on the real line, show that its complement (relative to the whole real line) is open.

5. Let E_n denote n-space. Prove the following properties of open sets in E_n:

(a) The empty set ϕ is open.

(b) E_n is open.

(c) The union of any collection of open sets is open.

(d) The intersection of a finite collection of open sets is open.

(e) Give an example to show that the intersection of an infinite collection of open sets is not necessarily open.

Let E_n denote n-space. A set S in E_n is called *closed* if its complement $E_n - S$ is open. The next three exercises discuss properties of closed sets.

6. In each of the following cases, let S be the set of all points (x, y) in E_2 satisfying the given conditions. Make a sketch showing the set S and give a geometric argument to explain whether S is open, closed, both open and closed, or neither open nor closed.

(a) $x^2 + y^2 \geq 0$.

(b) $x^2 + y^2 < 0$.

(c) $x^2 + y^2 \leq 1$.

(d) $1 < x^2 + y^2 < 2$.

(e) $1 \leq x^2 + y^2 \leq 2$.

(f) $1 < x^2 + y^2 \leq 2$.

(g) $1 \leq x \leq 2, 3 \leq y \leq 4$.

(h) $1 \leq x \leq 2, 3 \leq y < 4$.

(i) $y = x^2$.

(j) $y \geq x^2$.

(k) $y \geq x^2$ and $|x| < 2$.

(l) $y \geq x^2$ and $|x| \leq 2$.

7. (a) If A is a closed set in n-space and x is a point not in A, prove that $A \cup \{x\}$ is also closed.

(b) Prove that a closed interval $[a, b]$ on the real line is a closed set.

(c) If A and B are closed intervals on the real line, show that $A \cup B$ and $A \cap B$ are closed.

8. Prove the following properties of closed sets in E_n. You may use the results of Exercise 5. (Compare with Exercise 20 in Section 1.6.)

(a) The empty set ϕ is closed.

(b) E_n is closed.

(c) The intersection of any collection of closed sets is closed.

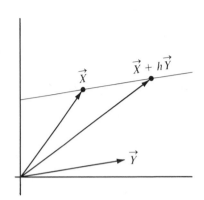
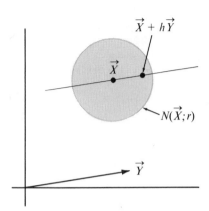

FIGURE 4.2   *The point $\vec{X} + h\vec{Y}$ lies on a line through $\vec{X}$ parallel to $\vec{Y}$.*   FIGURE 4.3   *The point $\vec{X} + h\vec{Y}$ lies in the neighborhood $N(\vec{X}; r)$ if $|h\vec{Y}| < r$.*

(d) The union of a finite number of closed sets is closed.

(e) Give an example to show that the union of an infinite collection of closed sets is not necessarily closed.

4.4   The derivative of a scalar field with respect to a vector

We turn now to the discussion of the derivative of a scalar field. In the course of this discussion we shall interpret many of the concepts geometrically by drawing pictures in 2-space or 3-space. Nevertheless, unless something is said to the contrary, all the definitions and theorems are applicable to higher dimensional spaces as well.

Suppose we have a scalar field f defined on an open set S. If $\vec{X}$ is a particular point of S we shall be interested in how the function changes as we move from $\vec{X}$ to a nearby point. In general, this change will depend on the direction in which we move away from $\vec{X}$. Suppose we specify this direction by means of another vector $\vec{Y}$. Then for each real number h the vector

$$\vec{X} + h\vec{Y}$$

lies on a line through $\vec{X}$ parallel to the vector $\vec{Y}$. An example in 2-space is shown in Figure 4.2. The distance from $\vec{X}$ to $\vec{X} + h\vec{Y}$ is $|h\vec{Y}| = |h|\,|\vec{Y}|$. Since the set S is open, there is a neighborhood of $\vec{X}$ of radius r, say, which lies within S. (See Figure 4.3.) This means that all points at a distance less than r from $\vec{X}$ lie in the set S. In particular, all points $\vec{X} + h\vec{Y}$ will be in S if h is chosen so that $|h|\,|\vec{Y}| < r$. If we keep $h \neq 0$ but small enough to guarantee that $\vec{X} + h\vec{Y} \; \varepsilon \; S$, we may form the difference quotient

$$\frac{f(\vec{X} + h\vec{Y}) - f(\vec{X})}{h}.$$

The numerator of this quotient tells us how much the function changes when we move from $\vec{X}$ to $\vec{X} + h\vec{Y}$. The quotient itself is called the *average rate of change* of f over the line segment joining $\vec{X}$ to $\vec{X} + h\vec{Y}$. We now study the behavior of this quotient as $h \to 0$. This leads us to the following definition:

DEFINITION OF THE DERIVATIVE OF A SCALAR FIELD WITH RESPECT TO A VECTOR. *Let f be a scalar field defined on an open set S in n-space. Let $\vec{X}$ be a point of S and let $\vec{Y}$ be an arbitrary vector in n-space. The derivative of f at the point $\vec{X}$ with respect to $\vec{Y}$ is denoted by the symbol $f'(\vec{X}; \vec{Y})$ and is defined by the equation*

$$f'(\vec{X}; \vec{Y}) = \lim_{h \to 0} \frac{f(\vec{X} + h\vec{Y}) - f(\vec{X})}{h}$$

when the limit on the right exists.

This definition includes, as a special case, the concept of a *partial derivative*. In particular, when $\vec{Y}$ is the kth unit coordinate vector $\vec{A}_k$ in n-space (all the components of $\vec{A}_k$ are zero except the kth, which has the value 1), the derivative $f'(\vec{X}; \vec{A}_k)$ is called the partial derivative with respect to $\vec{A}_k$, and is also denoted by the symbol $D_k f(\vec{X})$. If f is thought of as a function of n real variables, with $\vec{X} = (x_1, \ldots, x_n)$, we also use the following notations for the partial derivative $D_k f(\vec{X})$:

$$D_k f(x_1, \ldots, x_n), \quad \frac{\partial f(x_1, \ldots, x_n)}{\partial x_k}, \quad \text{and} \quad f'_{x_k}(x_1, \ldots, x_n).$$

In 2-space it is customary to write (x, y) instead of (x_1, x_2). The unit coordinate vectors are denoted by $\vec{i}$ and $\vec{j}$, and the partial derivatives $f'(\vec{X}; \vec{i})$ and $f'(\vec{X}; \vec{j})$ are written as

$$\frac{\partial f(x, y)}{\partial x} \quad \text{and} \quad \frac{\partial f(x, y)}{\partial y},$$

respectively. Similarly, in 3-space we write (x, y, z) instead of (x_1, x_2, x_3) and denote the partial derivatives $f'(\vec{X}; \vec{i}), f'(\vec{X}; \vec{j})$, and $f'(\vec{X}; \vec{k})$ by

$$\frac{\partial f(x, y, z)}{\partial x}, \frac{\partial f(x, y, z)}{\partial y}, \quad \text{and} \quad \frac{\partial f(x, y, z)}{\partial z}.$$

When $\vec{Y}$ is a *unit* vector, that is, when $|\vec{Y}| = 1$, the distance between the two points $\vec{X}$ and $\vec{X} + h\vec{Y}$ is $|h\vec{Y}| = |h|$. In this case the difference quotient $[f(\vec{X} + h\vec{Y}) - f(\vec{X})]/h$ represents the *average rate of change of f per unit distance* along the segment joining $\vec{X}$ to $\vec{X} + h\vec{Y}$, and the derivative $f'(\vec{X}; \vec{Y})$ is called the *directional derivative* of f at $\vec{X}$ in the direction of the vector $\vec{Y}$. The partial derivatives are merely the directional derivatives in the special directions of the unit coordinate vectors.

Example. Compute $f'(\vec{X}; \vec{Y})$ if $f(\vec{X}) = |\vec{X}|^2$.

Solution. We may write $f(\vec{X})$ as the dot product $\vec{X} \cdot \vec{X}$. From the algebraic properties of the dot product we have

$$f(\vec{X} + h\vec{Y}) - f(\vec{X}) = (\vec{X} + h\vec{Y}) \cdot (\vec{X} + h\vec{Y}) - \vec{X} \cdot \vec{X} = 2h\vec{X} \cdot \vec{Y} + h^2 \vec{Y} \cdot \vec{Y}.$$

Therefore, if $h \neq 0$ we have

$$\frac{f(\vec{X} + h\vec{Y}) - f(\vec{X})}{h} = 2\vec{X} \cdot \vec{Y} + h\vec{Y} \cdot \vec{Y}.$$

As $h \to 0$ the right member approaches the limit $2\vec{X} \cdot \vec{Y}$. Thus we see that the derivative $f'(\vec{X}; \vec{Y})$ exists and is given by the formula

$$f'(\vec{X}; \vec{Y}) = 2\vec{X} \cdot \vec{Y}.$$

Differentiation, when applied to a scalar field f, creates a new scalar field f' which is a function of two vectors $\vec{X}$ and $\vec{Y}$; the first vector $\vec{X}$ is a point in the open set S, and the second vector $\vec{Y}$ is an arbitrary point in n-space. A scalar field f is said to be *differentiable* on an open set S if the derivative $f'(\vec{X}; \vec{Y})$ exists for every point $\vec{X}$ in S and for every vector $\vec{Y}$. In the next few sections we shall extend some of the familiar properties of ordinary derivatives to differentiable scalar fields.

Most scalar fields that occur in practice are differentiable on some open set S. Also, for each fixed $\vec{Y}$, the derivative $f'(\vec{X}; \vec{Y})$ is a continuous function of $\vec{X}$. Continuity of scalar fields was defined in Chapter 2 for 2-space and 3-space. The extension to n-space may be stated as follows:

DEFINITION OF CONTINUITY OF A SCALAR FIELD. Let f be a scalar field defined at a point $\vec{A}$ in n-space. Assume that in every neighborhood of $\vec{A}$ there is at least one point different from $\vec{A}$ at which f is defined. The field f is said to be continuous at $\vec{A}$ if, for every $\epsilon > 0$, there exists a neighborhood $N(\vec{A})$ such that

$$|f(\vec{X}) - f(\vec{A})| < \epsilon$$

for every $\vec{X}$ in $N(\vec{A})$ at which f is defined.

Suppose now that f is differentiable on some open set S, and let $f'(\vec{A}; \vec{Y})$ be the derivative at $\vec{A}$ with respect to $\vec{Y}$. When we say that f' is continuous at $\vec{A}$ we mean that for the given vector $\vec{Y}$ and for every $\epsilon > 0$ there exists a neighborhood $N(\vec{A})$ such that

$$|f'(\vec{X}; \vec{Y}) - f'(\vec{A}; \vec{Y})| < \epsilon \qquad \text{whenever} \quad \vec{X} \, \varepsilon \, N(\vec{A}).$$

If this property holds for every point $\vec{A}$ in S and every vector $\vec{Y}$, the scalar field f is said to be *continuously differentiable* on S. Some theorems in the later sections use differentiability as part of their hypotheses, while others use *continuous* differentiability. The theorems of the second type require a stronger hypothesis than the existence of the derivative $f'(\vec{X}; \vec{Y})$; the added assumption of continuous differentiability enables us to carry through the proofs. It can be shown that a scalar field with continuous partial derivatives $D_1 f, \ldots, D_n f$ on an open set S is also continuously differentiable on S. (See Exercise 18 in Section 4.26.)

Continuity of scalar fields can also be defined in terms of limits.

DEFINITION OF THE LIMIT OF A SCALAR FIELD. Let $\vec{A}$ be a given point in n-space, and let f be a scalar field. Suppose every neighborhood of $\vec{A}$ contains at least one point different from $\vec{A}$ at which f is defined. (The function f may or may not be defined at the point $\vec{A}$ itself.) If L is a real number, the equation

(4.2) $$\lim_{\vec{X} \to \vec{A}} f(\vec{X}) = L$$

is defined to mean that, for every $\epsilon > 0$, there is a neighborhood $N(\vec{A})$ such that

$$|f(\vec{X}) - L| < \epsilon$$

for every point $\vec{X} \neq \vec{A}$ in $N(\vec{A})$ at which $f(\vec{X})$ is defined.

In 2-space we may write (x, y) for $\vec{X}$ and (a, b) for $\vec{A}$ and express Equation (4.2) as follows:

$$\lim_{(x,y)\to(a,b)} f(x, y) = L\,.$$

In 3-space we put $\vec{X} = (x, y, z)$ and $\vec{A} = (a, b, c)$ and write (4.2) in the form

$$\lim_{(x,y,z)\to(a,b,c)} f(x, y, z) = L\,.$$

To say that a scalar field is continuous at $\vec{A}$ means (in limit notation) that f is defined at $\vec{A}$ and that

$$\lim_{\vec{X}\to\vec{A}} f(\vec{X}) = f(\vec{A})\,.$$

The foregoing definitions of limit and continuity are straightforward generalizations of those in the one-dimensional case. Therefore it is not surprising that the usual theorems for dealing with limits and continuity of sums, products, and quotients also hold for scalar fields. The proofs are entirely analogous to those given in Volume I for the one-dimensional case and need not be discussed here.

There is an important difference between the one-dimensional case and more general scalar fields. In one-dimensional theory, existence of the derivative of a function f at a point x implies continuity of f at x. This is easily proved by choosing an $h \neq 0$ and writing

$$f(x + h) - f(x) = \frac{f(x + h) - f(x)}{h} \cdot h\,.$$

As $h \to 0$ the right side tends to the limit $f'(x) \cdot 0 = 0$ and hence $f(x + h) \to f(x)$. This shows that the existence of $f'(x)$ implies continuity of f at x. Suppose we apply the same argument to more general scalar fields. Assume the derivative $f'(\vec{A}; \vec{Y})$ exists for some vector $\vec{Y}$. Then if $h \neq 0$ we may write

$$f(\vec{A} + h\vec{Y}) - f(\vec{A}) = \frac{f(\vec{A} + h\vec{Y}) - f(\vec{A})}{h} \cdot h\,.$$

As $h \to 0$ the right side tends to the limit $f'(\vec{A}; \vec{Y}) \cdot 0 = 0$; hence the existence of $f'(\vec{A}; \vec{Y})$ for a given $\vec{Y}$ implies that

$$\lim_{h\to 0} f(\vec{A} + h\vec{Y}) = f(\vec{A})$$

for the same $\vec{Y}$. This means that $f(\vec{X}) \to f(\vec{A})$ as $\vec{X} \to \vec{A}$ *along a straight line through $\vec{A}$ having the same direction as $\vec{Y}$.* If $f'(\vec{A}; \vec{Y})$ exists for *every* vector $\vec{Y}$, then $f(\vec{X}) \to f(\vec{A})$ as $\vec{X} \to \vec{A}$ along any straight line through $\vec{A}$. This seems to suggest that f is continuous at $\vec{A}$. Surprisingly enough, this conclusion need not be true. A scalar field can have a directional derivative in *every* direction at some point and yet be discontinuous at that point. For example, consider the scalar field defined as follows:

$$f(x, y) = \begin{cases} \dfrac{xy^2}{x^2 + y^4} & \text{if } x \neq 0, \\ \\ 0 & \text{if } x = 0. \end{cases}$$

Let $\vec{Y} = a\vec{i} + b\vec{j}$ be any vector in 2-space with $a \neq 0$, and let $\vec{A} = \vec{0}$. If $h \neq 0$ we have

$$\frac{f(\vec{A} + h\vec{Y}) - f(\vec{A})}{h} = \frac{f(h\vec{Y}) - f(\vec{0})}{h} = \frac{f(ha, hb)}{h} = \frac{ab^2}{a^2 + h^2b^4}.$$

Letting $h \to 0$ we find $f'(\vec{0}; \vec{Y}) = b^2/a$. If $\vec{Y} = b\vec{j}$ we find, in a similar way, that $f'(\vec{0}; \vec{Y}) = 0$. Therefore the derivative $f'(\vec{0}; \vec{Y})$ exists for all directions $\vec{Y}$. Also, $f(\vec{X}) \to 0$ as $\vec{X} \to \vec{0}$ along any straight line through the origin. However, at each point of the parabola $x = y^2$ (except at the origin) the function f has the value $\frac{1}{2}$. Since such points exist arbitrarily close to the origin, and since $f(\vec{0}) = 0$, the function f cannot be continuous at $\vec{0}$. Later we shall prove that if a scalar field is *continuously differentiable* at a point $\vec{A}$, it is also continuous at $\vec{A}$. (See Theorem 4–6 in Section 4.9.)

Many of the exercises in the next section deal with properties of limits and continuity in the two-dimensional case. Special emphasis is placed on features that are not present in the one-dimensional case.

4.5 Exercises

1. A scalar field f is defined everywhere in n-space by the equation $f(\vec{X}) = |\vec{X}|^4$. Use the definition of derivative to compute $f'(\vec{X}; \vec{Y})$ for arbitrary vectors $\vec{X}$ and $\vec{Y}$.

2. For the scalar field in Exercise 1, find all points (x, y) in 2-space for which
   (a) $f'(2\vec{i} + 3\vec{j}; x\vec{i} + y\vec{j}) = 6$.
   (b) $f'(x\vec{i} + 3y\vec{j}; x\vec{i} - y\vec{j}) = 0$.

3. If $\lim\limits_{(x, y) \to (a, b)} f(x, y) = L$, and if the one-dimensional limits

$$\lim_{x \to a} f(x, y) \qquad \text{and} \qquad \lim_{y \to b} f(x, y)$$

both exist, prove that

$$\lim_{x \to a} [\lim_{y \to b} f(x, y)] = \lim_{y \to b} [\lim_{x \to a} f(x, y)] = L.$$

The two limits in this equation are called *iterated* limits; the exercise shows that the existence of the two-dimensional limit and of the two one-dimensional limits implies the existence and equality of the two iterated limits. (The converse is not always true. A counterexample is given in Exercise 5.)

4. Let $f(x, y) = (x - y)/(x + y)$ if $x + y \neq 0$. Show that

$$\lim_{x \to 0} [\lim_{y \to 0} f(x, y)] = 1 \qquad \text{but that} \qquad \lim_{y \to 0} [\lim_{x \to 0} f(x, y)] = -1.$$

Use this result along with Exercise 3 to deduce that $f(x, y)$ does not tend to a limit as $(x, y) \to (0, 0)$.

5. Let

$$f(x, y) = \frac{x^2y^2}{x^2y^2 + (x - y)^2} \qquad \text{whenever} \quad x^2y^2 + (x - y)^2 \neq 0.$$

Show that

$$\lim_{x \to 0} [\lim_{y \to 0} f(x, y)] = \lim_{y \to 0} [\lim_{x \to 0} f(x, y)] = 0$$

but that $f(x, y)$ does not tend to a limit as $(x, y) \to (0, 0)$. [*Hint.* Examine f on the line $y = x$.] This example shows that the converse of Exercise 3 is not always true.

6. Let

$$f(x, y) = \begin{cases} x \sin \dfrac{1}{y} & \text{if } y \neq 0, \\ 0 & \text{if } y = 0. \end{cases}$$

Show that $f(x, y) \to 0$ as $(x, y) \to (0, 0)$ but that

$$\lim_{y \to 0} [\lim_{x \to 0} f(x, y)] \neq \lim_{x \to 0} [\lim_{y \to 0} f(x, y)].$$

Explain why this does not contradict Exercise 3.

7. If $(x, y) \neq (0, 0)$, let $f(x, y) = (x^2 - y^2)/(x^2 + y^2)$. Find the limit of $f(x, y)$ as $(x, y) \to (0, 0)$ along the line $y = mx$. Is it possible to define $f(0, 0)$ so as to make f continuous at $(0, 0)$?

8. Let $f(x, y) = 0$ if $y \leq 0$ or if $y \geq x^2$ and let $f(x, y) = 1$ if $0 < y < x^2$. Show that $f(x, y) \to 0$ as $(x, y) \to (0, 0)$ along any straight line through the origin. Find a curve through the origin along which (except at the origin) $f(x, y)$ has the constant value 1. Is f continuous at the origin?

9. If $f(x, y) = [\sin(x^2 + y^2)]/(x^2 + y^2)$ when $(x, y) \neq (0, 0)$ how must $f(0, 0)$ be defined so as to make f continuous at the origin?

10. Let $f(x, y) = 2xy/(x^2 + y^2)$ if $(x, y) \neq (0, 0)$ and let $f(0, 0) = 0$. Show that:
    (a) For each fixed x, $f(x, y)$ is a continuous function of y.
    (b) For each fixed y, $f(x, y)$ is a continuous function of x.
    (c) f is not continuous at $(0, 0)$.
    (d) The partial derivatives $\partial f/\partial x$ and $\partial f/\partial y$ exist at $(0, 0)$ but are not continuous there. (This example shows that a function may possess partial derivatives at all points of a region, yet not be continuous everywhere in the region. This is in marked contrast to the case of a function of one variable, where the existence of a derivative at a point implies continuity at that point.)

11. In each of the following examples a scalar field f is defined by the given equation for all points (x, y) in the plane for which the expression on the right is defined. In each example determine the set of points (x, y) at which f is continuous, and compute the partial derivatives $\partial f/\partial x$ and $\partial f/\partial y$ whenever they exist. (To determine continuity of f you may use the theorem on continuity of composite functions mentioned in Section 2.11.)

    (a) $f(x, y) = x^4 + y^4 - 4x^2y^2$.
    (b) $f(x, y) = \log(x^2 + y^2)$.
    (c) $f(x, y) = \dfrac{1}{y} \cos x^2$.
    (d) $f(x, y) = \tan(x^2/y)$.
    (e) $f(x, y) = \arctan(y/x)$.
    (f) $f(x, y) = \arcsin \dfrac{x}{\sqrt{x^2 + y^2}}$.

    (g) $f(x, y) = \arctan \dfrac{x + y}{1 - xy}$.
    (h) $f(x, y) = \dfrac{x}{\sqrt{x^2 + y^2}}$.
    (i) $f(x, y) = x^{(y^2)}$.
    (j) $f(x, y) = \arccos \sqrt{x/y}$.

12. Let $v(r, t) = t^n e^{-r^2/(4t)}$. Find a value of the constant n such that v satisfies the following equation:

$$\frac{\partial v}{\partial t} = \frac{1}{r^2} \frac{\partial}{\partial r} \left(r^2 \frac{\partial v}{\partial r} \right).$$

13. Given $z = u(x, y) e^{ax+by}$ and $\partial^2 u/(\partial x \partial y) = 0$. Find values of the constants a and b such that

$$\frac{\partial^2 z}{\partial x \partial y} - \frac{\partial z}{\partial x} - \frac{\partial z}{\partial y} + z = 0.$$

14. Let f be a scalar field defined on an open set containing a point $\vec{A}$, and assume f is continuous at $\vec{A}$. If $f(\vec{A}) \neq 0$, prove that there is a neighborhood $N(\vec{A})$ in which f has the same sign as $f(\vec{A})$.

4.6　The mean-value theorem for scalar fields

This section extends the mean-value theorem of differential calculus to scalar fields defined on sets in n-space.

4–1　THEOREM. *Mean-value theorem.* Assume f is differentiable on an open set S in n-space. Let $\vec{X}$ be a point in S and let $\vec{Y}$ be a vector such that $\vec{X} + t\vec{Y} \in S$ whenever $0 \le t \le 1$. Then there exists a real number θ satisfying $0 < \theta < 1$ such that

(4.3)　　　　　　　$f(\vec{X} + \vec{Y}) - f(\vec{X}) = f'(\vec{Z}; \vec{Y})$,　　　where　$\vec{Z} = \vec{X} + \theta\vec{Y}$.

Note. As t runs through the interval $0 \le t \le 1$, the vector $\vec{X} + t\vec{Y}$ traces out the line segment joining $\vec{X}$ to $\vec{X} + \vec{Y}$. The assumption that this segment is in S is a restriction on the set S. Since $0 < \theta < 1$, the point $\vec{Z} = \vec{X} + \theta\vec{Y}$ is an interior point of the segment, as illustrated in Figure 4.4. Also, since S is open, S contains a neighborhood about $\vec{X}$ and one about $\vec{X} + \vec{Y}$. Therefore there is an $\alpha > 0$ such that the points $\vec{X} + t\vec{Y}$ are in S for all t satisfying $-\alpha \le t \le 1 + \alpha$. This means that the extended segment joining $\vec{X} - \alpha\vec{Y}$ to $\vec{X} + (1 + \alpha)\vec{Y}$ also lies in S.

Proof. We prove this theorem by reducing it to the one-dimensional case. For this purpose we keep $\vec{X}$ and $\vec{Y}$ fixed and introduce a new function g by means of the equation

$$g(t) = f(\vec{X} + t\vec{Y}) \qquad \text{if } -\alpha \le t \le 1 + \alpha,$$

where α is chosen so that $\vec{X} + t\vec{Y} \in S$ for all t in $(-\alpha, 1 + \alpha)$. Note that $g(1) = f(\vec{X} + \vec{Y})$ and $g(0) = f(\vec{X})$; hence the left side of Equation (4.3) is the difference $g(1) - g(0)$. We want to apply the ordinary mean-value theorem to g. To do this we need to know that g is continuous on $[0, 1]$ and that $g'(t)$ exists if $0 < t < 1$. In this case $g'(t)$ exists for all t in $(-\alpha, 1 + \alpha)$. In fact, if we take any t in $(-\alpha, 1 + \alpha)$ and then choose $h \ne 0$ such that $-\alpha \le t + h \le 1 + \alpha$, we have

$$\frac{g(t + h) - g(t)}{h} = \frac{f(\vec{X} + t\vec{Y} + h\vec{Y}) - f(\vec{X} + t\vec{Y})}{h}.$$

As $h \to 0$ the quotient on the right approaches $f'(\vec{X} + t\vec{Y}; \vec{Y})$; hence $g'(t)$ exists and is equal to $f'(\vec{X} + t\vec{Y}; \vec{Y})$. The mean-value theorem gives us

$$g(1) - g(0) = g'(\theta),$$

where $0 < \theta < 1$. If we replace $\vec{X} + \theta\vec{Y}$ by $\vec{Z}$, this equation reduces to Equation (4.3), and the proof is complete.

If we write $\vec{A}$ for $\vec{X}$ and $\vec{B}$ for $\vec{X} + \vec{Y}$, Equation (4.3) assumes a slightly different form:

(4.4)　　　　　　　　　$f(\vec{B}) - f(\vec{A}) = f'(\vec{Z}; \vec{B} - \vec{A})$,

where $\vec{Z}$ lies on the line segment joining $\vec{A}$ to $\vec{B}$. In this case we must assume that the segment joining $\vec{A}$ and $\vec{B}$ lies in the set S; in other words, that $t\vec{A} + (1 - t)\vec{B} \in S$ whenever $0 \le t \le 1$. If the set S has this property for *every* pair of points $\vec{A}$ and $\vec{B}$ in S, then

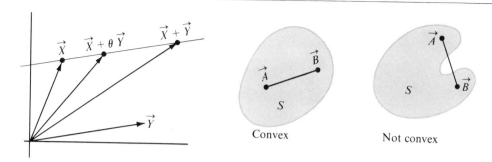

FIGURE 4.4 *The point $\vec{X} + \theta\vec{Y}$ lies on the segment joining $\vec{X}$ and $\vec{X} + \vec{Y}$.*   FIGURE 4.5 *In a convex set S, the segment joining $\vec{A}$ and $\vec{B}$ is in S for all points $\vec{A}$ and $\vec{B}$ in S.*

S is called *convex*. (See Figure 4.5.) For example, every neighborhood is a convex set. To prove this, let $S = N(\vec{C}; r)$ and choose two points $\vec{A}$ and $\vec{B}$ in S. Consider the point $\vec{X} = t\vec{A} + (1 - t)\vec{B}$, where $0 < t < 1$. Its distance from the center $\vec{C}$ is

$$|\vec{X} - \vec{C}| = |t\vec{A} + (1 - t)\vec{B} - \vec{C}| = |t(\vec{A} - \vec{C}) + (1 - t)(\vec{B} - \vec{C})|$$
$$\leq t|\vec{A} - \vec{C}| + (1 - t)|\vec{B} - \vec{C}| < tr + (1 - t)r = r.$$

Therefore $\vec{X} \varepsilon S$, so S is convex.

4.7 Exercises

1. Let f be the scalar field defined everywhere in 2-space by the equation $f(\vec{X}) = |\vec{X}|^2$.
   (a) If $\vec{X} = x_1\vec{i} + x_2\vec{j}$ and $\vec{Y} = y_1\vec{i} + y_2\vec{j}$, use the definition of $f'(\vec{X}; \vec{Y})$ to show that

   $$f'(\vec{X}; \vec{Y}) = 2x_1y_1 + 2x_2y_2.$$

   (b) Show that the point $\vec{Z}$ midway between $\vec{X}$ and $\vec{X} + \vec{Y}$ satisfies the equation

   $$f(\vec{X} + \vec{Y}) - f(\vec{X}) = f'(\vec{Z}; \vec{Y}).$$

   (c) Generalize parts (a) and (b) if $f(\vec{X}) = |\vec{X}|^2$ for every vector $\vec{X}$ in n-space.

2. (a) Assume f is differentiable on an open set S. Let $\vec{A}$ be a point in S and assume that $f'(\vec{X}; \vec{Y}) = 0$ for every $\vec{X}$ in some neighborhood $N(\vec{A})$ and for every vector $\vec{Y}$. Use the mean-value theorem to prove that f is constant on the neighborhood $N(\vec{A})$.

   (b) Suppose that $f'(\vec{X}; \vec{Y}) = 0$ for a *fixed* vector $\vec{Y}$ and for every $\vec{X}$ in some neighborhood $N(\vec{A})$. What can you conclude about f in this case?

3. If $f'(\vec{X}; \vec{Y}) = 0$ for every $\vec{X}$ in an open set S and for every vector $\vec{Y}$, it is not necessarily true that f is constant on S. Give an example to illustrate this statement. Then prove that f is constant on S when S is convex.

4. (a) Prove that there is no scalar field f such that $f'(\vec{X}; \vec{Y}) > 0$ for a fixed vector $\vec{X}$ and every nonzero vector $\vec{Y}$.

   (b) Give an example of a scalar field f such that $f'(\vec{X}; \vec{Y}) > 0$ for a fixed vector $\vec{Y}$ and every vector $\vec{X}$.

4.8   The linearity property of the derivative

In this section we prove that the derivative $f'(\vec{A}; \vec{Y})$ of a continuously differentiable scalar field f is a linear function of the second vector. That is, we have

(4.5) $$f'(\vec{A}; a\vec{Y} + b\vec{Z}) = a f'(\vec{A}; \vec{Y}) + b f'(\vec{A}; \vec{Z})$$

for all scalars a and b and all vectors $\vec{Y}$ and $\vec{Z}$. As a result of this property we can derive an important formula that enables us to express the derivative $f'(\vec{A}; \vec{Y})$ in terms of the partial derivatives of f. The special cases which appear in formulas (4.6) and (4.7) in the next two theorems suffice to prove the linearity property in Equation (4.5).

4– 2   THEOREM.   *Homogeneous property.* Assume the derivative $f'(\vec{A}; \vec{Y})$ exists. Then
          for every scalar c the derivative $f'(\vec{A}; c\vec{Y})$ also exists and we have

(4.6) $$f'(\vec{A}; c\vec{Y}) = c f'(\vec{A}; \vec{Y}).$$

Proof. When $c = 0$ both sides of (4.6) are zero because

$$f'(\vec{A}; \vec{0}) = \lim_{h \to 0} \frac{f(\vec{A}) - f(\vec{A})}{h} = 0;$$

in this case the theorem is clearly true. Assume, then, that $c \neq 0$ and consider the difference quotient

$$\frac{f(\vec{A} + hc\vec{Y}) - f(\vec{A})}{h} = c \frac{f(\vec{A} + hc\vec{Y}) - f(\vec{A})}{hc} = c \frac{f(\vec{A} + t\vec{Y}) - f(\vec{A})}{t},$$

where $t = hc$. Since $t \to 0$ as $h \to 0$, the last term on the right approaches $c f'(\vec{A}; \vec{Y})$ as $h \to 0$. Therefore the quotient on the extreme left also approaches $c f'(\vec{A}; \vec{Y})$. This proves that $f'(\vec{A}; c\vec{Y})$ exists and equals $c f'(\vec{A}; \vec{Y})$, as asserted.

4– 3   THEOREM.   *Additive property.* Assume f is a scalar field defined on an open set
          S. Let $\vec{A}$ be a point in S and let $\vec{Y}$ and $\vec{Z}$ be vectors such that both derivatives
          $f'(\vec{A}; \vec{Y})$ and $f'(\vec{A}; \vec{Z})$ exist. Assume also that $f'(\vec{X}; \vec{Z})$ exists for all $\vec{X}$ in some
          neighborhood $N(\vec{A}; r)$ and that, as a function of $\vec{X}$, $f'(\vec{X}; \vec{Z})$ is continuous at the
          point $\vec{X} = \vec{A}$. Then the derivative $f'(\vec{A}; \vec{Y} + \vec{Z})$ exists and is given by the sum

(4.7) $$f'(\vec{A}; \vec{Y} + \vec{Z}) = f'(\vec{A}; \vec{Y}) + f'(\vec{A}; \vec{Z}).$$

Proof. Choose $h \neq 0$ so that $|h(\vec{Y} + \vec{Z})| < r$ and $|h\vec{Y}| < r$. Then both $\vec{A} + h(\vec{Y} + \vec{Z})$ and $\vec{A} + h\vec{Y}$ are in the neighborhood $N(\vec{A}; r)$. We are interested in the behavior of the difference quotient

$$\frac{f(\vec{A} + h\vec{Y} + h\vec{Z}) - f(\vec{A})}{h}$$

as $h \to 0$. By adding and subtracting $f(\vec{A} + h\vec{Y})$, we may write the numerator of this quotient as a sum of two terms, namely:

$$f(\vec{A} + h\vec{Y} + h\vec{Z}) - f(\vec{A}) = [f(\vec{A} + h\vec{Y}) - f(\vec{A})] + [f(\vec{A} + h\vec{Y} + h\vec{Z}) - f(\vec{A} + h\vec{Y})].$$

Applying the mean-value theorem to the second term on the right we have†

$$f(\vec{A} + h\vec{Y} + h\vec{Z}) - f(\vec{A} + h\vec{Y}) = f'(\vec{A} + h\vec{Y} + \theta h\vec{Z}; h\vec{Z}),$$

where $0 < \theta < 1$. (The number θ depends on h.) Because of the homogeneous property derived in the foregoing theorem, the right member is equal to $h f'(\vec{A} + h\vec{Y} + \theta h\vec{Z}; \vec{Z})$. Therefore, dividing by h, we obtain

$$\frac{f(\vec{A} + h\vec{Y} + h\vec{Z}) - f(\vec{A})}{h} = \frac{f(\vec{A} + h\vec{Y}) - f(\vec{A})}{h} + f'(\vec{A} + h\vec{Y} + \theta h\vec{Z}; \vec{Z}).$$

Now we let $h \to 0$. The quotient on the right approaches $f'(\vec{A}; \vec{Y})$ as a limit. In the second term we have $0 < \theta < 1$ so $\theta h \to 0$ as $h \to 0$; hence, by the continuity of $f'(\vec{X}; \vec{Z})$ at $\vec{X} = \vec{A}$, this term approaches $f'(\vec{A}; \vec{Z})$ as a limit. Therefore the quotient on the left approaches $f'(\vec{A}; \vec{Y}) + f'(\vec{A}; \vec{Z})$, proving Equation (4.7).

By combining the additive property and the homogeneous property we obtain the linearity property shown in Equation (4.5). The linearity property may be extended by induction:

4- 4   THEOREM.   Assume f is continuously differentiable on some neighborhood of a point $\vec{X}$. Then for arbitrary vectors $\vec{Y}_1, \ldots, \vec{Y}_m$ and arbitrary scalars $a_1, \ldots, a_m$ we have

(4.8) $$f'\left(\vec{X}; \sum_{k=1}^{m} a_k \vec{Y}_k\right) = \sum_{k=1}^{m} a_k f'(\vec{X}; \vec{Y}_k).$$

An immediate corollary is the following theorem, which expresses the derivative $f'(\vec{X}; \vec{Y})$ as a linear combination of the partial derivatives of f.

4- 5   THEOREM.   Assume f is continuously differentiable on a neighborhood of $\vec{X}$, and let $\vec{Y} = (y_1, \ldots, y_n)$. Then we have

(4.9) $$f'(\vec{X}; \vec{Y}) = \sum_{k=1}^{n} y_k \, D_k f(\vec{X}).$$

Proof. We may express the vector $\vec{Y}$ as a sum, $\vec{Y} = y_1 \vec{A}_1 + \cdots + y_n \vec{A}_n$, where $\vec{A}_k$ denotes the kth unit coordinate vector (the kth component of $\vec{A}_k$ is 1 and the remaining components are zero). Applying (4.8) we have

$$f'(\vec{X}; \vec{Y}) = f'\left(\vec{X}; \sum_{k=1}^{n} y_k \vec{A}_k\right) = \sum_{k=1}^{n} y_k f'(\vec{X}; \vec{A}_k).$$

Since $f'(\vec{X}; \vec{A}_k)$ is the kth partial derivative $D_k f(\vec{X})$, this proves (4.9).

Note. The sum on the right of (4.9) may be expressed as the *dot product* of the vector $\vec{Y}$ with the vector

(4.10) $$(D_1 f(\vec{X}), \ldots, D_n f(\vec{X}))$$

whose components are the partial derivatives of f at $\vec{X}$. The vector in (4.10) is called the *gradient* of f at $\vec{X}$. It is of fundamental importance in the differential calculus of scalar fields; its principal properties are derived in the next section.

---

† The mean-value theorem is applicable because the neighborhood $N(\vec{A}; r)$ is convex.

4.9   The gradient of a scalar field

From a differentiable scalar field f we can always construct a vector field known as the gradient of f and defined as follows:

DEFINITION OF THE GRADIENT FIELD. Let f be a scalar field that is differentiable on an open set S in n-space. The gradient of f, denoted by ∇f, is a vector field whose value at an arbitrary point $\vec{X}$ in S is

$$\nabla f(\vec{X}) = (D_1 f(\vec{X}), \ldots, D_n f(\vec{X})).$$

Note. The notation grad f is also used instead of ∇f. The symbol ∇ is pronounced "del."

The gradient vector enables us to simplify many formulas in vector analysis. For example, Equation (4.9), which expresses the derivative $f'(\vec{X}; \vec{Y})$ as a linear combination of the partial derivatives of f, may be written as the dot product of $\nabla f(\vec{X})$ and $\vec{Y}$:

(4.11) $f'(\vec{X}; \vec{Y}) = \nabla f(\vec{X}) \cdot \vec{Y}.$

Also, Equation (4.4) in the mean-value theorem may now be written as

(4.12) $f(\vec{B}) - f(\vec{A}) = \nabla f(\vec{Z}) \cdot (\vec{B} - \vec{A}),$

where $\vec{Z}$ lies on the line segment joining $\vec{A}$ and $\vec{B}$. Expressed in this form, the mean-value theorem closely resembles the one-dimensional formulation, except that the gradient of f plays the role of the derivative.

As a consequence of (4.12) we can prove that every continuously differentiable scalar field is continuous. That is, we have

4–6   THEOREM.   Assume f is continuously differentiable on some neighborhood $N(\vec{A})$ of a point $\vec{A}$ in n-space. Then f is continuous at $\vec{A}$.

Proof. Let $\vec{X}$ be any point in $N(\vec{A})$, $\vec{X} \neq \vec{A}$. By the mean-value theorem, as expressed in (4.12), we have

$$f(\vec{X}) - f(\vec{A}) = \nabla f(\vec{Z}) \cdot (\vec{X} - \vec{A}),$$

where $\vec{Z} = \vec{A} + \theta(\vec{X} - \vec{A})$ for some θ satisfying $0 < \theta < 1$. By the Cauchy-Schwarz inequality for dot products† we have

(4.13) $| f(\vec{X}) - f(\vec{A})| \leq |\nabla f(\vec{Z})| \, |\vec{X} - \vec{A}|.$

In a moment, we shall prove that $\nabla f(\vec{Z}) \to \nabla f(\vec{A})$ as $\vec{X} \to \vec{A}$. Once we know this, we may let $\vec{X} \to \vec{A}$ in (4.13) and deduce that

$$\lim_{\vec{X} \to \vec{A}} f(\vec{X}) = f(\vec{A}).$$

This implies that f is continuous at $\vec{A}$.

We still need to prove that $\nabla f(\vec{Z}) \to \nabla f(\vec{A})$ as $\vec{X} \to \vec{A}$. This part of the proof uses the assumption that f is continuously differentiable. The kth component of $\nabla f(\vec{Z})$ is $D_k f(\vec{Z})$ $= f'(\vec{Z}; \vec{A}_k)$, where $\vec{A}_k$ is the kth unit coordinate vector. Since f is continuously differentiable and since $\vec{Z} \to \vec{A}$ as $\vec{X} \to \vec{A}$, it follows that $D_k f(\vec{Z}) \to D_k f(\vec{A})$ as $\vec{X} \to \vec{A}$. There-

† See Section 5.9 in Volume I.

fore $\nabla f(\vec{Z}) \rightarrow \nabla f(\vec{A})$, because limits of vector-valued functions are defined in terms of components. This completes the proof.

Note. In the course of the foregoing proof we have also shown that every continuously differentiable scalar field has continuous partial derivatives and hence also a continuous gradient.

In spaces of dimension not exceeding three, we may use the geometric interpretation of the dot product to write (4.11) as follows:

(4.14) $$f'(\vec{X}; \vec{Y}) = |\nabla f(\vec{X})| \, |\vec{Y}| \cos \theta \,,$$

where θ represents the angle between the two vectors $\vec{Y}$ and $\nabla f(\vec{X})$. When $\vec{Y}$ is a unit

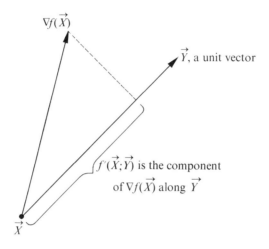

FIGURE 4.6 *Geometric interpretation of the directional derivative.*

vector, $f'(\vec{X}; \vec{Y})$ is the directional derivative of f at $\vec{X}$ in the direction of $\vec{Y}$. In this case $|\vec{Y}| = 1$ and Equation (4.14) becomes

$$f'(\vec{X}; \vec{Y}) = |\nabla f(\vec{X})| \cos \theta \,.$$

This shows that the directional derivative is simply the component of the gradient vector in the direction of $\vec{Y}$. Figure 4.6 shows the vectors $\nabla f(\vec{X})$ and $\vec{Y}$ attached to the point $\vec{X}$. The derivative is largest when $\cos \theta = 1$, that is, when $\vec{Y}$ has the same direction as $\nabla f(\vec{X})$. In other words, at a given point $\vec{X}$, the scalar field undergoes its maximum rate of change in the direction of the gradient vector; moreover, this maximum is equal to the length of the gradient vector. When $\nabla f(\vec{X})$ is perpendicular to $\vec{Y}$, the cosine of θ is zero and $f'(\vec{X}; \vec{Y}) = 0$.

In 2-space the gradient vector is usually written as

$$\nabla f(x, y) = \frac{\partial f(x, y)}{\partial x} \, \vec{i} + \frac{\partial f(x, y)}{\partial y} \, \vec{j} \,.$$

If a unit vector $\vec{Y}$ in the plane makes angles α and β with the positive x- and y-axes, respectively, we have $\vec{Y} = \cos \alpha \, \vec{i} + \cos \beta \, \vec{j}$ and the directional derivative is given by the formula

$$\nabla f(x, y) \cdot \vec{Y} = \frac{\partial f(x, y)}{\partial x} \cos \alpha + \frac{\partial f(x, y)}{\partial y} \cos \beta \,.$$

In 3-space the corresponding formulas are

$$\nabla f(x, y, z) = \frac{\partial f(x, y, z)}{\partial x} \vec{i} + \frac{\partial f(x, y, z)}{\partial y} \vec{j} + \frac{\partial f(x, y, z)}{\partial z} \vec{k}$$

and

$$\nabla f(x, y, z) \cdot \vec{Y} = \frac{\partial f(x, y, z)}{\partial x} \cos \alpha + \frac{\partial f(x, y, z)}{\partial y} \cos \beta + \frac{\partial f(x, y, z)}{\partial z} \cos \gamma \,,$$

where $\vec{Y} = \cos \alpha \, \vec{i} + \cos \beta \, \vec{j} + \cos \gamma \, \vec{k}$. The angles α, β, γ are the direction angles of $\vec{Y}$.

Sometimes it is convenient to think of the symbol ∇ as an "operator"† which converts a scalar field f into the vector field grad f. This operation is in many ways analogous to the operation of differentiation in elementary calculus. (Note the properties described in Exercise 7 of the next section.) For example, one property of the gradient is

$$\nabla(af + bg) = a \, \nabla f + b \, \nabla g \,,$$

where a and b are constants. This property is also shared by the ordinary derivative and many other operators. Any operator with this property is called a *linear operator*.

4.10   Exercises

1. Find the gradient vector at each point at which it exists for the scalar fields defined by the following equations:

(a) $f(x, y) = x^2 + y^2 \sin (xy)$.   (d) $f(x, y, z) = x^2 - y^2 + 2z^2$.
(b) $f(x, y) = e^x \cos y$.   (e) $f(x, y, z) = \log (x^2 + 2y^2 - 3z^2)$.
(c) $f(x, y, z) = x^2 y^3 z^4$.   (f) $f(x, y, z) = x^{y^z}$.

2. Evaluate the directional derivatives of the following scalar fields for the points and directions given:

(a) $f(x, y, z) = x^2 + 2y^2 + 3z^2$ at $(1, 1, 0)$ in the direction of $\vec{i} - \vec{j} + 2\vec{k}$.
(b) $f(x, y, z) = (x/y)^z$ at $(1, 1, 1)$ in the direction of $2\vec{i} + \vec{j} - \vec{k}$.

3. Find the points (x, y) and the directions for which the directional derivative of $f(x, y) = 3x^2 + y^2$ has its largest value, if (x, y) is restricted to be on the circle $x^2 + y^2 = 1$.

4. A scalar field f has, at the point $(1, 2)$, directional derivatives $+2$ in the direction toward $(2, 2)$ and -2 in the direction toward $(1, 1)$. Determine the gradient vector at $(1, 2)$ and compute the directional derivative in the direction toward $(4, 6)$.

---

† The word "operator" is used to denote a correspondence between two sets of functions. Therefore an operator is itself an example of a function. The domain of the gradient operator ∇ is the collection of all differentiable scalar fields; its range is the set of all vector fields that are gradients.

5. Find values of the constants a, b, and c such that the directional derivative of $f(x, y, z)$ $= axy^2 + byz + cz^2x^3$ at the point $(1, 2, -1)$ has a maximum value of 64 in a direction parallel to the z-axis.

6. Given a scalar field f which is continuously differentiable everywhere in 2-space. Suppose that at a point $\vec{X}$ we have $f'(\vec{X}; \vec{Y}) = 1$ and $f'(\vec{X}; \vec{Z}) = 2$, where $\vec{Y} = 2\,\vec{i} + 3\,\vec{j}$ and $\vec{Z} = \vec{i} + \vec{j}$. Make a sketch showing the set of all points (x, y) for which $f'(\vec{X}; x\,\vec{i} + y\,\vec{j}) = 6$. Also, find $\nabla f(\vec{X})$.

7. Let f and g denote scalar fields that are differentiable on a common open set S. Derive the following properties of the gradient:
    (a) grad $f = \vec{0}$ if f is constant on S.
    (b) grad $(f + g) = $ grad $f + $ grad g.
    (c) grad $(cf) = c$ grad f if c is a constant.
    (d) grad $(fg) = f$ grad $g + g$ grad f.
    (e) grad $\left(\dfrac{f}{g}\right) = \dfrac{g \text{ grad } f - f \text{ grad } g}{g^2}$ at points at which $g \neq 0$.

8. In 3-space, let $\vec{r}(x, y, z) = x\,\vec{i} + y\,\vec{j} + z\,\vec{k}$, and let $r(x, y, z) = |\vec{r}(x, y, z)|$.
    (a) Show that $\nabla r(x, y, z)$ is a unit vector in the direction of $\vec{r}(x, y, z)$.
    (b) Show that $\nabla(r^n) = nr^{n-2}\,\vec{r}$ if n is a positive integer. [*Hint.* Use Exercise 7(d).]
    (c) Is the formula of part (b) valid when n is a negative integer or zero?
    (d) Find a scalar field f such that $\nabla f = \vec{r}$.

9. Let f be continuously differentiable on an open set S in n-space. Let $\vec{A}$ be a point in S and assume that $f'(\vec{X}; \vec{Y}) = 0$ for n linearly independent vectors $\vec{Y}_1, \ldots, \vec{Y}_n$ and for every $\vec{X}$ in a neighborhood $N(\vec{A})$. Show that f is constant on the neighborhood $N(\vec{A})$.

10. Let f be continuously differentiable on an open set S in n-space and let $\vec{A}$ be a point in S.
    (a) If $\nabla f(\vec{X}) = \vec{0}$ for every $\vec{X}$ in some neighborhood $N(\vec{A})$, prove that f is constant on $N(\vec{A})$.
    (b) If $f(\vec{X}) \leq f(\vec{A})$ for all $\vec{X}$ in $N(\vec{A})$, prove that $\nabla f(\vec{A}) = \vec{0}$.

4.11 A chain rule for derivatives of scalar fields

In one-dimensional derivative theory, the chain rule enables us to compute the derivative of a composite function $g(t) = f[r(t)]$ by the formula

$$g'(t) = f'[r(t)] \cdot r'(t) \,.$$

This section provides an extension of the formula when f is replaced by a scalar field defined on a set in n-space and r is replaced by a vector-valued function of a real variable with values in the domain of f.

It is easy to conceive of examples in which the composition of a scalar field and a vector field might arise. For instance, suppose $f(\vec{X})$ measures the temperature at a point $\vec{X}$ of a solid in 3-space, and suppose we wish to know how the temperature changes as the point $\vec{X}$ moves along a curve C lying in the solid. If the curve is described by a vector-valued function $\vec{r}$ defined on an interval $[a, b]$, we may introduce a new function g by means of the formula

$$g(t) = f[\vec{r}(t)] \qquad \text{if} \quad a \leq t \leq b \,.$$

This composite function g expresses the temperature as a function of the parameter t, and its derivative $g'(t)$ measures the rate of change of the temperature along the curve. The following extension of the chain rule enables us to compute the derivative $g'(t)$ without determining $g(t)$ explicitly.

4–7   THEOREM.   Let f be a scalar field that is continuously differentiable on an open set S. Assume that $\vec{r}$ is a vector-valued function defined on an interval $[a, b]$ and that $\vec{r}(t) \in S$ whenever $a \leq t \leq b$. Define a new function g, the composition of f and $\vec{r}$, as follows:

$$g(t) = f[\vec{r}(t)] \qquad \text{if} \quad a \leq t \leq b.$$

Then at each point t at which $\vec{r}'(t)$ exists, the derivative $g'(t)$ also exists and is equal to the following dot product:

(4.15) $$g'(t) = \nabla f[\vec{r}(t)] \cdot \vec{r}'(t).$$

Proof. We begin by forming the difference quotient

(4.16) $$\frac{g(t + h) - g(t)}{h} = \frac{f[\vec{r}(t + h)] - f[\vec{r}(t)]}{h}.$$

Since S is open there is a neighborhood of $\vec{r}(t)$ that lies in S. We take $h \neq 0$ but small enough so that $\vec{r}(t + h)$ lies in this neighborhood. If we write $\vec{A}$ for $\vec{r}(t)$ and $\vec{B}$ for $\vec{r}(t + h)$, the numerator on the right of (4.16) is $f(\vec{B}) - f(\vec{A})$. Applying the mean-value theorem to this difference we have

$$f(\vec{B}) - f(\vec{A}) = \nabla f(\vec{Z}) \cdot (\vec{B} - \vec{A}),$$

where $\vec{Z} = \vec{A} + \theta(\vec{B} - \vec{A})$ for some θ satisfying $0 < \theta < 1$. Therefore the difference quotient in (4.16) may be written as

(4.17) $$\frac{g(t + h) - g(t)}{h} = \nabla f(\vec{Z}) \cdot \frac{\vec{r}(t + h) - \vec{r}(t)}{h}.$$

As $h \to 0$ the quotient on the right approaches $\vec{r}'(t)$; also $\vec{B} \to \vec{A}$, so $\vec{Z} \to \vec{A}$. Since f is continuously differentiable, ∇f is continuous, and hence $\nabla f(\vec{Z}) \to \nabla f(\vec{A}) = \nabla f[\vec{r}(t)]$. Therefore the right side of (4.17) approaches the limit $\nabla f[\vec{r}(t)] \cdot \vec{r}'(t)$. This proves that $g'(t)$ exists and is equal to the dot product in (4.15), as asserted.

Note. When the function $\vec{r}$ describes a curve C, the derivative $\vec{r}'$ is the velocity vector (tangent to the curve) and the derivative g' in Equation (4.15) is the derivative of f with respect to the velocity vector. If $\vec{T}(t)$ is a unit vector in the direction of $\vec{r}'(t)$ ($\vec{T}$ is the unit tangent vector), the dot product $\nabla f[\vec{r}(t)] \cdot \vec{T}(t)$ is called the directional derivative of f *along the curve C* or *in the direction of C*. For a plane curve we may write

$$\vec{T}(t) = \cos \alpha(t)\, \vec{i} + \cos \beta(t)\, \vec{j},$$

where $\alpha(t)$ and $\beta(t)$ are the angles made by the vector $\vec{T}(t)$ and the positive x- and y-axes; the directional derivative of f along C becomes

$$\nabla f[\vec{r}(t)] \cdot \vec{T}(t) = D_1 f[\vec{r}(t)] \cos \alpha(t) + D_2 f[\vec{r}(t)] \cos \beta(t).$$

This formula is often written more briefly as

$$\nabla f \cdot \vec{T} = \frac{\partial f}{\partial x} \cos \alpha + \frac{\partial f}{\partial y} \cos \beta.$$

(Some authors write df/ds for the directional derivative $\nabla f \cdot \vec{T}$.) Since the directional derivative along C is defined in terms of $\vec{T}$, its value depends on the parametric representation chosen for C. A change of the representation could reverse the direction of $\vec{T}$; this, in turn, would reverse the sign of the directional derivative.

Example 1. Find the directional derivative of the scalar field $f(x, y) = x^2 - 3xy$ along the parabola $y = x^2 - x + 2$ at the point $(1, 2)$.

Solution. At an arbitrary point (x, y) the gradient vector is

$$\nabla f(x, y) = \frac{\partial f}{\partial x} \vec{i} + \frac{\partial f}{\partial y} \vec{j} = (2x - 3y) \vec{i} - 3x\vec{j}.$$

At the point $(1, 2)$ we have $\nabla f(1, 2) = -4\vec{i} - 3\vec{j}$. The parabola may be represented parametrically by the vector equation $\vec{r}(t) = t\vec{i} + (t^2 - t + 2)\vec{j}$. Therefore, $\vec{r}(1) = \vec{i} + 2\vec{j}$, $\vec{r}'(t) = \vec{i} + (2t - 1)\vec{j}$, and $\vec{r}'(1) = \vec{i} + \vec{j}$. For this representation of C the unit tangent vector $\vec{T}(1)$ is $(\vec{i}+\vec{j})/\sqrt{2}$ and the required directional derivative is $\nabla f(1, 2) \cdot \vec{T}(1) = -7/\sqrt{2}$.

Example 2. Let f be a nonconstant scalar field, continuously differentiable everywhere in the plane, and let c be a constant. Assume the Cartesian equation $f(x, y) = c$ describes a curve C having a tangent at each of its points. Prove that f has the following properties at each point of C:
   (a) The gradient vector ∇f is normal to C.
   (b) The directional derivative of f is zero along C.
   (c) The directional derivative of f has its largest value in a direction normal to C.

Solution. If $\vec{T}$ is a unit tangent vector to C, the directional derivative of f along C is the dot product $\nabla f \cdot \vec{T}$. This product is zero if ∇f is perpendicular to $\vec{T}$, and it has its largest value if ∇f is parallel to $\vec{T}$. Therefore both statements (b) and (c) are consequences of (a). To prove (a), consider any plane curve Γ with a vector equation of the form $\vec{r}(t) = X(t) \vec{i} + Y(t) \vec{j}$ and introduce the function $\phi(t) = f[\vec{r}(t)]$. By the chain rule we have $\phi'(t) = \nabla f[\vec{r}(t)] \cdot \vec{r}'(t)$. When $\Gamma = C$, the function ϕ has the constant value c so $\phi'(t) = 0$ if $\vec{r}(t) \ \varepsilon \ C$. Since $\phi' = \nabla f \cdot \vec{r}'$, this shows that ∇f is perpendicular to $\vec{r}'$ on C; hence ∇f is normal to C.

For each c, the curve $f(x, y) = c$ is called a *level curve* of f; as we let c take on different values we obtain a whole family of level curves. Families of level curves occur in many physical applications. For example, if f represents temperature, the level curves of f (curves of constant temperature) are called *isothermals*. The flow of heat takes place in the direction of most rapid change in temperature. As we have just shown in Example 2, this direction is normal to the isothermals. Hence, in a thin flat sheet the flow of heat is along a family of curves orthogonal to the isothermals. These are called *lines of flow*; they are the orthogonal trajectories of the isothermals. Examples are shown in Figure 4.7. The three-dimensional analogs of level curves are the so-called *level surfaces*. These are discussed in the next section.

Example 3: A chain rule for vector-valued functions of a real variable. Let $\vec{F}$ be a vector field defined on an open set S in 2-space, say

$$\vec{F}(x, y) = P(x, y) \vec{i} + Q(x, y) \vec{j},$$

and assume the components P and Q are continuously differentiable on S. Let u and v be two real functions that are differentiable on an open interval (a, b), and assume that $(u(t), v(t)) \ \varepsilon \ S$ for each t in (a, b). Let $\vec{r}$ be the composite function defined on (a, b) by the equation

$$\vec{r}(t) = \vec{F}[u(t), v(t)].$$

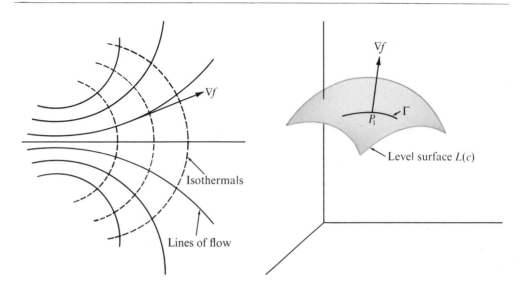

FIGURE 4.7 *The dotted curves are isothermals:*   FIGURE 4.8 *The gradient vector ∇f is normal to*
$f(x, y) = c$. The gradient vector ∇f points in the   *each curve Γ on the level surface $f(x, y, z) = c$.*
direction of the lines of flow.

Prove that

$$\vec{r}'(t) = D_1\vec{F}[u(t), v(t)]\, u'(t) + D_2\vec{F}[u(t), v(t)]\, v'(t)\,,$$

where $D_1\vec{F} = D_1P\,\vec{i} + D_1Q\,\vec{j}$ and $D_2\vec{F} = D_2P\,\vec{i} + D_2Q\,\vec{j}$.

Solution. Write $\vec{R}(t) = u(t)\,\vec{i} + v(t)\,\vec{j}$. Then we have

$$\vec{r}(t) = P[\vec{R}(t)]\,\vec{i} + Q[\vec{R}(t)]\,\vec{j}\,.$$

To compute the derivative $\vec{r}'(t)$ we apply the chain rule to each component of $\vec{r}(t)$ and we find

$$
\begin{aligned}
\vec{r}'(t) &= \nabla P[\vec{R}(t)] \cdot \vec{R}'(t)\,\vec{i} + \nabla Q[\vec{R}(t)] \cdot \vec{R}'(t)\,\vec{j} \\
&= \{D_1P[\vec{R}(t)]\,u'(t) + D_2P[\vec{R}(t)]\,v'(t)\}\,\vec{i} + \{D_1Q[\vec{R}(t)]\,u'(t) + D_2Q[\vec{R}(t)]\,v'(t)\}\,\vec{j} \\
&= \{D_1P[\vec{R}(t)]\,\vec{i} + D_1Q[\vec{R}(t)]\,\vec{j}\}\,u'(t) + \{D_2P[\vec{R}(t)]\,\vec{i} + D_2Q[\vec{R}(t)]\,\vec{j}\}\,v'(t) \\
&= D_1\vec{F}[\vec{R}(t)]\,u'(t) + D_2\vec{F}[\vec{R}(t)]\,v'(t)\,.
\end{aligned}
$$

This is equivalent to the required formula. The formula for $\vec{r}'(t)$ can also be written in the form

$$\vec{r}'(t) = \frac{\partial \vec{F}}{\partial x}\,u'(t) + \frac{\partial \vec{F}}{\partial y}\,v'(t)\,,$$

where the partial derivatives $\partial \vec{F}/\partial x$ and $\partial \vec{F}/\partial y$ are evaluated at $(u(t), v(t))$. It is clear that the formula can be extended in an obvious way to vector fields defined on open sets in *n*-space.

4.12 Applications to geometry

The chain rule may be used to give the gradient vector an important geometric interpretation. Suppose we have a continuously differentiable scalar field f defined on an open set S in n-space, and suppose we consider all those points $\vec{X}$ in S for which $f(\vec{X})$ has a constant value, say $f(\vec{X}) = c$. Denote this set by $L(c)$, so that

$$L(c) = \{\vec{X} \mid \vec{X} \; \varepsilon \; S \text{ and } f(\vec{X}) = c\} \,.$$

The set $L(c)$ is called a *level set* of f. We shall limit ourselves to the case in which the dimension n is 2 or 3. In 2-space, $L(c)$ is called a *level curve*; in 3-space, it is called a *level surface*.

As c takes on different values, $L(c)$ generates a whole family of level sets. For example, if $f(x, y) = x + y$, the level curves form a family of parallel straight lines, one for each real value of c. When $f(x, y, z) = x^2 + y^2 + z^2$ the level surfaces are spheres concentric with the origin. In this example only nonnegative values of c are of interest.

Consider a scalar field f defined in 3-space and examine one of its level surfaces, $L(c)$. Let $P_1 = (x_1, y_1, z_1)$ be a point on this surface, and consider a curve Γ which lies on the surface and passes through P_1, as suggested by Figure 4.8. We shall prove that the gradient vector $\nabla f(x_1, y_1, z_1)$ is *normal* to this curve at P_1. That is, we shall prove that ∇f is perpendicular to the tangent vector of Γ at P_1. For this purpose we assume that Γ is described parametrically by a vector-valued function $\vec{r}$, where

$$\vec{r}(t) = X(t) \, \vec{i} + Y(t) \, \vec{j} + Z(t) \, \vec{k}$$

for all t in an interval $[a, b]$. Since Γ lies on the level surface $L(c)$ the three functions X, Y, and Z are related by the equation

$$f[X(t), Y(t), Z(t)] = c$$

for all t in $[a, b]$. Now we introduce the composite function g defined as follows:

$$g(t) = f[X(t), Y(t), Z(t)] \qquad \text{if} \quad a \le t \le b \,.$$

By the chain rule we have

$$g'(t) = \nabla f[\vec{r}(t)] \cdot \vec{r}'(t) \,.$$

Since $g(t)$ is constant on $[a, b]$ we have $g'(t) = 0$ on (a, b). In particular, if the point P_1 corresponds to a value t_1 in (a, b), we have

$$\nabla f(x_1, y_1, z_1) \cdot \vec{r}'(t_1) = 0 \,.$$

This means that the gradient at P_1 is perpendicular to the tangent vector $\vec{r}'(t_1)$, as asserted.

Now we take a family of curves on the level surface $L(c)$, all passing through the point P_1. According to the foregoing discussion, the tangent vectors of all these curves are perpendicular to the gradient vector ∇f at P_1. If the gradient at P_1 is not the zero vector, these tangent vectors determine a plane, and the gradient is normal to this plane. (See Figure 4.9.) This particular plane is called the *tangent plane* of the surface $L(c)$ at the point P_1. We know from Section 5.12 of Volume I that the plane through (x_1, y_1, z_1) with normal vector $A\vec{i} + B\vec{j} + C\vec{k}$ has the Cartesian equation

(4.18) $$A(x - x_1) + B(y - y_1) + C(z - z_1) = 0 \,.$$

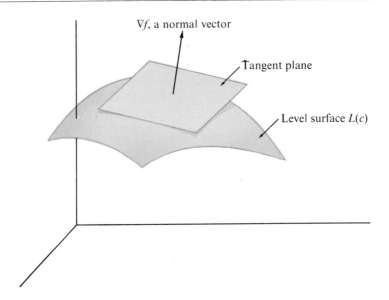

FIGURE 4.9   *The gradient vector ∇f is normal to the tangent plane of a level surface $f(x, y, z) = c$.*

In this case we may use the gradient vector $\nabla f(x_1, y_1, z_1)$ as a normal vector. Hence the coefficients A, B, and C are the components of the gradient, given by the formulas

$$A = D_1f(x_1, y_1, z_1)\,, \qquad B = D_2f(x_1, y_1, z_1)\,, \qquad C = D_3f(x_1, y_1, z_1)\,.$$

This discussion may be summarized by the following definition.

DEFINITION OF THE TANGENT PLANE TO A LEVEL SURFACE. Let f be continuously differentiable on an open set S in 3-space, and let $L(c)$ denote a level surface. Assume that at a point (x_1, y_1, z_1) on $L(c)$ there is a nonzero gradient vector $\nabla f(x_1, y_1, z_1) = A\vec{i} + B\vec{j} + C\vec{k}$. Then the plane with Cartesian equation (4.18) is called the tangent plane of the surface $L(c)$ at the point (x_1, y_1, z_1).

Note. We insist on *continuous* differentiability to ensure the continuity of the scalar field at each point at which a tangent plane exists. A given surface may be a level surface for more than one f, but all such f lead to the same tangent plane.

A similar discussion applies to scalar fields defined in 2-space. In Example 2 of Section 4.11 we proved that the gradient vector ∇f at a point $P_1 = (x_1, y_1)$ of a level curve is perpendicular to the tangent vector of the curve at P_1. Therefore the tangent line at P_1 of the level curve $L(c)$ has the Cartesian equation

$$A(x - x_1) + B(y - y_1) = 0\,,$$

where $A = D_1f(x_1, y_1)$ and $B = D_2f(x_1, y_1)$. These coefficients are, of course, the components of ∇f at P_1.

A scalar field f whose gradient is ∇f is sometimes called a *potential function* of the vector field ∇f. In the three-dimensional case the corresponding level surfaces are called *equipotential surfaces,* and in the two-dimensional case the level curves are called *equipotential lines.* (If f denotes temperature the word "equipotential" is replaced by "isothermal"; if f denotes pressure the word "isobaric" is used.)

An important example of a potential function is *Newton's gravitational potential.* This is a scalar field f defined everywhere in 3-space, except at the origin, by the equation

$$f(x, y, z) = \frac{mM}{r(x, y, z)},$$

where $r(x, y, z) = \sqrt{x^2 + y^2 + z^2}$. The constant m denotes the mass of a particle located at the origin, M denotes the mass of a particle located at (x, y, z), and $r(x, y, z)$ denotes the distance between the two particles. Newton's law of universal gravitation states that the force $\vec{F}(x, y, z)$ which the particle of mass m exerts on that of mass M is a vector of length $mM/r^2(x, y, z)$ having the direction of the vector from (x, y, z) to $(0, 0, 0)$. Since $-\vec{r}(x, y, z)/r(x, y, z)$ is a unit vector in this direction, where $\vec{r}(x, y, z) = x\,\vec{i} + y\,\vec{j} + z\,\vec{k}$, we may write

$$\vec{F}(x, y, z) = -\frac{mM}{r^3(x, y, z)}\,\vec{r}(x, y, z).$$

For any integer n we have $\nabla(r^n) = nr^{n-2}\vec{r}$ (see Exercise 8 of Section 4.10) and hence $\nabla f = \nabla(mMr^{-1}) = -mMr^{-3}\vec{r} = \vec{F}$. Thus we see that *the gravitational force $\vec{F}$ is the gradient of the Newtonian potential.* When we study line integration in Chapter 5 we shall prove that $f(x_1, y_1, z_1) - f(x_2, y_2, z_2)$ represents the amount of work done against the force field $\vec{F}$ in moving a particle from a point (x_1, y_1, z_1) to a point (x_2, y_2, z_2). The equipotential surfaces in this case are concentric spheres centered at the origin. Since f is constant on these spheres, no work is required to move a particle from one point to another on such a sphere (assuming, of course, that no other forces are present).

4.13 Exercises

1. In each case, evaluate the directional derivative of f for the points and directions specified:

(a) $f(x, y, z) = 3x - 5y + 2z$ at $(2, 2, 1,)$ in the direction of the outward normal to the sphere $x^2 + y^2 + z^2 = 9$.

(b) $f(x, y, z) = x^2 - y^2$ at a general point of the surface $x^2 + y^2 + z^2 = 4$ in the direction of the outward normal at that point.

(c) $f(x, y, z) = x^2 + y^2 - z^2$ at $(3, 4, 5)$ along the curve of intersection of the two surfaces $2x^2 + 2y^2 - z^2 = 25$ and $x^2 + y^2 = z^2$.

2. (a) Find a vector $\vec{V}(x, y, z)$ normal to the surface

$$z = \sqrt{x^2 + y^2} + (x^2 + y^2)^{3/2}$$

at a general point (x, y, z) of the surface, $(x, y, z) \neq (0, 0, 0)$.

(b) Find the cosine of the angle θ between $\vec{V}(x, y, z)$ and the z-axis and determine the limit of $\cos \theta$ as $(x, y, z) \to (0, 0, 0)$.

3. The two equations $e^u \cos v = x$ and $e^u \sin v = y$ define u and v as functions of x and y, say $u = U(x, y)$ and $v = V(x, y)$. Find explicit formulas for $U(x, y)$ and $V(x, y)$, valid for $x > 0$, and show that the gradient vectors $\nabla U(x, y)$ and $\nabla V(x, y)$ are perpendicular at each point (x, y).

4. Let $f(x, y) = \sqrt{|xy|}$.

(a) Verify that $\partial f/\partial x$ and $\partial f/\partial y$ are both zero at the origin.

(b) Does the surface $z = f(x, y)$ have a tangent plane at the origin? [*Hint.* Consider the section of the surface made by the plane $x = y$.]

5. If (x_0, y_0, z_0) is a point on the surface $z = xy$, then the two lines $z = y_0 x$, $y = y_0$ and $z = x_0 y$, $x = x_0$ intersect at (x_0, y_0, z_0) and lie on the surface. Verify that the tangent plane to this surface at the point (x_0, y_0, z_0) contains these two lines.

6. Find a Cartesian equation for the tangent plane to the surface $xyz = a^3$ at a general point (x_0, y_0, z_0). Show that the volume of the tetrahedron bounded by this plane and the three coordinate planes is $9a^3/2$.

7. Find a pair of linear Cartesian equations for the line which is tangent to both the surfaces $x^2 + y^2 + 2z^2 = 4$ and $z = e^{x-y}$ at the point $(1, 1, 1)$.

8. Find a constant c such that at any point of intersection of the two spheres

$$(x - c)^2 + y^2 + z^2 = 3 \quad \text{and} \quad x^2 + (y - 1)^2 + z^2 = 1$$

the corresponding tangent planes will be perpendicular to each other.

9. If r_1 and r_2 denote the distances from a point (x, y) on an ellipse to its foci, show that the equation $r_1 + r_2 = $ constant (satisfied by these distances) implies the relation

$$\vec{T} \cdot \nabla(r_1 + r_2) = 0 \,,$$

where $\vec{T}$ is the unit tangent to the curve. Interpret this result geometrically, thereby showing that the tangent makes equal angles with the lines joining (x, y) to the foci.

10. If $\nabla f(x, y, z)$ is always parallel to $x\vec{i} + y\vec{j} + z\vec{k}$, show that f must assume equal values at the points $(0, 0, a)$ and $(0, 0, -a)$.

11. In this exercise you may assume the existence and continuity of all derivatives under consideration. The equations $u = f(x, y)$, $x = X(t)$, $y = Y(t)$ define u as a function of t, say $u = F(t)$.

(a) Use an appropriate form of the chain rule to show that

$$F'(t) = \frac{\partial f}{\partial x} X'(t) + \frac{\partial f}{\partial y} Y'(t) \,,$$

where $\partial f/\partial x$ and $\partial f/\partial y$ are to be evaluated at $[X(t), Y(t)]$.

(b) In a similar way, express the second derivative $F''(t)$ in terms of derivatives of f, X, and Y. Remember that the partial derivatives in the formula of part (a) are composite functions given by

$$\frac{\partial f}{\partial x} = D_1 f[X(t), Y(t)] \,, \qquad \frac{\partial f}{\partial y} = D_2 f[X(t), Y(t)] \,.$$

12. Refer to Exercise 11 and compute $F'(t)$ and $F''(t)$ in terms of t for each of the following special cases:

(a) $f(x, y) = x^2 + y^2$, $X(t) = t$, $Y(t) = t^2$.
(b) $f(x, y) = e^{xy} \cos (xy^2)$, $X(t) = \cos t$, $Y(t) = \sin t$.
(c) $f(x, y) = \log[(1 + e^{x^2})/(1 + e^{y^2})]$, $X(t) = e^t$, $Y(t) = e^{-t}$.

13. Let f be a scalar field that is continuously differentiable on an open set S in n-space. We say that f is *homogeneous of degree p* over S if

$$f(t\vec{X}) = t^p f(\vec{X})$$

for every real t and for every $\vec{X}$ in S for which $t\vec{X} \in S$. For a homogeneous scalar field f of degree p show that we have

$$\vec{X} \cdot \nabla f(\vec{X}) = p f(\vec{X}) \qquad \text{for each} \quad \vec{X} \text{ in } S \,.$$

If $\vec{X} = (x_1, \ldots, x_n)$ this formula may also be expressed as

$$x_1 \frac{\partial f}{\partial x_1} + \cdots + x_n \frac{\partial f}{\partial x_n} = p f(x_1, \ldots, x_n) \,.$$

This is known as *Euler's theorem* for homogeneous functions. [*Hint.* For fixed $\vec{X}$ define $g(t) = f(t\vec{X})$ and compute $g'(1)$.]

14. Prove the converse of Euler's theorem. That is, show that if $\vec{X} \cdot \nabla f(\vec{X}) = p\, f(\vec{X})$ for all $\vec{X}$ in an open set S, f must be homogeneous of degree p over S. [*Hint.* For fixed $\vec{X}$ define $g(t) = f(t\vec{X}) - t^p f(\vec{X})$ and compute $g'(t)$.]

4.14 The generalized chain rule for scalar fields

Theorem 4–7 provides a chain rule for differentiating the composition of a scalar field f with a vector-valued function $\vec{r}$ of one real variable. A more general chain rule exists in which the function $\vec{r}$ is replaced by a more general vector field $\vec{U}$. The composition of a scalar field f with a vector field $\vec{U}$ gives rise to a new scalar field ϕ, where

$$\phi(\vec{T}) = f[\vec{U}(\vec{T})] \,.$$

For this equation to be meaningful, $\vec{T}$ must be a point at which $\vec{U}$ is defined and $\vec{U}(\vec{T})$ must be a point at which f is defined. The generalized chain rule provides a formula for computing the derivative $\phi'(\vec{T}; \vec{Y})$ in terms of derivatives of f and $\vec{U}$. This formula is analogous to (4.15) and expresses the derivative $\phi'(\vec{T}; \vec{Y})$ as the following dot product:

$$\phi'(\vec{T}; \vec{Y}) = \nabla f[\vec{U}(\vec{T})] \cdot \vec{U}'(\vec{T}; \vec{Y}) \,,$$

where $\vec{U}'$ is the derivative of the vector field $\vec{U}$, defined by the equation

$$\vec{U}'(\vec{T}; \vec{Y}) = \lim_{h \to 0} \frac{1}{h} [\vec{U}(\vec{T} + h\vec{Y}) - \vec{U}(\vec{T})] \,.$$

Notice that this definition is entirely analogous to that for a derivative of a scalar field. The limit process produces a new vector field $\vec{U}'$ from the given vector field $\vec{U}$. As in the case of scalar fields, the vector field $\vec{U}$ is said to be differentiable on an open set Q in m-space if $\vec{U}'(\vec{T}; \vec{Y})$ exists for each $\vec{T}$ in Q and each $\vec{Y}$ in m-space.

The exact formulation of the generalized chain rule may now be stated as follows:

4– 8   THEOREM. *Generalized chain rule.* Let f be a scalar field that is continuously differentiable on an open set S in n-space. Let $\vec{U}$ be a vector field that is differentiable on an open set Q in m-space and assume that $\vec{U}(\vec{T}) \,\varepsilon\, S$ whenever $\vec{T} \,\varepsilon\, Q$. Define a new scalar field, the composition ϕ of f and $\vec{U}$, as follows:

$$\phi(\vec{T}) = f[\vec{U}(\vec{T})] \qquad \text{whenever} \quad \vec{T} \,\varepsilon\, Q \,.$$

Then ϕ is differentiable on Q and the derivative $\phi'(\vec{T}; \vec{Y})$ is given by the dot product

(4.19) $$\phi'(\vec{T}; \vec{Y}) = \nabla f[\vec{U}(\vec{T})] \cdot \vec{U}'(\vec{T}; \vec{Y}) \,.$$

Note. The gradient ∇f and the derivative $\vec{U}'$ are n-dimensional vectors. The vectors $\vec{T}$ and $\vec{Y}$ are m-dimensional. The dimensions m and n may or may not be equal.

Proof. We must examine the difference quotient

(4.20) $$\frac{\phi(\vec{T} + h\vec{Y}) - \phi(\vec{T})}{h} = \frac{f[\vec{U}(\vec{T} + h\vec{Y})] - f[\vec{U}(\vec{T})]}{h} \,.$$

Since S is open there is a neighborhood of $\vec{U}(\vec{T})$ that lies in S. We take $h \neq 0$ but small enough to make sure that $\vec{U}(\vec{T} + h\vec{Y})$ is in this neighborhood. The numerator on the right of (4.20) may be written as $f(\vec{B}) - f(\vec{A})$, where $\vec{A} = \vec{U}(\vec{T})$ and $\vec{B} = \vec{U}(\vec{T} + h\vec{Y})$. By the mean-value theorem we have

$$f(\vec{B}) - f(\vec{A}) = \nabla f(\vec{Z}) \cdot (\vec{B} - \vec{A}),$$

where $\vec{Z} = \vec{A} + \theta(\vec{B} - \vec{A})$ for some θ satisfying $0 < \theta < 1$. Substituting in (4.20) we obtain

(4.21) $$\frac{\phi(\vec{T} + h\vec{Y}) - \phi(\vec{T})}{h} = \nabla f(\vec{Z}) \cdot \frac{\vec{U}(\vec{T} + h\vec{Y}) - \vec{U}(\vec{T})}{h}.$$

As $h \to 0$, the vector $\vec{Z}$ approaches $\vec{A} = \vec{U}(\vec{T})$ and the quotient multiplying $\nabla f(\vec{Z})$ approaches $\vec{U}'(\vec{T}; \vec{Y})$. Therefore the right-hand side of (4.21) approaches the dot product $\nabla f[\vec{U}(\vec{T})] \cdot \vec{U}'(\vec{T}; \vec{Y})$. This completes the proof.

———————

Next we deduce a number of special cases of the chain rule. These are obtained by expressing the vectors in terms of their components. First, if we introduce the unit co-ordinate vectors $\vec{A}_1, \ldots, \vec{A}_n$ (where all the components of $\vec{A}_k$ are 0 except the kth, which is 1) we may write

$$\vec{U}(\vec{T}) = u_1(\vec{T})\,\vec{A}_1 + u_2(\vec{T})\,\vec{A}_2 + \cdots + u_n(\vec{T})\,\vec{A}_n.$$

This equation defines n scalar fields $u_1, u_2, \ldots, u_n$ (called the components of $\vec{U}$) and the existence of the derivative $\vec{U}'(\vec{T}; \vec{Y})$ implies the existence of each of the derivatives $u_k'(\vec{T}; \vec{Y})$. Moreover, we have

$$\vec{U}'(\vec{T}; \vec{Y}) = \sum_{k=1}^{n} u_k'(\vec{T}; \vec{Y})\,\vec{A}_k.$$

We may also express the gradient ∇f in terms of the unit coordinate vectors $\vec{A}_1, \ldots, \vec{A}_n$, using the partial derivatives $D_k f$ as components. Thus, we have

$$\nabla f[\vec{U}(\vec{T})] = \sum_{k=1}^{n} D_k f[\vec{U}(\vec{T})]\,\vec{A}_k.$$

If we dot multiply these two sums, formula (4.19) of the chain rule becomes

(4.22) $$\phi'(\vec{T}; \vec{Y}) = \sum_{k=1}^{n} D_k f[\vec{U}(\vec{T})]\,u_k'(\vec{T}; \vec{Y}).$$

In particular, when $\vec{Y}$ is the ith unit coordinate vector in m-space, the derivatives $\phi'(\vec{T}; \vec{Y})$ and $u_k'(\vec{T}; \vec{Y})$ become the partial derivatives $D_i\phi(\vec{T})$ and $D_i u_k(\vec{T})$, respectively, and formula (4.22) may be written as follows:

(4.23) $$D_i\phi(\vec{T}) = \sum_{k=1}^{n} D_k f[\vec{U}(\vec{T})]\,D_i u_k(\vec{T}) \qquad \text{for each} \quad i = 1, 2, \ldots, m.$$

This is the form in which the generalized chain rule is usually stated. As i takes on the values $1, 2, \ldots, m$, Equation (4.23) yields m formulas for the partial derivatives $D_1\phi(\vec{T})$, $\ldots, D_m\phi(\vec{T})$. The collection of these m formulas is often referred to as the chain rule for partial derivatives.

Formula (4.23) is often written with a change in notation. We put $\vec{T} = (t_1, \ldots, t_m)$ and $\vec{X} = \vec{U}(\vec{T})$. Then we write $\vec{X} = (x_1, \ldots, x_n)$, where each component x_k is related to $\vec{T}$ by the equation $x_k = u_k(\vec{T})$. Formula (4.23) then becomes

$$(4.24) \qquad \frac{\partial \phi}{\partial t_i} = \frac{\partial f}{\partial x_1}\frac{\partial u_1}{\partial t_i} + \cdots + \frac{\partial f}{\partial x_n}\frac{\partial u_n}{\partial t_i} \qquad (i = 1, 2, \ldots, m),$$

where $\partial f/\partial x_k$ stands for the partial derivative $D_k f$, to be evaluated at the point $\vec{X} = \vec{U}(\vec{T})$, and $\partial u_k/\partial t_i$ stands for the partial derivative $D_i u_k$, to be evaluated at the point $\vec{T}$. The symbol $\partial \phi/\partial t_i$ on the left represents the partial derivative $D_i \phi$, to be evaluated at $\vec{T}$.

Example 1. The temperature of a thin plate is described by a scalar field f, the temperature at (x, y) being $f(x, y)$. Polar coordinates $x = r \cos \theta$, $y = r \sin \theta$ are introduced, and the temperature becomes a function of r and θ determined by the equation

$$\phi(r, \theta) = f(r \cos \theta, r \sin \theta) .$$

Express the partial derivatives $\partial \phi/\partial r$ and $\partial \phi/\partial \theta$ in terms of the partial derivatives $\partial f/\partial x$ and $\partial f/\partial y$.

Solution. The function ϕ is the composition of f with the vector field $\vec{U}(r, \theta) = u_1(r, \theta)\vec{i} + u_2(r, \theta)\vec{j}$, where

$$(4.25) \qquad u_1(r, \theta) = r \cos \theta \qquad \text{and} \qquad u_2(r, \theta) = r \sin \theta .$$

We use the chain rule, as expressed in Equation (4.24), with $m = n = 2$. We replace (x_1, x_2) by (x, y), and (t_1, t_2) by (r, θ), and obtain

$$(4.26) \qquad \frac{\partial \phi}{\partial r} = \frac{\partial f}{\partial x}\frac{\partial u_1}{\partial r} + \frac{\partial f}{\partial y}\frac{\partial u_2}{\partial r} , \qquad \frac{\partial \phi}{\partial \theta} = \frac{\partial f}{\partial x}\frac{\partial u_1}{\partial \theta} + \frac{\partial f}{\partial y}\frac{\partial u_2}{\partial \theta} .$$

Differentiating the functions u_1 and u_2 in (4.25) we get

$$(4.27) \qquad \frac{\partial u_1}{\partial r} = \cos \theta , \qquad \frac{\partial u_2}{\partial r} = \sin \theta , \qquad \frac{\partial u_1}{\partial \theta} = -r \sin \theta , \qquad \frac{\partial u_2}{\partial \theta} = r \cos \theta .$$

Substituting these formulas in (4.26) we find

$$(4.28) \qquad \frac{\partial \phi}{\partial r} = \frac{\partial f}{\partial x}\cos \theta + \frac{\partial f}{\partial y}\sin \theta , \qquad \frac{\partial \phi}{\partial \theta} = -r\frac{\partial f}{\partial x}\sin \theta + r\frac{\partial f}{\partial y}\cos \theta .$$

These are the required formulas for $\partial \phi/\partial r$ and $\partial \phi/\partial \theta$.

Note that the functions u_1 and u_2 do not appear in the final result. They were introduced merely to help us apply the chain rule properly. With a little practice, one may avoid the introduction of u_1 and u_2 and perform some of the steps mentally. To do this we write the equations in (4.26) as follows:

$$(4.29) \qquad \frac{\partial \phi}{\partial r} = \frac{\partial f}{\partial x}\frac{\partial x}{\partial r} + \frac{\partial f}{\partial y}\frac{\partial y}{\partial r} , \qquad \frac{\partial \phi}{\partial \theta} = \frac{\partial f}{\partial x}\frac{\partial x}{\partial \theta} + \frac{\partial f}{\partial y}\frac{\partial y}{\partial \theta} ,$$

where $\partial x/\partial r$, $\partial y/\partial r$, $\partial x/\partial \theta$, $\partial y/\partial \theta$ have been written for the partial derivatives $\partial u_1/\partial r$, $\partial u_2/\partial r$, $\partial u_1/\partial \theta$, $\partial u_2/\partial \theta$, respectively. Here we must keep in mind that in the derivatives

$\partial x/\partial r$, $\partial y/\partial r$, etc., x stands for $r \cos \theta$ and y stands for $r \sin \theta$. The equations in (4.27) now become

$$\frac{\partial x}{\partial r} = \cos \theta , \qquad \frac{\partial y}{\partial r} = \sin \theta , \qquad \frac{\partial x}{\partial \theta} = -r \sin \theta , \qquad \frac{\partial y}{\partial \theta} = r \cos \theta .$$

When these are substituted in (4.29) we obtain (4.28).

Example 2. Refer to Example 1 and express the second-order partial derivative $\partial^2 \phi/\partial \theta^2$ in terms of partial derivatives of f.

Solution. We begin with the formula for $\partial \phi/\partial \theta$ in (4.28) and differentiate with respect to θ, treating r as a constant. There are two terms on the right, each of which must be differentiated as a product. Thus we have

(4.30)
$$\frac{\partial^2 \phi}{\partial \theta^2} = -r \frac{\partial f}{\partial x} \frac{\partial (\sin \theta)}{\partial \theta} - r \sin \theta \frac{\partial}{\partial \theta} \left(\frac{\partial f}{\partial x} \right) + r \frac{\partial f}{\partial y} \frac{\partial (\cos \theta)}{\partial \theta} + r \cos \theta \frac{\partial}{\partial \theta} \left(\frac{\partial f}{\partial y} \right)$$

$$= -r \cos \theta \frac{\partial f}{\partial x} - r \sin \theta \frac{\partial}{\partial \theta} \left(\frac{\partial f}{\partial x} \right) - r \sin \theta \frac{\partial f}{\partial y} + r \cos \theta \frac{\partial}{\partial \theta} \left(\frac{\partial f}{\partial y} \right) .$$

To compute the derivatives of $\partial f/\partial x$ and $\partial f/\partial y$ with respect to θ we must keep in mind that, as functions of r and θ, $\partial f/\partial x$ and $\partial f/\partial y$ are *composite functions* given by

$$\frac{\partial f}{\partial x} = D_1 f(r \cos \theta, r \sin \theta) \qquad \text{and} \qquad \frac{\partial f}{\partial y} = D_2 f(r \cos \theta, r \sin \theta) .$$

Therefore, their derivatives with respect to θ must be determined by use of the chain rule. This gives us

$$\frac{\partial}{\partial \theta} \left(\frac{\partial f}{\partial x} \right) = \frac{\partial (D_1 f)}{\partial x} \frac{\partial x}{\partial \theta} + \frac{\partial (D_1 f)}{\partial y} \frac{\partial y}{\partial \theta} = \frac{\partial^2 f}{\partial x^2} (-r \sin \theta) + \frac{\partial^2 f}{\partial y \partial x} (r \cos \theta)$$

and

$$\frac{\partial}{\partial \theta} \left(\frac{\partial f}{\partial y} \right) = \frac{\partial (D_2 f)}{\partial x} \frac{\partial x}{\partial \theta} + \frac{\partial (D_2 f)}{\partial y} \frac{\partial y}{\partial \theta} = \frac{\partial^2 f}{\partial x \partial y} (-r \sin \theta) + \frac{\partial^2 f}{\partial y^2} (r \cos \theta) .$$

When these formulas are used in (4.30) we obtain

$$\frac{\partial^2 \phi}{\partial \theta^2} = -r \cos \theta \frac{\partial f}{\partial x} + r^2 \sin^2 \theta \frac{\partial^2 f}{\partial x^2} - r^2 \sin \theta \cos \theta \frac{\partial^2 f}{\partial y \partial x}$$

$$- r \sin \theta \frac{\partial f}{\partial y} - r^2 \sin \theta \cos \theta \frac{\partial^2 f}{\partial x \partial y} + r^2 \cos^2 \theta \frac{\partial^2 f}{\partial y^2} .$$

This is the required formula for $\partial^2 \phi/\partial \theta^2$. Analogous formulas for the second-order partial derivatives $\partial^2 \phi/\partial r^2$, $\partial^2 \phi/(\partial r \partial \theta)$, and $\partial^2 \phi/(\partial \theta \partial r)$ are requested in Exercise 8 of the next section.

Example 3: A generalized chain rule for vector fields. Let $\vec{F}$ be a two-dimensional vector field, say

$$\vec{F}(\vec{X}) = F_1(\vec{X}) \, \vec{i} + F_2(\vec{X}) \, \vec{j} ,$$

where F_1 and F_2 are continuously differentiable on an open set S in n-space. Let $\vec{U}$ be as in Theorem 4–8, and let $\vec{\Phi}$ denote the composite function defined by the equation

$$\vec{\Phi}(\vec{T}) = \vec{F}[\vec{U}(\vec{T})]$$

for $\vec{T}$ in Q. Then we may write

$$\vec{\Phi}(\vec{T}) = F_1[\vec{U}(\vec{T})]\,\vec{i} + F_2[\vec{U}(\vec{T})]\,\vec{j}\,.$$

If we apply Theorem 4–8 to each component of $\vec{\Phi}(\vec{T})$ we obtain the following chain rule for computing the derivative of the vector field $\vec{\Phi}$:

$$\vec{\Phi}'(\vec{T};\,\vec{Y}) = \nabla F_1[\vec{U}(\vec{T})] \cdot \vec{U}'(\vec{T};\,\vec{Y})\,\vec{i} + \nabla F_2[\vec{U}(\vec{T})] \cdot \vec{U}'(\vec{T};\,\vec{Y})\,\vec{j}\,.$$

This formula can be extended in an obvious way to vector fields $\vec{F}$ that are k-dimensional.

4.15 Exercises

In the exercises of this section you may assume the existence and continuity of all derivatives under consideration.

1. The substitution $t = g(x, y)$ converts $F(t)$ into $f(x, y)$, where $f(x, y) = F[g(x, y)]$.
   (a) Show that

   $$\frac{\partial f}{\partial x} = F'[g(x, y)]\,\frac{\partial g}{\partial x} \qquad \text{and} \qquad \frac{\partial f}{\partial y} = F'[g(x, y)]\,\frac{\partial g}{\partial y}\,.$$

   (b) Consider the special case $F(t) = e^{\sin t}$, $g(x, y) = \cos(x^2 + y^2)$. Compute $\partial f/\partial x$ and $\partial f/\partial y$ by use of the formulas in part (a). To check your result, determine $f(x, y)$ explicitly in terms of x and y and compute $\partial f/\partial x$ and $\partial f/\partial y$ directly from f.

2. A function u is defined by an equation of the form

   $$u = xy\, f\!\left(\frac{x + y}{xy}\right).$$

Show that u satisfies a partial differential equation of the form

$$x^2\,\frac{\partial u}{\partial x} - y^2\,\frac{\partial u}{\partial y} = G(x, y)\,u\,,$$

and find $G(x, y)$.

3. If k is a positive constant and $g(x, t) = \tfrac{1}{2}\,x/\sqrt{kt}$, let

   $$f(x, t) = \int_0^{g(x, t)} e^{-u^2}\,du\,.$$

Show that

$$k\,\frac{\partial^2 f}{\partial x^2} = \frac{\partial f}{\partial t}\,.$$

[*Hint.* Express $f(x, t)$ as a composite function, $f(x, t) = F[g(x, t)]$, for a suitable F; then use the chain rule.]

4. The equations $u = f(x, y)$, $x = X(s, t)$, $y = Y(s, t)$ define u as a function of s and t, say $u = F(s, t)$.
   (a) Use an appropriate form of the chain rule to express the partial derivatives $\partial F/\partial s$ and $\partial F/\partial t$ in terms of $\partial f/\partial x$, $\partial f/\partial y$, $\partial X/\partial s$, $\partial X/\partial t$, $\partial Y/\partial s$, $\partial Y/\partial t$.

(b) If $\partial^2 f/(\partial x \partial y) = \partial^2 f/(\partial y \partial x)$, show that

$$\frac{\partial^2 F}{\partial s^2} = \frac{\partial f}{\partial x}\frac{\partial^2 X}{\partial s^2} + \frac{\partial^2 f}{\partial x^2}\left(\frac{\partial X}{\partial s}\right)^2 + 2\frac{\partial X}{\partial s}\frac{\partial Y}{\partial s}\frac{\partial^2 f}{\partial x \partial y} + \frac{\partial f}{\partial y}\frac{\partial^2 Y}{\partial s^2} + \frac{\partial^2 f}{\partial y^2}\left(\frac{\partial Y}{\partial s}\right)^2 .$$

(c) Find similar formulas for the partial derivatives $\partial^2 F/(\partial s \partial t)$ and $\partial^2 F/\partial t^2$.

5. Solve Exercise 4 in each of the following special cases:

(a) $X(s, t) = s + t$, $Y(s, t) = st$.
(b) $X(s, t) = st$, $Y(s, t) = s/t$.
(c) $X(s, t) = (s - t)/2$, $Y(s, t) = (s + t)/2$.

6. The substitution $x = e^s$, $y = e^t$ converts $f(x, y)$ into $g(s, t)$, where $g(s, t) = f(e^s, e^t)$. If f is known to satisfy the partial differential equation

$$x^2 \frac{\partial^2 f}{\partial x^2} + y^2 \frac{\partial^2 f}{\partial y^2} + x \frac{\partial f}{\partial x} + y \frac{\partial f}{\partial t} = 0 ,$$

show that g satisfies a partial differential equation of the form

$$a \frac{\partial^2 g}{\partial s^2} + b \frac{\partial^2 g}{\partial t^2} + c \frac{\partial g}{\partial s} + d \frac{\partial g}{\partial t} = 0 ,$$

where a, b, c, d are constants. Determine the values of a, b, c, d.

7. The substitution $u = (x - y)/2$, $v = (x + y)/2$ changes $f(u, v)$ into $F(x, y)$. Use an appropriate form of the chain rule to express the partial derivatives $\partial F/\partial x$ and $\partial F/\partial y$ in terms of the partial derivatives $\partial f/\partial u$ and $\partial f/\partial v$.

8. The introduction of polar coordinates changes $f(x, y)$ into $\phi(r, \theta)$, where $x = r\cos\theta$ and $y = r\sin\theta$. Express the second-order partial derivatives $\partial^2\phi/\partial r^2$, $\partial^2\phi/(\partial r \partial\theta)$, and $\partial^2\phi/(\partial\theta\partial r)$ in terms of the partial derivatives of f. You may use the formulas derived in Example 1 of Section 4.14.

9. The equations $u = f(x, y, z)$, $x = X(r, s, t)$, $y = Y(r, s, t)$, and $z = Z(r, s, t)$ define u as a function of r, s, and t, say $u = F(r, s, t)$. Use an appropriate form of the chain rule to express the partial derivatives $\partial F/\partial r$, $\partial F/\partial s$, and $\partial F/\partial t$ in terms of partial derivatives of f, X, Y, and Z.

10. Solve Exercise 9 in each of the following special cases:

(a) $X(r, s, t) = r + s + t$, $Y(r, s, t) = r - 2s + 3t$, $Z(r, s, t) = 2r + s - t$.
(b) $X(r, s, t) = r^2 + s^2 + t^2$, $Y(r, s, t) = r^2 - s^2 - t^2$, $Z(r, s, t) = r^2 - s^2 + t^2$.

11. The equations $u = f(x, y, z)$, $x = X(s, t)$, $y = Y(s, t)$, $z = Z(s, t)$ define u as a function of s and t, say $u = F(s, t)$. Use an appropriate form of the chain rule to express the partial derivatives $\partial F/\partial s$ and $\partial F/\partial t$ in terms of partial derivatives of f, X, Y, and Z.

12. Solve Exercise 11 in each of the following special cases:

(a) $X(s, t) = s^2 + t^2$, $Y(s, t) = s^2 - t^2$, $Z(s, t) = 2st$.
(b) $X(s, t) = s + t$, $Y(s, t) = s - t$, $Z(s, t) = st$.

13. The equations $u = f(x, y)$, $x = X(r, s, t)$, $y = Y(r, s, t)$ define u as a function of r, s, and t, say $u = F(r, s, t)$. Use an appropriate form of the chain rule to express the partial derivatives $\partial F/\partial r$, $\partial F/\partial s$, and $\partial F/\partial t$ in terms of partial derivatives of f, X, and Y.

14. Solve Exercise 13 in each of the following special cases:

(a) $X(r, s, t) = r + s$, $Y(r, s, t) = t$.
(b) $X(r, s, t) = r + s + t$, $Y(r, s, t) = r^2 + s^2 + t^2$.
(c) $X(r, s, t) = r/s$, $Y(r, s, t) = s/t$.

15. If $\phi(\vec{T}) = f[\vec{U}(\vec{T})]$, where f, $\vec{U}$, and ϕ satisfy the hypotheses of Theorem 4-8, show that the gradient of ϕ may be expressed as a linear combination of the gradient vectors of the components of $\vec{U}$, as follows:

$$\nabla \phi(\vec{T}) = \sum_{k=1}^{n} a_k(\vec{T}) \, \nabla u_k(\vec{T}) \,.$$

Express the numbers $a_k(\vec{T})$ in terms of partial derivatives of f.

4.16 Derivatives of functions defined implicitly

In our study of analytic geometry in Volume I, we encountered many examples of surfaces defined by Cartesian equations of the form

$$(4.31) \qquad\qquad\qquad F(x, y, z) = 0 \,.$$

An equation like this is said to provide an implicit representation of the surface. Sometimes it is possible to solve this equation explicitly for one of the variables in terms of the other two, say for z in terms of x and y. This leads to an equation of the form

$$(4.32) \qquad\qquad\qquad z = f(x, y) \,,$$

which is said to provide an explicit representation of the surface. In actual practice it may not be an easy matter to obtain an explicit formula for z in terms of x and y. Nevertheless, a judicious use of the chain rule makes it possible to deduce various properties of the partial derivatives $\partial f / \partial x$ and $\partial f / \partial y$ without an explicit knowledge of $f(x, y)$. The procedure is described in the following paragraph.

Let us suppose that it is theoretically possible to solve Equation (4.31) for z in terms of x and y and that a solution is given by (4.32).† This means that if we replace z by $f(x, y)$ in (4.31) the equation is identically satisfied for all points (x, y) under consideration, say for all (x, y) in an open set S. That is, we have

$$(4.33) \qquad\qquad\qquad F[x, y, f(x, y)] = 0$$

for all (x, y) in S. Now we introduce a new function g defined as follows:

$$g(x, y) = F[x, y, f(x, y)] \qquad \text{if} \quad (x, y) \, \varepsilon \, S \,.$$

Then Equation (4.33) states that $g(x, y) = 0$ whenever $(x, y) \, \varepsilon \, S$; hence the partial derivatives $\partial g / \partial x$ and $\partial g / \partial y$ are also equal to 0 on S. We may also compute $\partial g / \partial x$ and $\partial g / \partial y$ by the chain rule. For this purpose we write

$$g(x, y) = F[u_1(x, y), u_2(x, y), u_3(x, y)] \,,$$

† When we say it is theoretically possible to solve Equation (4.31) for z in terms of x and y we mean a function f exists that makes $F[x, y, f(x, y)] = 0$ for all (x, y) in some open set S. We do not claim that there is a general method for actually determining f in every particular case. This is analogous to the fact that every polynomial of degree n has n zeros but no general method exists for finding them. For polynomials, the existence of zeros is guaranteed by the fundamental theorem of algebra. For Equation (4.31), a general theorem known as the *implicit function theorem* tells us when it is theoretically possible to solve for z. For the special case considered here, it states that if F and $D_3 F$ are continuous in some neighborhood of a point (x_0, y_0, z_0), and if $D_3 F(x_0, y_0, z_0) \neq 0$, a solution is theoretically possible in a sufficiently small neighborhood about (x_0, y_0, z_0). A discussion of the general implicit function theorem may be found in Chapter 7 of the author's *Mathematical Analysis*, Addison-Wesley, Reading, Mass., 1957. A special case is treated below in Section 9.12 (Theorem 9–8).

where $u_1(x, y) = x$, $u_2(x, y) = y$, and $u_3(x, y) = f(x, y)$. The chain rule gives us the formulas

$$\frac{\partial g}{\partial x} = D_1 F \frac{\partial u_1}{\partial x} + D_2 F \frac{\partial u_2}{\partial x} + D_3 F \frac{\partial u_3}{\partial x} \quad \text{and} \quad \frac{\partial g}{\partial y} = D_1 F \frac{\partial u_1}{\partial y} + D_2 F \frac{\partial u_2}{\partial y} + D_3 F \frac{\partial u_3}{\partial y},$$

where each partial derivative $D_k F$ is to be evaluated at $(x, y, f(x, y))$. Since we have

$$\frac{\partial u_1}{\partial x} = 1, \quad \frac{\partial u_2}{\partial x} = 0, \quad \frac{\partial u_3}{\partial x} = \frac{\partial f}{\partial x}, \quad \text{and} \quad \frac{\partial g}{\partial x} = 0,$$

the first of the foregoing equations becomes

$$D_1 F + D_3 F \frac{\partial f}{\partial x} = 0.$$

Solving this for $\partial f/\partial x$ we obtain

(4.34)
$$\frac{\partial f}{\partial x} = - \frac{D_1 F[x, y, f(x, y)]}{D_3 F[x, y, f(x, y)]}$$

at those points at which $D_3 F[x, y, f(x, y)] \neq 0$. By a similar argument we obtain a corresponding formula for $\partial f/\partial y$:

(4.35)
$$\frac{\partial f}{\partial y} = - \frac{D_2 F[x, y, f(x, y)]}{D_3 F[x, y, f(x, y)]}$$

at those points at which $D_3 F[x, y, f(x, y)] \neq 0$. These formulas are usually written more briefly as follows:

$$\frac{\partial f}{\partial x} = - \frac{\partial F/\partial x}{\partial F/\partial z}, \quad \frac{\partial f}{\partial y} = - \frac{\partial F/\partial y}{\partial F/\partial z}.$$

Example. Assume that the equation $y^2 + xz + z^2 - e^z - c = 0$ defines z as a function of x and y, say $z = f(x, y)$. Find a value of the constant c such that $f(0, e) = 2$, and compute the partial derivatives $\partial f/\partial x$ and $\partial f/\partial y$ at the point $(x, y) = (0, e)$.

Solution. When $x = 0$, $y = e$, and $z = 2$, the equation becomes $e^2 + 4 - e^2 - c = 0$, and this is satisfied by $c = 4$. Let $F(x, y, z) = y^2 + xz + z^2 - e^z - 4$. From (4.34) and (4.35) we have

$$\frac{\partial f}{\partial x} = - \frac{z}{x + 2z - e^z}, \quad \frac{\partial f}{\partial y} = - \frac{2y}{x + 2z - e^z}.$$

When $x = 0$, $y = e$, and $z = 2$ we find $\partial f/\partial x = 2/(e^2 - 4)$ and $\partial f/\partial y = 2e/(e^2 - 4)$. Note that we were able to compute the partial derivatives $\partial f/\partial x$ and $\partial f/\partial y$ using only the value of $f(x, y)$ at the single point $(0, e)$.

The foregoing discussion may be extended to functions of more than two variables.

If an equation of the form

$$F(x_1, x_2, \ldots, x_n) = 0$$

defines one of the variables as a function of the remaining variables, say we have $x_n = f(x_1, \ldots, x_{n-1})$, then for each $k = 1, 2, \ldots, n - 1$, the partial derivative $D_k f$ may be computed by the formula

(4.36)
$$D_k f = -\frac{D_k F}{D_n F}$$

at those points at which $D_n F \neq 0$. The partial derivatives $D_k F$ and $D_n F$ which appear on the right are to be evaluated at the point $(x_1, x_2, \ldots, x_{n-1}, f(x_1, \ldots, x_{n-1}))$.

The proof of Equation (4.36) is a direct extension of that given for Equation (4.34). Of course, we need to know that the functions F and f are such that the chain rule is applicable. It suffices to assume that f is differentiable and that F is continuously differentiable.

The discussion may be generalized in another way. Suppose we have two surfaces with the following implicit representations:

(4.37)
$$F(x, y, z) = 0, \qquad G(x, y, z) = 0.$$

If these surfaces intersect along a curve C, it may be possible to obtain a parametric representation of C by solving the two equations in (4.37) simultaneously for two of the variables in terms of the third, say for x and y in terms of z. Let us suppose that it is possible to solve for x and y and that solutions are given by the equations

$$x = X(z), \qquad y = Y(z)$$

for all z in some open interval (a, b). Then when x and y are replaced by $X(z)$ and $Y(z)$, respectively, the two equations in (4.37) are identically satisfied. That is, we may write $F[X(z), Y(z), z] = 0$ and $G[X(z), Y(z), z] = 0$ for all z in (a, b). Again, by using the chain rule, we may compute the derivatives $X'(z)$ and $Y'(z)$ without an explicit knowledge of $X(z)$ and $Y(z)$. To do this we introduce new functions f and g by means of the equations

$$f(z) = F[X(z), Y(z), z] \qquad \text{and} \qquad g(z) = G[X(z), Y(z), z].$$

Then $f(z) = g(z) = 0$ for every z in (a, b) and hence the derivatives $f'(z)$ and $g'(z)$ are also zero on (a, b). By the chain rule these derivatives are given by the formula

$$f'(z) = \frac{\partial F}{\partial x} X'(z) + \frac{\partial F}{\partial y} Y'(z) + \frac{\partial F}{\partial z}, \qquad g'(z) = \frac{\partial G}{\partial x} X'(z) + \frac{\partial G}{\partial y} Y'(z) + \frac{\partial G}{\partial z}.$$

Since $f'(z)$ and $g'(z)$ are both zero we may determine $X'(z)$ and $Y'(z)$ by solving the following pair of simultaneous *linear* equations:

$$\frac{\partial F}{\partial x} X'(z) + \frac{\partial F}{\partial y} Y'(z) = -\frac{\partial F}{\partial z},$$

$$\frac{\partial G}{\partial x} X'(z) + \frac{\partial G}{\partial y} Y'(z) = -\frac{\partial G}{\partial z}.$$

At those points at which the determinant of the system is not zero, these equations have a unique solution which may be expressed as follows:

$$(4.38) \qquad X'(z) = - \frac{\begin{vmatrix} \dfrac{\partial F}{\partial z} & \dfrac{\partial F}{\partial y} \\[2mm] \dfrac{\partial G}{\partial z} & \dfrac{\partial G}{\partial y} \end{vmatrix}}{\begin{vmatrix} \dfrac{\partial F}{\partial x} & \dfrac{\partial F}{\partial y} \\[2mm] \dfrac{\partial G}{\partial x} & \dfrac{\partial G}{\partial y} \end{vmatrix}}, \qquad Y'(z) = - \frac{\begin{vmatrix} \dfrac{\partial F}{\partial x} & \dfrac{\partial F}{\partial z} \\[2mm] \dfrac{\partial G}{\partial x} & \dfrac{\partial G}{\partial z} \end{vmatrix}}{\begin{vmatrix} \dfrac{\partial F}{\partial x} & \dfrac{\partial F}{\partial y} \\[2mm] \dfrac{\partial G}{\partial x} & \dfrac{\partial G}{\partial y} \end{vmatrix}}.$$

Notice that the determinants which appear in (4.38) are *Jacobian determinants*. If we use the notation for Jacobians introduced in Section 2.16, we may express the solutions in (4.38) more briefly by writing

$$(4.39) \qquad X'(z) = \frac{\partial(F, G)/\partial(y, z)}{\partial(F, G)/\partial(x, y)}, \qquad Y'(z) = \frac{\partial(F, G)/\partial(z, x)}{\partial(F, G)/\partial(x, y)}.$$

The method may be extended to treat more general situations in which m equations in n variables are given, where $n > m$, and we solve for m of the variables in terms of the remaining $n - m$ variables. The partial derivatives of the new functions so defined may be expressed as quotients of Jacobians, generalizing (4.39). An example with $m = 2$ and $n = 4$ is described in Exercise 10 of Section 4.18.

4.17 Worked examples

In this section we illustrate some of the concepts of the foregoing sections by solving various types of problems dealing with functions defined implicitly.

Example 1. Assume that the equation $g(x, y) = 0$ determines y as a function of x, say $y = Y(x)$ for all x in some open interval (a, b). Express the derivative $Y'(x)$ in terms of the partial derivatives of g.

Solution. Let $G(x) = g[x, Y(x)]$ for x in (a, b). Then the equation $g(x, y) = 0$ implies $G(x) = 0$ in (a, b). By the chain rule we have

$$G'(x) = \frac{\partial g}{\partial x} \cdot 1 + \frac{\partial g}{\partial y} Y'(x),$$

from which we obtain

$$(4.40) \qquad Y'(x) = - \frac{\partial g/\partial x}{\partial g/\partial y}$$

at those points x in (a, b) at which $\partial g/\partial y \neq 0$. The partial derivatives $\partial g/\partial x$ and $\partial g/\partial y$ are given by the formulas $\partial g/\partial x = D_1 g[x, Y(x)]$ and $\partial g/\partial y = D_2 g[x, Y(x)]$.

Example 2. When y is eliminated from the two equations $z = f(x, y)$ and $g(x, y) = 0$, the result can be expressed in the form $z = h(x)$. Express the derivative $h'(x)$ in terms of the partial derivatives of f and g.

Solution. Let us assume that the equation $g(x, y) = 0$ may be solved for y in terms of x and that a solution is given by $y = Y(x)$ for all x in some open interval (a, b). Then the function h is given by the formula

$$h(x) = f[x, Y(x)] \qquad \text{if} \quad x \, \varepsilon \, (a, b) \, .$$

Applying the chain rule we have

$$h'(x) = \frac{\partial f}{\partial x} + \frac{\partial f}{\partial y} Y'(x) \, .$$

Using Equation (4.40) of Example 1 we obtain the formula

$$h'(x) = \frac{\dfrac{\partial g}{\partial y} \dfrac{\partial f}{\partial x} - \dfrac{\partial f}{\partial y} \dfrac{\partial g}{\partial x}}{\dfrac{\partial g}{\partial y}} \, .$$

The partial derivatives on the right are to be evaluated at the point $(x, Y(x))$. Note that the numerator can also be expressed as a Jacobian, giving us

$$h'(x) = \frac{\partial(f, g)/\partial(x, y)}{\partial g/\partial y} \, .$$

Example 3. The two equations $2x = v^2 - u^2$ and $y = uv$ define u and v as functions of x and y. Find formulas for $\partial u/\partial x$, $\partial u/\partial y$, $\partial v/\partial x$, $\partial v/\partial y$.

Solution. If we hold y fixed and differentiate the two equations in question with respect to x, remembering that u and v are functions of x and y, we obtain

$$2 = 2v \frac{\partial v}{\partial x} - 2u \frac{\partial u}{\partial x} \qquad \text{and} \qquad 0 = u \frac{\partial v}{\partial x} + v \frac{\partial u}{\partial x} \, .$$

Solving these simultaneously for $\partial u/\partial x$ and $\partial v/\partial x$ we find

$$\frac{\partial u}{\partial x} = - \frac{u}{u^2 + v^2} \qquad \text{and} \qquad \frac{\partial v}{\partial x} = \frac{v}{u^2 + v^2} \, .$$

On the other hand, if we hold x fixed and differentiate the two given equations with respect to y we obtain the equations

$$0 = 2v \frac{\partial v}{\partial y} - 2u \frac{\partial u}{\partial y} \qquad \text{and} \qquad 1 = u \frac{\partial v}{\partial y} + v \frac{\partial u}{\partial y} \, .$$

Solving these simultaneously we find

$$\frac{\partial u}{\partial y} = \frac{v}{u^2 + v^2} \qquad \text{and} \qquad \frac{\partial v}{\partial y} = \frac{u}{u^2 + v^2} \, .$$

Example 4. Let u be defined as a function of x and y by means of the equation

$$u = F(x + u, yu) \, .$$

Find $\partial u/\partial x$ and $\partial u/\partial y$ in terms of the partial derivatives of F.

Solution. Suppose that the equation which defines u as a function of x and y leads to a solution which can be expressed as $u = g(x, y)$ for all (x, y) in some open set S. Substituting $g(x, y)$ for u in the original equation we must have

(4.41) $$g(x, y) = F[u_1(x, y), u_2(x, y)],$$

where $u_1(x, y) = x + g(x, y)$ and $u_2(x, y) = y\, g(x, y)$. Now we hold y fixed and differentiate both sides of (4.41) with respect to x, using the chain rule on the right, to obtain

(4.42) $$\frac{\partial g}{\partial x} = D_1 F \frac{\partial u_1}{\partial x} + D_2 F \frac{\partial u_2}{\partial x}.$$

But $\partial u_1/\partial x = 1 + \partial g/\partial x$, and $\partial u_2/\partial x = y\,\partial g/\partial x$. Hence (4.42) becomes

$$\frac{\partial g}{\partial x} = D_1 F \cdot \left(1 + \frac{\partial g}{\partial x}\right) + D_2 F \cdot \left(y\,\frac{\partial g}{\partial x}\right).$$

Solving this equation for $\partial g/\partial x$ (and writing $\partial u/\partial x$ for $\partial g/\partial x$) we obtain

$$\frac{\partial u}{\partial x} = \frac{-D_1 F}{D_1 F + y\, D_2 F - 1}.$$

In a similar way we find

$$\frac{\partial g}{\partial y} = D_1 F \frac{\partial u_1}{\partial y} + D_2 F \frac{\partial u_2}{\partial y} = D_1 F \frac{\partial g}{\partial y} + D_2 F \left(y\,\frac{\partial g}{\partial y} + g(x, y)\right).$$

This leads to the equation

$$\frac{\partial u}{\partial y} = \frac{-g(x, y)\, D_2 F}{D_1 F + y\, D_2 F - 1}.$$

The partial derivatives $D_1 F$ and $D_2 F$ are to be evaluated at the point $(x + g(x, y), y\, g(x, y))$.

Example 5. When u is eliminated from the two equations $x = u + v$ and $y = uv^2$, we get an equation of the form $F(x, y, v) = 0$ which defines v implicitly as a function of x and y, say $v = h(x, y)$. Prove that

$$\frac{\partial h}{\partial x} = \frac{h(x, y)}{3h(x, y) - 2x}$$

and find a similar formula for $\partial h/\partial y$.

Solution. Eliminating u from the two given equations, we obtain the relation

$$xv^2 - v^3 - y = 0.$$

Let F be the function defined by the equation

$$F(x, y, v) = xv^2 - v^3 - y.$$

The discussion in Section 4.16 is now applicable and we may write

(4.43) $$\frac{\partial h}{\partial x} = -\frac{\partial F/\partial x}{\partial F/\partial v} \quad \text{and} \quad \frac{\partial h}{\partial y} = -\frac{\partial F/\partial y}{\partial F/\partial v}.$$

But $\partial F/\partial x = v^2$, $\partial F/\partial v = 2xv - 3v^2$, and $\partial F/\partial y = -1$. Hence the equations in (4.43) become

$$\frac{\partial h}{\partial x} = -\frac{v^2}{2xv - 3v^2} = -\frac{v}{2x - 3v} = \frac{h(x, y)}{3h(x, y) - 2x}$$

and

$$\frac{\partial h}{\partial y} = -\frac{-1}{2xv - 3v^2} = \frac{1}{2xh(x, y) - 3h^2(x, y)}.$$

Example 6. The equation $F(x, y, z) = 0$ defines z implicitly as a function of x and y, say $z = f(x, y)$. Assuming that $\partial^2 F/(\partial x \partial z) = \partial^2 F/(\partial z \partial x)$, show that we have

(4.44) $$\frac{\partial^2 f}{\partial x^2} = -\frac{\left(\dfrac{\partial^2 F}{\partial z^2}\right)\left(\dfrac{\partial F}{\partial x}\right)^2 - 2\left(\dfrac{\partial^2 F}{\partial x \partial z}\right)\left(\dfrac{\partial F}{\partial z}\right)\left(\dfrac{\partial F}{\partial x}\right) + \left(\dfrac{\partial F}{\partial z}\right)^2\left(\dfrac{\partial^2 F}{\partial x^2}\right)}{\left(\dfrac{\partial F}{\partial z}\right)^3},$$

where the partial derivatives on the right are to be evaluated at $(x, y, f(x, y))$.

Solution. By Equation (4.34) of Section 4.16 we have

(4.45) $$\frac{\partial f}{\partial x} = -\frac{\partial F/\partial x}{\partial F/\partial z}.$$

We must remember that this quotient really means

$$-\frac{D_1 F[x, y, f(x, y)]}{D_3 F[x, y, f(x, y)]}.$$

Let us introduce $G(x, y) = D_1 F[x, y, f(x, y)]$ and $H(x, y) = D_3 F[x, y, f(x, y)]$. Our object is to evaluate the partial derivative with respect to x of the quotient

$$\frac{\partial f}{\partial x} = -\frac{G(x, y)}{H(x, y)},$$

holding y fixed. The rule for differentiating quotients gives us

(4.46) $$\frac{\partial^2 f}{\partial x^2} = -\frac{H\dfrac{\partial G}{\partial x} - G\dfrac{\partial H}{\partial x}}{H^2}.$$

Since G and H are composite functions, we use the chain rule to compute the partial derivatives $\partial G/\partial x$ and $\partial H/\partial x$. For $\partial G/\partial x$ we have

$$\frac{\partial G}{\partial x} = D_1(D_1 F) \cdot 1 + D_2(D_1 F) \cdot 0 + D_3(D_1 F) \cdot \frac{\partial f}{\partial x}$$

$$= \frac{\partial^2 F}{\partial x^2} + \frac{\partial^2 F}{\partial z \partial x}\frac{\partial f}{\partial x}.$$

Similarly, we find

$$\frac{\partial H}{\partial x} = D_1(D_3F) \cdot 1 + D_2(D_3F) \cdot 0 + D_3(D_3F) \cdot \frac{\partial f}{\partial x}$$

$$= \frac{\partial^2 F}{\partial x \partial z} + \frac{\partial^2 F}{\partial z^2} \frac{\partial f}{\partial x}.$$

Substituting these in (4.46) and replacing $\partial f/\partial x$ by the quotient in (4.45) we obtain the formula in (4.44).

Note. In the foregoing example we have assumed that the two mixed partials $\partial^2 F/(\partial x \partial z)$ and $\partial^2 F/(\partial z \partial x)$ are equal. Although this is not true for all functions, it *is* true at those points at which both mixed partials are continuous. A proof of this is given in Section 4.25.

4.18 Exercises

In the exercises in this section you may assume the existence and continuity of all derivatives under consideration.

1. Let F be a real-valued function of two real variables and assume that the partial derivatives D_1F and D_2F are never zero. Let u be another real-valued function of two real variables such that the partial derivatives $\partial u/\partial x$ and $\partial u/\partial y$ are related by the equation $F(\partial u/\partial x, \partial u/\partial y) = 0$. Prove that a constant n exists such that

$$\frac{\partial^2 u}{\partial x^2} \frac{\partial^2 u}{\partial y^2} = \left(\frac{\partial^2 u}{\partial x \partial y}\right)^n,$$

and find n. Assume that $\partial^2 u/(\partial x \partial y) = \partial^2 u/(\partial y \partial x)$.

2. The equation $x + z + (y + z)^2 = 6$ defines z implicitly as a function of x and y, say $z = f(x, y)$. Compute the partial derivatives $\partial f/\partial x$, $\partial f/\partial y$, and $\partial^2 f/(\partial x \partial y)$ in terms of x, y, and z.

3. The equation $\sin(x + y) + \sin(y + z) = 1$ defines z implicitly as a function of x and y, say $z = f(x, y)$. Compute the second derivative $D_{1,2}f$ in terms of x, y, and z.

4. The equation $F(x + y + z, x^2 + y^2 + z^2) = 0$ defines z implicitly as a function of x and y, say $z = f(x, y)$. Determine the partial derivatives $\partial f/\partial x$ and $\partial f/\partial y$ in terms of the partial derivatives D_1F and D_2F.

5. Let f and g be functions of one real variable and define $F(x, y) = f[x + g(y)]$. Find formulas for all the partial derivatives of F of first and second order, expressed in terms of the derivatives of f and g. Verify the relation

$$\frac{\partial F}{\partial x} \frac{\partial^2 F}{\partial x \partial y} = \frac{\partial F}{\partial y} \frac{\partial^2 F}{\partial x^2}.$$

6. The introduction of polar coordinates $x = r\cos\theta$, $y = r\sin\theta$ converts $f(x, y)$ into $F(r, \theta)$. Verify the formula

$$|\nabla f(r\cos\theta, r\sin\theta)|^2 = \left(\frac{\partial F}{\partial r}\right)^2 + \frac{1}{r^2}\left(\frac{\partial F}{\partial \theta}\right)^2.$$

7. The equation $f(y/x, z/x) = 0$ defines z implicitly as a function of x and y, say $z = g(x, y)$. Show that

$$x\frac{\partial g}{\partial x} + y\frac{\partial g}{\partial y} = g(x, y)$$

at those points at which $D_2 f[y/x, g(x, y)/x]$ is not zero.

8. The two equations $x + y = uv$ and $xy = u - v$ determine x and y implicitly as functions of u and v, say $x = X(u, v)$ and $y = Y(u, v)$. Show that $\partial X/\partial u = (xv - 1)/(x - y)$ if $x \neq y$, and find similar formulas for $\partial X/\partial v$, $\partial Y/\partial u$, $\partial Y/\partial v$.

9. The two equations $x + y = uv$ and $xy = u - v$ determine x and v as functions of u and y, say $x = X(u, y)$ and $v = V(u, y)$. Show that $\partial X/\partial u = (u + v)/(1 + yu)$ if $1 + yu \neq 0$, and find similar formulas for $\partial X/\partial y$, $\partial V/\partial u$, $\partial V/\partial y$.

10. The two equations $F(x, y, u, v) = 0$ and $G(x, y, u, v) = 0$ determine x and y implicitly as functions of u and v, say $x = X(u, v)$ and $y = Y(u, v)$. Show that

$$\frac{\partial X}{\partial u} = \frac{\partial(F, G)/\partial(y, u)}{\partial(F, G)/\partial(x, y)}$$

at points at which the Jacobian $\partial(F, G)/\partial(x, y) \neq 0$, and find similar formulas for the partial derivatives $\partial X/\partial v$, $\partial Y/\partial u$, and $\partial Y/\partial v$.

11. The intersection of the two surfaces given by the Cartesian equations $2x^2 + 3y^2 - z^2 = 25$ and $x^2 + y^2 = z^2$ contains a curve C passing through the point $P = (\sqrt{7}, 3, 4)$. These equations may be solved for x and y in terms of z to give a parametric representation of C with z as parameter.

(a) Find a unit tangent vector $\vec{T}$ to C at the point P without using an explicit knowledge of the parametric representation.

(b) Check the result in part (a) by determining a parametric representation of C with z as parameter.

12. The three equations $F(u, v) = 0$, $u = xy$, and $v = \sqrt{x^2 + z^2}$ define a surface in xyz-space. Find a normal vector to this surface at the point $x = 1, y = 1, z = \sqrt{3}$ if it is known that $D_1 F(1, 2) = 1$ and $D_2 F(1, 2) = 2$.

4.19 Existence of potential functions having a given gradient

In this section we consider the following important question: Suppose we have a vector field $\vec{V}$ defined on some portion of 3-space. Is $\vec{V}$ the gradient field of a scalar field f? That is, given $\vec{V}$, can we solve the equation $\nabla f = \vec{V}$ for f? When such an f exists, we say that the vector field $\vec{V}$ has a *potential function f*.

If we express the given vector field in terms of its components, say

$$\vec{V}(x, y, z) = P(x, y, z)\, \vec{i} + Q(x, y, z)\, \vec{j} + R(x, y, z)\, \vec{k}\,,$$

to solve the equation $\nabla f = \vec{V}$ means that we must find a scalar field f which satisfies the three partial differential equations

(4.47) $$\frac{\partial f}{\partial x} = P(x, y, z)\,, \qquad \frac{\partial f}{\partial y} = Q(x, y, z)\,, \qquad \frac{\partial f}{\partial z} = R(x, y, z)\,.$$

The first thing to notice is that there may not be *any f* which satisfies all three equations simultaneously. In fact, it is easy to see that the existence of such an f imposes severe restrictions on the three functions P, Q, and R. For example, let us suppose that the given vector field $\vec{V}$ is continuously differentiable in some region and let us differentiate the first two equations in (4.47) with respect to y and x, respectively. We find

$$\frac{\partial^2 f}{\partial y \partial x} = \frac{\partial P}{\partial y} \qquad \text{and} \qquad \frac{\partial^2 f}{\partial x \partial y} = \frac{\partial Q}{\partial x}\,.$$

Continuity of $\partial P/\partial y$ and $\partial Q/\partial x$ implies continuity and hence equality of the two mixed partials $\partial^2 f/(\partial y \partial x)$ and $\partial^2 f/(\partial x \partial y)$. (This is proved in Section 4.25.) Hence, the existence of a potential function f implies

(4.48)
$$\frac{\partial P}{\partial y} = \frac{\partial Q}{\partial x} .$$

Therefore, if we start out with a vector field $\vec{V}$ for which (4.48) does *not* hold there cannot be an f which satisfies (4.47). This is the case, for example, when $P(x, y, z) = Q(x, y, z) = x$.

The foregoing remarks show that Equation (4.48) is a *necessary* condition for the existence of an f satisfying (4.47). The same kind of argument shows that the two companion equations

$$\frac{\partial P}{\partial z} = \frac{\partial R}{\partial x} \quad \text{and} \quad \frac{\partial Q}{\partial z} = \frac{\partial R}{\partial y}$$

are also necessary. We shall now prove that if these three conditions on P, Q, and R are satisfied on a suitable region in space, an f does exist. In the course of the proof we shall outline a procedure for constructing f in terms of integrals involving P, Q, and R.

4–9 THEOREM. Consider a vector field $\vec{V} = P\,\vec{i} + Q\,\vec{j} + R\,\vec{k}$ that is continuously differentiable on an open rectangular parallelepiped S in 3-space. Then there exists a scalar field f such that $\nabla f = \vec{V}$ everywhere in S if, and only if, the following three equations hold at each point of S:

(4.49)
$$\frac{\partial P}{\partial y} = \frac{\partial Q}{\partial x} , \qquad \frac{\partial P}{\partial z} = \frac{\partial R}{\partial x} , \qquad \frac{\partial Q}{\partial z} = \frac{\partial R}{\partial y} .$$

Proof. We have already seen, in the remarks preceding this theorem, that the three equations in (4.49) are necessary for the existence of f. To prove the converse we assume that Equations (4.49) hold, and exhibit an f satisfying all three equations in (4.47). First we construct a function f_1 which satisfies the equation $\partial f_1/\partial x = P(x, y, z)$. Then we modify f_1 in a way that enables us to satisfy the remaining equations in (4.47).

To obtain f_1 we simply integrate $P(x, y, z)$ with respect to x, treating y and z as constants. For this purpose, we choose two points (x_0, y_0, z_0) and (x, y, z) in S and define

$$f_1(x, y, z) = \int_{x_0}^{x} P(t, y, z)\, dt .$$

Since S is a rectangular parallelepiped, all points (t, y, z) lie in S as t varies over the interval from x_0 to x, and the integration is meaningful. The derivative of f_1 with respect to x is obviously $P(x, y, z)$ but, of course, there is no reason to expect that its derivative with respect to y is Q or that its derivative with respect to z is R.

The function we are trying to construct can only differ from f_1 by a function of y and z alone. Moreover, if we add to $f_1(x, y, z)$ a function $f_2(y, z)$ independent of x, the sum $f_1 + f_2$ will also satisfy the first equation in (4.47). We try to choose $f_2(y, z)$ so that the first *two* equations in (4.47) are satisfied by the sum $f_1 + f_2$. For this, the equation $\partial(f_1 + f_2)/\partial y = Q$ must be true and hence f_2 must be such that

(4.50)
$$\frac{\partial f_2}{\partial y} = Q - \frac{\partial f_1}{\partial y} .$$

It is natural, therefore, to try to construct $f_2(y, z)$ by integrating the difference $Q - \partial f_1 / \partial y$ with respect to y, holding x and z fixed. Fortunately, the difference $Q - \partial f_1 / \partial y$ is independent of x because

$$\frac{\partial}{\partial x}\left(Q - \frac{\partial f_1}{\partial y}\right) = \frac{\partial Q}{\partial x} - \frac{\partial^2 f_1}{\partial x \partial y} = \frac{\partial Q}{\partial x} - \frac{\partial}{\partial y}\left(\frac{\partial f_1}{\partial x}\right) = \frac{\partial Q}{\partial x} - \frac{\partial P}{\partial y} = 0 .$$

Therefore the difference $Q - \partial f_1 / \partial y$ is a function of y and z alone; we may denote this difference by $g(y, z)$. If we define f_2 by the formula

$$f_2(y, z) = \int_{y_0}^{y} g(t, z) \, dt ,$$

where z is treated as a constant in the integration, we obtain a function f_2 satisfying (4.50), and hence the sum $f_1 + f_2$ satisfies the first two equations in (4.47). That is, we have

(4.51) $$\frac{\partial(f_1 + f_2)}{\partial x} = P \quad \text{and} \quad \frac{\partial(f_1 + f_2)}{\partial y} = Q .$$

The function we seek can only differ from $f_1 + f_2$ by a function of z alone, say $f_3(z)$. Therefore we try to construct f_3 in such a way that the derivative of the sum $f_1 + f_2 + f_3$ with respect to z is R. The equation $\partial(f_1 + f_2 + f_3)/\partial z = R$ requires that

$$f_3'(z) = R - \frac{\partial(f_1 + f_2)}{\partial z} .$$

Now the difference $R - \partial(f_1 + f_2)/\partial z$ is independent of *both* x and y because we have

$$\frac{\partial}{\partial x}\left[R - \frac{\partial(f_1 + f_2)}{\partial z}\right] = \frac{\partial R}{\partial x} - \frac{\partial}{\partial z}\left[\frac{\partial(f_1 + f_2)}{\partial x}\right] = \frac{\partial R}{\partial x} - \frac{\partial P}{\partial z} = 0$$

and

$$\frac{\partial}{\partial y}\left[R - \frac{\partial(f_1 + f_2)}{\partial z}\right] = \frac{\partial R}{\partial y} - \frac{\partial}{\partial z}\left[\frac{\partial(f_1 + f_2)}{\partial y}\right] = \frac{\partial R}{\partial y} - \frac{\partial Q}{\partial z} = 0 .$$

Therefore the difference $R - \partial(f_1 + f_2)/\partial z$ is a function of z alone, say $h(z) = R - \partial(f_1 + f_2)/\partial z$, and we may define $f_3(z)$ by the equation

$$f_3(z) = \int_{z_0}^{z} h(t) \, dt .$$

The derivative of f_3 is

(4.52) $$f_3'(z) = R - \partial(f_1 + f_2)/\partial z .$$

Therefore, if we put

$$f(x, y, z) = f_1(x, y, z) + f_2(y, z) + f_3(z) ,$$

we find $\partial f / \partial x = P$ and $\partial f / \partial y = Q$, because of (4.51); also

$$\frac{\partial f}{\partial z} = \frac{\partial(f_1 + f_2)}{\partial z} + f_3'(z) = R ,$$

because of (4.52). This establishes the existence of a potential function f such that $\nabla f = \vec{V}$.

The foregoing proof also provides a straightforward method for constructing f. If we use the Leibniz notation for indefinite integrals, we may summarize the procedure as follows: If $P\vec{i} + Q\vec{j} + R\vec{k}$ is a gradient, then a potential f is given by the formula

$$f(x, y, z) = f_1(x, y, z) + f_2(y, z) + f_3(z),$$

where

$$f_1(x, y, z) = \int P \, dx \qquad \text{(holding } y \text{ and } z \text{ fixed)},$$

$$f_2(y, z) = \int \left(Q - \frac{\partial f_1}{\partial y} \right) dy \qquad \text{(holding } z \text{ fixed)},$$

$$f_3(z) = \int \left(R - \frac{\partial f_1}{\partial z} - \frac{\partial f_2}{\partial z} \right) dz.$$

There is an alternative method for determining f that is often easier to carry out in actual practice. Using indefinite integrals, we write

$$(4.53) \qquad f(x, y, z) = \int P(x, y, z) \, dx + A(y, z),$$

where, as before, y and z are treated as constants in the integration. The function $A(y, z)$ is a "constant of integration" to be determined. The relation (4.53) comes from integrating the equation $\partial f / \partial x = P$ with respect to x. Similarly, if we integrate the equation $\partial f / \partial y = Q$ with respect to y and the equation $\partial f / \partial z = R$ with respect to z we obtain the further relations

$$(4.54) \qquad f(x, y, z) = \int Q(x, y, z) \, dy + B(x, z)$$

and

$$(4.55) \qquad f(x, y, z) = \int R(x, y, z) \, dz + C(x, y),$$

where $B(x, z)$ and $C(x, y)$ are functions to be determined. Finding f means finding three functions $A(y, z)$, $B(x, z)$, and $C(x, y)$ such that all three equations (4.53), (4.54), and (4.55) agree in their right-hand members. In many cases this can be done by inspection, as illustrated by the following example.

Example. Find a potential function f for the vector field

$$\vec{V}(x, y, z) = (2xyz + z^2 - 2y^2 + 1)\vec{i} + (x^2z - 4xy)\vec{j} + (x^2y + 2xz - 2)\vec{k}.$$

Solution. First we observe that the conditions in (4.49) are satisfied everywhere in 3-space; thus, by the foregoing theorem, a potential function must exist. To find f we use Equations (4.53), (4.54), and (4.55) to obtain

$$f(x, y, z) = \int (2xyz + z^2 - 2y^2 + 1)dx + A(y, z)$$

$$= x^2yz + xz^2 - 2xy^2 + x + A(y, z),$$

$$f(x, y, z) = \int (x^2z - 4xy)dy + B(x, z) = x^2yz - 2xy^2 + B(x, z),$$

$$f(x, y, z) = \int (x^2y + 2xz - 2)dz + C(x, y) = x^2yz + xz^2 - 2z + C(x, y).$$

By inspection we see that the choices $A(y, z) = -2z$, $B(x, z) = xz^2 + x - 2z$, and $C(x, y) = x - 2xy^2$ will make all three equations agree; hence the function f given by the equation

$$f(x, y, z) = x^2yz + xz^2 - 2xy^2 + x - 2z$$

is a potential of $\vec{V}$. Any other potential differs from this one only by an additive constant. [Since we found a potential it was not necessary to verify the conditions in (4.49) at the start of the solution.]

Theorem 4–9 was proved under the assumption that the set S in which the conditions (4.49) are required to hold is a rectangular parallelepiped. Actually, the assumption that S is a parallelepiped enabled us to carry out the integrations used in the construction of the potential function. The theorem is also true for some sets S that are more general than parallelepipeds. For example, in Chapter 6 we extend the theorem to open *convex* sets. However, the theorem is *not* true for arbitrary open sets. The reasons for this will become apparent when we return to this type of problem in connection with our study of line integrals and surface integrals.

Theorem 4–9 has a two-dimensional analogue. If $\vec{V}(x, y) = P(x, y)\vec{i} + Q(x, y)\vec{j}$ is a vector field that is continuously differentiable on an open rectangle S in the xy-plane, a necessary and sufficient condition for the existence of a potential function is that the equation

$$\frac{\partial P}{\partial y} = \frac{\partial Q}{\partial x}$$

be satisfied everywhere in S. When potential functions exist they may be constructed from $\vec{V}$ by methods entirely analogous to those just described for the three-dimensional case. Again, the theorem is true for some regions more general than rectangles but, as in the three-dimensional case, it is not true for arbitrary open sets.

4.20 Exercises

In each of Exercises 1 through 10, a vector field $\vec{V}$ is defined by the formulas given. In each case determine whether or not $\vec{V}$ is the gradient of a scalar field. When $\vec{V}$ is a gradient, find a corresponding potential function f.

1. $\vec{V}(x, y, z) = x\vec{i} + y\vec{j} + z\vec{k}$.
2. $\vec{V}(x, y, z) = (x + z)\vec{i} - (y + z)\vec{j} + (x - y)\vec{k}$.
3. $\vec{V}(x, y, z) = 2xy^3\vec{i} + x^2z^3\vec{j} + 3x^2yz^2\vec{k}$.
4. $\vec{V}(x, y, z) = 3y^4z^2\vec{i} + 4x^3z^2\vec{j} - 3x^2y^2\vec{k}$.
5. $\vec{V}(x, y, z) = (2x^2 + 8xy^2)\vec{i} + (3x^3y - 3xy)\vec{j} - (4y^2z^2 + 2x^3z)\vec{k}$.
6. $\vec{V}(x, y, z) = (y^2\cos x + z^3)\vec{i} - (4 - 2y\sin x)\vec{j} + (3xz^2 + 2)\vec{k}$.
7. $\vec{V}(x, y, z) = (4xy - 3x^2z^2 + 1)\vec{i} + 2(x^2 + 1)\vec{j} - (2x^3z + 3z^2)\vec{k}$.

8. $\vec{V}(x, y) = (2xe^y + y)\vec{i} + (x^2e^y + x - 2y)\vec{j}$.

9. $\vec{V}(x, y) = (\sin y - y \sin x + x)\vec{i} + (\cos x + x \cos y + y)\vec{j}$.

10. $\vec{V}(x, y) = [\sin(xy) + xy \cos(xy)]\vec{i} + x^2 \cos(xy)\,\vec{j}$.

11. A fluid flows in the xy-plane, each particle moving directly away from the origin. If a particle is at a distance r from the origin its speed is ar^n, where a and n are constants.

(a) Determine those values of a and n for which the velocity vector field is the gradient of some scalar field.

(b) Find a potential function of the velocity whenever the velocity is a gradient.

12. The tangent line to a plane curve C at an arbitrary point (a, b) of C has the Cartesian equation

$$9ax - 9ay = 9bx - 16by + 9a^2 + 16b^2 - 18ab\,.$$

Find a Cartesian equation for C if the point $(1, 1)$ lies on C.

13. A surface S containing the point $(1, 2, 3)$ has a tangent plane whose Cartesian equation at each point (x_1, y_1, z_1) of S is

$$(x_1 + z_1)(x - x_1) - (y_1 + z_1)(y - y_1) + (x_1 - y_1)(z - z_1) = 0\,.$$

Find a Cartesian equation for the surface S.

14. Let u denote a scalar field that is continuously differentiable on an open set S in the xy-plane. The function u is said to be *harmonic on S* if the second-order partial derivatives $\partial^2 u/\partial x^2$ and $\partial^2 u/\partial y^2$ exist and are continuous on S and if

$$\frac{\partial^2 u}{\partial x^2} + \frac{\partial^2 u}{\partial y^2} = 0$$

everywhere on S. This partial differential equation is known as *Laplace's equation*.

(a) If u is harmonic on an open rectangle S, show that there is a scalar field v such that

$$\nabla v = -\frac{\partial u}{\partial y}\,\vec{i} + \frac{\partial u}{\partial x}\,\vec{j}$$

everywhere on S. Such a function v is said to be *conjugate* to u.

(b) Let u be harmonic on an open rectangle S and let v be conjugate to u. If $\partial^2 u/(\partial x \partial y) = \partial^2 u/(\partial y \partial x)$ everywhere on S, show that v is also harmonic on S and that $-u$ is conjugate to v.

(c) Refer to part (b) and show that the two families of level curves $u = $ constant and $v = $ constant intersect orthogonally.

15. Refer to Exercise 14. Show that each of the following functions is harmonic in the region given and find a function v conjugate to u.

(a) $u(x, y) = e^x \cos y$; S any open rectangle.

(b) $u(x, y) = \cos x \cosh y$; S any open rectangle.

(c) $u(x, y) = \log \sqrt{x^2 + y^2}$; S any open rectangle not containing the origin.

16. In this exercise we give an example of a function satisfying Laplace's equation at a point of discontinuity. Define a scalar field u as follows:

$$u(x, y) = \begin{cases} \dfrac{xy}{(x^2 + y^2)^2} & \text{if } (x, y) \neq (0, 0)\,, \\ 0 & \text{if } (x, y) = (0, 0)\,. \end{cases}$$

(a) If $(x, y) \neq (0, 0)$ show that

$$\frac{\partial^2 u}{\partial x^2} = 12xy\,\frac{x^2 - y^2}{(x^2 + y^2)^4} \quad \text{and} \quad \frac{\partial^2 u}{\partial y^2} = 12xy\,\frac{y^2 - x^2}{(x^2 + y^2)^4}\,.$$

This proves that u satisfies Laplace's equation at all points $(x, y) \neq (0, 0)$.

(b) Show that $D_{1,1}u(0, 0) = D_{2,2}u(0, 0) = 0$. This proves that u also satisfies Laplace's equation at $(0, 0)$.

(c) Show that u is not continuous at $(0, 0)$.

4.21 Maxima, minima, and saddle points

A surface that is described explicitly by an equation of the form $z = F(x, y)$ can be thought of as a level surface of the scalar field f defined by the equation

$$f(x, y, z) = F(x, y) - z .$$

If F is continuously differentiable, the gradient of this field is given by the vector

$$\nabla f = \frac{\partial F}{\partial x} \vec{i} + \frac{\partial F}{\partial y} \vec{j} - \vec{k} .$$

A linear equation for the tangent plane at a point $P_1 = (x_1, y_1, z_1)$ may be written in the form

$$z - z_1 = A(x - x_1) + B(y - y_1),$$

where

$$A = D_1F(x_1, y_1) \quad \text{and} \quad B = D_2F(x_1, y_1) .$$

When both coefficients A and B are zero, the point P_1 is called a *stationary point* of the surface and the point (x_1, y_1) is called a *stationary point* of the function F. The tangent plane is horizontal at a stationary point. The stationary points of a surface are usually classified into three categories: maxima, minima, and saddle points. If the surface is thought of as a mountain landscape, these categories correspond, respectively, to mountain tops, bottoms of valleys, and mountain passes. Their mathematical descriptions follow.

A function F is said to have an *absolute maximum on a set S* if there is at least one point $\vec{A}$ in S such that

$$(4.56) \qquad\qquad F(\vec{X}) \leq F(\vec{A})$$

for all $\vec{X}$ in S. The number $F(\vec{A})$ is called the absolute maximum value of F on S. The function is said to have a *relative maximum at $\vec{A}$* if the inequality in (4.56) is satisfied for every $\vec{X}$ in some neighborhood of $\vec{A}$ lying in S. In other words, a relative maximum at $\vec{A}$ is the absolute maximum on some neighborhood of $\vec{A}$. The terms *absolute minimum* and *relative minimum* are defined in an analogous fashion, using the inequality opposite to that in (4.56). A number which is either a relative maximum or a relative minimum of F is called an *extremum* of F. Although these definitions are meaningful for scalar fields defined on sets in n-space, we shall discuss in detail only the two-dimensional case.

If F has an extremum at a point (x_1, y_1) and if the partial derivatives D_1F and D_2F exist in a neighborhood of (x_1, y_1), it is easy to prove that both derivatives $D_1F(x_1, y_1)$ and $D_2F(x_1, y_1)$ must be zero. (This is proved by holding one component fixed and reducing the problem to the one-dimensional case.) Geometrically, this means that there is a horizontal tangent plane to the surface $z = F(x, y)$ at the point $(x_1, y_1, F(x_1, y_1))$. On the other hand, it is easy to find examples in which the vanishing of both partial derivatives at a point (x_1, y_1) does not necessarily imply an extremum at the point. This

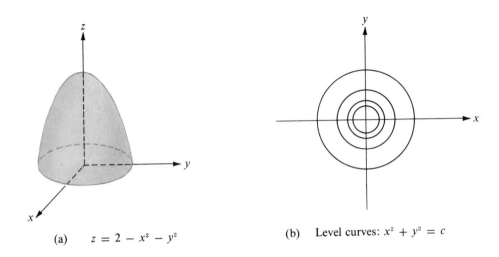

(a) $z = 2 - x^2 - y^2$ (b)   Level curves: $x^2 + y^2 = c$

FIGURE 4.10   *Example 1. Relative maximum at the origin.*

occurs at the so-called *saddle points*. A stationary point (x_1, y_1) of F is called a saddle point if every neighborhood of (x_1, y_1) contains points (x, y) such that $F(x, y) < F(x_1, y_1)$ and other points (x, y) such that $F(x, y) > F(x_1, y_1)$. Examples are described below. The situation is somewhat analogous to the one-dimensional case in which stationary points of a function are classified as maxima, minima, and points of inflection.

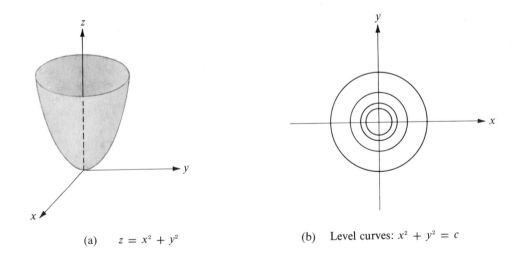

(a) $z = x^2 + y^2$ (b)   Level curves: $x^2 + y^2 = c$

FIGURE 4.11   *Example 2. Relative minimum at the origin.*

The following examples illustrate several types of stationary points. In each case the stationary point in question is at the origin.

Example 1: Relative maximum. $z = F(x, y) = 2 - x^2 - y^2$. This surface is a paraboloid of revolution. In the vicinity of the origin it has the shape shown in Figure 4.10(a). Its level curves are circles, some of which are shown in Figure 4.10(b). Since $F(x, y) = 2 - (x^2 + y^2) \leq 2 = F(0, 0)$ for all (x, y), it follows that F not only has a relative maximum at $(0, 0)$ but also an *absolute* maximum on any set containing the origin. Both partial derivatives $\partial F/\partial x$ and $\partial F/\partial y$ vanish at the origin.

Example 2: Relative minimum. $z = F(x, y) = x^2 + y^2$. This example, another paraboloid of revolution, is essentially the same as Example 1, except that there is a minimum at the origin rather than a maximum. The appearance of the surface near the origin is illustrated in Figure 4.11(a) and some of the level curves are shown in Figure 4.11(b).

Example 3: Saddle point. $z = F(x, y) = xy$. This surface is a hyperbolic paraboloid. Near the origin the surface is saddle shaped, as shown in Figure 4.12(a). Both partial derivatives $\partial F/\partial x$ and $\partial F/\partial y$ are zero at the origin but there is neither a relative maximum nor a relative minimum there. In fact, for points (x, y) in the first or third quadrants, x and y have the same sign, giving us $F(x, y) > 0 = F(0, 0)$, whereas for points in the second and fourth quadrants x and y have opposite signs, giving us $F(x, y) < 0 = F(0, 0)$. Therefore, in every neighborhood of the origin there are points at which the function is less than $F(0, 0)$ and points at which the function exceeds $F(0, 0)$, so the origin is a saddle point. The presence of the saddle point is also revealed by Figure 4.12(b), which shows some of the level curves near $(0, 0)$. These are hyperbolas having the x- and y-axes as asymptotes.

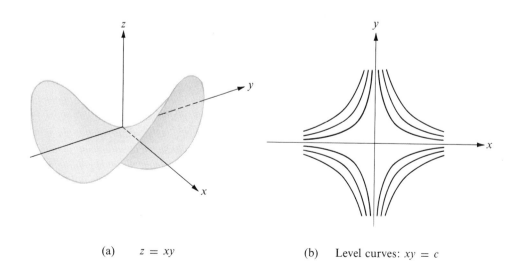

(a) $z = xy$ (b)   Level curves: $xy = c$

FIGURE 4.12   *Example 3. Saddle point at the origin.*

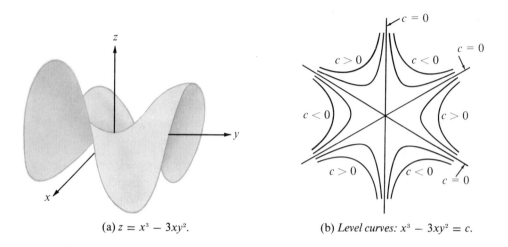

(a) $z = x^3 - 3xy^2$.   (b) *Level curves:* $x^3 - 3xy^2 = c$.

FIGURE 4.13   *Example 4. Saddle point at the origin.*

Example 4: Saddle point. $z = F(x, y) = x^3 - 3xy^2$. Near the origin, this surface has the appearance of a mountain pass in the vicinity of three peaks. This surface, sometimes referred to as a "monkey saddle," is shown in Figure 4.13(a). Some of the level curves are illustrated in Figure 4.13(b). It is clear that there is a saddle point at the origin.

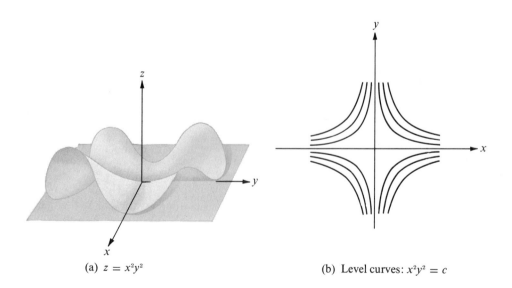

(a) $z = x^2y^2$ (b) Level curves: $x^2y^2 = c$

FIGURE 4.14   *Example 5. Relative minimum at the origin.*

Example 5: Relative minimum. $z = F(x,y) = x^2y^2$. This surface has the appearance of a valley surrounded by four mountains, as suggested by Figure 4.14(a). There is an absolute minimum at the origin, since $F(x, y) \geq F(0, 0)$ for all (x, y). The level curves [shown in Figure 4.14(b)] are hyperbolas having the x- and y-axes as asymptotes. Note that these level curves are similar to those in Example 3. In this case, however, the function assumes only nonnegative values on all its level curves.

Example 6: Relative maximum. $z = F(x, y) = 1 - x^2$. In this case the surface is a cylinder with generators parallel to the y-axis, as shown in Figure 4.15(a). Cross sections cut by planes parallel to the x-axis are parabolas. There is obviously an absolute maximum at the origin because $F(x, y) = 1 - x^2 \leq 1 = F(0, 0)$ for all (x, y). The level curves form a family of parallel straight lines as shown in Figure 4.15(b).

Sometimes it is possible to determine the nature of a stationary point entirely by analytic methods (that is, without having to draw the surface or its level curves). As in the case of functions of one variable, an examination of second derivatives often proves to be helpful. The simplest second-derivative test is described in the following theorem.

4–10   THEOREM.   *Second-derivative test for extrema of functions of two variables.* Assume F has continuous second-order partial derivatives in an open set S in the xy-plane. Suppose that (x_1, y_1) is a point of S at which both partial derivatives $\partial F/\partial x$ and $\partial F/\partial y$ are zero. Let $\Delta = AC - B^2$, where A, B, and C are the following second-order partial derivatives:

$$A = D_{1,1}F(x_1, y_1), \qquad B = D_{1,2}F(x_1, y_1), \qquad C = D_{2,2}F(x_1, y_1).$$

Then we have:
(a) If $\Delta > 0$ and $A > 0$, F has a relative minimum at (x_1, y_1).
(b) If $\Delta > 0$ and $A < 0$, F has a relative maximum at (x_1, y_1).
(c) If $\Delta < 0$, F has a saddle point at (x_1, y_1).
(d) If $\Delta = 0$, the test is inconclusive.

Note. Although the proof of this theorem is not difficult, it is lengthy; to avoid disrupting the discussion we have placed it in a separate starred section (Section 4.24) that may be omitted or postponed.

In Examples 4 and 5 shown above, all second-order partial derivatives are zero at the origin and hence $\Delta = 0$. In the first case there is a saddle point at the origin, and in the second case F has a relative minimum there. This shows that the condition $\Delta = 0$ is inconclusive. Tests involving higher order derivatives can be used to treat these examples, but we shall not discuss them here.

Even when Theorem 4–10 is applicable it may not be the simplest way to determine the nature of a stationary pient. For example, when $F(x, y) = e^{1/g(x, y)}$, where $g(x, y) = x^2 + 2 + \cos^2 y - 2 \cos y$, the test is applicable, but the computations are lengthy. In this case we may express $g(x, y)$ as a sum of squares by writing $g(x, y) = 1 + x^2 + (1 - \cos y)^2$. We see at once that F has relative maxima at the points at which $x^2 = 0$ and $(1 - \cos y)^2 = 0$. These are the points $(0, 2n\pi)$, where n is any integer.

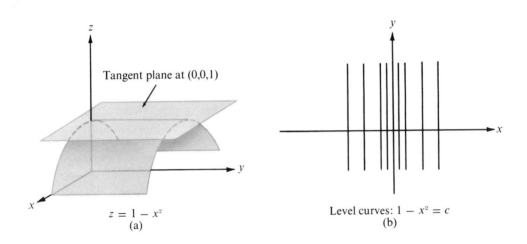

Tangent plane at (0,0,1)

$z = 1 - x^2$
(a)

Level curves: $1 - x^2 = c$
(b)

FIGURE 4.15   *Example 6. Relative maximum at the origin.*

4.22 Extrema with side conditions. Lagrange's multipliers

We turn now to a different type of extremum problem. Suppose $f(x, y, z)$ represents the temperature at the point (x, y, z) in 3-space and we ask for the maximum or minimum value of the temperature on a specific surface. If the equation of the surface is given explicitly in the form $z = h(x, y)$, we may replace z by $h(x, y)$ in the expression $f(x, y, z)$, thereby expressing the temperature on the surface as a function of x and y, say $F(x, y) = f[x, y, h(x, y)]$. The problem is now reduced to finding the extreme values of F.

In practice, difficulties arise when we attempt to solve a problem of this type. First of all, the equation of the surface may be given in an implicit form, say $g(x, y, z) = 0$, and it may not be possible to express z as a function of x and y, or even to express x or y in terms of the remaining variables. The problem may be further complicated when the extreme values of the temperature are sought at those points which lie on a given *curve* rather than on a given surface. Such a curve may be thought of as the intersection of two surfaces, say $g_1(x, y, z) = 0$ and $g_2(x, y, z) = 0$. If we could solve these two equations simultaneously, say for x and y in terms of z, we could introduce these expressions into $f(x, y, z)$ and obtain a new function of z alone, whose extrema we would then seek. However, this procedure can seldom be carried out in practice, so a more practicable method must be sought. An elegant and useful procedure for attacking such problems was developed by Lagrange. Before we describe the method of Lagrange in detail we shall consider a simple example.

Let us return to the problem of locating the extreme values of $f(x, y, z)$ when the point (x, y, z) is restricted so that it lies on a curve C. If we express the curve in terms of a parameter t, then on the curve C the field f becomes a function of t alone, say $f(x, y, z) = F(t)$, where t varies over an interval $[a, b]$. If F has a relative extremum at an interior point t_1 of the interval $[a, b]$ we must have $F'(t_1) = 0$. On the other hand, the chain rule

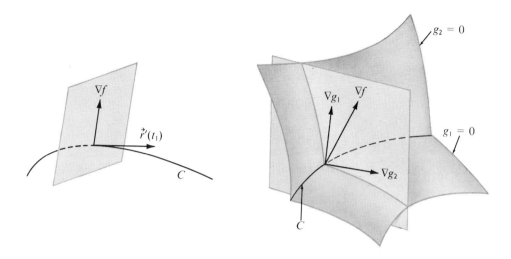

FIGURE 4.16   *The gradient vector ∇f lies in a*   FIGURE 4.17   *The vectors ∇g_1, ∇g_2, and ∇f*
plane normal to C.   *shown lying in the same plane.*

tells us that the derivative $F'(t)$ is the same as the derivative of the scalar field f with respect to the velocity vector of the curve. That is, we have

(4.57) $$F'(t) = \nabla f[\vec{r}(t)] \cdot \vec{r}'(t),$$

where $\vec{r}'$ represents the velocity vector of C. In particular, at the point corresponding to $t = t_1$ the gradient vector ∇f must be perpendicular to the velocity vector, since the dot product in (4.57) is zero. In other words, at this point the gradient vector ∇f lies in the plane normal to the curve C, as shown in Figure 4.16. Now suppose the curve C is the intersection of two surfaces whose Cartesian equations are $g_1(x, y, z) = 0$ and $g_2(x, y, z) = 0$. The two gradient vectors ∇g_1 and ∇g_2, which are normals to these surfaces, are also normal to C at each of its points. In particular, at the point corresponding to $t = t_1$ these normals must lie in the same plane as the gradient vector ∇f. (See Figure 4.17.) Therefore at this point the gradient ∇f may be expressed as a linear combination of ∇g_1 and ∇g_2, say

$$\nabla f = \lambda_1 \nabla g_1 + \lambda_2 \nabla g_2 .$$

When this vector equation is written out in component form, we obtain three scalar equations that must be satisfied by the coordinates (x, y, z) of any point at which $f(x, y, z)$ has a relative extremum along the curve C. These three equations, with the two equations $g_1(x, y, z) = 0$ and $g_2(x, y, z) = 0$, give us five equations altogether involving the five "unknowns" x, y, z, λ_1, and λ_2. If we can solve these equations simultaneously we obtain those points (x, y, z) *among which* $f(x, y, z)$ has an extremum along C. Each such point must be tested to determine if it yields a maximum, a minimum, or neither. The scalars λ_1 and λ_2 which are introduced to help us solve this type of problem are known as *Lagrange's multipliers.*

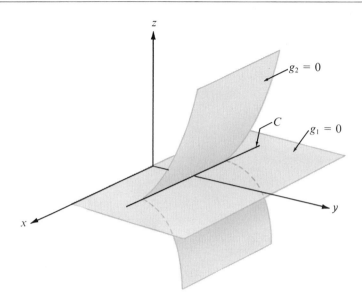

FIGURE 4.18   *An example where Lagrange's method is not applicable.*

If we ignore the geometrical aspects of the foregoing discussion, we may summarize the results entirely in analytical terms:

The method of Lagrange's multipliers. To find the relative extrema of $f(x, y, z)$, subject to the side conditions $g_1(x, y, z) = 0$ and $g_2(x, y, z) = 0$, solve these equations simultaneously with the three scalar equations obtained from the vector relation

$$(4.58) \qquad\qquad \nabla f = \lambda_1 \nabla g_1 + \lambda_2 \nabla g_2 \, .$$

The points (x, y, z) at which relative extrema occur are found among the solutions to these equations.

We tacitly assume that the surfaces $g_1(x, y, z) = 0$ and $g_2(x, y, z) = 0$ intersect in a curve, and that the two gradient vectors ∇g_1 and ∇g_2 are not collinear at the points at which the extrema occur. In fact, the method may fail if ∇g_1 and ∇g_2 are collinear. For example, suppose we try to apply the method to find the extreme values of $f(x, y, z) = x^2 + y^2$ on the curve of intersection of the two surfaces $g_1(x, y, z) = 0$ and $g_2(x, y, z) = 0$, where $g_1(x, y, z) = z$ and $g_2(x, y, z) = z^2 - (y - 1)^3$. The two surfaces, a plane and a cylinder, intersect along the straight line C shown in Figure 4.18. The problem obviously has a solution, because $f(x, y, z)$ represents the distance of the point (x, y, z) from the z-axis and this distance is a minimum on C when the point is at $(0, 1, 0)$. However, at this point the gradient vectors are $\nabla g_1 = \vec{k}$, $\nabla g_2 = \vec{0}$, and $\nabla f = 2\vec{j}$, and it is clear that there are no scalars λ_1 and λ_2 that satisfy Equation (4.58).

When the two gradient vectors ∇g_1 and ∇g_2 are collinear their cross product is the zero vector. This cross product may be written as follows:

$$\nabla g_1 \times \nabla g_2 = \begin{vmatrix} \vec{i} & \vec{j} & \vec{k} \\ \dfrac{\partial g_1}{\partial x} & \dfrac{\partial g_1}{\partial y} & \dfrac{\partial g_1}{\partial z} \\ \dfrac{\partial g_2}{\partial x} & \dfrac{\partial g_2}{\partial y} & \dfrac{\partial g_2}{\partial z} \end{vmatrix} = \frac{\partial(g_1, g_2)}{\partial(y, z)}\, \vec{i} + \frac{\partial(g_1, g_2)}{\partial(z, x)}\, \vec{j} + \frac{\partial(g_1, g_2)}{\partial(x, y)}\, \vec{k}\,.$$

Therefore, noncollinearity of ∇g_1 and ∇g_2 means that not all three of the Jacobians on the right are zero. It can be shown that Lagrange's method is applicable whenever this condition is satisfied.

The method of Lagrange's multipliers is more general than the above description indicates. It is applicable when f is a function of n variables $x_1, \ldots, x_n$ subject to m constraints, say

(4.59) $\qquad g_1(x_1, \ldots, x_n) = 0, \qquad \ldots, \qquad g_m(x_1, \ldots, x_n) = 0,$

where $m < n$. We consider the system of $n + m$ equations obtained by taking the m equations in (4.59) and the n equations determined by the vector relation

$$\nabla f = \lambda_1 \nabla g_1 + \lambda_2 \nabla g_2 + \cdots + \lambda_m \nabla g_m\,.$$

These equations are to be solved (if possible) for the $n + m$ unknowns $\lambda_1, \ldots, \lambda_m$ and $x_1, \ldots, x_n$. Each point $(x_1, \ldots, x_n)$ so obtained must then be tested to determine whether it yields a maximum, a minimum, or neither. One Lagrange multiplier is introduced for each side condition. The method is valid if not all the Jacobians of the m functions $g_1, \ldots, g_m$ with respect to m of the variables $x_1, \ldots, x_n$ are zero at the extreme value in question. The proof of the validity of the method in general is an important result in advanced calculus. (See Chapter 7 of the author's *Mathematical Analysis, ibid.*)

Note. When we seek relative extrema of a function F of one variable, we investigate those points x at which $F'(x) = 0$; for functions of two variables we investigate points (x, y) at which $D_1 F(x, y) = D_2 F(x, y) = 0$; and for a function F of n variables we investigate points $(x_1, x_2, \ldots, x_n)$ at which $D_i F(x_1, x_2, \ldots, x_n) = 0$ for all $i = 1, 2, \ldots, n$. Therefore, for any number of variables, the relative extrema of F occur among those points $\vec{X}$ at which $\nabla F(\vec{X}) = \vec{0}$. The same idea underlies Lagrange's method. If we seek the relative extrema of f subject to m constraints $g_1(\vec{X}) = \cdots = g_m(\vec{X}) = 0$, we investigate the points $\vec{X}$ at which $\nabla F(\vec{X}) = \vec{0}$, where now $F = f - \lambda_1 g_1 - \cdots - \lambda_m g_m$.

4.23 Exercises

In Exercises 1 through 15, locate and classify the stationary points (if any) of the surfaces having the Cartesian equations given.

1. $z = x^2 + (y - 1)^2$.

2. $z = x^2 - (y - 1)^2$.

3. $z = 1 + x^2 - y^2$.

4. $z = (x - y + 1)^2$.

5. $z = 2x^2 - xy - 3y^2 - 3x + 7y$.

6. $z = x^2 - xy + y^2 - 2x + y$.

7. $z = x^3 - 3xy^2 + y^3$.

8. $z = x^2 y^3 (6 - x - y)$.

9. $z = x^3 + y^3 - 3xy$.

10. $z = \sin x \cosh y$.

11. $z = e^{2x+3y}(8x^2 - 6xy + 3y^2)$.

12. $z = (5x + 7y - 25)\, e^{-(x^2+xy+y^2)}$.

13. $z = \sin x \sin y \sin(x + y)$, $0 \le x \le \pi$, $0 \le y \le \pi$.

14. $z = x - 2y + \log \sqrt{x^2 + y^2} + 3 \arc\tan \frac{y}{x}, x > 0$.

15. $z = (x^2 + y^2) e^{-(x^2+y^2)}$.

16. Let $f(x, y) = 3x^4 - 4x^2y + y^2$. Show that on every line $y = mx$ the function has a minimum at $(0, 0)$, but that there is no relative minimum in any two-dimensional neighborhood of the origin. Make a sketch indicating the set of points (x, y) at which $f(x, y) > 0$ and the set at which $f(x, y) < 0$.

17. Let $f(x, y) = (3 - x)(3 - y)(x + y - 3)$.

    (a) Make a sketch indicating the set of points (x, y) at which $f(x, y) \geq 0$.

    (b) Find all points (x, y) in the plane at which $D_1 f(x, y) = D_2 f(x, y) = 0$. [*Hint.* $D_1 f(x, y)$ has $(3 - y)$ as a factor.]

    (c) Which of the stationary points are relative maxima? Which are relative minima? Which are neither? Give reasons for your answers.

    (d) Does f have an absolute minimum or an absolute maximum on the whole plane? Give reasons for your answers.

18. Find the extreme values of $z = xy$ subject to the condition $x + y = 1$.

19. Find the maximum and minimum distances from the origin to the curve $5x^2 + 6xy + 5y^2 = 8$.

20. Assume a and b are fixed positive numbers.

    (a) Find the extreme values of $z = x/a + y/b$ subject to the condition $x^2 + y^2 = 1$.

    (b) Find the extreme values of $z = x^2 + y^2$ subject to the condition $x/a + y/b = 1$.
In each case, interpret the problem geometrically.

21. Find the extreme values of $z = \cos^2 x + \cos^2 y$ subject to the side condition $x - y = \pi/4$.

22. Find the extreme values of the scalar field $f(x, y, z) = x - 2y + 2z$ on the sphere $x^2 + y^2 + z^2 = 1$.

23. Find the points of the surface $z^2 - xy = 1$ nearest to the origin.

24. Find the shortest distance from the point $(1, 0)$ to the parabola $y^2 = 4x$.

25. Find the points on the curve of intersection of the two surfaces

$$x^2 - xy + y^2 - z^2 = 1 \quad \text{and} \quad x^2 + y^2 = 1$$

which are nearest to the origin.

26. If a, b, and c are positive numbers, find the maximum value of $f(x, y, z) = x^a y^b z^c$ subject to the side condition $x + y + z = 1$.

27. *Method of least squares.* Given n distinct numbers $x_1, \ldots, x_n$ and n further numbers $y_1, \ldots, y_n$ (not necessarily distinct), it is generally impossible to find a straight line $f(x) = ax + b$ which passes through all the points (x_i, y_i), that is, such that $f(x_i) = y_i$ for each i. However, we can try a linear function which makes the "total square error"

$$E(a, b) = \sum_{i=1}^{n} [f(x_i) - y_i]^2$$

a minimum. Determine values of a and b which do this.

28. Extend the method of least squares to 3-space. That is, find a linear function $f(x, y) = ax + by + c$ which minimizes the total square error

$$E(a, b, c) = \sum_{i=1}^{n} [f(x_i, y_i) - z_i]^2 ,$$

where (x_i, y_i) are n given distinct points and $z_1, \ldots, z_n$ are n given real numbers.

29. Given the conic section $Ax^2 + 2Bxy + Cy^2 = 1$, where $A > 0$ and $B^2 < AC$. Let m and

M denote the distances from the origin to the nearest and furthest points of the conic. Show that

$$M^2 = \frac{A + C + \sqrt{(A - C)^2 + 4B^2}}{2(AC - B^2)}$$

and find a companion formula for m^2.

30. Let $f(x, y) = Ax^2 + 2Bxy + Cy^2 + 2Dx + 2Ey + F$, where $A > 0$ and $B^2 < AC$.
   (a) Prove that a point (x_1, y_1) exists at which f has a minimum.
   (b) Prove that $f(x_1, y_1) = Dx_1 + Ey_1 + F$ at this minimum.
   (c) Show that

$$f(x_1, y_1) = \frac{1}{AC - B^2}\begin{vmatrix} A & B & D \\ B & C & E \\ D & E & F \end{vmatrix}.$$

31. Find the minimum volume bounded by the planes $x = 0$, $y = 0$, $z = 0$, and a plane which is tangent to the ellipsoid

$$\frac{x^2}{a^2} + \frac{y^2}{b^2} + \frac{z^2}{c^2} = 1$$

at a point in the octant $x > 0$, $y > 0$, $z > 0$.

32. Find the maximum of $\log x + \log y + 3 \log z$ on that portion of the sphere $x^2 + y^2 + z^2 = 5r^2$ where $x > 0$, $y > 0$, $z > 0$. Use the result to prove that for real positive numbers a, b, c we have

$$abc^3 \le 27\left(\frac{a + b + c}{5}\right)^5.$$

★4.24 Proof of the second-derivative test for extrema

Section 4.21 described a theorem for testing a stationary point (x_1, y_1) of a function F to determine whether it is a relative maximum, a relative minimum, or a saddle point. A proof of the theorem is given here. The reader should refer to Section 4.21 for the notation used in this proof.

The idea of the proof is to show that near the point (x_1, y_1) the surface $z = F(x, y)$ behaves very much like the quadric surface $z = Ax^2 + 2Bxy + Cy^2$ in the vicinity of the origin.

If we write $Q(x, y) = Ax^2 + 2Bxy + Cy^2$, by the process of completing the squares we find

(4.60) $$Q(x, y) = \frac{1}{A}[(Ax + By)^2 + (AC - B^2)y^2].$$

This equation is valid whenever $A \ne 0$. The expression $Q(x, y)$ is called a *quadratic form* in x and y and the number $\Delta = AC - B^2$ is called the *discriminant* of the quadratic form. When $\Delta > 0$, the expression multiplying $1/A$ in Equation (4.60) is the sum of two squares, and when $\Delta < 0$ it is the difference of two squares. This is why the nature of this quadratic form near the origin is determined by the algebraic sign of Δ.

The first step in the proof is to show that the given function F behaves like a quadratic form near the point (x_1, y_1). We choose a neighborhood N_1 of (x_1, y_1) that lies in S. Any point (x, y) in N_1 different from (x_1, y_1) can be written as $(x_1 + h, y_1 + k)$, where h and k are not both zero. Then the rectangle with vertices (x_1, y_1), $(x_1 + h, y_1)$, $(x_1 + h,$

$(x_1, y_1 + k)$ $(x_1 + h, y_1 + k)$

(x_1, y_1) $(x_1 + h, y_1)$

FIGURE 4.19

$y_1 + k$), and $(x_1, y_1 + k)$ lies in the given open set S. (An example with both $h > 0$ and $k > 0$ is shown in Figure 4.19.) We shall prove first that the difference $F(x_1 + h, y_1 + k) - F(x_1, y_1)$ is a quadratic form in h and k; that is,

$$(4.61) \qquad F(x_1 + h, y_1 + k) - F(x_1, y_1) = \tfrac{1}{2}(ah^2 + 2bhk + ck^2),$$

where the coefficients a, b, and c are second-order partial derivatives of F evaluated at some point $(\bar{x}, \bar{y})$ in the rectangle:

$$(4.62) \qquad a = D_{1,1}F(\bar{x}, \bar{y}), \qquad b = D_{1,2}F(\bar{x}, \bar{y}), \qquad c = D_{2,2}F(\bar{x}, \bar{y}).$$

To prove (4.61) we apply Taylor's formula with remainder† to a function g of one variable defined as follows:

$$g(t) = F(x_1 + ht, y_1 + kt) - F(x_1, y_1).$$

Then $F(x_1 + h, y_1 + k) - F(x_1, y_1) = g(1) - g(0)$ and Taylor's formula tells us that

$$(4.63) \qquad g(1) = g(0) + g'(0) + \tfrac{1}{2}g''(\theta)$$

for some θ satisfying $0 < \theta < 1$. The derivatives of g, computed by using the chain rule, are

$$g'(t) = h\, D_1F + k\, D_2F$$

and

$$g''(t) = h^2\, D_{1,1}F + hk\, D_{1,2}F + kh\, D_{2,1}F + k^2\, D_{2,2}F \, ;$$

all partial derivatives are evaluated at the point $(x_1 + ht, y_1 + kt)$. When $t = 0$ we have $g'(0) = 0$ and

$$g''(\theta) = ah^2 + 2bhk + ck^2 \, ,$$

where a, b, and c are given by (4.62). The point $(\bar{x}, \bar{y})$ is $(x_1 + \theta h, y_1 + \theta k)$, where θ is the number determined by (4.63). Substituting in Equation (4.63) we obtain (4.61).

At this stage we separate the proof into cases, depending on the algebraic sign of Δ.

† See Theorem 7–6 in Section 7.6 of Volume I.

CASE 1: Assume $\Delta > 0$. Since $\Delta = AC - B^2$, it follows that $A \neq 0$. Introduce a new function D, defined at each point of S by the equation

$$D(x, y) = D_{1,1}F(x, y) \, D_{2,2}F(x, y) - D_{1,2}^2 F(x, y).$$

Then $D(x_1, y_1) = \Delta > 0$. Because of the continuity of the second-order partials, the function D is continuous on S. Hence there is a neighborhood N_2 of (x_1, y_1), contained in N_1, in which $D(x, y) > 0$ and $D_{1,1}F(x, y)$ has the same sign as A. We now consider only points $(x, y) = (x_1 + h, y_1 + k)$ that lie in N_2, and we note that the rectangle of Figure 4.19 lies within N_2. Then the point $(\bar{x}, \bar{y})$ of (4.62) is in this rectangle; hence $ac - b^2$ is positive and a has the same sign as A. By completing the squares we may write Equation (4.61) as

(4.64) $\qquad F(x_1 + h, y_1 + k) - F(x_1, y_1) = \dfrac{1}{2a}[(ah + bk)^2 + (ac - b^2)k^2].$

The expression in square brackets is positive (since it is the sum of two squares) and hence the difference on the left has the same sign as a (which, in turn, has the same sign as A). From this it follows that F has a relative minimum at (x_1, y_1) if $A > 0$ and a relative maximum if $A < 0$. This proves parts (a) and (b) of the theorem.

CASE 2: Assume $\Delta < 0$. To prove that there is a saddle point at (x_1, y_1) we must show that every neighborhood of (x_1, y_1) contains points (x, y) for which $F(x, y) - F(x_1, y_1)$ is positive and points (x, y) for which it is negative.

If $A \neq 0$, we choose a neighborhood of (x_1, y_1) in which $D(x, y)$ is negative and in which $D_{1,1}F(x, y)$ has the same sign as A. Now we choose h and k so that the rectangle of Figure 4.19 is in this neighborhood. As before, Equation (4.64) holds with $ac - b^2 < 0$ and a having the same sign as A. If we take $k = 0$ and $h \neq 0$ the left-hand side of Equation (4.64) has the same sign as A. On the other hand, if we take $k \neq 0$ and let $h = -bk/a$, the left member of (4.64) has the sign opposite to that of A. Therefore, (x_1, y_1) is a saddle point. A similar argument holds when $C \neq 0$.

Finally, we treat the case $A = C = 0$. The condition $\Delta < 0$ implies $B \neq 0$. Let us now choose $h = k$. Then Equation (4.61) becomes

$$F(x_1 + h, y_1 + h) - F(x_1, y_1) = \frac{h^2}{2}(a + 2b + c),$$

and this leads to the limit relation:

$$\lim_{h \to 0} \frac{F(x_1 + h, y_1 + h) - F(x_1, y_1)}{h^2} = \lim_{h \to 0} \frac{a + 2b + c}{2} = \frac{A + C}{2} + B = B.$$

Hence for sufficiently small h the quotient

$$\frac{F(x_1 + h, y_1 + h) - F(x_1, y_1)}{h^2}$$

(and hence its numerator) has the same sign as B. On the other hand, if we choose $h = -k$ and apply the same type of argument, we find that the limit of this quotient is $-B$; hence for sufficiently small h the numerator of this quotient has the sign opposite to that of B. This shows that (x_1, y_1) is a saddle point when $A = C = 0$, which completes the proof of Case 2 and therefore of part (c) of the theorem. The proof of part (d) was demonstrated by examples in Section 4.21.

⋆4.25 A sufficient condition for the equality of mixed partial derivatives

If f is a real-valued function of two variables, the two mixed partial derivatives $D_{1,2}f$ and $D_{2,1}f$ are not necessarily equal. By $D_{1,2}f$ we mean $D_1(D_2f) = \partial^2 f/(\partial x \partial y)$, and by $D_{2,1}f$ we mean $D_2(D_1f) = \partial^2 f/(\partial y \partial x)$. For example, if f is defined by the equations

$$f(x, y) = xy \frac{x^2 - y^2}{x^2 + y^2} \quad \text{for} \quad (x, y) \neq (0, 0), \qquad f(0, 0) = 0,$$

it is easy to prove that $D_{2,1}f(0, 0) = -1$ and $D_{1,2}f(0, 0) = 1$. This may be seen as follows: The definition of $D_{2,1}f(0, 0)$ states that

$$(4.65) \qquad\qquad D_{2,1}f(0, 0) = \lim_{k \to 0} \frac{D_1f(0, k) - D_1f(0, 0)}{k}.$$

Now we have

$$D_1f(0, 0) = \lim_{h \to 0} \frac{f(h, 0) - f(0, 0)}{h} = 0$$

and, if $(x, y) \neq (0, 0)$, we find

$$D_1f(x, y) = \frac{y(x^4 + 4x^2y^2 - y^4)}{(x^2 + y^2)^2}.$$

Therefore, if $k \neq 0$ we have $D_1f(0, k) = -k^5/k^4 = -k$ and hence

$$\frac{D_1f(0, k) - D_1f(0, 0)}{k} = -1.$$

Using this in (4.65) we find that $D_{2,1}f(0, 0) = -1$. A similar argument shows that $D_{1,2}f(0, 0) = 1$, and hence $D_{2,1}f(0, 0) \neq D_{1,2}f(0, 0)$.

In the example just treated the two mixed partials $D_{1,2}f$ and $D_{2,1}f$ are not both continuous at the origin. It can be shown that the two mixed partials *are* equal at a point (a, b) if at least one of them is continuous in a neighborhood of the point. More precisely, we have the following theorem:

4–11   THEOREM. Assume f is a scalar field such that the partial derivatives D_1f, D_2f, and $D_{2,1}f$ are continuous in a neighborhood of a point (a, b). Then the derivative $D_{1,2}f(a, b)$ exists and we have

$$D_{1,2}f(a, b) = D_{2,1}f(a, b).$$

Proof. The definition of $D_{1,2}f(a, b)$ states that

$$(4.66) \qquad\qquad D_{1,2}f(a, b) = \lim_{h \to 0} \frac{D_2f(a + h, b) - D_2f(a, b)}{h}.$$

We are to prove that this limit exists and has the value $D_{2,1}f(a, b)$. Using the definition of D_2f we have

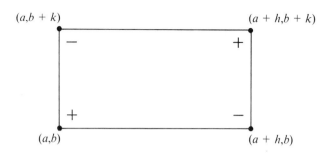

FIGURE 4.20

$$D_2 f(a, b) = \lim_{k \to 0} \frac{f(a, b + k) - f(a, b)}{k}$$

and

$$D_2 f(a + h, b) = \lim_{k \to 0} \frac{f(a + h, b + k) - f(a + h, b)}{k}.$$

Therefore the difference quotient in (4.66) may be written as

(4.67) $$\frac{D_2 f(a + h, b) - D_2 f(a, b)}{h} = \lim_{k \to 0} \frac{\Delta(h, k)}{hk},$$

where

$$\Delta(h, k) = f(a + h, b + k) - f(a + h, b) - f(a, b + k) + f(a, b).$$

Note that $\Delta(h, k)$ is a combination of the values of f at the vertices of the rectangle shown in Figure 4.20, taken with the algebraic signs indicated in the diagram.

To prove the theorem we must show that

$$\lim_{h \to 0} \left[\lim_{k \to 0} \frac{\Delta(h, k)}{hk} \right] = D_{2,1} f(a, b).$$

We begin by expressing $\Delta(h, k)$ in terms of the derivative $D_{2,1} f$. For this purpose we introduce a new function G of one variable defined by the equation

$$G(x) = f(x, b + k) - f(x, b)$$

for each x in the interval $a \leq x \leq a + h$. (Geometrically, we are considering the values of f at those points at which an arbitrary vertical line cuts the rectangle shown in Figure 4.20.) Then $\Delta(h, k)$ may be expressed in terms of G as follows:

$$\Delta(h, k) = G(a + h) - G(a).$$

Applying the one-dimensional mean-value theorem to the right-hand member we obtain

$$\Delta(h, k) = h\, G'(x_1), \quad \text{where} \quad a < x_1 < a + h.$$

Note that x_1 depends on k because x_1 depends on G which, in turn, depends on k. Since $G'(x) = D_1f(x, b + k) - D_1f(x, b)$, the foregoing equation becomes

$$\Delta(h, k) = h[D_1f(x_1, b + k) - D_1f(x_1, b)] ;$$

by another application of the mean-value theorem we obtain

(4.68) $\Delta(h, k) = hk\, D_{2,1}f(x_1, y_1) ,$ where $b < y_1 < b + k$.

This is the expression for $\Delta(h, k)$ that we were seeking. Notice that the point (x_1, y_1) is somewhere inside the rectangle shown in Figure 4.20. To complete the proof we must show that

(4.69) $$\lim_{h \to 0} \left[\lim_{k \to 0} D_{2,1}f(x_1, y_1) \right] = D_{2,1}f(a, b) .$$

When $k \to 0$, the point $y_1 \to b$, but the behavior of x_1 as a function of k is unknown. If we knew that x_1 approached some limit, say $\bar{x}$, as $k \to 0$, we could use the continuity of $D_{2,1}f$ to deduce that

$$\lim_{k \to 0} D_{2,1}f(x_1, y_1) = D_{2,1}f(\bar{x}, b) .$$

Since the limit $\bar{x}$ would have to lie in the interval $a \leq \bar{x} \leq a + h$, we could then let $h \to 0$ and deduce (4.69). However, the fact that $\bar{x}$ depends on k in an unknown fashion makes a slightly more involved argument necessary.

Because of Equations (4.67) and (4.68) we know that the following limit exists:

$$\lim_{k \to 0} D_{2,1}f(x_1, y_1) .$$

Let us denote this limit by $F(h)$. To complete the proof we must show that

$$\lim_{h \to 0} F(h) = D_{2,1}f(a, b) .$$

For this purpose we appeal to the definition of continuity of $D_{2,1}f$ at (a, b).

Let ϵ be a given positive number. Continuity of $D_{2,1}f$ at (a, b) means that there is a neighborhood $N(a, b)$, of radius δ, say, such that

(4.70) $|D_{2,1}f(x, y) - D_{2,1}f(a, b)| < \dfrac{\epsilon}{2}$ whenever $(x, y) \,\varepsilon\, N(a, b)$.

If we choose h and k so that $|h| < \delta/2$ and $|k| < \delta/2$, the entire rectangle shown in Figure 4.20 will lie in the neighborhood $N(a, b)$ and, specifically, the point (x_1, y_1) will be in $N(a, b)$. Therefore (4.70) is valid when $(x, y) = (x_1, y_1)$ and we may write

(4.71) $0 \leq |D_{2,1}f(x_1, y_1) - D_{2,1}f(a, b)| < \dfrac{\epsilon}{2} .$

Now keep h fixed and let $k \to 0$. The term $D_{2,1}f(x_1, y_1)$ approaches $F(h)$ and the other terms in (4.71) are independent of k. Therefore we have

$$0 \leq |F(h) - D_{2,1}f(a, b)| \leq \dfrac{\epsilon}{2} < \epsilon ,$$

provided that $0 < |h| < \delta/2$. But this is precisely the meaning of the statement

$$\lim_{h \to 0} F(h) = D_{2,1}f(a, b)$$

and, as we have already remarked, this completes the proof.

Note. It should be observed that the theorem is also valid if the roles of the two derivatives $D_{1,2}f$ and $D_{2,1}f$ are interchanged.

4.26 Miscellaneous exercises

1. If $f(x, y, z) = (\vec{r} \times \vec{A}) \cdot (\vec{r} \times \vec{B})$, where $\vec{r} = x\vec{i} + y\vec{j} + z\vec{k}$ and $\vec{A}$ and $\vec{B}$ are constant vectors, show that $\nabla f(x, y, z) = \vec{B} \times (\vec{r} \times \vec{A}) + \vec{A} \times (\vec{r} \times \vec{B})$.

2. Find a scalar field f satisfying both the following conditions:
    (a) The partial derivatives $D_1 f(0, 0)$ and $D_2 f(0, 0)$ exist and are zero.
    (b) The directional derivative at the origin in the direction of the vector $\vec{i} + \vec{j}$ exists and has the value 3. Explain why such an f cannot be continuously differentiable at $(0, 0)$.

3. Let f be defined as follows:

$$f(x, y) = y \frac{x^2 - y^2}{x^2 + y^2} \quad \text{if} \quad (x, y) \neq (0, 0), \quad f(0, 0) = 0.$$

Compute the following partial derivatives, when they exist: $D_1 f(0, 0), D_2 f(0, 0), D_{2,1} f(0, 0), D_{1,2} f(0, 0)$.

4. Let $\vec{r} = x\vec{i} + y\vec{j} + z\vec{k}$ and let $r = |\vec{r}|$. If $\vec{A}$ and $\vec{B}$ are constant vectors, show that:

(a) $\vec{A} \cdot \nabla\left(\dfrac{1}{r}\right) = -\dfrac{\vec{A} \cdot \vec{r}}{r^3}$.

(b) $\vec{B} \cdot \nabla\left(\vec{A} \cdot \nabla\left(\dfrac{1}{r}\right)\right) = \dfrac{3\vec{A} \cdot \vec{r}\,\vec{B} \cdot \vec{r}}{r^5} - \dfrac{\vec{A} \cdot \vec{B}}{r^3}$.

5. Assume that the equations $u = f(x, y)$, $x = X(t)$, $y = Y(t)$ define u as a function of t, say $u = F(t)$. Compute the third derivative $F'''(t)$ in terms of derivatives of f, X, and Y.

6. The change of variable $x = u + v$, $y = uv^2$ transforms $f(x, y)$ into $g(u, v)$. Compute the value of $\partial^2 g / (\partial v \partial u)$ at the point at which $u = 1$, $v = 1$, given that

$$\frac{\partial f}{\partial y} = \frac{\partial^2 f}{\partial x^2} = \frac{\partial^2 f}{\partial y^2} = \frac{\partial^2 f}{\partial x \partial y} = \frac{\partial^2 f}{\partial y \partial x} = 1$$

at that point.

7. Two functions F and G of one variable and a function z of two variables are related by the equation

$$[F(x) + G(y)]^2 \, e^{z(x, y)} = 2F'(x) \, G'(y)$$

whenever $F(x) + G(y) \neq 0$. Show that the mixed partial derivative $D_{2,1} f(x, y)$ is never zero. (You may assume the existence and continuity of all derivatives encountered.)

8. The three equations

$$\begin{aligned} x^2 - y \cos(uv) + z^2 &= 0, \\ x^2 + y^2 - \sin(uv) + 2z^2 &= 2, \\ xy - \sin u \cos v + z &= 0, \end{aligned}$$

define x, y, and z as functions of u and v. Compute the partial derivatives $\partial x / \partial u$ and $\partial x / \partial v$ at the point $x = y = 1$, $u = \pi/2$, $v = 0$, $z = 0$.

9. Let $\vec{r} = x\vec{i} + y\vec{j} + z\vec{k}$ and let $r = |\vec{r}|$. Let f be a continuously differentiable scalar field such that ∇f is always parallel to $\vec{r}$. Show that f is a function of r alone. That is, show that there is a function F such that $f(x, y, z) = F(r)$. [*Hint.* Express f in spherical coordinates.]

10. Let f be a scalar field that can be expressed as a function of r, where $r = |x\,\vec{i} + y\,\vec{j} + z\,\vec{k}|$, say $f(x, y, z) = F(r)$. If

$$\frac{\partial^2 f}{\partial x^2} + \frac{\partial^2 f}{\partial y^2} + \frac{\partial^2 f}{\partial z^2} = 0$$

everywhere except at the origin, prove that $F(r) = b + a/r$, where a and b are constants.

11. Find the locus of all points (a, b, c) in 3-space for which the two spheres $(x - a)^2 + (y - b)^2 + (z - c)^2 = 1$ and $x^2 + y^2 + z^2 = 1$ intersect orthogonally. (Their tangent planes should be perpendicular at each point of intersection.)

12. Let $z = f(x, y)$ be the equation of a surface not passing through the origin. Let (x_0, y_0, z_0) be a point on the surface at which the distance from the surface to the origin is a minimum. Show that the normal to the surface at (x_0, y_0, z_0) is parallel to the vector $x_0\,\vec{i} + y_0\,\vec{j} + z_0\,\vec{k}$.

13. A flat circular plate has the shape of the disk $x^2 + y^2 \leq 1$. The plate (including its boundary) is heated so that the temperature at any point (x, y) is $T(x, y) = x^2 + 2y^2 - x$. Locate the hottest and the coldest points of the plate and find the temperature at each of these points.

14. Find the shortest distance from the point $(0, b)$ to the parabola $x^2 = 4y$, expressing this distance as a function of b.

15. A cylinder whose equation is $y = f(x)$ is tangent to the surface $z^2 + 2xz + y = 0$ at all points common to the two surfaces. Find $f(x)$.

16. Use the method of Lagrange's multipliers to find the greatest and least distances of a point on the ellipse $x^2 + 4y^2 = 4$ from the straight line $x + y = 4$.

17. The cross section of a trough is an isosceles trapezoid. If the trough is made by bending up the sides of a strip of metal c inches wide, what should be the angle of inclination of the sides and the width across the bottom if the cross-sectional area is to be a maximum?

18. Let f be a scalar field with continuous partial derivatives $D_1 f$ and $D_2 f$ on an open set S in the plane.

(a) Prove that the derivative $f'(\vec{X}; \vec{Y})$ exists for every $\vec{X}$ in S and every $\vec{Y}$ in the plane. [*Hint*. If $\vec{Y} = y_1\vec{i} + y_2\vec{j}$, let $\vec{Z} = y_1\vec{i}$ and write

$$f(\vec{X} + h\vec{Y}) - f(\vec{X}) = [f(\vec{X} + h\vec{Y}) - f(\vec{X} + h\vec{Z})] + [f(\vec{X} + h\vec{Z}) - f(\vec{X})].$$

Now apply the one-dimensional mean-value theorem to each difference in square brackets.]

(b) Prove that f is continuously differentiable on S.

(c) Extend the results of this exercise to scalar fields with continuous partial derivatives $D_1 f, \ldots, D_n f$ on an open set S in n-space.

19. A scalar field f is bounded and continuous on a rectangle $R = [a, b] \times [c, d]$. A new scalar field g is defined on R as follows:

$$g(u, v) = \int_c^v \left[\int_a^u f(x, y)\, dx \right] dy\,.$$

(a) It can be shown that for each fixed u in $[a, b]$ the function A defined on $[c, d]$ by the equation $A(y) = \int_a^u f(x, y)\, dx$ is continuous on $[c, d]$. Use this fact and Exercise 18 to prove that g is continuously differentiable on the open rectangle $S = (a, b) \times (c, d)$.

(b) Prove that the mixed partial derivatives $D_{1,2}g(u, v)$ and $D_{2,1}g(u, v)$ exist and are equal at each point of S.

20. Refer to Exercise 19. Suppose u and v are expressed parametrically as follows: $u = A(t)$, $v = B(t)$; and let $\phi(t) = g[A(t), B(t)]$.

(a) Determine $\phi'(t)$ in terms of f, A', and B'.

(b) Compute $\phi'(t)$ in terms of t when $f(x, y) = e^{x+y}$ and $A(t) = B(t) = t^2$. (Assume R lies in the first quadrant.)

5

LINE INTEGRALS

5.1 Introduction

In Chapter 2, integration theory was extended from the real line to the plane and to 3-space by the introduction of multiple integrals. In this chapter, the integral $\int_a^b f(x)\,dx$ is generalized in yet another direction. The interval $[a, b]$ is replaced by a *curve C* described by a vector-valued function $\vec{r}$, and the integrand is replaced by a vector field $\vec{F}$ defined and bounded on C. The resulting integral (to be defined in Section 5.4) is called a *line integral* and is denoted by the symbol

$$\int_C \vec{F} \cdot d\vec{r}$$

or by a similar notation. The dot is meant to suggest the dot product of two vectors.

Line integrals are of fundamental importance in both pure and applied mathematics. They occur in connection with work, potential energy, heat flow, change in entropy, circulation of a fluid, and other physical situations in which the behavior of a vector or scalar field is studied along a curve. To make the definition of the line integral more meaningful we first discuss the concept of work.

5.2 The concept of work

If a constant force $\vec{F}$ displaces a particle along a vector $\vec{R}$, the amount of work done by this force is defined to be the product of the magnitude of the displacement and the component of the force in the direction of the displacement. In vector notation, this is simply the dot product $\vec{F} \cdot \vec{R}$.† Consider now a force $\vec{F}$ which may vary with the position of the particle. Such a force determines a vector field. Also, assume the particle moves along a curve C joining two points A and B. The problem of determining the amount of work done by $\vec{F}$ in moving the particle from A to B along C is now more complicated. In fact, the real problem here is to decide on a reasonable *definition* of what is meant by the work done. The following discussion suggests such a definition.

---

† If θ is the angle between $\vec{F}$ and $\vec{R}$, the number $|\vec{F}| \cos \theta$ represents the component of the force in the direction of motion, and $|\vec{R}|$ represents the magnitude of the displacement. Hence the amount of work done is $(|\vec{F}| \cos \theta) |\vec{R}| = \vec{F} \cdot \vec{R}$.

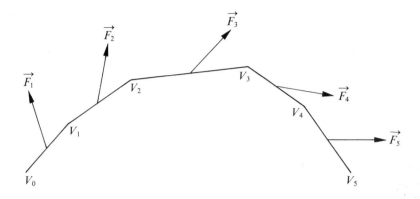

FIGURE 5.1   *Work done by a force field $\vec{F}$ along a polygonal path.*

We begin with a discussion of work done along polygonal curves. Suppose C is a polygonal path with n edges, and suppose the vertices $V_0, V_1, \ldots, V_n$, taken in succession, are the terminal points of the vectors $\vec{V}_0, \vec{V}_1, \ldots, \vec{V}_n$. The n edges of C may be described by the vectors

$$\vec{V}_1 - \vec{V}_0, \ \vec{V}_2 - \vec{V}_1, \ldots, \ \vec{V}_n - \vec{V}_{n-1} \ .$$

(An example with $n = 5$ is shown in Figure 5.1.) Let $\vec{F}$ be a force field defined everywhere on C in such a way that $\vec{F}$ is constant on each of the open edges of C. Let $\vec{F}_k$ denote the constant value of $\vec{F}$ on the open segment joining V_{k-1} to V_k. The sum of dot products

(5.1) $$\sum_{k=1}^{n} \vec{F}_k \cdot (\vec{V}_k - \vec{V}_{k-1})$$

is defined to be the work done by $\vec{F}$ in moving a particle from V_0 to V_n along C. Note that the sum in (5.1) does not depend on the particular values of $\vec{F}$ at the vertices. Now we shall introduce a parametric representation of C and express this sum as an integral.

Let $[a, b]$ denote an interval of real numbers, and consider any partition $P = \{t_0, t_1, \ldots, t_n\}$ of $[a, b]$ into n subintervals. Let $\vec{r}$ be the vector-valued function defined on $[a, b]$ as follows:

$$\vec{r}(t) = \frac{t - t_{k-1}}{t_k - t_{k-1}} \vec{V}_k + \frac{t_k - t}{t_k - t_{k-1}} \vec{V}_{k-1} \qquad \text{if} \quad t_{k-1} \le t \le t_k \,, \qquad k = 1, 2, \ldots, n \,.$$

The function $\vec{r}$ is *linear* in the kth subinterval $[t_{k-1}, t_k]$. Moreover,

$$\vec{r}(t_{k-1}) = \vec{V}_{k-1} \qquad \text{and} \qquad \vec{r}(t_k) = \vec{V}_k \,,$$

so $\vec{r}$ describes the polygonal path C.

Next we note that the derivative of $\vec{r}$ exists in each open subinterval (t_{k-1}, t_k) and is given by the formula

(5.2) $$\vec{r}'(t) = \frac{1}{t_k - t_{k-1}} \vec{V}_k - \frac{1}{t_k - t_{k-1}} \vec{V}_{k-1} = \frac{1}{t_k - t_{k-1}} (\vec{V}_k - \vec{V}_{k-1}) \,.$$

This shows that $\vec{r}'$ is constant on each open subinterval (t_{k-1}, t_k) and that $\vec{V}_k - \vec{V}_{k-1}$ $= \vec{r}'(t)(t_k - t_{k-1})$ for each t in (t_{k-1}, t_k). Since we also have $\vec{F}_k = \vec{F}[\vec{r}(t)]$ in the kth open subinterval (t_{k-1}, t_k), the sum in (5.1) can be written as

$$\text{(5.3)} \qquad \sum_{k=1}^{n} \vec{F}[\vec{r}(t)] \cdot \vec{r}'(t)(t_k - t_{k-1}),$$

where it is understood that in the kth term of this sum t is restricted to the open interval (t_{k-1}, t_k). Since both $\vec{F}[\vec{r}(t)]$ and $\vec{r}'(t)$ are constant on the open subinterval (t_{k-1}, t_k), we can consider the dot product $\vec{F}[\vec{r}(t)] \cdot \vec{r}'(t)$ as a *step function* defined on $[a, b]$†; the sum in (5.3) is the integral of this step function:

$$\text{(5.4)} \qquad \int_a^b \vec{F}[\vec{r}(t)] \cdot \vec{r}'(t) \, dt.$$

If the parametric interval $[a, b]$ is chosen so that $b - a$ is the length of the polygon, and if the partition P is chosen so that $t_k - t_{k-1} = |\vec{V}_k - \vec{V}_{k-1}|$ (the length of the kth edge), then Equation (5.2) shows that $\vec{r}'(t)$ is a unit vector tangent to C. In this case the dot product $\vec{F}[\vec{r}(t)] \cdot \vec{r}'(t)$ is the component of $\vec{F}$ in the direction of the curve, and, as we have just shown, the integral of this component is equal to the work done by $\vec{F}$ along the polygonal path C.

For a more general curve C and a more general force field $\vec{F}$, we shall use the integral in (5.4) as the *definition* of work.

DEFINITION OF WORK. Let C be a curve described by a vector-valued function $\vec{r}$ defined on an interval $[a, b]$. Assume that $\vec{F}$ is a force field defined on C and that the dot product $\vec{F} \cdot \vec{r}'$ is integrable on $[a, b]$. Then the work done by $\vec{F}$ in moving a particle from $\vec{r}(a)$ to $\vec{r}(b)$ along C is defined to be the integral

$$\int_a^b \vec{F}[\vec{r}(t)] \cdot \vec{r}'(t) \, dt.$$

Example 1. A two-dimensional force field $\vec{F}$ is given by the equation

$$\vec{F}(x, y) = \sqrt{y}\,\vec{i} + (x - y)\,\vec{j}.$$

Calculate the amount of work done by this force in moving a particle from $(0, 0)$ to $(1, 1)$ along (a) the line $y = x$, (b) the curve $y^2 = x^3$.

Solution. For the path in part (a) we may use the vector representation

$$\vec{r}(t) = t\,\vec{i} + t\vec{j} \qquad \text{where } 0 \leq t \leq 1.$$

Then $\vec{F}[\vec{r}(t)] \cdot \vec{r}'(t) = (\sqrt{t}\,\vec{i}) \cdot (\vec{i} + \vec{j}) = \sqrt{t}$, and the work is equal to the integral $\int_0^1 \sqrt{t}\, dt = \frac{2}{3}$.

For the path in part (b) we may use the vector equation

$$\vec{r}(t) = t^2\,\vec{i} + t^3\,\vec{j} \qquad \text{where } 0 \leq t \leq 1.$$

---

† Although the derivative $\vec{r}'$ may not exist at the partition points t_k, we will arbitrarily define $\vec{r}'$ to be $\vec{0}$ at these points. This assignment of values ensures that the dot product $\vec{F}[\vec{r}(t)] \cdot \vec{r}'(t)$ is defined everywhere on $[a, b]$ and does not affect the subsequent discussion.

Then we have

$$\vec{F}[\vec{r}(t)] \cdot \vec{r}'(t) = [t^{3/2} \vec{i} + (t^2 - t^3) \vec{j}] \cdot [2t \vec{i} + 3t^2 \vec{j}] = 2t^{5/2} + 3t^4 - 3t^5,$$

and the work done is the integral

$$\int_0^1 (2t^{5/2} + 3t^4 - 3t^5) \, dt = \frac{4}{7} + \frac{3}{5} - \frac{1}{2} = \frac{47}{70}.$$

Notice that this answer is not the same as that obtained in part (a). This illustrates the fact that the work done in moving a particle from one point to another may depend on the path joining the two points.

Now let us carry out the calculations for part (b) once more, using a different parametric representation for the curve. The same curve may be described by the vector equation

$$\vec{r}(t) = t \vec{i} + t^{3/2} \vec{j} \qquad \text{where} \quad 0 \le t \le 1.$$

This leads to the relation

$$\vec{F}[\vec{r}(t)] \cdot \vec{r}'(t) = [t^{3/4} \vec{i} + (t - t^{3/2}) \vec{j}] \cdot \left[\vec{i} + \frac{3}{2} t^{1/2} \vec{j}\right] = t^{3/4} + \frac{3}{2} t^{3/2} - \frac{3}{2} t^2,$$

the integral of which from 0 to 1 is 47/70, as before. This calculation illustrates that the work done is independent of the parametric representation used to describe the curve. This general property will be discussed further in Section 5.7 in connection with the study of line integrals.

Example 2. Calculate the amount of work done by the force field $\vec{F}(x, y, z) = x \vec{i} + y \vec{j} + z \vec{k}$ in moving a particle from the point $(a, 0, 0)$ to $(a, 0, 2\pi b)$ along the circular helix whose vector equation is

$$\vec{r}(t) = a \cos t \, \vec{i} + a \sin t \, \vec{j} + bt \, \vec{k}, \qquad 0 \le t \le 2\pi.$$

Solution. Since $\vec{r}'(t) = -a \sin t \, \vec{i} + a \cos t \, \vec{j} + b \, \vec{k}$, we have

$$\vec{F}[\vec{r}(t)] \cdot \vec{r}'(t) = (a \cos t \, \vec{i} + a \sin t \, \vec{j} + bt \, \vec{k}) \cdot (-a \sin t \, \vec{i} + a \cos t \, \vec{j} + b \, \vec{k})$$

$$= -a^2 \sin t \cos t + a^2 \sin t \cos t + b^2 t = b^2 t.$$

Therefore the work done is $\int_0^{2\pi} b^2 t \, dt = 2\pi^2 b^2$. The reader may verify that the same amount of work is done if $\vec{F}$ moves the particle along a straight line joining $(a, 0, 0)$ to $(a, 0, 2\pi b)$.

Example 3. The principle of work and energy. A particle of mass m moves along a curve under the action of a force field $\vec{F}$. If the speed of the particle at time t is $v(t)$, its kinetic energy is defined to be $\frac{1}{2} mv^2(t)$. Prove that *the change in kinetic energy in any time interval is equal to the work done by $\vec{F}$ during this time interval.*

Solution. Let $\vec{r}(t)$ denote the position of the particle at time t. We wish to prove that

$$\int_{t_0}^{t_1} \vec{F}[\vec{r}(t)] \cdot \vec{r}'(t) \, dt = \frac{1}{2} mv^2(t_1) - \frac{1}{2} mv^2(t_0).$$

From Newton's second law of motion we have

$$\vec{F}[\vec{r}(t)] = m\vec{r}''(t) = m\,\vec{v}'(t),$$

where $\vec{v}(t)$ denotes the velocity vector at time t. The speed is the length of the velocity vector, $v(t) = |\vec{v}(t)|$. Therefore,

$$\vec{F}[\vec{r}(t)] \cdot \vec{r}'(t) = \vec{F}[\vec{r}(t)] \cdot \vec{v}(t) = m\vec{v}'(t) \cdot \vec{v}(t) = \tfrac{1}{2}m\,\frac{d}{dt}\,(\vec{v}(t) \cdot \vec{v}(t)) = \tfrac{1}{2}m\,\frac{d}{dt}\,(v^2(t)).$$

Integrating from t_0 to t_1 we obtain

$$\int_{t_0}^{t_1} \vec{F}[\vec{r}(t)] \cdot \vec{r}'(t)\, dt = \tfrac{1}{2}mv^2(t)\Big|_{t_0}^{t_1} = \tfrac{1}{2}mv^2(t_1) - \tfrac{1}{2}mv^2(t_0),$$

as required.

5.3 Exercises

In each of Exercises 1 through 8, compute the work done by the force field $\vec{F}$ along the curve C described.

1. $\vec{F}(x, y) = (x^2 - 2xy)\vec{i} + (y^2 - 2xy)\vec{j}$. The path C joins $(-1, 1)$ to $(1, 1)$ along the parabola $y = x^2$.

2. $\vec{F}(x, y) = (x^2 + y^2)\vec{i} + (x^2 - y^2)\vec{j}$. The path C joins $(0, 0)$ to $(2, 0)$ along the curve $y = 1 - |1 - x|$.

3. $\vec{F}(x, y) = (x + y)\,\vec{i} + (x - y)\vec{j}$. The path C is the ellipse $b^2x^2 + a^2y^2 = a^2b^2$ traversed in a counterclockwise direction.

4. $\vec{F}(x, y) = (2a - y)\,\vec{i} + x\vec{j}$. The path C is described by the vector equation $\vec{r}(t) = a(t - \sin t)\vec{i} + a(1 - \cos t)\vec{j}$, $0 \le t \le 2\pi$.

5. $\vec{F}(x, y, z) = (y^2 - z^2)\vec{i} + 2yz\vec{j} - x^2\vec{k}$. The path C is described by the vector equation $\vec{r}(t) = t\vec{i} + t^2\vec{j} + t^3\vec{k}$, $0 \le t \le 1$.

6. $\vec{F}(x, y, z) = 2xy\vec{i} + (x^2 + z)\vec{j} + y\vec{k}$. The path C is the line segment from $(1, 0, 2)$ to $(3, 4, 1)$.

7. $\vec{F}(x, y, z) = (y - z)\vec{i} + (z - x)\vec{j} + (x - y)\vec{k}$. The path C is the curve of intersection of the sphere $x^2 + y^2 + z^2 = a^2$ and the plane $y = x \tan \alpha$, where $a > 0$ and $0 < \alpha < \pi$. Show that the amount of work done is $\pm 2\pi \sqrt{2}\, a^2 \sin(\tfrac{1}{4}\pi - \alpha)$ and explain the significance of the $\pm$ sign.

8. $\vec{F}(x, y, z) = y^2\vec{i} + z^2\vec{j} + x^2\vec{k}$. The path C is the curve of intersection of the sphere $x^2 + y^2 + z^2 = a^2$ and the cylinder $x^2 + y^2 = ax$, where $z \ge 0$ and $a > 0$. The path is traversed in a direction that appears clockwise when viewed from high above the xy-plane.

9. Find the amount of work done by the force $\vec{F}(x, y) = (x^2 - y^2)\vec{i} + 2xy\vec{j}$ in moving a particle (in a counterclockwise direction) once around the square bounded by the coordinate axes and the lines $x = a$ and $y = a$, $a > 0$.

10. A two-dimensional force field $\vec{F}$ is given by the equation $\vec{F}(x, y) = cxy\,\vec{i} + x^6y^2\,\vec{j}$, where c is a positive constant. This force acts on a particle which must move from $(0, 0)$ to the line $x = 1$ along a curve of the form

$$y = ax^b, \qquad \text{where} \quad a > 0 \quad \text{and} \quad b > 0.$$

Find a value of a (in terms of c) such that the work done by this force is independent of b.

5.4   The definition of the line integral

The discussion of the concept of work in Section 5.2 suggests the following definition of the line integral.

DEFINITION OF THE LINE INTEGRAL. Let C be a curve described by a vector-valued function $\vec{r}$ defined on an interval $[a, b]$. Let $\vec{F}$ be a vector field that is defined and bounded on C. The line integral of $\vec{F}$ along C is denoted by the symbol $\int_C \vec{F} \cdot d\vec{r}$ and is defined by the equation

$$(5.5) \qquad \int_C \vec{F} \cdot d\vec{r} = \int_a^b \vec{F}[\vec{r}(t)] \cdot \vec{r}'(t) \, dt$$

whenever the integral on the right exists.

Note. Although this definition is meaningful when $\vec{F}$ and $\vec{r}$ are vectors in n-space, we shall be interested here only in the cases $n = 2$ and $n = 3$.

In most examples that occur in practice, the curve C is *piecewise smooth*. By this we mean that the function $\vec{r}$ has a bounded derivative $\vec{r}'$ which is continuous everywhere in $[a, b]$ except (possibly) at a finite number of points. Interpreted geometrically, the property of being piecewise smooth means that the curve has a tangent line at all but a finite number of its points. These exceptional points subdivide the curve into arcs, along each of which the tangent line turns continuously. *All the curves discussed in this book will be assumed to be piecewise smooth,*† unless stated otherwise. Also, the force fields discussed here will be bounded on C and continuous at all points of C except (possibly) at a finite number of points. Under these circumstances the integral in (5.5) always exists.

Other notations. When $\vec{F}$ and $\vec{r}$ are expressed in terms of their components, say

$$\vec{F} = P\,\vec{i} + Q\,\vec{j} + R\,\vec{k} \qquad \text{and} \qquad \vec{r}(t) = X(t)\,\vec{i} + Y(t)\,\vec{j} + Z(t)\,\vec{k}\,,$$

the integral on the right of (5.5) becomes

$$(5.6) \qquad \int_a^b \{P[\vec{r}(t)]\,X'(t) + Q[\vec{r}(t)]\,Y'(t) + R[\vec{r}(t)]\,Z'(t)\}\,dt\,.$$

In this case the line integral is also denoted by the symbol

$$(5.7) \qquad \int_C P\,dx + Q\,dy + R\,dz\,.$$

This notation is suggested by the following considerations: If we introduce the symbolic "vector" $d\vec{r} = dx\,\vec{i} + dy\,\vec{j} + dz\,\vec{k}$, the "dot product" $\vec{F} \cdot d\vec{r}$ becomes $P\,dx + Q\,dy + R\,dz$. To convert the integral in (5.7) to that in (5.6) we simply make a formal substitution; we replace x by $X(t)$, y by $Y(t)$, z by $Z(t)$, dx by $X'(t)\,dt$, dy by $Y'(t)\,dt$, and dz by $Z'(t)\,dt$.

If the curve C is represented parametrically in terms of arc length s, the integrand in (5.6) is exactly equal to the dot product $\vec{F} \cdot \vec{T}$, where $\vec{T}$ is the *unit tangent vector* of the curve, $\vec{T} = d\vec{r}/ds$. Because of this relation, the line integral $\int_C \vec{F} \cdot d\vec{r}$ is also written in

---

† With the aid of Riemann-Stieltjes integrals, the definition of the line integral can be extended to arbitrary *rectifiable* curves, that is, to curves having a finite arc length. (See Chapter 10 of the author's *Mathematical Analysis*, Addison-Wesley, 1957.) All piecewise smooth curves are rectifiable, but not all rectifiable curves are piecewise smooth.

the form $\int_C \vec{F} \cdot \vec{T} \, ds$. The unit tangent vector $\vec{T}$ may be expressed in terms of its direction cosines by writing $\vec{T} = \cos \alpha \; \vec{i} + \cos \beta \; \vec{j} + \cos \gamma \; \vec{k}$, in which case the line integral $\int_C \vec{F} \cdot \vec{T} \, ds$ is also written as $\int_C (P \cos \alpha + Q \cos \beta + R \cos \gamma) \, ds$. Therefore, we have the following equations:

$$\int_C \vec{F} \cdot d\vec{r} = \int_C P \, dx + Q \, dy + R \, dz = \int_C \vec{F} \cdot \vec{T} \, ds$$
$$= \int_C (P \cos \alpha + Q \cos \beta + R \cos \gamma) \, ds \; ;$$

the last three symbols are simply different notations for the first.

Let $\vec{A} = \vec{r}(a)$ and $\vec{B} = \vec{r}(b)$ denote the end points of the curve C. The line integral $\int_C \vec{F} \cdot d\vec{r}$ is sometimes written $\int_{\vec{A}}^{\vec{B}} \vec{F} \cdot d\vec{r}$ and is called the integral of $\vec{F}$ *from $\vec{A}$ to $\vec{B}$ along* C. When this notation is used it should be kept in mind that the integral depends not only on the end points $\vec{A}$ and $\vec{B}$ but also on the curve C which joins them. When $\vec{A} = \vec{B}$, the curve C is said to be *closed*. The symbol $\oint$ is often used to indicate integration along a closed curve.

If s denotes the arc-length function of C, the derivative of s is the speed; that is,

$$s'(t) = |\vec{r}'(t)| \; .$$

If f is a scalar field defined and bounded on C, the *line integral of f with respect to arc length along* C is denoted by the symbol $\int_C f \, ds$ and is defined by the equation

(5.8)
$$\int_C f \, ds = \int_a^b f[\vec{r}(t)] \, s'(t) \, dt$$

whenever the integral on the right exists. When the scalar field f is the dot product of a vector field $\vec{F}$ and the unit tangent vector $\vec{T}$, the line integral in (5.8) is the same as $\int_C \vec{F} \cdot d\vec{r}$ because

$$\vec{F} \cdot \vec{r}' = \vec{F} \cdot \frac{d\vec{r}}{dt} = \vec{F} \cdot \frac{d\vec{r}}{ds} \frac{ds}{dt} = \vec{F} \cdot \vec{T} \, s'(t) = f[\vec{r}(t)] \, s'(t) \; .$$

When $\vec{F}$ denotes a velocity field, the dot product $\vec{F} \cdot \vec{T}$ is the tangential component of velocity, and the line integral $\int_C \vec{F} \cdot \vec{T} \, ds$ is called the *flow integral* of $\vec{F}$ along C. When C is a closed curve, the flow integral is called the *circulation* of $\vec{F}$ along C. These terms are commonly used in the theory of fluid flow.

5.5 Further applications of line integrals

The definition of work, as given in Section 5.4, can be expressed as a line integral. In fact, if $\vec{F}$ is a force field acting along a curve C described by a vector-valued function $\vec{r}$, the line integral $\int_C \vec{F} \cdot d\vec{r}$ represents the work done by $\vec{F}$.

There are many other applications of line integrals. For example, think of a curve C as a wire made of a thin material of varying density. Assume the density is described by a scalar field f, where $f(x, y, z)$ is the *mass per unit length* at the point (x, y, z) of C. Then the *total mass* M of the wire is defined to be the line integral of f with respect to arc length:

$$M = \int_C f(x, y, z) \, ds \; .$$

The center of mass of the wire is defined to be the point $(\bar{x}, \bar{y}, \bar{z})$ whose coordinates are determined by the equations

$$\bar{x}M = \int_C x\, f(x, y, z)\, ds, \qquad \bar{y}M = \int_C y\, f(x, y, z)\, ds, \qquad \bar{z}M = \int_C z\, f(x, y, z)\, ds.$$

Example 1. Compute the mass M of one coil of a spring having the shape of the helix whose vector equation is

$$\vec{r}(t) = a \cos t\, \vec{i} + a \sin t\, \vec{j} + bt\, \vec{k}$$

if the density at (x, y, z) is $x^2 + y^2 + z^2$.

Solution. The integral for M is

$$M = \int_C (x^2 + y^2 + z^2)\, ds = \int_0^{2\pi} (a^2 \cos^2 t + a^2 \sin^2 t + b^2 t^2)\, s'(t)\, dt.$$

Since $s'(t) = |\vec{r}'(t)|$ and $\vec{r}'(t) = -a \sin t\, \vec{i} + a \cos t\, \vec{j} + b\, \vec{k}$, we have $s'(t) = \sqrt{a^2 + b^2}$ and hence

$$M = \sqrt{a^2 + b^2} \int_0^{2\pi} (a^2 + b^2 t^2)\, dt = \sqrt{a^2 + b^2} \left(2\pi a^2 + \frac{8}{3}\, \pi^3 b^2 \right).$$

In this example the z-coordinate $\bar{z}$ of the center of mass is given by

$$\bar{z}M = \int_C z(x^2 + y^2 + z^2)\, ds = \sqrt{a^2 + b^2} \int_0^{2\pi} bt(a^2 + b^2 t^2)\, dt$$

$$= b\sqrt{a^2 + b^2}\, (2\pi^2 a^2 + 4\pi^4 b^2).$$

The coordinates $\bar{x}$ and $\bar{y}$ are requested in Exercise 11 of Section 5.6.

Line integrals can be used to define the moment of inertia of a wire with respect to an axis. If $\delta(x, y, z)$ represents the perpendicular distance from a point (x, y, z) of C to an axis L, the moment of inertia I_L is defined to be the line integral

$$I_L = \int_C \delta^2(x, y, z)\, f(x, y, z)\, ds,$$

where $f(x, y, z)$ is the density at (x, y, z). The moments of inertia about the coordinate axes are denoted by I_x, I_y, and I_z.

Example 2. Compute the moment of inertia I_z of the spring coil in Example 1.

Solution. Here $\delta^2(x, y, z) = x^2 + y^2 = a^2$ and $f(x, y, z) = x^2 + y^2 + z^2$, so we have

$$I_z = \int_C (x^2 + y^2)(x^2 + y^2 + z^2)\, ds = a^2 \int_C (x^2 + y^2 + z^2)\, ds = Ma^2,$$

where M is the mass, as computed in Example 1.

Other applications of line integrals will be encountered later in this chapter.

5.6 Exercises

In each of Exercises 1 through 10, compute the value of the given line integral.

1. $\int_C (x^2 - 2xy) \, dx + (y^2 - 2xy) \, dy$, where C is a path from $(-2, 4)$ to $(1, 1)$ along the parabola $y = x^2$.

2. $\int_C \vec{F} \cdot d\vec{r}$, where $\vec{F}(x, y, z) = x\,\vec{i} + y\,\vec{j} + (xz - y)\,\vec{k}$ if (a) C is the line segment from $(0, 0, 0)$ to $(1, 2, 4)$, (b) C has the vector equation $\vec{r}(t) = t^2\,\vec{i} + 2t\,\vec{j} + 4t^3\,\vec{k}$, $0 \le t \le 1$.

3. $\displaystyle \int_C \frac{(x + y)\,dx - (x - y)\,dy}{x^2 + y^2}$,

where C is the circle $x^2 + y^2 = a^2$, traversed in a counterclockwise direction.

4. $\displaystyle \int_C \frac{dx + dy}{|x| + |y|}$,

where C is the square with vertices $(1, 0)$, $(0, 1)$, $(-1, 0)$, and $(0, -1)$, traversed in a counterclockwise direction.

5. $\int_C (x + y) \, ds$, where C is the triangle with vertices $(0, 0)$, $(1, 0)$, and $(0, 1)$, traversed in a counterclockwise direction.

6. $\int_C y^2 \, ds$, where C has the vector equation

$$\vec{r}(t) = a(t - \sin t)\,\vec{i} + a(1 - \cos t)\,\vec{j}, \qquad 0 \le t \le 2\pi.$$

7. $\int_C (x^2 + y^2) \, ds$, where C has the vector equation

$$\vec{r}(t) = a(\cos t + t \sin t)\,\vec{i} + a(\sin t - t \cos t)\,\vec{j}, \qquad 0 \le t \le 2\pi.$$

8. $\int_C z \, ds$, where C has the vector equation

$$\vec{r}(t) = t \cos t\,\vec{i} + t \sin t\,\vec{j} + t\,\vec{k}, \qquad 0 \le t \le t_0.$$

9. $\int_C y \, dx + z \, dy + x \, dz$, where

(a) C is the curve of intersection of the two surfaces $x + y = 2$ and $x^2 + y^2 + z^2 = 2(x + y)$. The curve is to be traversed in a direction that appears clockwise when viewed from the origin.

(b) C is the intersection of the two surfaces $z = xy$ and $x^2 + y^2 = 1$, traversed in a direction that appears counterclockwise when viewed from high above the xy-plane.

10. $\int_C [(3x^2 + 6y) \cos \alpha - 14yz \cos \beta + 20xz^2 \cos \gamma] \, ds$, where C has the vector equation $\vec{r}(t) = t\,\vec{i} + t^2\,\vec{j} + t^3\,\vec{k}$, $0 \le t \le 1$, and α, β, γ are the direction cosines of the unit tangent vector $\vec{T} = d\vec{r}/ds$.

11. Determine the coordinates $\bar{x}$ and $\bar{y}$ of the center of mass of the spring coil described in Example 1 of Section 5.5.

12. Find the mass of a wire whose shape is that of the curve of intersection of the sphere $x^2 + y^2 + z^2 = 1$ and the plane $x + y + z = 0$ if the density of the wire at (x, y, z) is x^2.

13. A uniform wire ("uniform" means constant density) has the shape of that portion of the curve of intersection of the two surfaces $x^2 + y^2 = z^2$ and $y^2 = x$ connecting the points $(0, 0, 0)$ and $(1, 1, \sqrt{2})$. Find the z-coordinate of its center of mass.

14. (a) Show that the moment of inertia of a homogeneous circular wire of radius a with respect to an axis through a diameter is $\frac{1}{2}Ma^2$, where M is the mass of the wire.

(b) A wire has the shape of the circle $x^2 + y^2 = a^2$. Determine its moment of inertia about a diameter if the density at (x, y) is $|x| + |y|$.

15. For the spring coil described in Example 1 of Section 5.5, compute the moments of inertia I_x and I_y.

5.7   Basic properties of line integrals

As might be expected, line integrals share many of the properties of ordinary integrals. They have a *linearity property* with respect to the integrand:

$$(5.9) \qquad \int_C (a\vec{F} + b\vec{G}) \cdot d\vec{r} = a \int_C \vec{F} \cdot d\vec{r} + b \int_C \vec{G} \cdot d\vec{r} \,,$$

and an *additive property* with respect to the path of integration:

$$(5.10) \qquad \int_C \vec{F} \cdot d\vec{r} = \int_{C_1} \vec{F} \cdot d\vec{r} + \int_{C_2} \vec{F} \cdot d\vec{r} \,,$$

where the two curves C_1 and C_2 make up the curve C. That is, C is described by a vector-valued function $\vec{r}$ defined on an interval $[a, b]$, and the curves C_1 and C_2 are those traced out by $\vec{r}(t)$ as t varies over subintervals $[a, c]$ and $[c, b]$, respectively, for some c satisfying $a < c < b$. The proofs of (5.9) and (5.10) follow immediately from the definition of the line integral; they are left as exercises for the reader.

The next theorem describes another important property of line integrals, known as *invariance under a change of parameter.*

5– 1   THEOREM.   *Let C be a piecewise smooth curve described by a vector-valued function $\vec{r}_1$ defined on an interval $[a, b]$. Let $\vec{r}_2$ be another vector-valued function defined on an interval $[c, d]$, and suppose that $\vec{r}_2$ is related to $\vec{r}_1$ as follows:*

$$(5.11) \qquad \vec{r}_2(t) = \vec{r}_1[h(t)] \qquad \text{if} \quad c \leq t \leq d \,,$$

where h is a real-valued function that is differentiable and strictly increasing on $[c, d]$ and such that $h(c) = a$ and $h(d) = b$. [See Figure 5.2(a).] Then $\vec{r}_2$ describes the same curve C and we have

$$(5.12) \qquad \int_C \vec{F} \cdot d\vec{r}_1 = \int_C \vec{F} \cdot d\vec{r}_2 \,.$$

Proof. The two functions $\vec{r}_1$ and $\vec{r}_2$ obviously describe the same curve C. We shall establish the equality of the two line integrals in (5.12). From the definition of a line integral we have

$$(5.13) \qquad \int_C \vec{F} \cdot d\vec{r}_2 = \int_c^d \vec{F}[\vec{r}_2(t)] \cdot \vec{r}_2'(t) \, dt \,.$$

Using Equation (5.11) and the chain rule we find

$$\vec{r}_2'(t) = \vec{r}_1'[h(t)] \, h'(t) \,.$$

Therefore Equation (5.13) becomes

$$(5.14) \qquad \int_C \vec{F} \cdot d\vec{r}_2 = \int_c^d \vec{F}\{\vec{r}_1[h(t)]\} \cdot \vec{r}_1'[h(t)] \, h'(t) \, dt \,.$$

In the last integral we introduce the substitution $u = h(t)$. Then $du = h'(t) \, dt$, and when t takes the values c and d, u takes the values $h(c) = a$ and $h(d) = b$, respectively. Equation (5.14) is transformed into

$$(5.15) \qquad \int_C \vec{F} \cdot d\vec{r}_2 = \int_a^b \vec{F}[\vec{r}_1(u)] \cdot \vec{r}_1'(u) \, du \,.$$

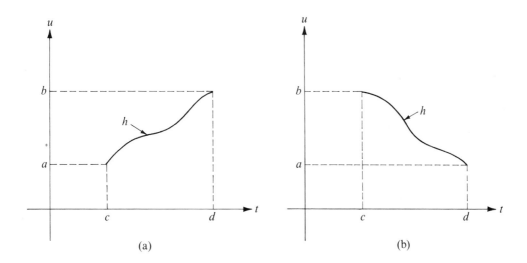

FIGURE 5.2   *A change of parameter defined by u = h(t). In (a), the function h preserves orientation. In (b), the function h reverses the orientation.*

Since the integral on the right is, by definition, $\int_C \vec{F} \cdot d\vec{r}_1$, this completes the proof of the theorem.

If $\vec{r}_2$ is related to $\vec{r}_1$ by an equation of the form

(5.16) $$\vec{r}_2(t) = \vec{r}_1[h(t)] \qquad \text{for} \quad c \leq t \leq d,$$

where h is differentiable and strictly *decreasing* on $[c, d]$ and such that $h(c) = b$ and $h(d) = a$, then $\vec{r}_2$ and $\vec{r}_1$ again describe the same curve C and the foregoing proof undergoes only one change—in Equation (5.15) the limits of integration must be interchanged on the right because $h(c) = b$ and $h(d) = a$. [See Figure 5.2(b).] Therefore in this case we find

$$\int_C \vec{F} \cdot d\vec{r}_2 = -\int_C \vec{F} \cdot d\vec{r}_1 .$$

When a function $\vec{r}_2$ is related to $\vec{r}_1$ by an equation of the form (5.11), where h is strictly *increasing*, $h(c) = a$, and $h(d) = b$, we say that the two radius vectors $\vec{r}_1$ and $\vec{r}_2$ trace out the curve C in the *same direction*. On the other hand, two radius vectors $\vec{r}_1$ and $\vec{r}_2$ are said to trace out C in *opposite directions* if they are related by an equation of the form (5.16), where h is strictly decreasing, $h(c) = b$, and $h(d) = a$. In the first case the function h is said to be *orientation preserving*; in the second case h is said to be *orientation reversing*. Thus, the foregoing theorem is sometimes described as follows: *A line integral remains unchanged under a change of parameter that preserves orientation; it reverses its sign if the change of parameter reverses orientation.* This latter property is often indicated symbolically by writing

$$\int_{-C} \vec{F} \cdot d\vec{r} = -\int_{C} \vec{F} \cdot d\vec{r} .$$

5.8   The line integral of a gradient. Independence of the path

The second fundamental theorem of calculus states that

$$\int_{a}^{b} f'(x) \, dx = f(b) - f(a)$$

when f has a continuous derivative. In theoretical discussions, this formula relates the concepts of differentiation and integration. In practice, it enables us to compute integrals of derivatives by subtraction. This section extends the second fundamental theorem to line integrals.

5–2   THEOREM.   *Second fundamental theorem of calculus for line integrals. Let f be a scalar field that is continuously differentiable on an open set S, and let ∇f denote the gradient of f. Let $\vec{A}$ and $\vec{X}$ be two points of S that can be connected by a piecewise smooth curve lying in S. If C is such a curve, described by a vector-valued function $\vec{r}$ defined on an interval $[a, b]$, where $\vec{r}(a) = \vec{A}$ and $\vec{r}(b) = \vec{X}$, then we have*

(5.17) $$\int_{C} \nabla f \cdot d\vec{r} = f(\vec{X}) - f(\vec{A}) .$$

Before we prove this theorem we shall mention some of its important consequences. First, we note that the right member of (5.17) depends only on the end points $\vec{A}$ and $\vec{X}$. This means that the value of the integral does not change if we replace C by any other piecewise smooth curve C_1 joining $\vec{A}$ to $\vec{X}$ and lying within S (see Figure 5.3). This property is described by saying that *the line integral of a gradient is independent of the path.* If C is a *closed* curve, then $\vec{r}(a) = \vec{r}(b)$ and $\vec{A} = \vec{X}$, so $f(\vec{X}) - f(\vec{A}) = 0$. In other words, *the line integral of a gradient is zero around every closed path.*

An important application of Theorem 5–2 occurs in mechanics. Suppose a force field $\vec{F}$ is the gradient of a scalar potential, say $\vec{F} = \nabla f$. By Equation (5.17), the work done by $\vec{F}$ in moving a particle from $\vec{A}$ to $\vec{X}$ along any curve C is $f(\vec{X}) - f(\vec{A})$. In Example 3 of Section 5.2 we proved that this work is also equal to the change in kinetic energy of the particle. If we denote by $k(\vec{X})$ the kinetic energy of the particle when it is located at $\vec{X}$, then Equation (5.17) gives the relation

$$k(\vec{X}) - k(\vec{A}) = f(\vec{X}) - f(\vec{A}) ,$$

or

(5.18) $$k(\vec{X}) - f(\vec{X}) = k(\vec{A}) - f(\vec{A}) .$$

The scalar $-f(\vec{X})$ is called the potential energy† of the particle. If $\vec{A}$ is kept fixed and $\vec{X}$

---

† Some authors refer to $-f$ as the potential function of $\vec{F}$ so that the potential energy at $\vec{X}$ will be equal to the value of the potential function at $\vec{X}$.

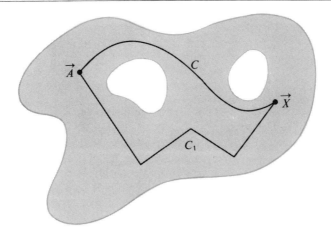

FIGURE 5.3   *The line integral of a gradient is independent of the path.*

is allowed to vary over the set S, Equation (5.18) tells us that the sum of $k(\vec{X})$ and $-f(\vec{X})$ is constant. In other words, *if a force field is a gradient, the sum of the kinetic and potential energies of a particle moving in this field is constant.* In mechanics this is called the principle of conservation of (mechanical) energy. A force field with a potential function is said to be *conservative* because the total energy, kinetic plus potential, is conserved. In a conservative field, no net work is done in moving a particle around a closed curve back to its starting point. A force field will not be conservative if friction or viscosity exists in the system, since these tend to convert mechanical energy into heat energy.

An important example of a conservative force field is the gravitational field $\vec{F}$ encountered earlier in Section 4.12. In this case we have

$$\vec{F}(x, y, z) = -\frac{mM}{r^3}\,\vec{r}$$

for all $(x, y, z) \neq (0, 0, 0)$, where $\vec{r} = x\vec{i} + y\vec{j} + z\vec{k}$ and $r = |\vec{r}|$. This $\vec{F}$ is the gradient of the Newtonian potential f given by

$$f(x, y, z) = \frac{mM}{r}$$

if $r \neq 0$. To calculate the amount of work done *against* this force field in moving a particle from a point $P_1 = (x_1, y_1, z_1)$ to a point $P_2 = (x_2, y_2, z_2)$ we compute the line integral of $-\vec{F}$ from P_1 to P_2, which is the same as the integral of $\vec{F}$ from P_2 to P_1. By Theorem 5-2, this is equal to

$$f(x_1, y_1, z_1) - f(x_2, y_2, z_2) = mM\left(\frac{1}{r_1} - \frac{1}{r_2}\right),$$

where $r_1 = \sqrt{x_1^2 + y_1^2 + z_1^2}$ and $r_2 = \sqrt{x_2^2 + y_2^2 + z_2^2}$. Thus we see that the amount of work done is independent of the path joining P_1 and P_2. The equipotential surfaces in this example are spheres centered at the origin. If P_1 and P_2 lie on the same equipotential surface, then $r_1 = r_2$ and no net work is required to move the particle from P_1 to P_2.

We turn now to the proof of Theorem 5–2.

Proof. The definition of the line integral states that

$$(5.19) \qquad \int_C \nabla f \cdot d\vec{r} = \int_a^b \nabla f[\vec{r}(t)] \cdot \vec{r}'(t)\, dt\,.$$

Since the curve is piecewise smooth we may subdivide the interval $[a, b]$ into a finite number (say n) of subintervals $[t_{k-1}, t_k]$ such that $\vec{r}'$ is continuous on each open subinterval (t_{k-1}, t_k), where $a = t_0 < t_1 < \cdots < t_n = b$. The integral on the right of (5.19) is the sum of n integrals over these subintervals; hence we may write

$$(5.20) \qquad \int_C \nabla f \cdot d\vec{r} = \sum_{k=1}^n \int_{t_{k-1}}^{t_k} \nabla f[\vec{r}(t)] \cdot \vec{r}'(t)\, dt.$$

If we introduce the composite function g defined by the equation

$$g(t) = f[\vec{r}(t)] \qquad \text{if} \quad a \le t \le b\,,$$

the chain rule tells us that the derivative of g is given by the formula

$$g'(t) = \nabla f[\vec{r}(t)] \cdot \vec{r}'(t)$$

in each open subinterval (t_{k-1}, t_k). Therefore Equation (5.20) becomes

$$\int_C \nabla f \cdot d\vec{r} = \sum_{k=1}^n \int_{t_{k-1}}^{t_k} g'(t)\, dt = \sum_{k=1}^n [g(t_k) - g(t_{k-1})] = g(b) - g(a)$$

$$= f[\vec{r}(b)] - f[\vec{r}(a)] = f(\vec{X}) - f(\vec{A})\,.$$

This completes the proof.

Not every pair of points in an open set S can be joined by a curve lying in S. For example, the open set S in Figure 5.4 is the union of two disjoint open circular disks; it is clear that a point in one disk cannot be connected to a point in the other by a curve lying entirely within S. On the other hand, in the open set shown in Figure 5.3, *every* pair of points can be connected by a piecewise smooth curve lying in S. Sets with this property are said to be *arcwise connected*. It can be shown that a set which is both open and arcwise connected is also *polygonally* connected; that is, every pair of points in S may be joined by a polygon lying in S. As a matter of fact, they may be joined by a polygon with sides parallel to the coordinate axes. We shall refer to such a polygon as a *step polygon*. In an open polygonally connected set every pair of points can be joined by a *simple* step polygon, that is, one having no self-intersections. (Examples are shown in Figure 5.5.) Any open set with this property will be referred to here as an *open connected set*. The region shown in Figure 5.3 and the three examples in Figure 5.5 are open connected sets in a plane. Examples in 3-space analogous to those in Figure 5.5 would be (a) a solid ellipsoid, (b) a solid polyhedron, and (c) a solid torus; in each case only the interior points are considered.

An open set S is said to be *disconnected* if S is the union of two disjoint nonempty

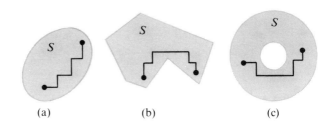

(a)   (b)   (c)

FIGURE 5.4 *A disconnected set S, the union of two disjoint circular disks.*

FIGURE 5.5 *Examples of open connected sets. (The boundary points are not included.)*

open sets. An example is the set S in Figure 5.4. It can be shown that the class of open connected sets is identical with the class of open sets that are not disconnected.†

Theorem 5–2 implies the following statement: *If a scalar field f is continuously differentiable on an open connected set S, the line integral of its gradient ∇f is independent of the path in S.* That is, if $\vec{A}$ and $\vec{X}$ are arbitrary points of S, and if C and C_1 are two piecewise smooth curves in S joining these points, we have

$$\int_C \nabla f \cdot d\vec{r} = \int_{C_1} \nabla f \cdot d\vec{r}_1 \, ,$$

where $\vec{r}$ describes C and $\vec{r}_1$ describes C_1. In Section 5.10 we shall prove (in Theorem 5–3) that gradients are the *only* vector fields with this property. That is, if $\vec{F}$ is a vector field whose line integral is independent of the path in an open connected set S, then $\vec{F} = \nabla f$ for some scalar field f. Theorems 5–2 and 5–3 together show that a necessary and sufficient condition for a vector field $\vec{F}$ to be a gradient in an open connected set S is for the line integral of $\vec{F}$ to be independent of the path in S. Equivalent formulations of this condition will be discussed in Section 5.12 (Theorem 5–4).

5.9 Exercises

1. For each of the following vector fields use Theorem 4–9 of Section 4.19 to prove that $\vec{F}$ is not a gradient. Then find a closed path C such that $\int_C \vec{F} \cdot d\vec{r} \neq 0$.

   (a) $\vec{F}(x, y) = y\vec{i} - x\vec{j}$.

   (b) $\vec{F}(x, y) = y\vec{i} + (xy - x)\vec{j}$.

   (c) $\vec{F}(x, y, z) = y\vec{i} + x\vec{j} + x\vec{k}$.

   (d) $\vec{F}(x, y, z) = xy\vec{i} + (x^2 + 1)\vec{j} + z^2\vec{k}$.

2. A force field $\vec{F}$ is defined in 3-space by the equation

   $$\vec{F}(x, y, z) = y\,\vec{i} + z\,\vec{j} + yz\,\vec{k}\,.$$

   (a) Determine whether or not $\vec{F}$ is conservative.

   (b) Calculate the work done in moving a particle along the curve

† For a further discussion of connectedness, see Chapter 8 of the author's *Mathematical Analysis, ibid.*

$$\vec{r}(t) = \cos t \; \vec{i} + \sin t \; \vec{j} + e^t \; \vec{k}$$

as t runs from 0 to π.

3. A two-dimensional force field $\vec{F}$ is described by the equation

$$\vec{F}(x, y) = (x + y) \; \vec{i} + (x - y) \; \vec{j}.$$

(a) Show that the work done by this force in moving a particle along a curve

$$\vec{r}(t) = f(t) \; \vec{i} + g(t) \; \vec{j}, \qquad a \le t \le b,$$

depends only on $f(a)$, $f(b)$, $g(a)$, $g(b)$.

(b) Find the amount of work done when $f(a) = 1$, $f(b) = 2$, $g(a) = 3$, $g(b) = 4$.

4. A force field is given in polar coordinates by the equation

$$\vec{F}(r, \theta) = -4 \sin \theta \; \vec{i} + 4 \sin \theta \; \vec{j}.$$

Compute the work done in moving a particle from the point $(1, 0)$ to the origin along the spiral whose polar equation is $r = e^{-\theta}$.

5. A radial or "central" force field $\vec{F}$ in the plane may be written in the form $\vec{F}(x, y) = f(r) \; \vec{r}$, where $\vec{r} = x \; \vec{i} + y \; \vec{j}$ and $r = |\vec{r}|$. Show that such a force field is conservative.

6. Find the work required to push a particle from $(1, 0)$ to $(-1, 0)$ along the ellipse $b^2 x^2 + y^2 = b^2$ against the force $\vec{F}(x, y) = (3y^2 + 2) \; \vec{i} + 16x \; \vec{j}$. Which ellipse (that is, which value of b) makes the work a minimum? Give a reason for your answer.

7. Each of the following sets S is an open connected set in the xy-plane. In each case, choose two arbitrary distinct points in S and explain how you would find a simple step polygon in S connecting the two points.

(a) $S = \{(x, y) \mid x^2 + y^2 \ge 0\}$.
(b) $S = \{(x, y) \mid x^2 + y^2 > 0\}$.
(c) $S = \{(x, y) \mid x^2 + y^2 < 1\}$.
(d) $S = \{(x, y) \mid 1 < x^2 + y^2 < 2\}$.
(e) $S = \{(x, y) \mid x^2 + y^2 > 1 \text{ and } (x - 3)^2 + y^2 > 1\}$.

5.10 The first fundamental theorem of calculus for line integrals. Construction of potential functions by line integration

Section 5.8 extended the second fundamental theorem of calculus to line integrals. This section extends the first fundamental theorem. We recall that the first fundamental theorem states that every indefinite integral of a continuous function f has a derivative equal to f. That is, if

$$\phi(x) = \int_a^x f(t) \; dt \, ,$$

then at the points of continuity of f we have

$$\phi'(x) = f(x) \, .$$

To extend this theorem to line integrals we begin with a vector field $\vec{F}$, continuous on an open connected set S, and integrate it along a curve C from a fixed point $\vec{A}$ in S to an arbitrary point $\vec{X}$. Then we let ϕ denote the scalar field defined by the line integral

$$\phi(\vec{X}) = \int_{\vec{A}}^{\vec{X}} \vec{F} \cdot d\vec{r} \, ,$$

where $\vec{r}$ describes C. (Since S is connected, each point $\vec{X}$ in S can be reached by such a curve.) For this definition of $\phi(\vec{X})$ to be unambiguous, we need to know that the integral depends only on $\vec{X}$ and not on the particular path used to join $\vec{A}$ to $\vec{X}$. Therefore, it is natural to require the line integral of $\vec{F}$ to be independent of the path in S. Under these conditions, the extension of the first fundamental theorem takes the following form:

5–3   THEOREM. *First fundamental theorem for line integrals.* Let $\vec{F}$ be a vector field that is continuous on an open connected set S. Let $\vec{A}$ be a fixed point of S. Assume that for every $\vec{X}$ in S the line integral of $\vec{F}$ from $\vec{A}$ to $\vec{X}$ has the same value for every simple step polygon connecting $\vec{A}$ to $\vec{X}$. Define a scalar field ϕ on S by the equation

$$\phi(\vec{X}) = \int_{\vec{A}}^{\vec{X}} \vec{F} \cdot d\vec{r} \,,$$

where the line integral is taken along any simple step polygon in S joining $\vec{A}$ to $\vec{X}$. Then ϕ is differentiable on S and its gradient, $\nabla\phi$, is equal to $\vec{F}$; that is,

(5.21) $$\nabla\phi(\vec{X}) = \vec{F}(\vec{X}) \qquad \text{for every } \vec{X} \text{ in } S \,.$$

Before we discuss the proof of this theorem we note that it gives us another method for constructing a potential function of a given gradient. If $\vec{F}$ is a gradient, the line integral of $\vec{F}$ is independent of the path in S (by Theorem 5–2). Therefore we may find a potential ϕ simply by integrating $\vec{F}$ from a fixed point $\vec{A}$ to an arbitrary point $\vec{X}$ in S, using any piecewise smooth path lying in S. The scalar field ϕ so obtained depends on the choice of the initial point $\vec{A}$. If we begin the integration from another initial point, say $\vec{B}$, we obtain a new potential function ψ. But, because of the additive property of line integrals, ϕ and ψ can differ only by a constant, this constant being the integral of $\vec{F}$ from $\vec{A}$ to $\vec{B}$. An alternative method for constructing a potential of a given gradient was outlined earlier in Section 4.19. In practice, the method in Section 4.19 is usually simpler than a direct application of Theorem 5–3. When a potential is constructed by line integration the calculations are often simplified considerably by connecting $\vec{A}$ and $\vec{X}$ by a step polygon.

We turn now to the proof of Theorem 5–3.

Proof. We shall prove that the derivative $\phi'(\vec{X}; \vec{Y})$ exists for every unit coordinate vector $\vec{Y}$, and that

(5.22) $$\phi'(\vec{X}; \vec{Y}) = \vec{F}(\vec{X}) \cdot \vec{Y} \,.$$

This implies (5.21), because when $\vec{Y}$ is the kth unit coordinate vector, Equation (5.22) becomes

$$D_k\phi(\vec{X}) = F_k(\vec{X}) \qquad \text{(for all } k) \,,$$

where $F_k(\vec{X})$ denotes the kth component of $\vec{F}(\vec{X})$.

Let $N(\vec{X}; r)$ be any neighborhood of $\vec{X}$ of radius r lying entirely in the set S. Then $\vec{X} + h\vec{Y}$ also lies in S for every real h satisfying $0 < |h| < r$, and we may form the difference quotient

$$\frac{\phi(\vec{X} + h\vec{Y}) - \phi(\vec{X})}{h} \,.$$

Because of the additive property of line integrals, the numerator of this quotient may be written as

(5.23) $\phi(\vec{X} + h\vec{Y}) - \phi(\vec{X}) = \int_{\vec{X}}^{\vec{X}+h\vec{Y}} \vec{F} \cdot d\vec{r}$,

and the path joining $\vec{X}$ to $\vec{X} + h\vec{Y}$ may be any simple step polygon lying in S. In particular, we may use the line segment described by the vector equation

$$\vec{r}(t) = t(\vec{X} + h\vec{Y}) + (1 - t)\vec{X} , \qquad \text{where} \quad 0 \leq t \leq 1 .$$

Since $\vec{r}'(t) = (\vec{X} + h\vec{Y}) - \vec{X} = h\vec{Y}$, the integral in (5.23) becomes

$$\phi(\vec{X} + h\vec{Y}) - \phi(\vec{X}) = h \int_0^1 \vec{F}[\vec{r}(t)] \cdot \vec{Y} \, dt .$$

If we write $\vec{F}[\vec{r}(t)] = \vec{F}(\vec{X}) + \vec{F}[\vec{r}(t)] - \vec{F}(\vec{X})$ in the integrand and divide both sides by h we find

$$\frac{\phi(\vec{X} + h\vec{Y}) - \phi(\vec{X})}{h} - \vec{F}(\vec{X}) \cdot \vec{Y} = \int_0^1 \{\vec{F}[\vec{r}(t)] - \vec{F}(\vec{X})\} \cdot \vec{Y} \, dt .$$

Using the Cauchy-Schwarz inequality in the form $|\vec{A} \cdot \vec{B}| \leq |\vec{A}| \, |\vec{B}|$, we obtain

(5.24) $\left| \dfrac{\phi(\vec{X} + h\vec{Y}) - \phi(\vec{X})}{h} - \vec{F}(\vec{X}) \cdot \vec{Y} \right| \leq \displaystyle\int_0^1 |\vec{F}[\vec{r}(t)] - \vec{F}(\vec{X})| \, dt$,

since $|\vec{Y}| = 1$. This inequality is valid so long as $0 < |h| < r$, where r is the radius of any neighborhood of $\vec{X}$ that lies within S. Now we shall make a special choice of this neighborhood.

Continuity of $\vec{F}$ at $\vec{X}$ means that for every $\epsilon > 0$ a neighborhood $N(\vec{X})$ exists such that

$$|\vec{F}(\vec{T}) - \vec{F}(\vec{X})| < \frac{\epsilon}{2} \qquad \text{whenever} \quad \vec{T} \, \varepsilon \, N(\vec{X}) .$$

If we apply the foregoing argument to this neighborhood the point $\vec{r}(t)$ is in $N(\vec{X})$ for each t in [0, 1] and hence $|\vec{F}[\vec{r}(t)] - \vec{F}(\vec{X})| < \epsilon/2$. Integrating this inequality from 0 to 1 we find

$$\int_0^1 |\vec{F}[\vec{r}(t)] - \vec{F}(\vec{X})| \, dt \leq \frac{\epsilon}{2} < \epsilon .$$

Therefore inequality (5.24) becomes

(5.25) $\left| \dfrac{\phi(\vec{X} + h\vec{Y}) - \phi(\vec{X})}{h} - \vec{F}(\vec{X}) \cdot \vec{Y} \right| < \epsilon$.

That is, we have shown that for every $\epsilon > 0$ an $r > 0$ exists such that (5.25) holds whenever $0 < |h| < r$. This means that the derivative $\phi'(\vec{X}; \vec{Y})$ exists and has the value $\vec{F}(\vec{X}) \cdot \vec{Y}$, as asserted.

5.11 Exercises

In the following exercises, S denotes the set of all points (x, y) in the plane different from the origin, and $\vec{F}(x, y) = P(x, y) \, \vec{i} + Q(x, y) \, \vec{j}$, where

$$P(x, y) = -\frac{y}{x^2 + y^2} \quad \text{and} \quad Q(x, y) = \frac{x}{x^2 + y^2}.$$

These exercises show that $\vec{F}$ is a gradient on every open rectangle not containing the origin, but that $\vec{F}$ is *not* a gradient on the entire set S. In other words, for every open rectangle R not containing the origin, there is a scalar field ϕ such that $\vec{F} = \nabla\phi$ in R, but there is *no* ϕ that serves as a potential in the entire set S. The trouble is that each ϕ depends, in general, on the rectangle R, and there is no way to put them all together to construct a continuously differentiable gradient on the whole of S.

1. (a) Prove that S is an open connected set.
   (b) Prove that $\vec{F}$ is continuously differentiable on S.
   (c) Verify that $\partial P/\partial y = \partial Q/\partial x$ for every point (x, y) in S. From this and Theorem 4-9 of Section 4.19 it follows that $\vec{F}$ is the gradient of a potential in every open rectangle not containing the origin.

2. Continuing Exercise 1, let A and B denote the intersections of S with the upper and lower half planes, respectively. That is, A is the set of all $(x, y) \neq (0, 0)$ with $y \geq 0$, and B is the set of all $(x, y) \neq (0, 0)$ with $y \leq 0$.
   (a) Prove that the line integral $\int P\,dx + Q\,dy$ is independent of the path in A.
   (b) If $(a, b) \in A$, define

$$f(a, b) = \int_{(1, 0)}^{(a, b)} P\,dx + Q\,dy,$$

where the path lies in the set A. Show that

$$f(a, b) = \begin{cases} \operatorname{arc\,tan} \dfrac{b}{a} & \text{if } a > 0, \\[2mm] \pi/2 & \text{if } a = 0, \\[2mm] \operatorname{arc\,tan} \dfrac{b}{a} + \pi & \text{if } a < 0. \end{cases}$$

This f is a potential for $\vec{F}$ in A. [Recall the definition of the arc tangent function: For any real t, arc tan t is the unique real number θ which satisfies the two conditions $\tan \theta = t$ and $-\pi/2 < \theta < \pi/2$.]
   (c) Prove that the line integral $\int P\,dx + Q\,dy$ is independent of the path in B.
   (d) If $(a, b) \in B$, define

$$g(a, b) = \int_{(1, 0)}^{(a, b)} P\,dx + Q\,dy,$$

where the path lies in the set B. Show that

$$g(a, b) = \begin{cases} \operatorname{arc\,tan} \dfrac{b}{a} & \text{if } a > 0, \\[2mm] -\pi/2 & \text{if } a = 0, \\[2mm] \operatorname{arc\,tan} \dfrac{b}{a} - \pi & \text{if } a < 0. \end{cases}$$

This g is a potential for $\vec{F}$ in B.
   (e) Prove that the line integral $\int P\,dx + Q\,dy$ is *not* independent of the path in S. [*Hint.* Integrate from $(1, 0)$ to $(-1, 0)$ first along a path in A and then along a path in B.] This shows that

if a line integral is independent of the path in each of two sets A and B it need not be independent of the path in their union.

(f) The function f in part (b) is a potential for $\vec{F}$ in the set A and the function g in part (d) is a potential in B. Prove that there is *no* function that is a potential for $\vec{F}$ in the set S. This result, along with Exercise 1(c), shows that the equality of the two derivatives $\partial P/\partial y$ and $\partial Q/\partial x$ everywhere in S is not sufficient to guarantee the existence of a potential for $\vec{F}$ in S.

3. Let T denote the set of all $(x, y) \neq (0, 0)$ that do not lie on the negative x-axis. Prove that $\int P\, dx + Q\, dy$ is independent of the path in T and find a potential for $\vec{F}$ in T.

5.12   Necessary and sufficient conditions for a vector field to be a gradient

Theorems 5–2 and 5–3 together tell us that a necessary and sufficient condition for a continuous vector field to be a gradient is for its line integral between any two points to be independent of the path. We shall prove now that this condition is equivalent to the statement that the line integral is zero around every piecewise smooth *closed* path. All these conditions are summarized in the following theorem:

5– 4   THEOREM.   Let $\vec{F}$ be a vector field that is continuous on an open connected set S. Then the following three statements are equivalent:

(a) $\vec{F}$ is the gradient of some scalar field in S.

(b) If C_1 and C_2 are two arbitrary piecewise smooth curves in S, described by $\vec{r}_1$ and $\vec{r}_2$, respectively, with the same initial and terminal points, then

$$\int_{C_1} \vec{F} \cdot d\vec{r}_1 = \int_{C_2} \vec{F} \cdot d\vec{r}_2 \,.$$

(c) If C is an arbitrary piecewise smooth closed curve in S (described by $\vec{r}$), then

$$\int_C \vec{F} \cdot d\vec{r} = 0 \,.$$

Note. It is important to realize exactly what this theorem does and does not assert. For example, part (c) does *not* state that $\int_C \vec{F} \cdot d\vec{r} = 0$ for *every* vector field $\vec{F}$; rather, it states that this integral is zero around every closed curve in S if, and only if, $\vec{F}$ is the gradient of a scalar field in S. The theorem asserts that if any one of the three statements (a), (b), or (c) is true, the other two are also true; if any one of them does not hold, neither of the other two holds.

Proof. In Section 5.8 we proved that (a) implies (b) and in Section 5.10 we proved that (b) implies (a). We shall prove next that (a) implies (c).

If (a) holds, then $\vec{F} = \nabla f$ for some f and Equation (5.17) states that

$$\int_C \vec{F} \cdot d\vec{r} = \int_C \nabla f \cdot d\vec{r} = f(\vec{X}) - f(\vec{A})$$

for any two points $\vec{A}$ and $\vec{X}$ of S connected by a piecewise smooth curve C lying in S. For a *closed* curve we may choose $\vec{X} = \vec{A}$, making the integral zero. This proves that (a) implies (c).

Finally, we shall prove that (c) implies (b). Assume the integral of $\vec{F}$ is zero around any closed curve and let C_1 and C_2 be two curves in S with the same end points. Suppose C_1 is described by a function $\vec{r}_1$ defined over an interval $[a, b]$, and C_2 is described by a function $\vec{r}_2$ defined over $[c, d]$. Define a new function $\vec{r}$ as follows:

$$\vec{r}(t) = \begin{cases} \vec{r}_1(t) & \text{if } a \le t \le b, \\ \vec{r}_2(b + d - t) & \text{if } b \le t \le b + d - c. \end{cases}$$

Then $\vec{r}$ describes a closed curve C such that $\int_C \vec{F} \cdot d\vec{r} = \int_{C_1} \vec{F} \cdot d\vec{r}_1 - \int_{C_2} \vec{F} \cdot d\vec{r}_2$; since $\int_C \vec{F} \cdot d\vec{r} = 0$, this proves (b). Thus, (a), (b), and (c) are equivalent.

Warning: If a line integral $\int_C \vec{F} \cdot d\vec{r}$ is zero for a *particular* closed curve C or even for *infinitely many* closed curves, it does not necessarily follow that $\vec{F}$ is a gradient. For example, the reader can easily verify that the line integral $\int_C \vec{F} \cdot d\vec{r}$ of the vector field $\vec{F}(x, y) = x\vec{i} + xy\vec{j}$ is zero for every circle C with center at the origin. Nevertheless, this particular vector field is not a gradient.

5.13 Applications to exact differential equations of first order

Some differential equations of the first order can be solved with the aid of potential functions. Suppose we have a first-order differential equation of the form

$$y' = f(x, y).$$

If we multiply both sides by a nonvanishing factor $Q(x, y)$ we transform this equation to the form $Q(x, y)y' - f(x, y)Q(x, y) = 0$. If we then write $P(x, y)$ for $-f(x, y)Q(x, y)$ and use the Leibniz notation for derivatives, writing dy/dx for y', the differential equation takes the form

(5.26) $$P(x, y) \, dx + Q(x, y) \, dy = 0.$$

We assume that P and Q are continuous on some open connected set S in the plane. With each such differential equation we can associate a vector field $\vec{V}$, where

$$\vec{V}(x, y) = P(x, y)\vec{i} + Q(x, y)\vec{j}.$$

The components P and Q are the coefficients of dx and dy in Equation (5.26). The differential equation in (5.26) is said to be *exact* in S if the vector field $\vec{V}$ is the gradient of a potential; that is, if $\vec{V}(x, y) = \nabla\phi(x, y)$ for each point (x, y) in S, where ϕ is some scalar field. When such a ϕ exists we have $\partial\phi/\partial x = P$ and $\partial\phi/\partial y = Q$, and the differential equation in (5.26) becomes

$$\frac{\partial\phi}{\partial x} \, dx + \frac{\partial\phi}{\partial y} \, dy = 0.$$

We shall prove now that each solution of this differential equation satisfies the relation $\phi(x, y) = C$, where C is a constant. More precisely, assume there is a solution Y of the differential equation (5.26) defined on an open interval (a, b) such that the point $(x, Y(x))$ is in S for each x in (a, b). We shall prove that

$$\phi[x, Y(x)] = C$$

for some constant C. For this purpose we introduce the composite function g defined on (a, b) by the equation

$$g(x) = \phi[x, Y(x)].$$

By the chain rule, the derivative of g is given by

(5.27) $g'(x) = D_1\phi[x, Y(x)] + D_2\phi[x, Y(x)] \, Y'(x) = P(x, y) + Q(x, y)y'$,

where $y = Y(x)$ and $y' = Y'(x)$. If y satisfies (5.26), $P(x, y) + Q(x, y)y' = 0$, so $g'(x) = 0$ for each x in (a, b) and, therefore, g is constant on (a, b). This proves that every solution y satisfies the equation $\phi(x, y) = C$.

Now we may turn this argument around to find a solution of the differential equation. Suppose the equation

(5.28) $\phi(x, y) = C$

defines y as a differentiable function of x, say $y = Y(x)$ for x in an interval (a, b), and let $g(x) = \phi[x, Y(x)]$. Equation (5.28) implies that g is constant on (a, b). Hence, by (5.27), $P(x, y) + Q(x, y)y' = 0$, so y is a solution. Therefore, we have proved the following theorem:

5–5   THEOREM.   Assume that the differential equation

(5.29) $P(x, y) \, dx + Q(x, y) \, dy = 0$

is exact in an open connected set S, and let ϕ be a scalar field satisfying

$$\frac{\partial\phi}{\partial x} = P \quad \text{and} \quad \frac{\partial\phi}{\partial y} = Q$$

everywhere in S. Then every solution $y = Y(x)$ of (5.29) whose graph lies in S satisfies the equation $\phi[x, Y(x)] = C$ for some constant C. Conversely, if the equation

$$\phi(x, y) = C$$

defines y implicitly as a differentiable function of x, then this function is a solution of the differential equation (5.29).

The foregoing theorem provides a straightforward method for solving exact differential equations of the first order. We simply construct a potential function ϕ and then write the equation $\phi(x, y) = C$, where C is a constant. Whenever this equation defines y implicitly as a function of x, the corresponding y satisfies (5.29). Therefore we can use Equation (5.28) as a representation of a one-parameter family of integral curves. Of course, the only admissible values of C are those for which $\phi(x_0, y_0) = C$ for some (x_0, y_0) in S.

Example 1. Consider the differential equation

$$\frac{dy}{dx} = -\frac{3x^2 + 6xy^2}{6x^2y + 4y^3}.$$

Clearing the fractions we may write the equation as

$$(3x^2 + 6xy^2) \, dx + (6x^2y + 4y^3) \, dy = 0.$$

This is now a special case of (5.29) with $P(x, y) = 3x^2 + 6xy^2$ and $Q(x, y) = 6x^2y + 4y^3$. Since $\partial P/\partial y = \partial Q/\partial x = 12xy$ for all (x, y), Theorem 4–9 (Section 4.19) tells us that the vector field $P\vec{i} + Q\vec{j}$ is a gradient in every rectangle. A potential function ϕ is given by the formula

$$\phi(x, y) = x^3 + 3x^2y^2 + y^4 .$$

By Theorem 5-5, each solution of the differential equation satisfies

$$x^3 + 3x^2y^2 + y^4 = C$$

for some C. This provides an implicit representation of a family of integral curves. In this particular case the equation is quadratic in y^2 and can be solved to give an explicit formula for y in terms of x and C.

Example 2. Consider the first-order differential equation

(5.30) $$y \, dx + 2x \, dy = 0 .$$

Here $P(x, y) = y$ and $Q(x, y) = 2x$. Since $\partial P/\partial y = 1$ and $\partial Q/\partial x = 2$, this differential equation is not exact. However, if we multiply both sides by y we obtain an equation that *is* exact:

(5.31) $$y^2 \, dx + 2xy \, dy = 0 .$$

A potential of the vector field $y^2\vec{i} + 2xy\vec{j}$ is $\phi(x, y) = xy^2$, and every solution of (5.31) satisfies the relation $xy^2 = C$. This relation also represents a family of integral curves for Equation (5.30).

The multiplier y which converted (5.30) into an exact equation is called an *integrating factor*. In general, if multiplication of a first-order linear equation by a nonzero factor $\mu(x, y)$ results in an exact equation, the multiplier $\mu(x, y)$ is called an integrating factor of the original equation. A differential equation may have more than one integrating factor. For example, $\mu(x, y) = 2xy^3$ is another integrating factor of (5.30). Some special differential equations for which integrating factors can easily be found are discussed in the following set of exercises.

5.14 Exercises

Show that the differential equations in Exercises 1 through 5 are exact, and in each case find a one-parameter family of integral curves.

1. $(x + 2y) \, dx + (2x + y) \, dy = 0$.
2. $2xy \, dx + x^2 \, dy = 0$.
3. $(x^2 - y) \, dx - (x + \sin^2 y) \, dy = 0$.
4. $4 \sin x \sin 3y \cos x \, dx - 3 \cos 3y \cos 2x \, dy = 0$.
5. $(3x^2y + 8xy^2) \, dx + (x^3 + 8x^2y + 12ye^y) \, dy = 0$.
6. Show that a linear first-order equation, $y' + P(x)y = Q(x)$, has the integrating factor $\mu(x) = e^{\int P(x)dx}$. Use this to solve the equation.
7. Let $\mu(x, y)$ be an integrating factor of the differential equation $P(x, y) \, dx + Q(x, y) \, dy = 0$. Show that

$$\frac{\partial P}{\partial y} - \frac{\partial Q}{\partial x} = Q \frac{\partial}{\partial x} \log |\mu| - P \frac{\partial}{\partial y} \log |\mu| .$$

Use this equation to deduce the following rules for finding integrating factors:

(a) If $(\partial P/\partial y - \partial Q/\partial x)/Q$ is a function of x alone, say $f(x)$, then $e^{\int f(x)\,dx}$ is an integrating factor.

(b) If $(\partial Q/\partial x - \partial P/\partial y)/P$ is a function of y alone, say $g(y)$, then $e^{\int g(y)\,dy}$ is an integrating factor.

8. Use Exercise 7 to find integrating factors for the following equations, and determine a one-parameter family of integral curves.

(a) $y\,dx - (2x + y)\,dy = 0$.

(b) $(x^3 + y^3)\,dx - xy^2\,dy = 0$.

9. If $\partial P/\partial y - \partial Q/\partial x = f(x)Q(x, y) - g(y)P(x, y)$, show that

$$e^{\int f(x)\,dx + \int g(y)\,dy}$$

is an integrating factor of the differential equation $P(x, y)\,dx + Q(x, y)\,dy = 0$. Find such an integrating factor for each of the following equations and obtain a one-parameter family of integral curves.

(a) $(2x^2y + y^2)\,dx + (2x^3 - xy)\,dy = 0$.

(b) $(e^x \sec y - \tan y)\,dx + dy = 0$.

10. The following differential equations have an integrating factor in common. Find such an integrating factor and obtain a one-parameter family of integral curves for each equation.

$$(3y + 4xy^2)\,dx + (4x + 5x^2y)\,dy = 0 ,$$
$$(6y + x^2y^2)\,dx + (8x + x^3y)\,dy = 0 .$$

5.15   Green's theorem in the plane

In Section 5.8 we generalized the second fundamental theorem of calculus by showing that the line integral of a gradient ∇f along a path joining two points $\vec{A}$ and $\vec{B}$ may be expressed in terms of the function values $f(\vec{A})$ and $f(\vec{B})$. There is a two-dimensional analog of the second fundamental theorem which expresses a double integral over a region R as a line integral taken along a closed curve forming the boundary of R. This theorem is usually referred to as *Green's theorem*,† but it is sometimes called Gauss's theorem. It may be stated in several ways; the most common is in the form of the identity:

$$(5.32) \qquad \iint\limits_{R} \left(\frac{\partial Q}{\partial x} - \frac{\partial P}{\partial y} \right) dx\,dy = \oint_{C} P\,dx + Q\,dy .$$

The curve C which appears on the right is the boundary of the region R, and the integration symbol $\oint$ indicates that the curve is to be traversed in the counterclockwise direction, as suggested by the example shown in Figure 5.6.

Two types of assumptions are required for the validity of this identity. First, conditions of an analytic nature are imposed on the functions P and Q to ensure the existence of the integrals. The usual assumptions are that P and Q are continuously differentiable on an open set S containing the region R. This implies continuity of P and Q on C as well as continuity of $\partial P/\partial y$ and $\partial Q/\partial x$ on R, although the theorem is also valid under less stringent hypotheses. Second, there are conditions of a geometric nature that are

---

† In honor of George Green (1793–1841), an English mathematician who wrote on the applications of mathematics to electricity and magnetism, fluid flow, and the reflection and refraction of light and sound. The theorem which bears Green's name appeared earlier in the researches of Gauss and Lagrange.

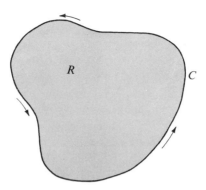

FIGURE 5.6 *The curve C is the boundary of R, traversed in a counterclockwise direction.*

imposed on the region R and its boundary curve C. The curve C may be any *rectifiable simple closed curve*. The term "rectifiable" means, of course, that C has a finite arc length. To explain what is meant by a simple closed curve, we refer to the vector-valued function which describes the curve.

Suppose C is described by a continuous vector-valued function $\vec{r}$ defined on an interval $[a, b]$. If $\vec{r}(a) = \vec{r}(b)$, the curve is *closed*. A closed curve such that $\vec{r}(t_1) \neq \vec{r}(t_2)$ for every pair of values $t_1 \neq t_2$ in the half-open interval $(a, b]$ is called a *simple* closed curve. This means that, except for the end points of the interval $[a, b]$, distinct values of t lead to distinct points on the curve. A circle is the prototype of a simple closed curve.

Simple closed curves that lie in a plane are usually called *Jordan curves* in honor of Camille Jordan (1838–1922), a famous French mathematician who did much of the pioneering work on such concepts as simple closed curves and arc length. Every Jordan curve C decomposes the plane into two disjoint open connected sets having the curve C as their common boundary. One of these regions is *bounded* and is called the *interior* (or *inner region*) of C. (An example is the shaded region in Figure 5.6.) The other is unbounded and is called the *exterior* (or *outer region*) of C. For some familiar Jordan curves such as circles, ellipses, or elementary polygons, it is intuitively evident that the curve divides the plane into an inner and an outer region, but to prove that this is true for an *arbitrary* Jordan curve is not easy. Jordan was the first to point out that this statement requires proof; the result is now known as the *Jordan curve theorem*. Toward the end of the 19th century Jordan and others published incomplete proofs. In 1905 the American mathematician Oswald Veblen (1880–   ) gave the first complete proof of this theorem. Green's theorem is valid whenever C is a rectifiable Jordan curve, and the region R is the union of C and its interior.† Since we have not defined line integrals along arbitrary rectifiable curves, we restrict our discussion here to piecewise smooth curves.

There is another technical difficulty associated with the formulation of Green's theorem. We have already remarked that, for the validity of the identity in (5.32), the

---

† A proof of Green's theorem for regions of this generality may be found in Chapter 10 of the author's *Mathematical Analysis, ibid.*

curve C must be traversed in the counterclockwise direction. Intuitively, this means that a man walking along the curve in this direction always has the region R to his left. Again, for some familiar Jordan curves, such as those mentioned earlier, the meaning of the expression "traversing a curve in the counterclockwise direction" is intuitively evident. However, in a strictly rigorous treatment of Green's theorem one would have to define this expression in completely analytic terms, that is, in terms of the vector-valued function $\vec{r}$ that describes the curve. One possible definition is outlined in Section 5.27.

Having pointed out some of the difficulties associated with the formulation of Green's theorem, we shall state the theorem in a rather general form and then indicate briefly why it is true for certain special regions. In this discussion the meaning of "counterclockwise" will be intuitive, so the treatment is not completely rigorous.

5- 6   THEOREM. *Green's theorem for plane regions bounded by piecewise smooth Jordan curves.* Let P and Q be scalar fields that are continuously differentiable on an open set S in the xy-plane. Let C be a piecewise smooth Jordan curve, and let R denote the union of C and its interior. Assume R lies in the set S. Then we have the identity

(5.33)
$$\iint\limits_{R} \left(\frac{\partial Q}{\partial x} - \frac{\partial P}{\partial y} \right) dx\, dy = \oint_{C} P\, dx + Q\, dy\, ,$$

where the line integral is taken around C in the counterclockwise direction.

Note. The identity in (5.33) is equivalent to the *two* formulas

(5.34)
$$\iint\limits_{R} \frac{\partial Q}{\partial x} dx\, dy = \oint_{C} Q\, dy$$

and

(5.35)
$$-\iint\limits_{R} \frac{\partial P}{\partial y} dx\, dy = \oint_{C} P\, dx\, .$$

In fact, if both of these are true, (5.33) follows by addition. Conversely, if (5.33) is true we may obtain (5.34) and (5.35) as special cases by taking $P = 0$ and $Q = 0$, respectively.

We shall outline a proof of (5.35) for special regions of the type shown in Figure 5.7. Here we assume that vertical lines intersect the boundary curve in two points at most. Thus, C may be decomposed into a lower arc C_1 and an upper arc C_2, traversed in the directions indicated in Figure 5.7. These curves are the graphs of two functions, say f and g, defined on a common interval $[a, b]$ on the x-axis. The region R is the set

$$R = \{(x, y) \mid a \leq x \leq b \text{ and } f(x) \leq y \leq g(x)\}\, .$$

Therefore the double integral $\iint\limits_{R} (\partial P/\partial y)\, dx\, dy$ may be evaluated by iterated integration. Integrating first with respect to y we have

(5.36)
$$\iint\limits_{R} \frac{\partial P}{\partial y} dx\, dy = \int_{a}^{b} \left[\int_{f(x)}^{g(x)} \frac{\partial P}{\partial y} dy \right] dx$$
$$= \int_{a}^{b} P[x, g(x)]\, dx - \int_{a}^{b} P[x, f(x)]\, dx\, .$$

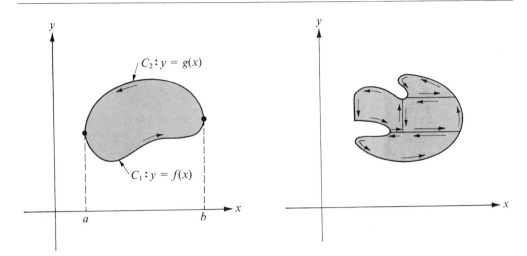

FIGURE 5.7   *Proof of Green's theorem for a spe-*   FIGURE 5.8   *Proof of Green's theorem for a more*
cial region.   *general region.*

On the other hand, the line integral $\oint_C P\,dx$ may be written as follows:

$$\oint_C P\,dx = \int_{C_1} P\,dx - \int_{(-C_2)} P\,dx\,.$$

To evaluate the integral over C_1 we use the vector representation $\vec{r}(t) = t\,\vec{i} + f(t)\,\vec{j}$; to evaluate the integral over $-C_2$ we use the representation $\vec{r}(t) = t\,\vec{i} + g(t)\,\vec{j}$. In both cases t varies from a to b. We now have

$$\int_{C_1} P\,dx - \int_{(-C_2)} P\,dx = \int_a^b P[t, f(t)]\,dt - \int_a^b P[t, g(t)]\,dt\,.$$

Comparing this equation with the formula in (5.36) we obtain (5.35).

A similar argument may be used to prove (5.34) when horizontal lines cut C twice at most. In this way a proof of Green's theorem is obtained for curves that are intersected at most twice by any horizontal or vertical line. If the boundary contains horizontal or vertical line segments the above arguments may be modified slightly and the same kind of proof carried out. Once this is done, the theorem can be proved for those regions R that can be decomposed into a finite number of regions of the types just discussed. "Crosscuts" are introduced as shown in Figure 5.8, the theorem is applied to each subregion, and the results are added together. The line integrals along the crosscuts cancel in pairs, as suggested in the figure, and the sum of the line integrals along the boundaries of the subregions is equal to the line integral along the boundary of R.

5.16   Some applications of Green's theorem

Let $\vec{F} = P\,\vec{i} + Q\,\vec{j}$ be a vector field that is continuously differentiable on an open set S in the plane. In Section 4.19 we proved that if $\vec{F}$ is the gradient of a potential, we have

$\partial P/\partial y = \partial Q/\partial x$ everywhere in S. Therefore the condition $\partial P/\partial y = \partial Q/\partial x$ is *necessary* for $\vec{F}$ to be a gradient. The Exercises in Section 5.11 show that the equality of the two partial derivatives $\partial P/\partial y$ and $\partial Q/\partial x$ everywhere in S is *not sufficient* to guarantee the existence of a potential for $\vec{F}$. We shall prove now that this condition *is* sufficient for a restricted class of regions. The regions of this class are called *simply connected*; they are defined as follows:

DEFINITION OF A SIMPLY CONNECTED PLANE SET. Let S be a polygonally connected set in the plane. Then S is called simply connected if, for every Jordan curve C which lies in S, the inner region of C is also a subset of S.

An annulus (the set of points lying between two concentric circles) is not simply connected because the entire inner region of the outermost circle is not a subset of the annulus. Intuitively speaking, we say that S is simply connected when it has no "holes." Another way to describe simple connectedness is to say that a curve C_1 in S connecting any two points may be continuously deformed into any other curve C_2 in S joining these two points, with all intermediate curves during the deformation lying completely in S. An alternative definition, which can be shown to be equivalent to the one given here, states that a set S is simply connected if its complement (relative to the whole plane) is connected. For example, an annulus is not simply connected because its complement is disconnected. A polygonally connected set that is not simply connected is called *multiply connected*.

The following important theorem provides a useful sufficient condition for the existence of potential functions.

5–7   THEOREM.   Let $\vec{F} = P\vec{i} + Q\vec{j}$ be a vector field whose components P and Q are continuously differentiable on an open connected set S in the plane. If S is simply connected, the following statements are equivalent:

    (a) $\partial P/\partial y = \partial Q/\partial x$ everywhere in S.
    (b) $\vec{F}$ is a gradient in S.
    (c) The line integral $\int P\, dx + Q\, dy$ is independent of the path in S.

Proof. Statements (b) and (c) are equivalent because of Theorem 5–4. Also, we proved in Section 4.19 that (b) implies (a). We prove next that (a) implies (b). For this we need only show that the line integral of $\vec{F}$ from a fixed point $\vec{A}$ to an arbitrary point $\vec{X}$ in S has the same value for all simple step polygons in S joining $\vec{A}$ to $\vec{X}$. Part (b) then follows by Theorem 5–3.

Let C_1 and C_2 be two simple step polygons in S joining $\vec{A}$ to $\vec{X}$. Portions of these polygons may coincide along certain line segments. The remaining portions will intersect at most a finite number of times, and will form the boundaries of a finite number of polygonal regions, say $R_1, \ldots, R_m$. Since S is assumed to be simply connected, each of the regions R_k is a subset of S. An example is shown in Figure 5.9. The solid line represents C_1, the dotted line represents C_2, and the shaded regions represent $R_1, \ldots, R_m$. (These two particular polygons coincide along the segment pq.)

We observe next that the line integral of $\vec{F}$ from $\vec{A}$ to $\vec{X}$ along C_1 plus the integral from $\vec{X}$ back to $\vec{A}$ along C_2 is zero because the integral along the closed path is a sum of integrals taken over the line segments common to C_1 and C_2 plus a sum of integrals taken around the boundaries of the regions R_k. The integrals over the common segments cancel in pairs, since each common segment is traversed twice, in opposite directions, and

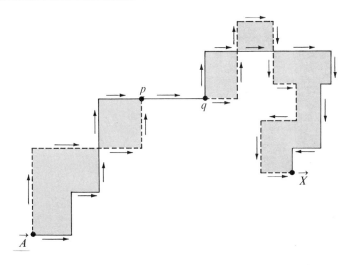

FIGURE 5.9   *Independence of the path in a simply connected region.*

their sum is zero. The integral over the boundary Γ_k of each region R_k is also zero because, by Green's theorem, we may write

$$\oint_{\Gamma_k} \vec{F} \cdot d\vec{r} = \oint_{\Gamma_k} P \, dx + Q \, dy = \pm \iint_{R_k} \left(\frac{\partial Q}{\partial x} - \frac{\partial P}{\partial y} \right) dx \, dy \,,$$

and the integrand of the double integral is zero because of the hypothesis $\partial Q/\partial x = \partial P/\partial y$. It follows that the integral from $\vec{A}$ to $\vec{X}$ along C_1 is equal to that along C_2. As we have already noted, this implies that $\vec{F}$ is a gradient in S and that the line integral of $\vec{F}$ is independent of the path in S.

In Theorem 5–4 (Section 5.12) we stated a number of necessary and sufficient conditions for a continuously differentiable vector field $P\vec{i} + Q\vec{j}$ to be a gradient on an open connected set S. For an open *simply* connected set, Theorem 5–7 gives a further necessary and sufficient condition, namely, $\partial P/\partial y = \partial Q/\partial x$. In practice, this condition provides the easiest method, by far, for determining whether or not a vector field is a gradient.

Further applications of Green's theorem are illustrated by the following examples.

Example 1. Use Green's theorem to compute the work done by the force field $\vec{F}(x, y)$ $= (y + 3x)\vec{i} + (2y - x)\vec{j}$ in moving a particle once around the ellipse $4x^2 + y^2 = 4$ in the counterclockwise direction.

Solution. The work is equal to $\oint_C P \, dx + Q \, dy$, where $P = y + 3x$, $Q = 2y - x$, and C is the ellipse. Since $\partial Q/\partial x - \partial P/\partial y = -2$, Green's theorem gives us

$$\oint_C P \, dx + Q \, dy = \iint_R (-2) \, dx \, dy = -2 \, A \,,$$

where A is the area of the region enclosed by the ellipse. Since this ellipse has semiaxes $a = 1$ and $b = 2$, its area A is $\pi ab = 2\pi$ and the value of the line integral is -4π.

Example 2. Evaluate the line integral $\oint_C (5 - xy - y^2)\, dx - (2xy - x^2)\, dy$, where C is the square with vertices $(0, 0)$, $(1, 0)$, $(1, 1)$, $(0, 1)$.

Solution. Here $P = 5 - xy - y^2$, $Q = x^2 - 2xy$, and $\partial Q/\partial x - \partial P/\partial y = 3x$. Hence, by Green's theorem, we have

$$\oint_C P\, dx + Q\, dy = 3 \iint_R x\, dx\, dy = 3\,\bar{x},$$

where $\bar{x}$ is the x-coordinate of the centroid of the square. Since $\bar{x}$ is obviously $1/2$, the value of the line integral is $3/2$.

Example 3. The area of a region R enclosed by a Jordan curve C is given by the line integral $\frac{1}{2} \oint_C -y\, dx + x\, dy$ since, by Green's theorem, this is equal to $\iint_R dx\, dy$.

5.17   Exercises

1. Use Green's theorem to evaluate the line integral $\oint_C y^2\, dx + x\, dy$ when
   (a) C is the square with vertices $(0, 0)$, $(2, 0)$, $(2, 2)$, $(0, 2)$.
   (b) C is the square with vertices $(\pm 1, \pm 1)$.
   (c) C is the square with vertices $(\pm 2, 0)$, $(0, \pm 2)$.
   (d) C is the circle of radius 2 and center at the origin.
   (e) C has the vector equation $\vec{r}(t) = 2\cos^3 t\,\vec{i} + 2\sin^3 t\,\vec{j}$, $0 \le t \le 2\pi$.

2. If $P(x, y) = x\, e^{-y^2}$ and $Q(x, y) = -x^2 y\, e^{-y^2} + 1/(x^2 + y^2)$, evaluate the line integral $\oint P\, dx + Q\, dy$ around the boundary of the square of side $2a$ determined by the inequalities $|x| \le a$ and $|y| \le a$.

3. Let C be a simple closed curve in the xy-plane and let I_z denote the moment of inertia (about the z-axis) of the region enclosed by C. Show that an integer n exists such that

$$n\, I_z = \oint_C x^3\, dy - y^3\, dx.$$

4. Given two scalar fields u and v that are continuously differentiable on an open set containing the circular disk R whose boundary is the circle $x^2 + y^2 = 1$. Define two vector fields $\vec{F}$ and $\vec{G}$ as follows:

$$\vec{F}(x, y) = v(x, y)\,\vec{i} + u(x, y)\,\vec{j}, \quad \vec{G}(x, y) = \left(\frac{\partial u}{\partial x} - \frac{\partial u}{\partial y}\right)\vec{i} + \left(\frac{\partial v}{\partial x} - \frac{\partial v}{\partial y}\right)\vec{j}.$$

Find the value of the double integral $\iint_R \vec{F} \cdot \vec{G}\, dx\, dy$ if it is known that on the boundary of R we have $u(x, y) = 1$ and $v(x, y) = y$.

5. If f and g are continuously differentiable in an open connected set S in the plane, show that $\oint_C f\nabla g \cdot d\vec{r} = -\oint_C g\nabla f \cdot d\vec{r}$ for every piecewise smooth Jordan curve C in S.

6. Let u and v be scalar fields having continuous first- and second-order partial derivatives in an open connected set S in the plane. Let R be a region in S bounded by a piecewise smooth Jordan curve C. Show that:

(a) $\displaystyle\oint_C uv\, dx + uv\, dy = \iint_R \left\{ v\left(\frac{\partial u}{\partial x} - \frac{\partial u}{\partial y}\right) + u\left(\frac{\partial v}{\partial x} - \frac{\partial v}{\partial y}\right) \right\} dx\, dy.$

(b) $\dfrac{1}{2} \oint_C \left(v\dfrac{\partial u}{\partial x} - u\dfrac{\partial v}{\partial x} \right) dx + \left(u\dfrac{\partial v}{\partial y} - v\dfrac{\partial u}{\partial y} \right) dy = \iint_R \left(u\dfrac{\partial^2 v}{\partial x \partial y} - v\dfrac{\partial^2 u}{\partial x \partial y} \right) dx\, dy\;.$

Normal derivatives. In Section 5.4 we defined line integrals with respect to arc length in such a way that the following equation holds:

$$\int_C P\, dx + Q\, dy = \int_C \vec{F} \cdot \vec{T}\, ds\;,$$

where $\vec{F} = P\,\vec{i} + Q\,\vec{j}$ and $\vec{T}$ is the unit tangent vector to C. (The dot product $\vec{F} \cdot \vec{T}$ is called the *tangential component* of $\vec{F}$ along C.) If C is a Jordan curve described by a continuously differentiable function $\vec{r}$, say $\vec{r}(t) = X(t)\,\vec{i} + Y(t)\,\vec{j}$, the unit *outer normal* $\vec{n}$ of C is defined by the equation

$$\vec{n}(t) = \dfrac{1}{|\vec{r}'(t)|}\,(Y'(t)\,\vec{i} - X'(t)\,\vec{j})$$

whenever $|\vec{r}'(t)| \neq 0$. If f is a scalar field with a gradient ∇f on C, the *normal derivative* $\partial f / \partial n$ is defined on C by the equation

$$\dfrac{\partial f}{\partial n} = \nabla f \cdot \vec{n}\;.$$

This is, of course, the directional derivative of f in the direction of $\vec{n}$. These concepts occur in the remaining exercises of this section.

7. If $\vec{F} = Q\,\vec{i} - P\,\vec{j}$, show that

$$\int_C P\, dx + Q\, dy = \int_C \vec{F} \cdot \vec{n}\, ds\;.$$

(The dot product $\vec{F} \cdot \vec{n}$ is called the *normal component* of $\vec{F}$ along C.)

8. Let f and g be scalar fields with continuous first- and second-order partial derivatives on an open set S in the plane. Let R denote a region (in S) whose boundary is a piecewise smooth Jordan curve C. Prove the following identities, where $\nabla^2 u = \partial^2 u/\partial x^2 + \partial^2 u/\partial y^2$.

(a) $\displaystyle \oint_C \dfrac{\partial g}{\partial n}\, ds = \iint_R \nabla^2 g\, dx\, dy\;.$

(b) $\displaystyle \oint_C f\dfrac{\partial g}{\partial n}\, ds = \iint_R (f\,\nabla^2 g + \nabla f \cdot \nabla g)\, dx\, dy\;.$

(c) $\displaystyle \oint_C \left(f\dfrac{\partial g}{\partial n} - g\dfrac{\partial f}{\partial n} \right) ds = \iint_R (f\,\nabla^2 g - g\,\nabla^2 f)\, dx\, dy\;.$

The identity in (c) is known as *Green's formula*; it shows that

$$\oint_C f\dfrac{\partial g}{\partial n}\, ds = \oint_C g\dfrac{\partial f}{\partial n}\, ds$$

whenever f and g are both harmonic on R (that is, when $\nabla^2 f = \nabla^2 g = 0$ on R).

9. Suppose the differential equation

$$P(x, y)\, dx + Q(x, y)\, dy = 0$$

has an integrating factor $\mu(x, y)$ which leads to a one-parameter family of solutions of the form

$\phi(x, y) = C$. If the slope of the curve $\phi(x, y) = C$ at (x, y) is $\tan \theta$, the unit normal vector $\vec{n}$ is taken to mean

$$\vec{n} = \sin \theta \, \vec{i} - \cos \theta \, \vec{j} \,.$$

There is a scalar field $g(x, y)$ such that the normal derivative of ϕ is given by the formula

$$\frac{\partial \phi}{\partial n} = \mu(x, y) g(x, y) \,,$$

where $\partial \phi / \partial n = \nabla \phi \cdot \vec{n}$. Find an explicit formula for $g(x, y)$ in terms of $P(x, y)$ and $Q(x, y)$.

5.18 Green's theorem for multiply connected regions

Green's theorem may be generalized to apply to certain multiply connected regions. The modification runs as follows:

5– 8   THEOREM. *Green's theorem for multiply connected regions.* Let $C_1, \ldots, C_n$ be n piecewise smooth Jordan curves having the following properties:
    (a) No two of the curves intersect.
    (b) The curves $C_2, \ldots, C_n$ all lie in the interior of C_1.
    (c) Curve C_i lies in the exterior of curve C_j for each $i \neq j$, $i > 1$, $j > 1$.
Let R denote the region which consists of the union of C_1 with that portion of the interior of C_1 that is not inside any of the curves $C_2, C_3, \ldots, C_n$. (An example of such a region is shown in Figure 5.10.) Let P and Q be continuously differentiable on an open set S containing R. Then we have the following identity:

$$(5.37) \qquad \iint\limits_{R} \left(\frac{\partial Q}{\partial x} - \frac{\partial P}{\partial y} \right) dx \, dy = \oint_{C_1} (P \, dx + Q \, dy) - \sum_{k=2}^{n} \oint_{C_k} (P \, dx + Q \, dy) \,.$$

The theorem may be proved by introducing crosscuts which transform R into a union of a finite number of simply connected regions bounded by Jordan curves. Green's theorem is applied to each part separately, and the results are added together. We shall illustrate how this proof may be carried out when $n = 2$. The more general case may be dealt with by using induction on the number n of curves.

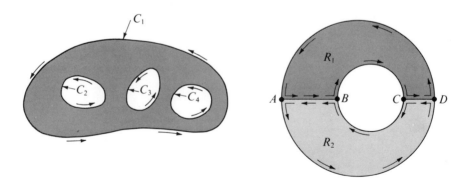

FIGURE 5.10   *A multiply connected region.*   FIGURE 5.11   *Proof of Green's theorem for a multiply connected region.*

The idea of the proof when $n = 2$ is illustrated by the example shown in Figure 5.11, where C_1 and C_2 are two circles, C_1 being the larger circle. Introduce the crosscuts AB and CD, as shown in the figure. Let K_1 denote the Jordan curve consisting of the upper half of C_2, the upper half of C_1, and the segments AB and CD. Let K_2 denote the Jordan curve consisting of the lower half of C_1, the lower half of C_2, and the two segments AB and CD. Now apply Green's theorem to each of the regions bounded by K_1 and K_2 and add the two identities so obtained. The line integrals along the crosscuts cancel out (since each crosscut is traversed once in each direction), resulting in the equation

$$\iint_R \left(\frac{\partial Q}{\partial x} - \frac{\partial P}{\partial y} \right) dx\, dy = \oint_{C_1} (P\, dx + Q\, dy) - \oint_{C_2} (P\, dx + Q\, dy).$$

The minus sign appears because of the direction in which C_2 is traversed. This is Equation (5.37) when $n = 2$.

For a simply connected region, the condition $\partial P/\partial y = \partial Q/\partial x$ implies that the line integral $\int P\, dx + Q\, dy$ is independent of the path (Theorem 5–7). As we have already noted, if S is *not* simply connected, the condition $\partial P/\partial y = \partial Q/\partial x$ does not necessarily imply independence of the path. However, in this case there is a substitute for independence that may be deduced from Theorem 5–8.

5– 9   THEOREM. *Invariance of a line integral under deformation of the path.* Let P and Q be continuously differentiable on an open connected set S in the plane, and assume that $\partial P/\partial y = \partial Q/\partial x$ everywhere on S. Let C_1 and C_2 be two piecewise smooth Jordan curves lying in S and satisfying the following conditions:

(a) C_2 lies in the interior of C_1.

(b) Those points inside C_1 which lie outside C_2 are in S. (An example is shown in Figure 5.12.)

Then we have

(5.38) $$\oint_{C_1} P\, dx + Q\, dy = \oint_{C_2} P\, dx + Q\, dy,$$

where both curves are traversed in the same direction.

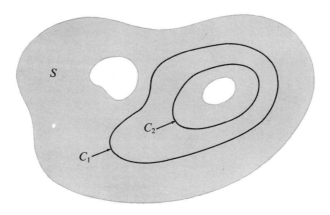

FIGURE 5.12   *Invariance of a line integral under deformation of the path.*

Proof. Under the conditions stated, Equation (5.37) is applicable when $n = 2$. The region R consists of those points lying between the two curves C_1 and C_2 and the curves themselves. Since $\partial P/\partial y = \partial Q/\partial x$ in S, the left member of Equation (5.37) is zero and we obtain (5.38).

Theorem 5–9 is sometimes described by saying that if $\partial P/\partial y = \partial Q/\partial x$ in S the value of a line integral along a simple closed curve in S is unaltered if the path is deformed to any other simple closed curve in S, provided all intermediate curves remain within the set S during the deformation. The set S is assumed to be open and connected—it need not be simply connected.

5.19   Exercises

1. Let $S = \{(x, y) \mid x^2 + y^2 > 0\}$, and let

$$P(x, y) = \frac{y}{x^2 + y^2}, \qquad Q(x, y) = \frac{-x}{x^2 + y^2}$$

if $(x, y) \in S$. Let C be a piecewise smooth Jordan curve lying in S.

   (a) If $(0, 0)$ is inside C, show that the line integral $\int_C P\,dx + Q\,dy$ has the value $\pm 2\pi$, and explain when the plus sign occurs.

   (b) Compute the value of the line integral $\int_C P\,dx + Q\,dy$ when $(0, 0)$ is outside C.

2. If $\vec{r} = x\vec{i} + y\vec{j}$ and $r = |\vec{r}|$, let

$$\vec{F}(x, y) = \frac{\partial(\log r)}{\partial y}\,\vec{i} - \frac{\partial(\log r)}{\partial x}\,\vec{j}$$

for $r > 0$. Let C be a piecewise smooth Jordan curve lying in the annulus $1 < x^2 + y^2 < 25$, and find all possible values of the line integral of $\vec{F}$ along C.

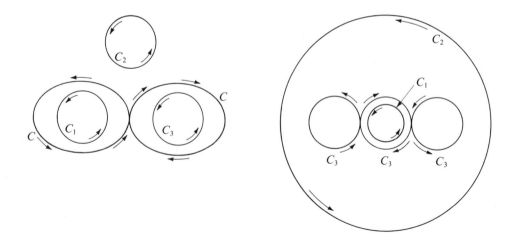

FIGURE 5.13   *Exercise 5.*   FIGURE 5.14   *Exercise 6.*

3. A connected plane region with exactly one "hole" is called *doubly connected.* (The annulus $1 < x^2 + y^2 < 2$ is an example.) If P and Q are continuously differentiable on an open doubly connected region R, and if $\partial P/\partial y = \partial Q/\partial x$ everywhere in R, how many distinct values are possible for line integrals $\int_C P\,dx + Q\,dy$ taken around piecewise smooth Jordan curves in R?

4. Solve Exercise 3 for triply connected regions, that is, for connected plane regions with exactly two holes.

5. Let P and Q be two scalar fields which have continuous derivatives satisfying $\partial P/\partial y = \partial Q/\partial x$ everywhere in the plane except at three points. Let C_1, C_2, C_3 be three nonintersecting circles having centers at these three points, as shown in Figure 5.13, and let $I_k = \oint_{C_k} P\,dx + Q\,dy$. Assume that $I_1 = 12$, $I_2 = 10$, $I_3 = 15$.

(a) Find the value of $\int_C P\,dx + Q\,dy$, where C is the figure-eight curve shown.

(b) Draw another closed curve Γ along which $\int P\,dx + Q\,dy = 1$. Indicate on your drawing the direction in which Γ is traversed.

(c) If $I_1 = 12$, $I_2 = 9$, and $I_3 = 15$, show that there is no closed curve Γ along which $\int P\,dx + Q\,dy = 1$.

6. Let $I_k = \oint_{C_k} P\,dx + Q\,dy$, where

$$P(x, y) = -y\left[\frac{1}{(x-1)^2 + y^2} + \frac{1}{x^2 + y^2} + \frac{1}{(x+1)^2 + y^2}\right]$$

and

$$Q(x, y) = \frac{x-1}{(x-1)^2 + y^2} + \frac{x}{x^2 + y^2} + \frac{x+1}{(x+1)^2 + y^2}.$$

In Figure 5.14, C_1 is the smallest circle, $x^2 + y^2 = 1/8$ (traced counterclockwise), C_2 is the largest circle, $x^2 + y^2 = 4$ (traced counterclockwise), and C_3 is the curve made up of the three intermediate circles $(x-1)^2 + y^2 = 1/4$, $x^2 + y^2 = 1/4$, and $(x+1)^2 + y^2 = 1/4$ traced out as shown. If $I_2 = 6\pi$ and $I_3 = 2\pi$, find the value of I_1.

5.20 Curl and divergence of a vector field

While integration enables us to deal satisfactorily with the concept of work and other problems connected with vector and scalar fields, some physical problems are better treated by differentiation. In Chapter 4 we extended the concepts of differential calculus to scalar fields by introducing the derivative of a scalar field with respect to a vector. We recall that the derivative $\phi'(\vec{X}; \vec{Y})$ was defined by the equation

(5.39)
$$\phi'(\vec{X}; \vec{Y}) = \lim_{h \to 0} \frac{\phi(\vec{X} + h\vec{Y}) - \phi(\vec{X})}{h}.$$

We then proved that for a continuously differentiable scalar field the derivative $\phi'(\vec{X}; \vec{Y})$ is linear in $\vec{Y}$. This enabled us to express the derivative as the dot product of the gradient vector $\nabla\phi(\vec{X})$ with $\vec{Y}$:

(5.40)
$$\phi'(\vec{X}; \vec{Y}) = \nabla\phi(\vec{X}) \cdot \vec{Y}.$$

We now introduce two new concepts, *curl* and *divergence,* that occur in the differential calculus of *vector* fields. Many of the theorems on line integrals discussed earlier in this chapter can be expressed very simply in terms of curl and divergence.

By analogy with (5.39), the derivative of a vector field $\vec{F}$ with respect to a vector $\vec{Y}$ is defined by the equation

$$\vec{F}'(\vec{X};\ \vec{Y}) = \lim_{h \to 0} \frac{\vec{F}(\vec{X} + h\vec{Y}) - \vec{F}(\vec{X})}{h}.$$

Here, the vectors $\vec{X}$ and $\vec{Y}$ are in m-space, and $\vec{F}(\vec{X})$ is in n-space, where m and n may or may not be equal. This derivative appeared earlier (in Section 4.14) in connection with the generalized chain rule (Theorem 4–8). We found that the components of $\vec{F}'(\vec{X};\ \vec{Y})$ are the derivatives of the components of $\vec{F}$. In fact, if the unit coordinate vectors in n-space are denoted by $\vec{A}_1, \vec{A}_2, \ldots, \vec{A}_n$, we have

$$\vec{F}(\vec{X}) = \sum_{i=1}^{n} F_i(\vec{X})\ \vec{A}_i$$

and

(5.41) $$\vec{F}'(\vec{X};\ \vec{Y}) = \sum_{i=1}^{n} F_i'(\vec{X};\ \vec{Y})\ \vec{A}_i.$$

Since each derivative $F_i'(\vec{X};\ \vec{Y})$ in this sum is linear in $\vec{Y}$, the same is true of $\vec{F}'(\vec{X};\ \vec{Y})$. By (5.40), each derivative $F_i'(\vec{X};\ \vec{Y})$ is a dot product, $\nabla F_i(\vec{X}) \cdot \vec{Y}$. If we express this dot product in terms of the components of $\nabla F_i(\vec{X})$ and $\vec{Y}$, we find

$$F_i'(\vec{X};\ \vec{Y}) = \nabla F_i(\vec{X}) \cdot \vec{Y} = \sum_{k=1}^{m} D_k F_i(\vec{X})\ y_k,$$

where $\vec{Y} = (y_1, y_2, \ldots, y_m)$. Substituting this sum in Equation (5.41) we obtain the following formula for expressing $\vec{F}'(\vec{X};\ \vec{Y})$ in terms of the components of $\vec{Y}$:

(5.42) $$\vec{F}'(\vec{X};\ \vec{Y}) = \sum_{i=1}^{n} \sum_{k=1}^{m} D_k F_i(\vec{X})\ y_k\ \vec{A}_i.$$

This shows that, as a function of $\vec{X}$, the derivative $\vec{F}'(\vec{X};\ \vec{Y})$ is completely determined by the mn partial derivatives $D_k F_i(\vec{X})$ appearing in this sum. These derivatives may be displayed in a rectangular array as follows:

$$\begin{bmatrix} D_1 F_1(\vec{X}) & D_2 F_1(\vec{X}) & \cdots & D_m F_1(\vec{X}) \\ D_1 F_2(\vec{X}) & D_2 F_2(\vec{X}) & \cdots & D_m F_2(\vec{X}) \\ \cdot & & & \cdot \\ \cdot & & & \cdot \\ \cdot & & & \cdot \\ D_1 F_n(\vec{X}) & D_2 F_n(\vec{X}) & \cdots & D_m F_n(\vec{X}) \end{bmatrix}.$$

The array is called the *Jacobian matrix* of $\vec{F}$ at $\vec{X}$ and will be denoted by $D\vec{F}(\vec{X})$. The ith row of the matrix consists of the partial derivatives of F_i, and the jth column consists of the partial derivatives D_j of the components of $\vec{F}$.

Readers familiar with matrix algebra will recognize that Equation (5.42) can be expressed more simply as a matrix equation, namely,

(5.43) $\vec{F}'(\vec{X};\ \vec{Y}) = D\vec{F}(\vec{X})\vec{Y}$,

where $D\vec{F}(\vec{X})$ is the Jacobian matrix and the vectors $\vec{F}'(\vec{X};\ \vec{Y})$ and $\vec{Y}$ are column matrices. The product $D\vec{F}(\vec{X})\vec{Y}$ is matrix multiplication. Formula (5.43) is the analog of (5.40) for vector fields, with the Jacobian matrix playing the role of the gradient.

Further discussion of the derivative $\vec{F}'(\vec{X};\ \vec{Y})$ in a general n-space is best carried out with the aid of matrix algebra. It would take us too far afield to develop the necessary algebraic tools for such a discussion, so from now on we assume that the vectors $\vec{X}$, $\vec{Y}$, and $\vec{F}(\vec{X})$ are in 3-space. We shall not require any knowledge of matrix algebra. Matrices will be used here only as a convenient device for keeping track of the nine derivatives $D_k F_i$.

We change notation and write

$$\vec{F}(x,\ y,\ z) = P(x,\ y,\ z)\vec{i} + Q(x,\ y,\ z)\vec{j} + R(x,\ y,\ z)\vec{k} .$$

The corresponding Jacobian matrix now consists of three rows and columns†:

$$D\vec{F}(x,\ y,\ z) = \begin{bmatrix} \dfrac{\partial P}{\partial x} & \dfrac{\partial P}{\partial y} & \dfrac{\partial P}{\partial z} \\[2mm] \dfrac{\partial Q}{\partial x} & \dfrac{\partial Q}{\partial y} & \dfrac{\partial Q}{\partial z} \\[2mm] \dfrac{\partial R}{\partial x} & \dfrac{\partial R}{\partial y} & \dfrac{\partial R}{\partial z} \end{bmatrix} .$$

Two special combinations of the partial derivatives in this matrix are called, respectively, the *divergence* and *curl* of the vector field $\vec{F}$. The divergence is a *scalar field*, denoted by div $\vec{F}$, and defined by the equation

$$\text{div } \vec{F} = \frac{\partial P}{\partial x} + \frac{\partial Q}{\partial y} + \frac{\partial R}{\partial z} .$$

The curl, on the other hand, is a *vector field*, denoted by curl $\vec{F}$, and defined by the equation

(5.44) $\text{curl } \vec{F} = \left(\dfrac{\partial R}{\partial y} - \dfrac{\partial Q}{\partial z}\right)\vec{i} + \left(\dfrac{\partial P}{\partial z} - \dfrac{\partial R}{\partial x}\right)\vec{j} + \left(\dfrac{\partial Q}{\partial x} - \dfrac{\partial P}{\partial y}\right)\vec{k} .$

If we refer to the Jacobian matrix we see that the divergence is simply the sum of the elements appearing on the main diagonal (from the upper left-hand corner to the lower right-hand corner). In matrix theory, this sum is called the *trace* of the matrix. The components of the curl are the differences of elements located symmetrically with respect to the main diagonal. The physical significance of the curl and divergence will be discussed in a later section. At this stage we shall consider some examples and mention some of the fundamental mathematical properties of the curl and divergence.

Example 1. Let $\vec{F}(x,\ y,\ z) = x\vec{i} + y\vec{j} + z\vec{k}$. Then we have

$$P(x,\ y,\ z) = x ,\qquad Q(x,\ y,\ z) = y ,\qquad R(x,\ y,\ z) = z ,$$

---

† The determinant of this matrix was referred to earlier as the Jacobian $\partial(P,\ Q,\ R)/\partial(x,\ y,\ z)$. In this discussion we are dealing with matrices, not determinants.

and the corresponding Jacobian matrix is

$$\begin{bmatrix} 1 & 0 & 0 \\ 0 & 1 & 0 \\ 0 & 0 & 1 \end{bmatrix}.$$

Therefore

$$\text{div } \vec{F} = 3 \qquad \text{and} \qquad \text{curl } \vec{F} = \vec{0}.$$

More generally, if $\vec{F}(x, y, z) = f(x)\vec{i} + g(y)\vec{j} + h(z)\vec{k}$, the Jacobian matrix has the elements $f'(x)$, $g'(y)$, $h'(z)$ on the main diagonal and zeros elsewhere, so

$$\text{div } \vec{F} = f'(x) + g'(y) + h'(z) \qquad \text{and} \qquad \text{curl } \vec{F} = \vec{0}.$$

Example 2. Let $\vec{F}(x, y, z) = xy^2z^2\,\vec{i} + z^2 \sin y\,\vec{j} + x^2e^y\,\vec{k}$. The Jacobian matrix is

$$\begin{bmatrix} y^2z^2 & 2xyz^2 & 2xy^2z \\ 0 & z^2\cos y & 2z \sin y \\ 2xe^y & x^2e^y & 0 \end{bmatrix}.$$

Therefore,

$$\text{div } \vec{F} = y^2z^2 + z^2\cos y$$

and

$$\text{curl } \vec{F} = (x^2e^y - 2z \sin y)\,\vec{i} + (2xy^2z - 2xe^y)\,\vec{j} - 2xyz^2\,\vec{k}.$$

Example 3: The divergence and curl of a gradient. Suppose $\vec{F}$ is a gradient, say $\vec{F} = \text{grad } \phi = \partial\phi/\partial x\,\vec{i} + \partial\phi/\partial y\,\vec{j} + \partial\phi/\partial z\,\vec{k}$. The Jacobian matrix is

(5.45)

$$\begin{bmatrix} \dfrac{\partial^2\phi}{\partial x^2} & \dfrac{\partial^2\phi}{\partial y\,\partial x} & \dfrac{\partial^2\phi}{\partial z\,\partial x} \\[2ex] \dfrac{\partial^2\phi}{\partial x\,\partial y} & \dfrac{\partial^2\phi}{\partial y^2} & \dfrac{\partial^2\phi}{\partial z\,\partial y} \\[2ex] \dfrac{\partial^2\phi}{\partial x\,\partial z} & \dfrac{\partial^2\phi}{\partial y\,\partial z} & \dfrac{\partial^2\phi}{\partial z^2} \end{bmatrix}.$$

Therefore

$$\text{div } \vec{F} = \frac{\partial^2\phi}{\partial x^2} + \frac{\partial^2\phi}{\partial y^2} + \frac{\partial^2\phi}{\partial z^2}.$$

The expression on the right is called the *Laplacian* of ϕ and is often written more briefly as $\nabla^2\phi$. Thus, the divergence of a gradient $\nabla\phi$ is the Laplacian of ϕ. In symbols, this is written

(5.46) $$\text{div}(\nabla\phi) = \nabla^2\phi.$$

When $\nabla^2\phi = 0$, the function ϕ is called *harmonic*. Equation (5.46) shows that the gradient of a harmonic function has zero divergence. When the mixed partial derivatives in matrix (5.45) are continuous, the elements located symmetrically with respect to the main diagonal are equal and curl $\vec{F}$ is zero. In other words,

$$\text{curl}(\text{grad } \phi) = \vec{0}$$

for every scalar field ϕ with continuous second-order mixed partial derivatives. This example shows that the condition curl $\vec{F} = \vec{0}$ is necessary for a continuously differentiable vector field $\vec{F}$ to be a gradient. In other words, if curl $\vec{F} \neq \vec{0}$ on an open set S, $\vec{F}$ is not a gradient on S. We know also, from Theorem 4–9 (Section 4.19), that if curl $\vec{F} = \vec{0}$ on an open rectangular parallelepiped S, $\vec{F}$ is a gradient on S. In Chapter 6 (Section 6.11) we shall prove that the statement is also true if S is convex.

Example 4: A vector field with zero divergence and zero curl. Let S be the set of all $(x, y) \neq (0, 0)$, and let

$$\vec{F}(x, y) = -\frac{y}{x^2 + y^2}\, \vec{i} + \frac{x}{x^2 + y^2}\, \vec{j}$$

if $(x, y) \varepsilon S$. From the work in Section 5.11 we know that $\vec{F}$ *is not a gradient on S* (although $\vec{F}$ *is* a gradient on every rectangle not containing the origin). The Jacobian matrix is

$$D\vec{F}(x, y) = \begin{bmatrix} \dfrac{2xy}{(x^2 + y^2)^2} & \dfrac{y^2 - x^2}{(x^2 + y^2)^2} & 0 \\[3ex] \dfrac{y^2 - x^2}{(x^2 + y^2)^2} & \dfrac{-2xy}{(x^2 + y^2)^2} & 0 \\[3ex] 0 & 0 & 0 \end{bmatrix},$$

and we see at once that div $\vec{F} = 0$ and curl $\vec{F} = \vec{0}$.

Example 5: The divergence and curl of a curl. If $\vec{F} = P\vec{i} + Q\vec{j} + R\vec{k}$, the curl of $\vec{F}$ is a new vector field, given by Equation (5.44), and we can compute *its* divergence and curl. The Jacobian matrix of curl $\vec{F}$ is

$$\begin{bmatrix} \dfrac{\partial^2 R}{\partial x\, \partial y} - \dfrac{\partial^2 Q}{\partial x\, \partial z} & \dfrac{\partial^2 R}{\partial y^2} - \dfrac{\partial^2 Q}{\partial y\, \partial z} & \dfrac{\partial^2 R}{\partial z\, \partial y} - \dfrac{\partial^2 Q}{\partial z^2} \\[3ex] \dfrac{\partial^2 P}{\partial x\, \partial z} - \dfrac{\partial^2 R}{\partial x^2} & \dfrac{\partial^2 P}{\partial y\, \partial z} - \dfrac{\partial^2 R}{\partial y\, \partial x} & \dfrac{\partial^2 P}{\partial z^2} - \dfrac{\partial^2 R}{\partial z\, \partial x} \\[3ex] \dfrac{\partial^2 Q}{\partial x^2} - \dfrac{\partial^2 P}{\partial x\, \partial y} & \dfrac{\partial^2 Q}{\partial y\, \partial x} - \dfrac{\partial^2 P}{\partial y^2} & \dfrac{\partial^2 Q}{\partial z\, \partial x} - \dfrac{\partial^2 P}{\partial z\, \partial y} \end{bmatrix}.$$

If we assume that all the mixed partial derivatives are continuous, we find that

$$\text{div}(\text{curl } \vec{F}) = 0$$

and

(5.47) $$\text{curl}(\text{curl } \vec{F}) = \text{grad}(\text{div } \vec{F}) - \nabla^2 \vec{F},$$

where $\nabla^2\vec{F}$ is defined by the equation

$$\nabla^2\vec{F} = (\nabla^2 P)\vec{i} + (\nabla^2 Q)\vec{j} + (\nabla^2 R)\vec{k}.$$

The identity in (5.47) relates all four operators, gradient, curl, divergence, and Laplacian. The verification of (5.47) is requested in Exercise 7 of Section 5.21.

The curl and divergence have some general properties in common with ordinary derivatives. First, they are *linear operators*. That is, if a and b are constants, we have

$$(5.48) \qquad \operatorname{div}(a\vec{F} + b\vec{G}) = a \operatorname{div} \vec{F} + b \operatorname{div} \vec{G} \,,$$

and

$$(5.49) \qquad \operatorname{curl}(a\vec{F} + b\vec{G}) = a \operatorname{curl} \vec{F} + b \operatorname{curl} \vec{G} \,.$$

They also have a property analogous to the formula for differentiating a product:

$$(5.50) \qquad \operatorname{div}(\phi\vec{F}) = \phi \operatorname{div} \vec{F} + \nabla\phi \cdot \vec{F} \,,$$

and

$$(5.51) \qquad \operatorname{curl}(\phi\vec{F}) = \phi \operatorname{curl} \vec{F} + \nabla\phi \times \vec{F} \,,$$

where ϕ is any differentiable scalar field. These properties are immediate consequences of the definitions of curl and divergence; their proofs are requested in Exercise 6 of Section 5.21.

There is a useful notation that helps us remember various formulas involving curl and divergence. We treat the symbol ∇ as though it were a vector:

$$\nabla = \frac{\partial}{\partial x} \vec{i} + \frac{\partial}{\partial y} \vec{j} + \frac{\partial}{\partial z} \vec{k} \,.$$

If $\vec{F} = P\vec{i} + Q\vec{j} + R\vec{k}$, we form the "dot product" $\nabla \cdot \vec{F}$ in a purely formal way, interpreting the "product" of $\partial/\partial x$ and P as the partial derivative $\partial P/\partial x$. We then find that

$$\nabla \cdot \vec{F} = \frac{\partial P}{\partial x} + \frac{\partial Q}{\partial y} + \frac{\partial R}{\partial z} \,.$$

Thus, the dot product $\nabla \cdot \vec{F}$ can be interpreted as the divergence of $\vec{F}$. Similarly, if we form the cross product $\nabla \times \vec{F}$ in a purely formal way we find

$$\nabla \times \vec{F} = \begin{vmatrix} \vec{i} & \vec{j} & \vec{k} \\ \dfrac{\partial}{\partial x} & \dfrac{\partial}{\partial y} & \dfrac{\partial}{\partial z} \\ P & Q & R \end{vmatrix} = \left(\frac{\partial R}{\partial y} - \frac{\partial Q}{\partial z} \right)\vec{i} + \left(\frac{\partial P}{\partial z} - \frac{\partial R}{\partial x} \right)\vec{j} + \left(\frac{\partial Q}{\partial x} - \frac{\partial P}{\partial y} \right)\vec{k} \,,$$

so the cross product $\nabla \times \vec{F}$ can be interpreted as the curl of $\vec{F}$. In line with this point of view, it is interesting to note that formal multiplication of ∇ by a scalar field ϕ gives us the vector field

$$\nabla\phi = \frac{\partial\phi}{\partial x} \vec{i} + \frac{\partial\phi}{\partial y} \vec{j} + \frac{\partial\phi}{\partial z} \vec{k} \,,$$

which is, of course, the gradient of ϕ. Thus, the gradient, the divergence, and the curl may be represented symbolically by the three "products" $\nabla\phi$, $\nabla \cdot \vec{F}$, and $\nabla \times \vec{F}$.

With this notation, each of the formulas in (5.50) and (5.51) takes a form which resembles more closely the usual rule for differentiating a product:

$$\nabla \cdot (\phi \vec{F}) = \phi \, \nabla \cdot \vec{F} + \nabla \phi \cdot \vec{F}$$

and

$$\nabla \times (\phi \vec{F}) = \phi \, \nabla \times \vec{F} + \nabla \phi \times \vec{F}.$$

In Example 3 the Laplacian of a scalar field, $\nabla^2 \phi$, was defined to be $\partial^2 \phi / \partial x^2 + \partial^2 \phi / \partial y^2 + \partial^2 \phi / \partial z^2$. In Example 5 the Laplacian $\nabla^2 \vec{F}$ of a vector field was defined by components. We get correct formulas for both $\nabla^2 \phi$ and $\nabla^2 \vec{F}$ if we interpret ∇^2 as the symbolic operator

$$\nabla^2 = \frac{\partial^2}{\partial x^2} + \frac{\partial^2}{\partial y^2} + \frac{\partial^2}{\partial z^2}.$$

This formula for ∇^2 also arises by dot multiplication of the symbolic vector ∇ with itself. Thus, we have $\nabla^2 = \nabla \cdot \nabla$ and we can write

$$\nabla^2 \phi = (\nabla \cdot \nabla)\phi \qquad \text{and} \qquad \nabla^2 \vec{F} = (\nabla \cdot \nabla)\vec{F}.$$

Now consider the formula $\nabla \cdot \nabla \phi$. This can be read as $(\nabla \cdot \nabla)\phi$, which is $\nabla^2 \phi$; or as $\nabla \cdot (\nabla \phi)$, which is $\mathrm{div}(\nabla \phi)$. In Example 3 we showed that $\mathrm{div}(\nabla \phi) = \nabla^2 \phi$, so we have

$$(\nabla \cdot \nabla)\phi = \nabla \cdot (\nabla \phi);$$

hence we can write $\nabla \cdot \nabla \phi$ for either of these expressions without danger of ambiguity. This is not true, however, when ϕ is replaced by a vector field $\vec{F}$. The expression $(\nabla \cdot \nabla)\vec{F}$ is $\nabla^2 \vec{F}$, which has been defined. However, $\nabla \cdot (\nabla \vec{F})$ is meaningless because $\nabla \vec{F}$ is not defined. Therefore the expression $\nabla \cdot \nabla \vec{F}$ is meaningful only when it is interpreted as $(\nabla \cdot \nabla)\vec{F}$. These remarks illustrate that although symbolic formulas sometimes serve as a convenient notation and memory aid, care is needed in manipulating the symbols.

5.21 Exercises

1. For each of the following vector fields determine the Jacobian matrix and compute the curl and divergence.

(a) $\vec{F}(x, y, z) = (x^2 + yz)\vec{i} + (y^2 + xz)\vec{j} + (z^2 + xy)\vec{k}$.

(b) $\vec{F}(x, y, z) = (2z - 3y)\vec{i} + (3x - z)\vec{j} + (y - 2x)\vec{k}$.

(c) $\vec{F}(x, y, z) = (z + \sin y)\vec{i} - (z - x \cos y)\vec{j}$.

(d) $\vec{F}(x, y, z) = e^{xy}\vec{i} + \cos xy \, \vec{j} + \cos xz^2 \, \vec{k}$.

(e) $\vec{F}(x, y, z) = x^2 \sin y \, \vec{i} + y^2 \sin xz \, \vec{j} + xy \sin(\cos z)\vec{k}$.

2. If $\vec{r} = x\vec{i} + y\vec{j} + z\vec{k}$ and $r = |\vec{r}|$, compute curl $[f(r)\vec{r}]$, where f is a differentiable function.

3. If $\vec{r} = x\vec{i} + y\vec{j} + z\vec{k}$ and $\vec{A}$ is a constant vector, show that curl$(\vec{A} \times \vec{r}) = 2\vec{A}$.

4. If $\vec{r} = x\vec{i} + y\vec{j} + z\vec{k}$ and $r = |\vec{r}|$, find all integers n for which div$(r^n \vec{r}) = 0$.

5. Find a vector field whose curl is $x\vec{i} + y\vec{j} + z\vec{k}$ or prove that no such vector field exists.

6. Prove the elementary properties of curl and divergence in Equations (5.48) through (5.51).

7. Prove that curl(curl $\vec{F}$) = grad(div $\vec{F}$) $- \nabla^2 \vec{F}$ if the components of $\vec{F}$ have continuous mixed partial derivatives of second order.

8. Prove the identity

$$\nabla \cdot (\vec{F} \times \vec{G}) = \vec{G} \cdot (\nabla \times \vec{F}) - \vec{F} \cdot (\nabla \times \vec{G}),$$

where $\vec{F}$ and $\vec{G}$ are differentiable vector fields.

9. A vector field $\vec{F}$ will not be the gradient of a potential unless curl $\vec{F} = \vec{0}$. However, it may be possible to find a nonzero scalar field μ such that $\mu\vec{F}$ is a gradient. Prove that if such a μ exists, $\vec{F}$ is always perpendicular to its curl. When the field is two-dimensional, say $\vec{F} = P\vec{i} + Q\vec{j}$, this exercise gives us a necessary condition for the differential equation $P\,dx + Q\,dy = 0$ to have an integrating factor. (The converse is also true. That is, if $\vec{F} \cdot$ curl $\vec{F} = 0$ in a suitable region, a nonzero μ exists such that $\mu\vec{F}$ is a gradient. The proof of the converse is not required.)

10. Let $\vec{F}(x, y, z) = y^2z^2\,\vec{i} + z^2x^2\,\vec{j} + x^2y^2\,\vec{k}$. Show that curl $\vec{F}$ is not always zero, but that $\vec{F} \cdot$ curl $\vec{F} = 0$. Find a scalar field μ such that $\mu\vec{F}$ is a gradient.

11. Suppose that two vector fields $\vec{F}$ and $\vec{G}$ satisfy the equations

(5.52)   curl $\vec{F} = c\vec{G}$ and   curl $\vec{G} = c\vec{F}$,

where c is a nonzero constant.

(a) Show that div $\vec{F} =$ div $\vec{G} = 0$, and that $\vec{F}$ and $\vec{G}$ satisfy the partial differential equation

$$\nabla^2\vec{V} + c^2\vec{V} = \vec{0} .$$

(b) If $\vec{A}$ is any vector field satisfying $\nabla^2\vec{A} + c^2\vec{A} =$ grad ϕ for some scalar field ϕ with a continuously differentiable gradient, show that the vectors $\vec{F} = c$ curl $\vec{A}$ and $\vec{G} =$ curl(curl $\vec{A}$) satisfy (5.52).

(c) If $\vec{r} = x\vec{i} + y\vec{j} + z\vec{k}$, and u and v are two scalar fields satisfying the partial differential equation $\nabla^2w + c^2w = 0$, show that the two vector fields

$$\vec{F}(x, y) = \text{curl}[\text{curl}(u\,\vec{r})] + c\,\text{curl}(v\,\vec{r}) \qquad \text{and} \qquad \vec{G}(x, y) = c\,\text{curl}(u\,\vec{r}) + \text{curl}[\text{curl}(v\,\vec{r})]$$

satisfy (5.52).

(d) Can you discover any connection between the representations in parts (b) and (c) of the solutions of (5.52)?

5.22 Physical interpretation of curl and divergence

In this section we illustrate the physical interpretation of curl and divergence in connection with fluid flow. We imagine that a fluid is a collection of points called *particles*. At each particle (x, y, z) we attach a vector $\vec{V}(x, y, z)$ which represents the velocity of that particular particle. This is the velocity field of the flow. The velocity field may or may not change with time. We shall consider only *steady-state* flows, that is, flows for which the velocity $\vec{V}(x, y, z)$ depends only on the position of the particle and not on time.

We denote by $\rho(x, y, z)$ the density (mass per unit volume) of the fluid at the point (x, y, z). If the fluid is incompressible the density ρ will be constant throughout the fluid. For a compressible fluid, such as a gas, the density may vary from point to point. In any case, the density is a scalar field associated with the flow. The product of the density and the velocity we denote by $\vec{F}$; that is,

$$\vec{F}(x, y, z) = \rho(x, y, z)\,\vec{V}(x, y, z) .$$

This is a vector field called the *flux density* of the flow. The vector $\vec{F}(x, y, z)$ has the same direction as the velocity, and its length has the dimensions

$$\frac{\text{mass}}{\text{unit volume}} \cdot \frac{\text{distance}}{\text{unit time}} = \frac{\text{mass}}{(\text{unit area})(\text{unit time})} .$$

In other words, the flux density vector $\vec{F}(x, y, z)$ tells us how much mass of fluid per unit area per unit time is flowing in the direction of $\vec{V}(x, y, z)$ at the point (x, y, z). We

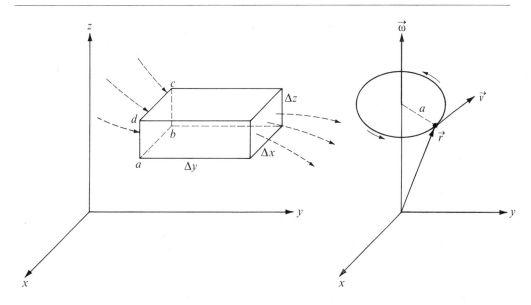

FIGURE 5.15 *Fluid flow through a parallelepiped.*

FIGURE 5.16 *A rigid body rotating with constant angular velocity $\vec{\omega}$. The curl of the velocity $\vec{v}$ is $2\vec{\omega}$.*

now give an argument which suggests that the divergence of $\vec{F}$ represents the time rate of change of mass per unit volume at (x, y, z).

For this purpose, we consider a small rectangular parallelepiped of fluid, with one vertex at (x, y, z), and with dimensions Δx, Δy, Δz, as illustrated in Figure 5.15. Let us determine the mass of fluid passing through the face *abcd* in unit time. The point b represents (x, y, z). If the box is not too large, and if the density ρ and the velocity $\vec{V}$ are continuous functions, the flux density vector $\vec{F}$ will be nearly constant over the entire face *abcd*. For the sake of the argument, let us assume that the flux density has the same value at each point of the face *abcd*, and that this value is $\vec{F}(x, y, z)$. The component of $\vec{F}(x, y, z)$ in the y-direction is $\vec{F}(x, y, z) \cdot \vec{j}$. When this is multiplied by the area of the face *abcd* we obtain

$$\vec{F}(x, y, z) \cdot \vec{j}\,(\Delta x \,\Delta z),$$

which represents the mass of fluid flowing into the box in unit time in a direction normal to the face *abcd*. Similarly, the product

$$\vec{F}(x, y + \Delta y, z) \cdot \vec{j}\,(\Delta x \,\Delta z)$$

represents the mass per unit time flowing out of the box normal to the face opposite to *abcd*. Therefore, the net flow out of the box in the y-direction (mass per unit time) is the difference

$$[\vec{F}(x, y + \Delta y, z) - \vec{F}(x, y, z)] \cdot \vec{j}\,(\Delta x \,\Delta z).$$

A similar argument shows that $[\vec{F}(x + \Delta x, y, z) - \vec{F}(x, y, z)] \cdot \vec{i}\,(\Delta y \,\Delta z)$ represents the net flow out of the box in the x-direction, and that $[\vec{F}(x, y, z + \Delta z) - \vec{F}(x, y, z)] \cdot \vec{k}$ $(\Delta x\, \Delta y)$ represents the net flow in the z-direction.

Next we assume that the total change of mass per unit time is the sum of these three expressions. If we divide this sum by the volume of the box $\Delta x\, \Delta y\, \Delta z$ and let the dimensions of the box shrink to zero, the limit of the quotient is the rate of change of mass per unit volume per unit time at the point (x, y, z). This limit is the sum

$$\frac{\partial \vec{F}}{\partial x} \cdot \vec{i} + \frac{\partial \vec{F}}{\partial y} \cdot \vec{j} + \frac{\partial \vec{F}}{\partial z} \cdot \vec{k} = \operatorname{div} \vec{F}.$$

That is, the divergence of $\vec{F}$ at (x, y, z) is the time rate of change of mass per unit volume at that point. If the divergence is positive at a point, either there is a "source" of fluid at that point or the density of the fluid is diminishing. If the divergence is negative at a point, either there is a "sink" at the point (the fluid is being destroyed or carried away) or the fluid is being compressed so that its density increases. For an incompressible fluid flow with no sources or sinks the divergence is zero at each point.

Next we interpret the curl physically. Suppose a rigid body is rotating about an axis with constant angular velocity vector $\vec{\omega}$. For the sake of simplicity, let us take the axis of rotation to be the z-axis and assume that $\vec{\omega}$ is directed toward the positive z-direction, so that we may write $\vec{\omega} = \omega \vec{k}$, where $\omega = |\vec{\omega}|$ is the angular speed of rotation. Let a denote the radius of the circle in which a point (x, y, z) of the body is rotating (see Figure 5.16). If the point is initially at $(a, 0, z)$ its position at time t may be described by the vector

$$\vec{r} = a \cos \omega t\, \vec{i} + a \sin \omega t \vec{j} + z\, \vec{k},$$

where z is independent of t. Differentiating, we get

$$\vec{v} = \frac{d\vec{r}}{dt} = \omega(-a \sin \omega t\, \vec{i} + a \cos \omega t\, \vec{j}) = -\omega y\, \vec{i} + \omega x\, \vec{j},$$

and hence

$$\operatorname{curl} \vec{v} = \begin{vmatrix} \vec{i} & \vec{j} & \vec{k} \\ \dfrac{\partial}{\partial x} & \dfrac{\partial}{\partial y} & \dfrac{\partial}{\partial z} \\ -\omega y & \omega x & 0 \end{vmatrix} = 2\omega \vec{k} = 2\vec{\omega}.$$

Therefore, for a rigid body rotating with angular velocity vector $\vec{\omega}$ about the z-axis, the curl of the velocity $\vec{v}$ of each particle is $2\vec{\omega}$. The same is true for rotation about an arbitrary axis. This suggests that curl $\vec{v}$ can be used as a measure of the local rotational effect of a fluid flow whose velocity is $\vec{v}$. For this reason, a vector field is said to be *irrotational* at points at which curl $\vec{v} = \vec{0}$.

5.23   Vector formulation of Green's theorem

The identity in Green's theorem,

$$(5.53) \qquad \iint\limits_{R} \left(\frac{\partial Q}{\partial x} - \frac{\partial P}{\partial y} \right) dx\, dy = \oint_{C} P\, dx + Q\, dy,$$

may be restated in terms of the divergence and the curl. To obtain a formulation in terms of the divergence, we introduce the unit outer normal $\vec{n}$ of the boundary curve C. The easiest way to do this is to write the vector equation of C using the arc length s as parameter:

$$\vec{r}(s) = X(s)\,\vec{i} + Y(s)\,\vec{j},$$

where the functions X and Y are so chosen that the radius vector $\vec{r}$ traces out the curve in the counterclockwise direction as s varies from 0 to the length of C. Then the unit tangent vector $\vec{T}$ is $X'(s)\,\vec{i} + Y'(s)\,\vec{j}$ and the unit outer normal is $\vec{n} = Y'(s)\,\vec{i} - X'(s)\,\vec{j}$. Now let $\vec{V}$ be the two-dimensional vector field defined by the equation

$$\vec{V}(x, y) = Q(x, y)\,\vec{i} - P(x, y)\,\vec{j}.$$

Then we have

$$\operatorname{div} \vec{V} = \left(\frac{\partial Q}{\partial x} - \frac{\partial P}{\partial y}\right) \quad \text{and} \quad \vec{V} \cdot \vec{n} = Q\,Y'(s) + P\,X'(s).$$

Therefore Equation (5.53) may be written as

$$(5.54) \qquad \iint\limits_{R} (\operatorname{div} \vec{V})\, dx\, dy = \oint_{C} \vec{V} \cdot \vec{n}\, ds.$$

When stated in this form, Green's theorem can be interpreted physically as follows: Let $\vec{V}$ represent the velocity vector of a plane fluid flow. If the fluid is *incompressible* the density is constant everywhere. For the sake of the argument, let us say the density is 1 everywhere. Then $\operatorname{div} \vec{V}$ measures the amount of mass being transported away from each point (x, y) per unit time. This will be different from zero only when there are sources or sinks present. The double integral $\iint\limits_{R} (\operatorname{div} \vec{V})\, dx\, dy$ measures the net mass of fluid introduced in R per unit time by these sources and sinks. The fluid must escape from (or enter) the region R by crossing the boundary curve C; the line integral $\oint_{C} \vec{V} \cdot \vec{n}\, ds$ measures the net flow across C. The equality of the two integrals is simply the statement of conservation of mass in R. Formula (5.54) will be extended to 3-space in Chapter 6. The three-dimensional analog is called the *divergence theorem*.

Green's theorem can also be formulated in terms of the curl. Let $\vec{F}(x, y) = P(x, y)\,\vec{i} + Q(x, y)\,\vec{j}$. Then we have

$$\operatorname{curl} \vec{F} = \left(\frac{\partial Q}{\partial x} - \frac{\partial P}{\partial y}\right)\vec{k} \quad \text{and} \quad (\operatorname{curl} \vec{F}) \cdot \vec{k} = \frac{\partial Q}{\partial x} - \frac{\partial P}{\partial y},$$

so Equation (5.53) becomes

$$\iint\limits_{R} (\operatorname{curl} \vec{F}) \cdot \vec{k}\, dx\, dy = \oint_{C} \vec{F} \cdot d\vec{r}.$$

A three-dimensional analog of this formula, called Stokes' theorem, will be discussed in Chapter 6.

5.24 Exercises

1. Let $\vec{F}$ be a two-dimensional vector field, continuously differentiable on an open connected set S in the plane. Consider the following statements:

A. curl $\vec{F} = \vec{0}$ in S.
B. $\vec{F}$ is a gradient in S.
C. $\oint_C \vec{F} \cdot d\vec{r} = 0$ for every piecewise smooth closed curve C in S.
D. The line integral $\int \vec{F} \cdot d\vec{r}$ is independent of the path in S.

Some of the following implications are always true; the others are sometimes false. For those that are true, state the theorem (or theorems) from which they follow. For each false implication give a counterexample, and then amend the statements A, B, C, D so the implication becomes true.

(a) A implies B.	(f) D implies A.
(b) B implies A.	(g) B implies C.
(c) A implies C.	(h) C implies B.
(d) C implies A.	(i) C implies D.
(e) A implies D.	(j) D implies C.

2. Let f and g be scalar fields with continuously differentiable gradients on an open connected set S in the plane. Let R be a region in S bounded by a piecewise smooth Jordan curve C. Show that

$$\iint_R \nabla f \times \nabla g \cdot \vec{k} \, dx \, dy = \oint_C f \nabla g \cdot d\vec{r} \,.$$

3. Refer to Exercise 2. If ∇f is perpendicular to the vector $\partial g/\partial y \, \vec{i} - \partial g/\partial x \, \vec{j}$ everywhere on S, show that $\oint_C f \nabla g \cdot d\vec{r} = 0$.

4. Let $\vec{V}(x, y) = y^c \, \vec{i} + x^c \, \vec{j}$, where c is a positive constant, and let $\vec{r}(x, y) = x \, \vec{i} + y \, \vec{j}$. Let R be a plane region bounded by a piecewise smooth Jordan curve C. Compute $\text{div}(\vec{V} \times \vec{r})$ and $\text{curl}(\vec{V} \times \vec{r})$, and use Green's theorem to show that

$$\oint_C \vec{V} \times \vec{r} \cdot d\vec{r} = 0 \,.$$

5. Show that Green's theorem may be expressed as follows:

$$\iint_R (\text{curl } \vec{V}) \cdot \vec{k} \, dx \, dy = \oint_C \vec{V} \cdot \vec{T} \, ds \,,$$

where $\vec{T}$ is the unit tangent to C and s denotes arc length.

6. A plane region R is bounded by a piecewise smooth Jordan curve C. The moments of inertia of R about the x- and y-axes are known to be a and b, respectively. Compute the line integral

$$\oint_C \nabla(r^4) \cdot \vec{n} \, ds$$

in terms of a and b. Here $r = |x\vec{i} + y\vec{j}|$, $\vec{n}$ denotes the unit outward normal of C, and s denotes arc length. The curve is traversed counterclockwise.

7. Let $\vec{F}$ be a two-dimensional vector field. State a definition for the vector-valued line integral $\int_C \vec{F} \times d\vec{r}$. Your definition should be such that the following formula is a consequence of Green's theorem:

$$\int_C \vec{F} \times d\vec{r} = \vec{k} \iint_R (\text{div } \vec{F}) \, dx \, dy \,,$$

where R is a plane region bounded by a simple closed curve C.

5.25 Reconstruction of a vector field from its curl

In our study of the gradient we learned how to determine whether or not a given vector field is a gradient. We now ask a similar question concerning the curl. Given a vector field $\vec{F}$, is there a $\vec{G}$ such that curl $\vec{G} = \vec{F}$? Suppose we write $\vec{F} = P\vec{i} + Q\vec{j} + R\vec{k}$ and $\vec{G} = L\vec{i} + M\vec{j} + N\vec{k}$. To solve the equation curl $\vec{G} = \vec{F}$ we must solve the system of partial differential equations

$$(5.55) \qquad \frac{\partial N}{\partial y} - \frac{\partial M}{\partial z} = P, \qquad \frac{\partial L}{\partial z} - \frac{\partial N}{\partial x} = Q, \qquad \frac{\partial M}{\partial x} - \frac{\partial L}{\partial y} = R$$

for the three unknown functions L, M, and N when P, Q, and R are given.

It is not always possible to solve such a system. For example, we proved in Section 5.20 that the divergence of a curl is always zero. Therefore, for the system (5.55) to have a solution in some open set S it is necessary to have

$$(5.56) \qquad \frac{\partial P}{\partial x} + \frac{\partial Q}{\partial y} + \frac{\partial R}{\partial z} = 0$$

everywhere in S. As it turns out, this condition is also sufficient for system (5.55) to have a solution if we suitably restrict the set S in which (5.56) is satisfied. We shall prove now that condition (5.56) suffices when S is a rectangular parallelepiped.

5–10   THEOREM. *Let $\vec{F}$ be continuously differentiable on an open rectangular parallelepiped S in 3-space. Then there exists a vector field $\vec{G}$ such that curl $\vec{G} = \vec{F}$ if, and only if, div $\vec{F} = 0$ everywhere in S.*

Proof. The necessity of the condition div $\vec{F} = 0$ has already been established, since the divergence of a curl is always zero. To establish the sufficiency we must exhibit three functions L, M, and N that satisfy the three equations in (5.55). Let us try to make a choice with $L = 0$. Then the second and third equations in (5.55) become

$$\frac{\partial N}{\partial x} = -Q \qquad \text{and} \qquad \frac{\partial M}{\partial x} = R.$$

This means that we must have

$$N(x, y, z) = - \int_{x_0}^{x} Q(t, y, z)dt + f(y, z)$$

and

$$M(x, y, z) = \int_{x_0}^{x} R(t, y, z)dt + g(y, z),$$

where each integration is along a line segment in S and the "constants of integration" $f(y, z)$ and $g(y, z)$ are independent of x. Let us try to find a solution with $f(y, z) = 0$. The first equation in (5.55) requires

$$(5.57) \qquad \frac{\partial N}{\partial y} - \frac{\partial M}{\partial z} = P.$$

For the choice of M and N just described we have

$$(5.58) \qquad \frac{\partial N}{\partial y} - \frac{\partial M}{\partial z} = - \frac{\partial}{\partial y} \int_{x_0}^{x} Q(t, y, z)dt - \frac{\partial}{\partial z} \int_{x_0}^{x} R(t, y, z)dt - \frac{\partial g}{\partial z}.$$

At this stage we shall interchange the two operations of partial differentiation and integration (a step that will be justified later). That is, we write

(5.59)
$$\frac{\partial}{\partial y} \int_{x_0}^{x} Q(t, y, z) \, dt = \int_{x_0}^{x} D_2 Q(t, y, z) \, dt$$

and

(5.60)
$$\frac{\partial}{\partial z} \int_{x_0}^{x} R(t, y, z) \, dt = \int_{x_0}^{x} D_3 R(t, y, z) \, dt \, .$$

Then Equation (5.58) becomes

(5.61)
$$\frac{\partial N}{\partial y} - \frac{\partial M}{\partial z} = \int_{x_0}^{x} [-D_2 Q(t, y, z) - D_3 R(t, y, z)] \, dt - \frac{\partial g}{\partial z} \, .$$

Using condition (5.56) we may replace the integrand in (5.61) by $D_1 P(t, y, z)$; Equation (5.61) becomes

$$\frac{\partial N}{\partial y} - \frac{\partial M}{\partial z} = \int_{x_0}^{x} D_1 P(t, y, z) \, dt - \frac{\partial g}{\partial z} = P(x, y, z) - P(x_0, y, z) - \frac{\partial g}{\partial z} \, .$$

Therefore (5.57) will be satisfied if we choose g so that $\partial g / \partial z = -P(x_0, y, z)$. Thus, for example, we may take

$$g(y, z) = - \int_{z_0}^{z} P(x_0, y, u) \, du \, .$$

This argument leads us to consider the vector field $\vec{G} = L\vec{i} + M\vec{j} + N\vec{k}$, where $L(x, y, z) = 0$ and

$$M(x, y, z) = \int_{x_0}^{x} R(t, y, z) \, dt - \int_{z_0}^{z} P(x_0, y, u) \, du \, , \qquad N(x, y, z) = - \int_{x_0}^{x} Q(t, y, z) \, dt \, .$$

For this choice of L, M, and N it is easy to verify, with the help of (5.59) and (5.60), that the three equations in (5.55) are satisfied, giving us curl $\vec{G} = \vec{F}$, as required.

To complete the proof we must justify the interchange of the operations of partial differentiation and integration in Equations (5.59) and (5.60). To prove (5.59) we write

$$Q(t, y, z) = Q(t, y_0, z) + \int_{y_0}^{y} D_2 Q(t, u, z) \, du \, .$$

If we integrate both sides of this equation with respect to t from x_0 to x, and then differentiate with respect to y, we find

(5.62)
$$\frac{\partial}{\partial y} \int_{x_0}^{x} Q(t, y, z) \, dt = \frac{\partial}{\partial y} \int_{x_0}^{x} \left[\int_{y_0}^{y} D_2 Q(t, u, z) \, du \right] dt.$$

Now we appeal to Theorem 2–4 (Section 2.8) and interchange the order of integration. (Theorem 2–4 is applicable because of the continuity of $D_2 Q$.) Thus, Equation (5.62) becomes

$$\frac{\partial}{\partial y} \int_{x_0}^{x} Q(t, y, z) \, dt = \frac{\partial}{\partial y} \int_{y_0}^{y} \left[\int_{x_0}^{x} D_2 Q(t, u, z) \, dt \right] du = \int_{x_0}^{x} D_2 Q(t, y, z) \, dt \, .$$

This proves Equation (5.59). Equation (5.60) is proved in a similar way, completing the proof of Theorem 5-10.

It should be noted that the foregoing proof not only establishes the existence of a vector field $\vec{G}$ whose curl is $\vec{F}$, but also provides a straightforward method for determining $\vec{G}$ by integration involving the components of $\vec{F}$.

For a given $\vec{F}$, the vector field $\vec{G}$ that we have constructed is not the only solution of the equation curl $\vec{G} = \vec{F}$. If we add to this $\vec{G}$ any continuously differentiable gradient $\nabla\phi$ we obtain another solution because

$$\text{curl}(\vec{G} + \nabla\phi) = \text{curl } \vec{G} + \text{curl}(\nabla\phi) = \text{curl } \vec{G} = \vec{F},$$

since $\text{curl}(\nabla\phi) = \vec{0}$. Moreover, it is easy to show that *all* continuously differentiable solutions must be of the form $\vec{G} + \nabla\phi$. Indeed, if $\vec{H}$ is another solution, then curl $\vec{H}$ = curl $\vec{G}$, so $\text{curl}(\vec{H} - \vec{G}) = \vec{0}$. By Theorem 4-9 it follows that $\vec{H} - \vec{G} = \nabla\phi$ for some continuously differentiable gradient $\nabla\phi$; hence $\vec{H} = \vec{G} + \nabla\phi$, as asserted.

A vector field $\vec{F}$ for which div $\vec{F} = 0$ is sometimes called *solenoidal*. Theorem 5-10 states that a vector field is solenoidal on an open rectangular parallelepiped S if, and only if, it is the curl of another vector field on S. The theorem is also true for open sets more general than rectangular parallelepipeds, but it is not true for *arbitrary* open sets. The set S must be such that every closed surface in S forms the complete boundary of a solid lying entirely in S. The reasons for a restriction of this kind will be more apparent later when we study surface integrals. (See Section 6.11.)

5.26 Exercises

1. Find a vector field $\vec{G}(x, y, z)$ whose curl is $2\vec{i} + \vec{j} + 3\vec{k}$ everywhere in 3-space. What is the most general continuously differentiable vector field with this property?

2. Show that the vector field $\vec{F}(x, y, z) = (y - z)\vec{i} + (z - x)\vec{j} + (x - y)\vec{k}$ is solenoidal, and find a vector field $\vec{G}$ such that $\vec{F} = \text{curl } \vec{G}$.

3. Let $\vec{F}(x, y, z) = -z\vec{i} + xy\vec{k}$. Find a continuously differentiable vector field $\vec{G}$ of the form $\vec{G}(x, y, z) = L(x, y, z)\vec{i} + M(x, y, z)\vec{j}$ such that $\vec{F} = \text{curl } \vec{G}$ on every rectangular parallelepiped in 3-space. What is the most general $\vec{G}$ of this form?

4. If two vector fields $\vec{U}$ and $\vec{V}$ are both irrotational, show that the vector field $\vec{U} \times \vec{V}$ is solenoidal.

5. Let $\vec{r} = x\vec{i} + y\vec{j} + z\vec{k}$ and $r = |\vec{r}|$. Show that $n = -3$ is the only value of n for which $r^n \vec{r}$ is solenoidal for $r \neq 0$. For this n, choose a rectangular parallelepiped S not containing the origin and express $r^{-3} \vec{r}$ as a curl in S. [*Warning.* Although $r^{-3} \vec{r}$ is a curl in every such S, it is *not* a curl on the set of all points different from $(0, 0, 0)$. We shall prove this in Section 6.11 with the help of Stokes' theorem.]

6. Find the most general continuously differentiable function f of one real variable such that the vector field $f(r)\vec{r}$ will be solenoidal, where $\vec{r} = x\vec{i} + y\vec{j} + z\vec{k}$ and $r = |\vec{r}|$.

7. Let $\vec{V}$ denote a vector field that is continuously differentiable on some open rectangular parallelepiped S in 3-space. Consider the following two statements about $\vec{V}$:

(i) curl $\vec{V} = \vec{0}$ and $\vec{V} = \text{curl } \vec{U}$ for some continuously differentiable vector field $\vec{U}$ (everywhere on S).

(ii) A scalar field ϕ exists such that $\nabla\phi$ is continuously differentiable and such that

$$\vec{V} = \text{grad } \phi \quad \text{and} \quad \nabla^2\phi = 0 \quad \text{everywhere on } S.$$

(a) Prove that (i) implies (ii). In other words, a vector field that is both irrotational and solenoidal in S is the gradient of a harmonic function in S.

(b) Prove that (ii) implies (i), or give a counterexample.

8. Assume continuous differentiability of all vector fields involved, on an open parallelepiped S. Suppose $\vec{H} = \vec{F} + \vec{G}$, where $\vec{F}$ is solenoidal and $\vec{G}$ is irrotational. Then there exists a vector field $\vec{U}$ such that $\vec{F} = \operatorname{curl} \vec{U}$ and a scalar field ϕ such that $\vec{G} = \nabla\phi$ in S. Show that $\vec{U}$ and ϕ satisfy the following partial differential equations in S:

$$\nabla^2\phi = \operatorname{div} \vec{H}, \qquad \operatorname{grad}(\operatorname{div} \vec{U}) - \nabla^2\vec{U} = \operatorname{curl} \vec{H}.$$

Note. This exercise has widespread applications, because it can be shown that every continuously differentiable vector field $\vec{H}$ on S can be expressed in the form $\vec{H} = \vec{F} + \vec{G}$, where $\vec{F}$ is solenoidal and $\vec{G}$ is irrotational.

9. Let $\vec{H}(x, y, z) = x^2 y\,\vec{i} + y^2 z\,\vec{j} + z^2 x\,\vec{k}$. Find vector fields $\vec{F}$ and $\vec{G}$, where $\vec{F}$ is a curl and $\vec{G}$ is a gradient, such that $\vec{H} = \vec{F} + \vec{G}$.

★5.27　The winding number

We have seen that the value of a line integral often depends both on the curve along which the integration takes place and on the direction in which the curve is traversed. For example, the identity in Green's theorem requires the line integral to be taken in the counterclockwise direction. In a completely rigorous treatment of Green's theorem it would be necessary to describe analytically what it means to traverse a closed curve in the "counterclockwise direction." For some special curves this may be done by making specific statements about the vector-valued function $\vec{r}$ which describes the curve. For example, the vector-valued function $\vec{r}$ defined on the interval $[0, 2\pi]$ by the equation

$$(5.63) \qquad \vec{r}(t) = (a \cos t + x_0)\,\vec{i} + (a \sin t + y_0)\,\vec{j}$$

describes a circle of radius a with center at (x_0, y_0). This particular function is said to describe the circle in a *positive* or *counterclockwise* direction. On the other hand, if we replace t by $-t$ on the right of (5.63) we obtain a new function which is said to describe the circle in a *negative* or *clockwise* direction. In this way we have given a completely analytical description of "clockwise" and "counterclockwise" for a circle. However, it is not so simple to describe the same idea for an *arbitrary* closed curve. For piecewise smooth curves this may be done by introducing the concept of the *winding number*, an analytic device which gives us a mathematically precise way of counting the number of times a radius vector $\vec{r}$ "winds around" a given point as it traces out a given closed curve. In this section we shall describe briefly one method for introducing the winding number. Then we shall indicate how it may be used to assign positive and negative directions to closed curves.

Let C be a piecewise smooth closed curve in the plane described by a vector-valued function $\vec{r}$ defined on an interval $[a, b]$, say

$$\vec{r}(t) = X(t)\,\vec{i} + Y(t)\,\vec{j} \qquad \text{if} \quad a \leq t \leq b\,.$$

Let $P_0 = (x_0, y_0)$ be a point which does not lie on the curve C. Then the winding number of $\vec{r}$ with respect to the point P_0 is denoted by $W(\vec{r}; P_0)$; it is defined to be the value of the following integral:

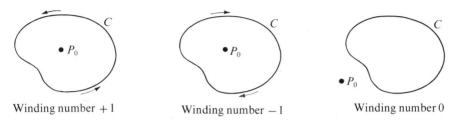

Winding number $+1$ Winding number -1 Winding number 0

FIGURE 5.17 *Illustrating the possible values of the winding number of a Jordan curve C with respect to P_0.*

(5.64) $$W(\vec{r}; P_0) = \frac{1}{2\pi} \int_a^b \frac{[X(t) - x_0]\, Y'(t) - [Y(t) - y_0]\, X'(t)}{[X(t) - x_0]^2 + [Y(t) - y_0]^2}\, dt \,.$$

This is the same as the line integral

(5.65) $$\frac{1}{2\pi} \oint_C \frac{-(y - y_0)\, dx + (x - x_0)\, dy}{(x - x_0)^2 + (y - y_0)^2} \,.$$

It can be shown that the value of this integral is always an *integer*, positive, negative, or zero. Moreover, if C is a *Jordan* curve (*simple* closed curve) this integer is 0 if P_0 is *outside* C and has the value $+1$ or -1 if P_0 is *inside* C. (See Figure 5.17.) Furthermore, $W(\vec{r}; P_0)$ is either $+1$ for *every* point P_0 inside C or it is -1 for every such point. This enables us to define positive and negative orientations for C as follows: If the winding number $W(\vec{r}; P_0)$ is $+1$ for every point P_0 inside C we say that $\vec{r}$ traces out C in the *positive* or *counterclockwise direction*. If the winding number is -1 we say that $\vec{r}$ traces out C in the *negative* or *clockwise direction*. [An example of the integral in (5.65) with $x_0 = y_0 = 0$ was encountered earlier in the Exercises of Section 5.11.]

To prove that the integral for the winding number is always $+1$ or -1 for a simple closed curve enclosing (x_0, y_0) we use Theorem 5–9. Let S denote the open connected region consisting of all points in the plane except (x_0, y_0). Then the line integral in (5.65) may be written as $\int_C P\, dx + Q\, dy$, and it is easy to verify that $\partial P/\partial y = \partial Q/\partial x$ everywhere in S. Therefore, if (x_0, y_0) is inside C, Theorem 5–9 tells us that we may replace the curve C by a circle with center at (x_0, y_0) without changing the value of the integral. Now we verify that for a circle the integral for the winding number is either $+1$ or -1, depending on whether the circle is positively or negatively oriented. For a positively oriented circle we may use the representation in Equation (5.63). In this case we have

$$X(t) = a \cos t + x_0 \,, \qquad Y(t) = a \sin t + y_0 \,,$$

and the integrand in (5.64) is identically equal to 1. Therefore we obtain

$$W(\vec{r}; P_0) = \frac{1}{2\pi} \int_0^{2\pi} 1\, dt = 1 \,.$$

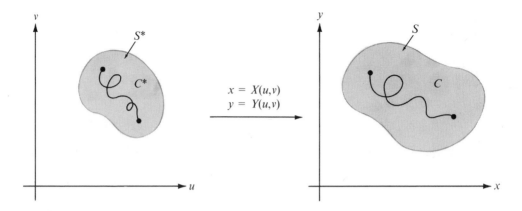

FIGURE 5.18   *A mapping which carries a curve C* in S* into a curve C in S.*

By a similar argument we find that the integral is -1 when C is negatively oriented. This proves that the winding number is either $+1$ or -1 for a simple closed curve enclosing the point (x_0, y_0).

5.28   A transformation law for line integrals

Suppose the two equations

(5.66) $$x = X(u, v), \qquad y = Y(u, v)$$

define a mapping which carries an open set S^* of the uv-plane into an open set S of the xy-plane. Such a mapping carries a curve C^* lying in S^* into a curve C lying in S, as suggested by Figure 5.18. In this section we shall derive a formula which tells us how a line integral along C is transformed into a line integral along C^*. The mapping is not assumed to be one-to-one.

5–11   THEOREM.   Let $\vec{G}$ be a continuously differentiable vector field which maps an open set S^* in the uv-plane into an open set S in the xy-plane. Suppose that

$$\vec{G}(u, v) = X(u, v)\,\vec{i} + Y(u, v)\,\vec{j}\,.$$

If $\vec{F}$ is a continuous vector field defined on S, let $\vec{F}^*$ denote the composite function defined on S^* by the equation

(5.67) $$\vec{F}^*(u, v) = \vec{F}[\vec{G}(u, v)]\,.$$

Then if C^* is any piecewise smooth curve in S^* whose image in S is C, we have

(5.68) $$\int_C \vec{F} \cdot d\vec{r} = \int_{C^*} \left(\vec{F}^* \cdot \frac{\partial \vec{G}}{\partial u}\right) du + \left(\vec{F}^* \cdot \frac{\partial \vec{G}}{\partial v}\right) dv\,.$$

Proof. We begin with a parametric representation of $C*$ and use this to find a representation of C. Let the curve $C*$ be described by a function $\vec{R}$ defined on an interval $[a, b]$, say

$$\vec{R}(t) = U(t)\,\vec{i} + V(t)\,\vec{j}\,,$$

and let

(5.69) $$\vec{r}(t) = \vec{G}[U(t), V(t)]\,.$$

Then as t varies over the interval $[a, b]$, the radius vector $\vec{R}(t)$ traces out the curve $C*$ and the radius vector $\vec{r}(t)$ traces out the curve C. Hence we may write

(5.70) $$\int_C \vec{F} \cdot d\vec{r} = \int_a^b \vec{F}[\vec{r}(t)] \cdot \vec{r}'(t)\, dt\,.$$

Now Equations (5.67) and (5.69) together imply that $\vec{F}[\vec{r}(t)] = \vec{F}*[\vec{R}(t)]$. Also, the chain rule, applied to (5.69) gives us

$$\vec{r}'(t) = \frac{\partial \vec{G}}{\partial u}\,U'(t) + \frac{\partial \vec{G}}{\partial v}\,V'(t)\,,$$

where $\partial \vec{G}/\partial u$ and $\partial \vec{G}/\partial v$ are to be evaluated at $(U(t), V(t))$. Therefore (5.70) becomes

$$\int_a^b \vec{F}[\vec{r}(t)] \cdot \vec{r}'(t)\, dt = \int_a^b \vec{F}*[\vec{R}(t)] \cdot \left[\frac{\partial \vec{G}}{\partial u}\,U'(t) + \frac{\partial \vec{G}}{\partial v}\,V'(t) \right] dt\,.$$

The last integral on the right is by definition the line integral over $C*$ which appears in (5.68), so the proof is complete.

If $\vec{F}$, $\vec{G}$, and $\vec{F}*$ are expressed in terms of their components, say

$$\vec{F} = P\,\vec{i} + Q\,\vec{j}\,, \qquad \vec{G} = X\,\vec{i} + Y\,\vec{j}\,, \qquad \vec{F}* = P*\,\vec{i} + Q*\,\vec{j}\,,$$

Equation (5.68) becomes

(5.71) $$\int_C P\,dx + Q\,dy = \int_{C*} \left\{ \left(P*\frac{\partial X}{\partial u} + Q*\frac{\partial Y}{\partial u} \right) du + \left(P*\frac{\partial X}{\partial v} + Q*\frac{\partial Y}{\partial v} \right) dv \right\}.$$

Example. Suppose we take $P(x, y) = 0$, $Q(x, y) = x$, and let $\vec{G}(u, v) = X(u, v)\vec{i} + Y(u, v)\vec{j}$. Then $\vec{F}(x, y) = 0\vec{i} + x\vec{j} = x\vec{j}$ and

$$\vec{F}*(u, v) = \vec{F}[X(u, v)\vec{i} + Y(u, v)\vec{j}] = X(u, v)\vec{j}\,.$$

Therefore $P*(u, v)\vec{i} + Q*(u, v)\vec{j} = X(u, v)\vec{j}$, so

$$P*(u, v) = 0 \qquad \text{and} \qquad Q*(u, v) = X(u, v)\,.$$

Transformation formula (5.71) becomes

$$\int_C x\,dy = \int_{C*} X\frac{\partial Y}{\partial u}\,du + X\frac{\partial Y}{\partial v}\,dv\,.$$

There is, of course, an extension of Theorem 5–11 to line integrals in 3-space. If the three equations

(5.72) $x = X(u, v, w)\,, \qquad y = Y(u, v, w)\,, \qquad z = Z(u, v, w)$

define a mapping of a region S^* in the uvw-space into a region S of the xyz-space, then the analog of (5.68) is the formula

(5.73) $$\int_C \vec{F} \cdot d\vec{r} = \int_{C^*} \left(\vec{F}^* \cdot \frac{\partial \vec{G}}{\partial u} \right) du + \left(\vec{F}^* \cdot \frac{\partial \vec{G}}{\partial v} \right) dv + \left(\vec{F}^* \cdot \frac{\partial \vec{G}}{\partial w} \right) dw \,,$$

where $\vec{G}(u, v, w) = X(u, v, w)\,\vec{i} + Y(u, v, w)\,\vec{j} + Z(u, v, w)\,\vec{k}$ and $\vec{F}^*(u, v, w) = \vec{F}[\vec{G}(u, v, w)]$. The curve C^* lies in the region S^* and C is its image in S. The proof of (5.73) is a direct extension of the proof of (5.68). When $\vec{F}$, $\vec{G}$, and $\vec{F}^*$ are expressed in terms of their components, (5.73) assumes the form

(5.74)

$$\int_C P\,dx + Q\,dy + R\,dz = \int_{C^*} \left\{ \left(P^* \frac{\partial X}{\partial u} + Q^* \frac{\partial Y}{\partial u} + R^* \frac{\partial Z}{\partial u} \right) du \right.$$

$$\left. + \left(P^* \frac{\partial X}{\partial v} + Q^* \frac{\partial Y}{\partial v} + R^* \frac{\partial Z}{\partial v} \right) dv + \left(P^* \frac{\partial X}{\partial w} + Q^* \frac{\partial Y}{\partial w} + R^* \frac{\partial Z}{\partial w} \right) dw \right\}.$$

Equation (5.74) is applicable when C^* is a *plane* curve and C a space curve; for example, when the three functions in (5.72) are independent of w. We shall use (5.74) in this form in Chapter 6 when we prove Stokes' theorem.

As an application of Theorem 5–11 we shall prove the transformation law for double integrals that was discussed in Chapter 2 (Section 2.16). The formula states that

(5.75) $$\iint_S f(x, y)\,dx\,dy = \iint_{S^*} f[X(u, v),\, Y(u, v)]\,|J(u, v)|\,du\,dv \,,$$

where S denotes a region in the xy-plane and S^* denotes its image under a one-to-one mapping which we may take to be the inverse of that given by the pair of equations in (5.66). The factor $|J(u, v)|$ is the absolute value of the Jacobian determinant,

$$J(u, v) = \begin{vmatrix} \dfrac{\partial X}{\partial u} & \dfrac{\partial X}{\partial v} \\[2mm] \dfrac{\partial Y}{\partial u} & \dfrac{\partial Y}{\partial v} \end{vmatrix}.$$

In Section 2.21 we proved that the general formula in (5.75) is a consequence of the special case in which $f(x, y) = 1$ and S is a rectangle R. (See Figure 5.19.) Therefore, we must show that we have

(5.76) $$\iint_R dx\,dy = \iint_{R^*} |J(u, v)|\,du\,dv \,,$$

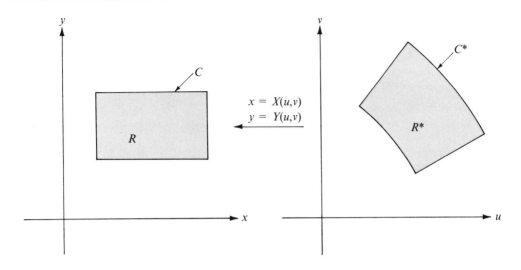

FIGURE 5.19   *The transformation law for double integrals derived from Green's theorem.*

which we can do with the aid of Green's theorem. We express each double integral in (5.76) as a line integral around the respective boundary curves C and C^*; then we establish the equality of the two line integrals by using the transformation law in Theorem 5-11. In the proof we shall assume that the functions in (5.66) have continuous second-order partial derivatives and that the Jacobian $J(u, v)$ is never 0 in R^*. Then $J(u, v)$ is either positive everywhere or negative everywhere. The significance of the sign of $J(u, v)$ is that when a point (x, y) traces out the boundary of R in the positive direction, the image point (u, v) traces out the boundary of R^* in the positive direction if $J(u, v)$ is positive and in the negative direction if $J(u, v)$ is negative. In the proof we shall assume that $J(u, v) > 0$.

To prove (5.76) we begin with the double integral in the xy-plane, writing

$$\iint_R dx\, dy = \iint_R \left(\frac{\partial Q}{\partial x} - \frac{\partial P}{\partial y} \right) dx\, dy\,,$$

where $Q(x, y) = x$ and $P(x, y) = 0$. By Green's theorem this double integral is equal to the line integral $\int_C P\, dx + Q\, dy = \int_C x\, dy$. The transformation formula in (5.71) tells us that

$$\int_C x\, dy = \int_{C^*} \left\{ X \frac{\partial Y}{\partial u}\, du + X \frac{\partial Y}{\partial v}\, dv \right\}.$$

Applying Green's theorem once more to the integral along C^* gives us

$$\int_C x\, dy = \iint_{R^*} \left\{ \frac{\partial}{\partial u}\left(X \frac{\partial Y}{\partial v} \right) - \frac{\partial}{\partial v}\left(X \frac{\partial Y}{\partial u} \right) \right\} du\, dv$$

$$= \iint\limits_{R^*} \left(\frac{\partial X}{\partial u} \frac{\partial Y}{\partial v} + X \frac{\partial^2 Y}{\partial u \partial v} - X \frac{\partial^2 Y}{\partial v \partial u} - \frac{\partial X}{\partial v} \frac{\partial Y}{\partial u} \right) du\, dv$$

$$= \iint\limits_{R^*} \left(\frac{\partial X}{\partial u} \frac{\partial Y}{\partial v} - \frac{\partial X}{\partial v} \frac{\partial Y}{\partial u} \right) du\, dv = \iint\limits_{R^*} J(u,\, v)\, du\, dv\,.$$

This proves (5.76).

6

SURFACE INTEGRALS

6.1 Parametric representation of a surface

A deeper study of vector fields in 3-space requires the use of surface integrals. A surface integral can be thought of as a two-dimensional analog of a line integral where the region of integration is a surface rather than a curve. Before we can discuss surface integrals intelligently, we must agree on what we shall mean by a surface.

Roughly speaking, a surface is the locus of a point moving in space with two degrees of freedom. In our study of analytic geometry in Volume I we discussed two methods for describing such a locus by mathematical formulas. One is the *implicit representation* in which we describe a surface as a set of points (x, y, z) satisfying an equation of the form $F(x, y, z) = 0$. Sometimes we can solve such an equation for one of the coordinates in terms of the other two, say for z in terms of x and y. When this is possible we obtain an *explicit representation* given by one or more equations of the form $z = f(x, y)$. For example, a sphere of radius 1 and center at the origin has the implicit representation $x^2 + y^2 + z^2 - 1 = 0$. When this equation is solved for z it leads to two solutions, $z = \sqrt{1 - x^2 - y^2}$ and $z = -\sqrt{1 - x^2 - y^2}$. The first gives an explicit representation of the upper hemisphere and the second of the lower hemisphere.

A third method for describing surfaces is more useful in the study of surface integrals; this is the *parametric* or *vector* representation in which we have three equations expressing x, y, and z in terms of two parameters u and v:

$$(6.1) \qquad x = X(u, v), \qquad y = Y(u, v), \qquad z = Z(u, v).$$

Here the point (u, v) is allowed to vary over some two-dimensional connected set T in the uv-plane, and the corresponding points (x, y, z) trace out a portion of a surface in xyz-space. This method for describing a surface is analogous to the representation of a space curve by three parametric equations involving one parameter. The presence of the two parameters in (6.1) makes it possible to transmit two degrees of freedom to the point (x, y, z), as suggested by Figure 6.1. Another way of describing the same idea is to say that a surface is the image of a plane region T under the mapping defined by (6.1).

If we introduce the radius vector $\vec{r}$ from the origin to a general point (x, y, z) of the surface, we may combine the three parametric equations in (6.1) into one vector equation of the form

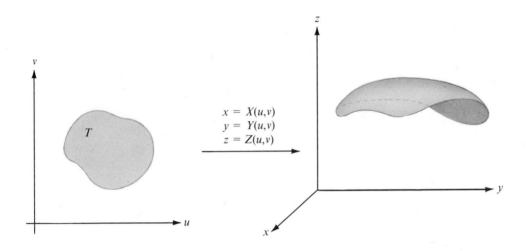

$$x = X(u,v)$$
$$y = Y(u,v)$$
$$z = Z(u,v)$$

FIGURE 6.1   *Parametric representation of a surface.*

(6.2) $\vec{r}(u, v) = X(u, v)\,\vec{i} + Y(u, v)\,\vec{j} + Z(u, v)\,\vec{k}$,   where $(u, v) \varepsilon T$.

This is called a *vector equation* for the surface.

There are, of course, many parametric representations for the same surface. One of these can always be obtained from an explicit form $z = f(x, y)$ by taking $X(u, v) = u$, $Y(u, v) = v$, $Z(u, v) = f(u, v)$. On the other hand, if it is possible to eliminate u and v from the parametric equations—for example, if we can solve the first two equations in (6.1) for u and v in terms of x and y and substitute in the third—we obtain an explicit representation $z = f(x, y)$.

Example 1: A parametric representation of a sphere. The three equations

(6.3) $x = a \cos u \cos v$, $y = a \sin u \cos v$, $z = a \sin v$

serve as parametric equations for a sphere of radius a and center at the origin. If we square and add the three equations in (6.3) we find $x^2 + y^2 + z^2 = a^2$, and we see that every point (x, y, z) satisfying (6.3) lies on the sphere. The parameters u and v in this example may be interpreted geometrically as the angles shown in Figure 6.2. If we let the point (u, v) vary over the rectangle $T = [0, 2\pi] \times [-\tfrac{1}{2}\pi, \tfrac{1}{2}\pi]$, the points determined by (6.3) trace out the whole sphere. The upper hemisphere is the image of the rectangle $[0, 2\pi] \times [0, \tfrac{1}{2}\pi]$ and the lower hemisphere is the image of $[0, 2\pi] \times [-\tfrac{1}{2}\pi, 0]$. Figure 6.3 gives a concrete idea of how the rectangle $[0, 2\pi] \times [0, \tfrac{1}{2}\pi]$ is mapped onto the upper hemisphere. Imagine that the rectangle is made of a flexible plastic material capable of being stretched or shrunk. Figure 6.3 shows the rectangle being deformed into a hemisphere. The base AB eventually becomes the equator, the opposite edges AD and BC are brought into coincidence, and the upper edge DC shrinks to a point (the North Pole).

Example 2: A parametric representation of a cone. The vector equation

$$\vec{r}(u, v) = v \sin \alpha \cos u\,\vec{i} + v \sin \alpha \sin u\,\vec{j} + v \cos \alpha\,\vec{k}$$

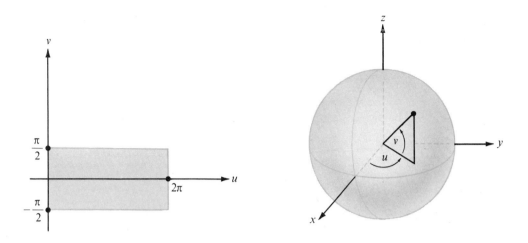

FIGURE 6.2   *Parametric representation of a sphere.*

represents the right circular cone shown in Figure 6.4, where α denotes half the vertex angle. Again, the parameters u and v may be given geometric interpretations; v is the distance from the vertex to the point (x, y, z) on the cone, and u is the polar-coordinate angle. When (u, v) is allowed to vary over a rectangle of the form $[0, 2\pi] \times [0, h]$, the corresponding points (x, y, z) trace out a cone of altitude $h \cos \alpha$. A plastic rectangle may be physically deformed into the cone by bringing the edges AD and BC into coincidence, as suggested by Figure 6.5, and letting the edge AB shrink to a point (the vertex of the cone). The surface in Figure 6.5 shows an intermediate stage of the deformation.

In the general study of surfaces, the functions X, Y, and Z that occur in the parametric equations (6.1) or in the vector equation (6.2) are assumed to be continuous on T. The image of T under the mapping $\vec{r}$ is called a *parametric surface* and will be denoted by the symbol $\vec{r}(T)$. In many of the examples we shall discuss, T will be a rectangle, a circular disk, or some other simply connected set bounded by a simple closed curve. If the function $\vec{r}$ is one-to-one on T, the image $\vec{r}(T)$ will be called a *simple parametric surface*. In

FIGURE 6.3   *Deformation of a rectangle into a hemisphere.*

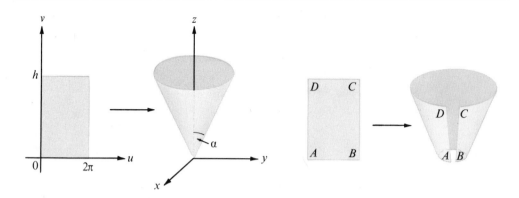

FIGURE 6.4   *Parametric representation of a cone.*   FIGURE 6.5   *Deformation of a rectangle into a cone.*

such a case, distinct points of T map onto distinct points of the surface. In particular, every simple closed curve in R maps onto a simple closed curve lying on the surface.

A parametric surface $\vec{r}(T)$ may degenerate to a point or to a curve. For example, if all three functions X, Y, and Z are constant, the image $\vec{r}(T)$ is a single point. If X, Y, and Z are independent of v, the image $\vec{r}(T)$ is a curve. Another example of a degenerate surface occurs when $X(u, v) = u + v$, $Y(u, v) = (u + v)^2$, and $Z(u, v) = (u + v)^3$, where $T = [0, 1] \times [0, 1]$. If we write $t = u + v$ we see that the surface degenerates to the space curve having parametric equations $x = t$, $y = t^2$, and $z = t^3$, where $0 \leq t \leq 2$. Such degeneracies can be avoided by placing further restrictions on the mapping function $\vec{r}$, as described in the next section.

6.2   The fundamental vector product

Consider a surface described by the vector equation

$$\vec{r}(u, v) = X(u, v)\, \vec{i} + Y(u, v)\, \vec{j} + Z(u, v)\, \vec{k}, \qquad \text{where} \quad (u, v) \in T.$$

If X, Y, and Z are differentiable on T we may consider the two vectors

$$\frac{\partial \vec{r}}{\partial u} = \frac{\partial X}{\partial u}\, \vec{i} + \frac{\partial Y}{\partial u}\, \vec{j} + \frac{\partial Z}{\partial u}\, \vec{k}$$

and

$$\frac{\partial \vec{r}}{\partial v} = \frac{\partial X}{\partial v}\, \vec{i} + \frac{\partial Y}{\partial v}\, \vec{j} + \frac{\partial Z}{\partial v}\, \vec{k}.$$

The cross product of these two vectors $\partial \vec{r}/\partial u \times \partial \vec{r}/\partial v$ will be referred to as the *fundamental vector product* of the representation $\vec{r}$. Its components may be expressed as Jacobian determinants. In fact, we have

$$\frac{\partial \vec{r}}{\partial u} \times \frac{\partial \vec{r}}{\partial v} = \begin{vmatrix} \vec{i} & \vec{j} & \vec{k} \\ \dfrac{\partial X}{\partial u} & \dfrac{\partial Y}{\partial u} & \dfrac{\partial Z}{\partial u} \\ \dfrac{\partial X}{\partial v} & \dfrac{\partial Y}{\partial v} & \dfrac{\partial Z}{\partial v} \end{vmatrix} = \begin{vmatrix} \dfrac{\partial Y}{\partial u} & \dfrac{\partial Z}{\partial u} \\ \dfrac{\partial Y}{\partial v} & \dfrac{\partial Z}{\partial v} \end{vmatrix} \vec{i} + \begin{vmatrix} \dfrac{\partial Z}{\partial u} & \dfrac{\partial X}{\partial u} \\ \dfrac{\partial Z}{\partial v} & \dfrac{\partial X}{\partial v} \end{vmatrix} \vec{j} + \begin{vmatrix} \dfrac{\partial X}{\partial u} & \dfrac{\partial Y}{\partial u} \\ \dfrac{\partial X}{\partial v} & \dfrac{\partial Y}{\partial v} \end{vmatrix} \vec{k}$$

(6.4)
$$= \frac{\partial(Y, Z)}{\partial(u, v)} \vec{i} + \frac{\partial(Z, X)}{\partial(u, v)} \vec{j} + \frac{\partial(X, Y)}{\partial(u, v)} \vec{k}.$$

If (u, v) is a point in T at which $\partial \vec{r}/\partial u$ and $\partial \vec{r}/\partial v$ are continuous and the fundamental vector product is nonzero, then the image point $\vec{r}(u, v)$ is called a *regular point* of $\vec{r}$. Points at which $\partial \vec{r}/\partial u$ or $\partial \vec{r}/\partial v$ fails to be continuous or $\partial \vec{r}/\partial u \times \partial \vec{r}/\partial v = \vec{0}$ are called *singular points* of $\vec{r}$. A surface $\vec{r}(T)$ is called *smooth* if all its points are regular points. Every surface has more than one parametric representation. Some of the examples discussed below show that a point of a surface may be a regular point for one representation but a singular point for some other representation. The geometric significance of regular and singular points may be explained as follows:

Consider a horizontal line segment in T. Its image under $\vec{r}$ is a curve (called a *u*-curve) lying on the surface $\vec{r}(T)$. The vector $\partial \vec{r}/\partial u$ is the velocity vector of this curve. (See Figure 6.6.) Likewise, $\partial \vec{r}/\partial v$ is the velocity vector of a *v*-curve obtained by setting $u = $ constant. There is a *u*-curve and a *v*-curve passing through each point of the surface. The restriction $\partial \vec{r}/\partial u \times \partial \vec{r}/\partial v \neq \vec{0}$ means that the velocity vectors $\partial \vec{r}/\partial u$ and $\partial \vec{r}/\partial v$ are not collinear at this point. For a fixed v, let us think of the parameter u as representing "time." When u changes by an amount Δu, a point originally at $\vec{r}(u, v)$ moves along a *u*-curve a distance approximately equal to $|\partial \vec{r}/\partial u| \, \Delta u$ (since $|\partial \vec{r}/\partial u|$ represents the speed along the *u*-curve).

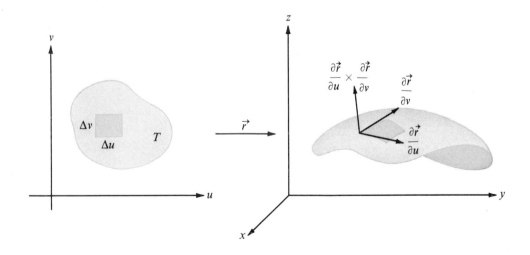

FIGURE 6.6 *Geometric interpretation of the vectors* $\dfrac{\partial \vec{r}}{\partial u}, \dfrac{\partial \vec{r}}{\partial v},$ *and* $\dfrac{\partial \vec{r}}{\partial u} \times \dfrac{\partial \vec{r}}{\partial v}.$

Similarly, for a fixed u a point of a v-curve moves in time Δv a distance nearly equal to $|\partial \vec{r}/\partial v| \, \Delta v$. A rectangle in T having area $\Delta u \, \Delta v$ is traced onto a portion of $\vec{r}(T)$ which we shall approximate by the parallelogram determined by the vectors $(\partial \vec{r}/\partial u) \, \Delta u$ and $(\partial \vec{r}/\partial v) \, \Delta v$. (See Figure 6.6.) The area of the parallelogram spanned by $(\partial \vec{r}/\partial u) \, \Delta u$ and $(\partial \vec{r}/\partial v) \, \Delta v$ is the magnitude of their cross product,

$$\left| \frac{\partial \vec{r}}{\partial u} \Delta u \times \frac{\partial \vec{r}}{\partial v} \Delta v \right| = \left| \frac{\partial \vec{r}}{\partial u} \times \frac{\partial \vec{r}}{\partial v} \right| \Delta u \, \Delta v \,.$$

Therefore the length of the fundamental vector product may be thought of as a local magnification factor for areas. At the points at which this vector product is zero the parallelogram collapses to a curve or point, and degeneracies occur. At each regular point the vectors $\partial \vec{r}/\partial u$ and $\partial \vec{r}/\partial v$ determine a plane having the vector $\partial \vec{r}/\partial u \times \partial \vec{r}/\partial v$ as a normal. Later in this section we shall prove that $\partial \vec{r}/\partial u \times \partial \vec{r}/\partial v$ is normal to every smooth curve on the surface; for this reason the plane determined by $\partial \vec{r}/\partial u$ and $\partial \vec{r}/\partial v$ is called the *tangent plane* of the surface. Continuity of $\partial \vec{r}/\partial u$ and $\partial \vec{r}/\partial v$ implies continuity of $\partial \vec{r}/\partial u \times \partial \vec{r}/\partial v$; this, in turn, means that the tangent plane turns continuously on a smooth surface. Thus we see that continuity of $\partial \vec{r}/\partial u$ and $\partial \vec{r}/\partial v$ prevents the occurrence of sharp edges or corners on the surface; the nonvanishing of $\partial \vec{r}/\partial u \times \partial \vec{r}/\partial v$ prevents degeneracies.

Example 1: Surfaces with an explicit representation, $z = f(x, y)$. For a surface with an explicit representation of the form $z = f(x, y)$, we can use x and y as the parameters, which gives us the vector equation

$$\vec{r}(x, y) = x\vec{i} + y\vec{j} + f(x, y)\vec{k} \,.$$

This representation always gives a simple parametric surface. The region T is called the projection of the surface on the xy-plane. (An example is shown in Figure 6.7.) To compute the fundamental vector product we note that

$$\frac{\partial \vec{r}}{\partial x} = \vec{i} + \frac{\partial f}{\partial x} \vec{k} \quad \text{and} \quad \frac{\partial \vec{r}}{\partial y} = \vec{j} + \frac{\partial f}{\partial y} \vec{k} \,.$$

This gives us

$$(6.5) \qquad \frac{\partial \vec{r}}{\partial x} \times \frac{\partial \vec{r}}{\partial y} = \begin{vmatrix} \vec{i} & \vec{j} & \vec{k} \\ 1 & 0 & \dfrac{\partial f}{\partial x} \\ 0 & 1 & \dfrac{\partial f}{\partial y} \end{vmatrix} = -\frac{\partial f}{\partial x} \vec{i} - \frac{\partial f}{\partial y} \vec{j} + \vec{k} \,.$$

Since the z-component of $\partial \vec{r}/\partial x \times \partial \vec{r}/\partial y$ is 1, the fundamental vector product is never zero. Therefore the only singular points that can occur for this representation are points at which at least one of the partial derivatives $\partial f/\partial x$ or $\partial f/\partial y$ fails to be continuous.

A specific case is the equation $z = \sqrt{1 - x^2 - y^2}$, which represents a hemisphere of radius 1 and center at the origin, if $x^2 + y^2 \leq 1$. The vector equation

$$\vec{r}(x, y) = x\vec{i} + y\vec{j} + \sqrt{1 - x^2 - y^2} \, \vec{k}$$

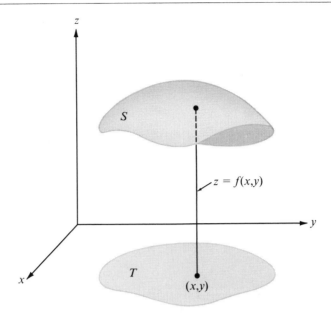

FIGURE 6.7   *A surface S with an explicit representation, $z = f(x, y)$. The region T is the projection of S on the xy-plane.*

maps the unit disk $T = \{(x, y) \mid x^2 + y^2 \leq 1\}$ onto the hemisphere in a one-to-one fashion. The partial derivatives $\partial \vec{r}/\partial x$ and $\partial \vec{r}/\partial y$ exist and are continuous everywhere in the interior of this disk, but they do not exist on the boundary. Therefore every point on the equator is a singular point of this representation.

Example 2. We consider the same hemisphere as in Example 1, but this time as the image of the rectangle $T = [0, 2\pi] \times [0, \tfrac{1}{2}\pi]$ under the mapping

$$\vec{r}(u, v) = a \cos u \cos v \, \vec{i} + a \sin u \cos v \, \vec{j} + a \sin v \, \vec{k}.$$

The vectors $\partial \vec{r}/\partial u$ and $\partial \vec{r}/\partial v$ are given by the formulas

$$\frac{\partial \vec{r}}{\partial u} = -a \sin u \cos v \, \vec{i} + a \cos u \cos v \, \vec{j},$$

$$\frac{\partial \vec{r}}{\partial v} = -a \cos u \sin v \, \vec{i} - a \sin u \sin v \, \vec{j} + a \cos v \, \vec{k}.$$

An easy calculation shows that their cross product is equal to

$$\frac{\partial \vec{r}}{\partial u} \times \frac{\partial \vec{r}}{\partial v} = a \cos v \, \vec{r}(u, v).$$

The image of T is not a simple parametric surface because this mapping is not one-to-one on T. In fact, every point on the line segment $v = \tfrac{1}{2}\pi$, $0 \leq u \leq 2\pi$, is mapped onto the point $(0, 0, a)$ (the North Pole). Also, because of the periodicity of the sine and cosine, $\vec{r}$ takes the same values at the points $(0, v)$ and $(2\pi, v)$, so the right and left edges of T are mapped onto the same curve, a circular arc joining the North Pole to the point $(a, 0, 0)$ on the equator. (See Figure 6.3.) The vectors $\partial \vec{r}/\partial u$ and $\partial \vec{r}/\partial v$ are continuous everywhere in T. Since $|\partial \vec{r}/\partial u \times \partial \vec{r}/\partial v| = a^2 \cos v$, the only singular points of this representation occur when $\cos v = 0$. The North Pole is the only such point.

We shall prove now that at each point P on a smooth parametric surface $\vec{r}(T)$, the vector $\partial \vec{r}/\partial u \times \partial \vec{r}/\partial v$ is normal to every smooth curve on the surface passing through P. Let C be such a curve, and suppose that C is the image $\vec{r}(C^*)$ of a smooth curve C^* in T. If C^* is described by a function $\vec{\alpha}$ defined on an interval $[a, b]$, say

$$\vec{\alpha}(t) = U(t)\vec{i} + V(t)\vec{j},$$

the image curve C is described by the composite function

$$\vec{\rho}(t) = \vec{r}[\vec{\alpha}(t)] = X[\vec{\alpha}(t)]\vec{i} + Y[\vec{\alpha}(t)]\vec{j} + Z[\vec{\alpha}(t)]\vec{k}.$$

We wish to prove that the derivative $\vec{\rho}'(t)$ is perpendicular to the vector $\partial \vec{r}/\partial u \times \partial \vec{r}/\partial v$ when the partial derivatives $\partial \vec{r}/\partial u$ and $\partial \vec{r}/\partial v$ are evaluated at $(U(t), V(t))$. To compute $\vec{\rho}'(t)$ we differentiate each component of $\vec{\rho}(t)$ by the chain rule (Theorem 4–8) to obtain

$$(6.6) \qquad \vec{\rho}'(t) = \nabla X \cdot \vec{\alpha}'(t)\vec{i} + \nabla Y \cdot \vec{\alpha}'(t)\vec{j} + \nabla Z \cdot \vec{\alpha}'(t)\vec{k},$$

where the gradient vectors ∇X, ∇Y, and ∇Z are evaluated at $(U(t), V(t))$. Equation (6.6) can be rewritten as

$$\vec{\rho}'(t) = \frac{\partial \vec{r}}{\partial u} U'(t) + \frac{\partial \vec{r}}{\partial v} V'(t),$$

where the derivatives $\partial \vec{r}/\partial u$ and $\partial \vec{r}/\partial v$ are evaluated at $(U(t), V(t))$. Since $\partial \vec{r}/\partial u$ and $\partial \vec{r}/\partial v$ are each perpendicular to the cross product $\partial \vec{r}/\partial u \times \partial \vec{r}/\partial v$, the same is true of $\vec{\rho}'(t)$. This proves that $\partial \vec{r}/\partial u \times \partial \vec{r}/\partial v$ is normal to C, as asserted. For this reason, the vector $\partial \vec{r}/\partial u \times \partial \vec{r}/\partial v$ is said to be *normal* to the surface $\vec{r}(T)$. At each regular point P of $\vec{r}(T)$ the vector $\partial \vec{r}/\partial u \times \partial \vec{r}/\partial v$ is nonzero; the plane through P having this vector as a normal is called the *tangent plane* to the surface at P.

6.3 Exercises

In Exercises 1 through 6, eliminate the parameters u and v to obtain a Cartesian equation, thus showing that the given vector equation represents a portion of the surface named. Also, compute the fundamental vector product $\partial \vec{r}/\partial u \times \partial \vec{r}/\partial v$ in terms of u and v.

1. *Plane*:
   $\vec{r}(u, v) = (x_0 + a_1 u + b_1 v)\vec{i} + (y_0 + a_2 u + b_2 v)\vec{j} + (z_0 + a_3 u + b_3 v)\vec{k}.$
2. *Elliptic paraboloid*:
   $\vec{r}(u, v) = au \cos v \, \vec{i} + bu \sin v \, \vec{j} + u^2 \vec{k}.$
3. *Ellipsoid*:
   $\vec{r}(u, v) = a \sin u \cos v \, \vec{i} + b \sin u \sin v \, \vec{j} + c \cos u \, \vec{k}.$
4. *Surface of revolution*:
   $\vec{r}(u, v) = u \cos v \, \vec{i} + u \sin v \, \vec{j} + f(u) \, \vec{k}.$

5. *Cylinder*:

$\vec{r}(u, v) = u\vec{i} + a \sin v \, \vec{j} + b \cos v \, \vec{k}.$

6. *Torus*:

$\vec{r}(u, v) = (a + b \cos u) \sin v \, \vec{i} + (a + b \cos u) \cos v \, \vec{j} + b \sin u \, \vec{k}$, where $0 < b < a$. What are the geometric meanings of a and b?

In Exercises 7 through 10 compute the magnitude of the fundamental vector product $\partial \vec{r}/\partial u \times \partial \vec{r}/\partial v$ in terms of u and v.

7. $\vec{r}(u, v) = a \sin u \cosh v \, \vec{i} + b \cos u \cosh v \, \vec{j} + c \sinh v \, \vec{k}.$
8. $\vec{r}(u, v) = (u + v) \, \vec{i} + (u - v) \, \vec{j} + 4v^2 \, \vec{k}.$
9. $\vec{r}(u, v) = (u + v) \, \vec{i} + (u^2 + v^2) \, \vec{j} + (u^3 + v^3) \, \vec{k}.$
10. $\vec{r}(u, v) = u \cos v \, \vec{i} + u \sin v \, \vec{j} + \frac{1}{2} u^2 \sin 2v \, \vec{k}.$

6.4 Area of a parametric surface

Let $S = \vec{r}(T)$ be a parametric surface described by a vector-valued function $\vec{r}$ defined on a region T in the uv-plane. In Section 6.2 we found that the length of the fundamental vector product $\partial \vec{r}/\partial u \times \partial \vec{r}/\partial v$ could be interpreted as a local magnification factor for areas. (See Figure 6.6.) A rectangle in T of area $\Delta u \, \Delta v$ is mapped by $\vec{r}$ onto a curvilinear parallelogram on S with area nearly equal to

$$\left| \frac{\partial \vec{r}}{\partial u} \times \frac{\partial \vec{r}}{\partial v} \right| \Delta u \, \Delta v \, .$$

This observation suggests that we define the area of S by the following double integral:

(6.7)
$$\text{area of } S = \iint_T \left| \frac{\partial \vec{r}}{\partial u} \times \frac{\partial \vec{r}}{\partial v} \right| du \, dv \, .$$

In other words, to determine the area of S we first compute the fundamental vector product $\partial \vec{r}/\partial u \times \partial \vec{r}/\partial v$ and then integrate its length over the region T. When $\partial \vec{r}/\partial u \times \partial \vec{r}/\partial v$ is expressed in terms of its components, by means of Equation (6.4), we have

(6.8)
$$\text{area of } S = \iint_T \sqrt{\left(\frac{\partial(Y, Z)}{\partial(u, v)} \right)^2 + \left(\frac{\partial(Z, X)}{\partial(u, v)} \right)^2 + \left(\frac{\partial(X, Y)}{\partial(u, v)} \right)^2} \, du \, dv \, .$$

Written in this form, the integral for surface area resembles the integral for computing the arc length of a curve.†

If S is given explicitly by an equation of the form $z = f(x, y)$ we may use x and y as the parameters. The fundamental vector product is given by Equation (6.5), so we have

---

† Since the integral in (6.7) involves $\vec{r}$, the area of a surface will depend on the function used to describe the surface. When we discuss surface integrals we shall prove (in Section 6.7) that under certain general conditions the area is independent of the parametric representation. The result is analogous to Theorem 5–1, in which we discussed the invariance of line integrals under a change of parameter.

$$\left| \frac{\partial \vec{r}}{\partial x} \times \frac{\partial \vec{r}}{\partial y} \right| = \left| -\frac{\partial f}{\partial x} \vec{i} - \frac{\partial f}{\partial y} \vec{j} + \vec{k} \right| = \sqrt{1 + \left(\frac{\partial f}{\partial x}\right)^2 + \left(\frac{\partial f}{\partial y}\right)^2} \, .$$

In this case the integral for surface area becomes

(6.9)   area of $S = \iint\limits_T \sqrt{1 + \left(\frac{\partial f}{\partial x}\right)^2 + \left(\frac{\partial f}{\partial y}\right)^2} \, dx \, dy \, ,$

where the region T is now the projection of S on the xy-plane, as illustrated in Figure 6.7.

When S lies in a plane parallel to the xy-plane, the function f is constant, so $\partial f/\partial x = \partial f/\partial y = 0$, and Equation (6.9) becomes

$$\text{area of } S = \iint\limits_T dx \, dy \, .$$

This agrees with the usual formula for areas of plane regions.

Equation (6.9) can be written in another form that gives further insight into its geometric significance. At each point of S, let γ denote the angle between the normal vector $\vec{N} = \partial \vec{r}/\partial x \times \partial \vec{r}/\partial y$ and the unit coordinate vector $\vec{k}$. (See Figure 6.8.) Since the z-component of $\vec{N}$ is 1, we have

$$\cos \gamma = \frac{\vec{N} \cdot \vec{k}}{|\vec{N}| \, |\vec{k}|} = \frac{1}{|\vec{N}|} = \frac{1}{\left| \dfrac{\partial \vec{r}}{\partial x} \times \dfrac{\partial \vec{r}}{\partial y} \right|} \, ,$$

and hence $|\partial \vec{r}/\partial x \times \partial \vec{r}/\partial y| = 1/\cos \gamma$. Therefore Equation (6.9) becomes

(6.10)   area of $S = \iint\limits_T \frac{1}{\cos \gamma} \, dx \, dy \, .$

Suppose now that S lies in a plane not perpendicular to the xy-plane. Then γ is constant and Equation (6.10) states that the area of $S = $ (area of T)/cos γ, or that

(6.11)   area of $T = $ (area of S) cos γ .

Equation (6.11) is sometimes referred to as the *area cosine principle*. It tells us that if a region S in one plane is projected onto a region T in another plane, making an angle γ with the first plane, the area of T is cos γ times that of S. This formula is obviously true when S is the rectangle shown in Figure 6.9, because distances in one direction are shortened by the factor cos γ while those in a perpendicular direction are unaltered by projection. Equation (6.11) extends this property to any plane region S having an area.

Suppose now that S is given by an implicit representation $F(x, y, z) = 0$. If S can be projected in a one-to-one fashion on the xy-plane, the equation $F(x, y, z) = 0$ defines z as a function of x and y, say $z = f(x, y)$, and the partial derivatives $\partial f/\partial x$ and $\partial f/\partial y$ are related to those of F by the equations

$$\frac{\partial f}{\partial x} = -\frac{\partial F/\partial x}{\partial F/\partial z} \quad \text{and} \quad \frac{\partial f}{\partial y} = -\frac{\partial F/\partial y}{\partial F/\partial z}$$

for those points at which $\partial F/\partial z \neq 0$. Substituting these quotients in (6.9), we find

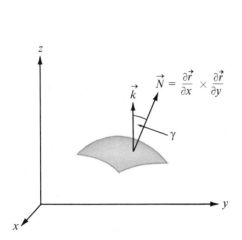

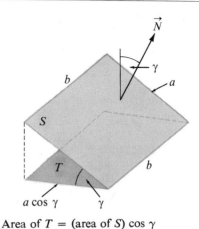

Area of $T = $ (area of S) $\cos \gamma$

FIGURE 6.8   *The length of $\dfrac{\partial \vec{r}}{\partial x} \times \dfrac{\partial \vec{r}}{\partial y}$ is $1/\cos \gamma$.*   FIGURE 6.9   *The area cosine principle for a rectangle.*

(6.12) $$\text{area of } S = \iint\limits_{T} \frac{\sqrt{(\partial F/\partial x)^2 + (\partial F/\partial y)^2 + (\partial F/\partial z)^2}}{|\partial F/\partial z|} \, dx \, dy \,.$$

Example 1: Area of a hemisphere. Consider a hemisphere S of radius a and center at the origin. We have at our disposal the implicit representation $x^2 + y^2 + z^2 = a^2, z \geq 0$; the explicit representation $z = \sqrt{a^2 - x^2 - y^2}$; and the parametric representation

(6.13) $$\vec{r}(u, v) = a \cos u \cos v \, \vec{i} + a \sin u \cos v \, \vec{j} + a \sin v \, \vec{k} \,.$$

To compute the area of S from the implicit representation we refer to Equation (6.12) with

$$F(x, y, z) = x^2 + y^2 + z^2 - a^2 \,.$$

The partial derivatives of F are $\partial F/\partial x = 2x$, $\partial F/\partial y = 2y$, $\partial F/\partial z = 2z$. The hemisphere S projects in a one-to-one fashion onto the circular disk $D = \{(x, y) \mid x^2 + y^2 \leq a^2\}$ in the xy-plane. We cannot apply Equation (6.12) directly because the partial derivative $\partial F/\partial z$ is zero on the boundary of D. However, the derivative $\partial F/\partial z$ is nonzero everywhere in the interior of D, so we can consider the smaller concentric disk $D(R)$ of radius R, where $R < a$. If $S(R)$ denotes the corresponding portion of the upper hemisphere, Equation (6.12) is now applicable and we find

$$\text{area of } S(R) = \iint\limits_{D(R)} \frac{\sqrt{(2x)^2 + (2y)^2 + (2z)^2}}{|2z|} \, dx \, dy$$

$$= \iint\limits_{D(R)} \frac{a}{z} \, dx \, dy = a \iint\limits_{D(R)} \frac{1}{\sqrt{a^2 - x^2 - y^2}} \, dx \, dy \,.$$

The last integral may be easily evaluated by the use of polar coordinates, giving us

$$\text{area of } S(R) = a \int_0^{2\pi} \left[\int_0^R \frac{1}{\sqrt{a^2 - r^2}} \, r \, dr \right] d\theta = 2\pi a(a - \sqrt{a^2 - R^2}).$$

When $R \to a$ this approaches the limit $2\pi a^2$.

We can avoid the limiting process in the foregoing calculation by using the parametric representation in (6.13). The calculations of Example 2 in Section 6.2 show that

$$\left| \frac{\partial \vec{r}}{\partial u} \times \frac{\partial \vec{r}}{\partial v} \right| = | \, a \cos v \, \vec{r}(u, v) | = a^2 |\cos v| \,.$$

Therefore we may apply Equation (6.7), taking for the region T the rectangle $[0,2\pi] \times [0,\tfrac{1}{2}\pi]$. We find

$$\text{area of } S = a^2 \iint_T |\cos v| \, du \, dv = a^2 \int_0^{2\pi} \left[\int_0^{\pi/2} \cos v \, dv \right] du = 2\pi a^2 \,.$$

Example 2: Another theorem of Pappus. One of the theorems of Pappus states that a surface of revolution, obtained by rotating a plane curve of length L about an axis in the plane of the curve, has area $2\pi Lh$, where h is the distance from the centroid of the curve to the axis of rotation. We shall use Equation (6.7) to prove this theorem for a special surface of revolution.

Suppose a curve C, initially in the xz-plane, is rotated about the z-axis. Let its equation in the xz-plane be $z = f(x)$, where $a \le x \le b$, $a \ge 0$. The surface of revolution S so generated may be described by the vector equation

$$\vec{r}(u, v) = u \cos v \, \vec{i} + u \sin v \, \vec{j} + f(u) \, \vec{k} \,,$$

where $(u, v) \, \varepsilon \, [a, b] \times [0,2\pi]$. The parameters u and v can be interpreted as the radius and angle of polar coordinates, as illustrated in Figure 6.10. If $a \le u \le b$, all points (x, y, z) at a given distance u from the z-axis have the same z-coordinate, $f(u)$, so they all lie on the surface. The fundamental vector product of this representation is

$$\frac{\partial \vec{r}}{\partial u} \times \frac{\partial \vec{r}}{\partial v} = \begin{vmatrix} \vec{i} & \vec{j} & \vec{k} \\ \cos v & \sin v & f'(u) \\ -u \sin v & u \cos v & 0 \end{vmatrix} = -u f'(u) \cos v \, \vec{i} - u f'(u) \sin v \, \vec{j} + u \, \vec{k} \,,$$

and hence

$$\left| \frac{\partial \vec{r}}{\partial u} \times \frac{\partial \vec{r}}{\partial v} \right| = u \sqrt{1 + [f'(u)]^2} \,.$$

Therefore Equation (6.7) becomes

$$\text{area of } S = \int_0^{2\pi} \left[\int_a^b u \sqrt{1 + [f'(u)]^2} \, du \right] dv = 2\pi \int_a^b u \sqrt{1 + [f'(u)]^2} \, du \,.$$

The integral that remains can be expressed as $\int_C x \, ds$, a line integral with respect to arc length along the curve C. As such, it is equal to $\bar{x} \, L$, where $\bar{x}$ is the x-coordinate of the centroid of C and L is the length of C. (See Section 5.5.) Therefore the area of S is $2\pi L \bar{x}$. This proves the theorem of Pappus for the special surface considered.

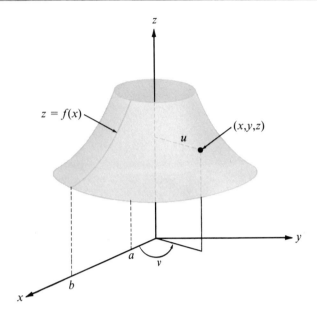

FIGURE 6.10   *Area of a surface of revolution determined by Pappus' theorem.*

6.5   Exercises

1. Let S be a parallelogram not parallel to any of the coordinate planes. Let S_1, S_2, and S_3 denote the areas of the projections of S on the three coordinate planes. Show that the area of S is $\sqrt{S_1^2 + S_2^2 + S_3^2}$.

2. Compute the area of the region cut from the plane $x + y + z = a$ by the cylinder $x^2 + y^2 = a^2$.

3. Compute the surface area of that portion of the sphere $x^2 + y^2 + z^2 = a^2$ lying within the cylinder $x^2 + y^2 = ay$, where $a > 0$.

4. Compute the area of that portion of the surface $z^2 = 2xy$ which lies above the first quadrant of the xy-plane and is cut off by the planes $x = 2$ and $y = 1$.

5. A parametric surface S is described by the vector equation

$$\vec{r}(u, v) = u \cos v \, \vec{i} + u \sin v \, \vec{j} + u^2 \, \vec{k} ,$$

where $0 \leq u \leq 4$ and $0 \leq v \leq 2\pi$.

(a) Show that S is a portion of a quadric surface. Name this quadric, sketch it, and indicate the geometric meanings of the parameters u and v on the surface.

(b) Compute the fundamental vector product $\partial \vec{r}/\partial u \times \partial \vec{r}/\partial v$ in terms of u and v.

(c) The area of S is $\pi(65 \sqrt{65} - 1)/n$, where n is an integer. Compute the value of n.

6. Compute the area of that portion of the conical surface $x^2 + y^2 = z^2$ which lies above the xy-plane and is cut off by the sphere $x^2 + y^2 + z^2 = 2ax$.

7. Compute the area of that portion of the conical surface $x^2 + y^2 = z^2$ which lies between the two planes $z = 0$ and $x + 2z = 3$.

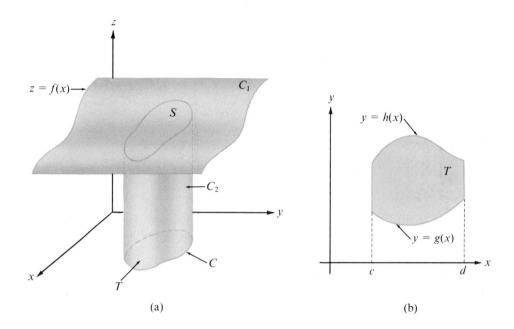

FIGURE 6.11   *Exercise 10.*

8. Compute the area of that portion of the paraboloid $x^2 + z^2 = 2ay$ which is cut off by the plane $y = a$.

9. Compute the area of the torus described by the vector equation

$$\vec{r}(u, v) = (a + b \cos u) \sin v \ \vec{i} + (a + b \cos u) \cos v \ \vec{j} + b \sin u \ \vec{k},$$

where $0 < b < a$ and $0 \le u \le 2\pi$, $0 \le v \le 2\pi$. Use the theorem of Pappus to check your answer.

10. A cylinder C_1 with generators parallel to the y-axis intersects the xz-plane along a curve with Cartesian equation $z = f(x)$, $a \le x \le b$. A cylinder C_2 with generators parallel to the z-axis traces out a simple closed curve C in the xy-plane forming the boundary of a plane region T as shown in Figure 6.11(a). The x-coordinate of each point of T satisfies $a < x < b$. Let

$$s(x) = \int_a^x \sqrt{1 + [f'(t)]^2} \ dt \ .$$

[This is the arc-length function for the curve $z = f(x)$.] Let S be that portion of C_1 cut out by C_2.
    (a) Show that

$$\text{area of } S = \iint_T s'(x) \ dx \ dy \ .$$

    (b) Show that

$$\text{area of } S = \oint_C s(x) \ dy \ ,$$

where the integral is a line integral taken around C in a counterclockwise direction.

Assume now that the boundary curve C consists of portions of two curves $y = g(x)$ and $y = h(x)$ and (possibly) two line segments, as shown in Figure 6.11(b), where $g(x) < h(x)$ for $c < x < d$, and $a < c < d < b$. If $c \le x \le d$, let $A(x)$ denote the area of that portion of T above the interval $[c, x]$.

(c) Show that

$$\text{area of } S = \int_c^d A'(x)\, s'(x)\, dx \, .$$

(d) If the curves $y = h(x)$ and $y = g(x)$ are parallel, show that

$$\text{area of } S = [h(c) - g(c)][s(d) - s(c)] \, .$$

Justify this formula geometrically by referring to a suitable rectangle having the same area as S.

(e) If the curves $y = h(x)$ and $y = g(x)$ intersect when $x = c$ and when $x = d$, show that

$$\text{area of } S = \int_c^d [g'(x) - h'(x)]\, s(x)\, dx \, .$$

11. A sphere is inscribed in a right circular cylinder. The sphere is sliced by two parallel planes perpendicular to the axis of the cylinder. Show that the portions of the sphere and cylinder lying between these planes have equal surface areas.

6.6 Surface integrals

Surface integrals are, in many respects, analogous to line integrals; the integration takes place along a surface rather than along a curve. The definition of the line integral was suggested by a study of the concept of work. The definition of the surface integral will be motivated by a physical problem taken from the theory of fluid flow.

Suppose we have a fluid flowing in space with velocity vector $\vec{V}(x, y, z)$ and density $\rho(x, y, z)$ at each point (x, y, z). As we observed earlier in connection with the physical interpretation of divergence (Section 5.22), the flux density vector

$$\vec{F}(x, y, z) = \rho(x, y, z)\, \vec{V}(x, y, z)$$

measures the rate of flow (mass per unit area) at (x, y, z). We wish now to measure the total mass of fluid that flows through a given surface S in unit time. The following discussion is purely heuristic and is only intended to suggest a reasonable definition of the total mass flowing through S in unit time.

Let $S = \vec{r}(T)$ be a simple parametric surface given by an equation of the form

$$\vec{r}(u, v) = X(u, v)\, \vec{i} + Y(u, v)\, \vec{j} + Z(u, v)\, \vec{k} \, ,$$

where (u, v) ranges over a rectangular region T in the uv-plane. At each regular point of S let $\vec{n}$ denote the unit normal having the same direction as the fundamental vector product. That is, let

(6.14)
$$\vec{n} = \frac{\dfrac{\partial \vec{r}}{\partial u} \times \dfrac{\partial \vec{r}}{\partial v}}{\left| \dfrac{\partial \vec{r}}{\partial u} \times \dfrac{\partial \vec{r}}{\partial v} \right|} \, .$$

To measure the mass of fluid that flows through S in unit time in the direction indicated by $\vec{n}$, we partition the rectangle T into subrectangles $T_1, \ldots, T_m$, and let $S_1, \ldots, S_m$ be the corresponding surface patches on S. Let ΔS_k denote the area of the kth patch S_k. If the density ρ and the velocity $\vec{V}$ are constant on S_k and if S_k is nearly planar, the fluid flowing through S_k in unit time fills out a slanted cylindrical solid with base S_k and axis

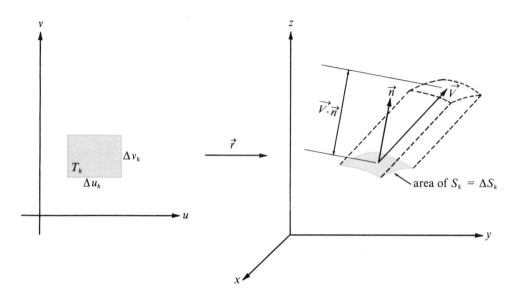

FIGURE 6.12   *Fluid flowing through S_k in unit time fills out a cylindrical solid with volume $\vec{V} \cdot \vec{n}\, \Delta S_k$.*

determined by the velocity vector $\vec{V}$. (See Figure 6.12.) The volume of this solid is the product of the area of its base ΔS_k with its altitude $\vec{V} \cdot \vec{n}$. Therefore the mass of fluid in this solid is $\rho \vec{V} \cdot \vec{n}\, \Delta S_k = \vec{F} \cdot \vec{n}\, \Delta S_k$. This suggests that the sum

$$(6.15) \qquad\qquad \sum_{k=1}^{m} \vec{F} \cdot \vec{n}\, \Delta S_k$$

should be a reasonable approximation to the total mass of fluid flowing through S in unit time. Now we shall express this sum in terms of the rectangles T_k in the uv-plane. If the dimensions of the kth subrectangle T_k are Δu_k and Δv_k, the image S_k has an area ΔS_k approximately equal to $|\partial \vec{r}/\partial u \times \partial \vec{r}/\partial v|\, \Delta u_k\, \Delta v_k$, since $|\partial \vec{r}/\partial u \times \partial \vec{r}/\partial v|$ represents a local magnification factor for areas. Therefore, if we let $\phi = \vec{F} \cdot \vec{n}$, the sum in (6.15) is nearly equal to

$$(6.16) \qquad\qquad \sum_{k=1}^{m} \phi \left| \frac{\partial \vec{r}}{\partial u} \times \frac{\partial \vec{r}}{\partial v} \right| \Delta u_k\, \Delta v_k \,.$$

If $\phi\, |\partial \vec{r}/\partial u \times \partial \vec{r}/\partial v|$ were constant on the open subrectangle T_k, the product $\phi\, |\partial \vec{r}/\partial u \times \partial \vec{r}/\partial v|$ would be a step function, and the sum in (6.16) would be the double integral of this step function over T. In this case the total mass of fluid flowing through S in unit time in the direction of $\vec{n}$ is

$$(6.17) \qquad \iint_T \phi \left| \frac{\partial \vec{r}}{\partial u} \times \frac{\partial \vec{r}}{\partial v} \right| du\, dv = \iint_T \vec{F} \cdot \vec{n} \left| \frac{\partial \vec{r}}{\partial u} \times \frac{\partial \vec{r}}{\partial v} \right| du\, dv \,.$$

When the integrand is not a step function we shall use this integral as the *definition* of the total mass of fluid flowing through S in unit time in the direction of $\vec{n}$. This discussion also serves to motivate the following definition of a surface integral:

DEFINITION OF A SURFACE INTEGRAL. Let $S = \vec{r}(T)$ be a parametric surface described by a function $\vec{r}$ defined on a region T in the uv-plane, and let ϕ be a scalar field defined and bounded on S. The surface integral of ϕ over S is denoted by the symbol $\iint_{\vec{r}(T)} \phi \, dS$ [or by $\iint_{S} \phi(x, y, z) \, dS$], and is defined by the equation

$$(6.18) \qquad \iint_{\vec{r}(T)} \phi \, dS = \iint_{T} \phi[\vec{r}(u, v)] \left| \frac{\partial \vec{r}}{\partial u} \times \frac{\partial \vec{r}}{\partial v} \right| du \, dv$$

whenever the double integral on the right exists.

Note. Since the double integral in (6.18) involves the function $\vec{r}$ in the integrand, the value of the surface integral $\iint_{\vec{r}(T)} \phi \, dS$ may depend on the particular representation used to describe the surface. In Section 6.7 we shall prove that under certain general conditions the value of the integral is independent of the representation.

The following examples illustrate some applications of surface integrals.

Example 1: Surface area. When $\phi = 1$, Equation (6.18) becomes

$$\iint_{\vec{r}(T)} dS = \iint_{T} \left| \frac{\partial \vec{r}}{\partial u} \times \frac{\partial \vec{r}}{\partial v} \right| du \, dv \,.$$

The double integral on the right is that used earlier in Section 6.4 to define surface area. Thus, the area of S is equal to the surface integral $\iint_{\vec{r}(T)} dS$. For this reason, the symbol dS is sometimes referred to as an "element of surface area," and the surface integral $\iint_{\vec{r}(T)} \phi \, dS$ is said to be an integral of ϕ with respect to the element of surface area, extended over the surface $\vec{r}(T)$.

Example 2: Fluid flow. If $\vec{F}$ is the flux density of a fluid flow and if $\vec{n}$ is the unit normal to S, given by Equation (6.14), the surface integral $\iint_{\vec{r}(T)} \vec{F} \cdot \vec{n} \, dS$ represents the total mass of fluid flowing through S in unit time in the direction of $\vec{n}$. In fact, we have

$$\iint_{\vec{r}(T)} \vec{F} \cdot \vec{n} \, dS = \iint_{T} \vec{F} \cdot \vec{n} \left| \frac{\partial \vec{r}}{\partial u} \times \frac{\partial \vec{r}}{\partial v} \right| du \, dv \,,$$

so the surface integral $\iint_{\vec{r}(T)} \vec{F} \cdot \vec{n} \, dS$ is equal to the double integral in (6.17).

Example 3: Center of mass. Moment of inertia. If the scalar field ϕ is interpreted as the density (mass per unit area) of a thin material in the shape of the surface S, the total mass M of the surface is defined by the equation

$$M = \iint_{S} \phi(x, y, z) \, dS \,.$$

Its center of mass is the point $(\bar{x}, \bar{y}, \bar{z})$ determined by the equations

$$\bar{x}M = \iint\limits_{S} x\,\phi(x, y, z)\,dS\,, \qquad \bar{y}M = \iint\limits_{S} y\,\phi(x, y, z)\,dS\,, \qquad \bar{z}M = \iint\limits_{S} z\,\phi(x, y, z)\,dS\,.$$

The moment of inertia I_L of S about an axis L is defined by the equation

$$I_L = \iint\limits_{S} \delta^2(x, y, z)\,\phi(x, y, z)\,dS\,,$$

where $\delta(x, y, z)$ denotes the perpendicular distance from a general point (x, y, z) of S to the line L.

To illustrate, let us determine the center of mass of a uniform hemispherical surface of radius a. We use the parametric representation

$$\vec{r}(u, v) = a \cos u \cos v\,\vec{i} + a \sin u \cos v\,\vec{j} + a \sin v\,\vec{k}\,,$$

where $(u, v)\,\varepsilon\,[0, 2\pi] \times [0, \tfrac{1}{2}\pi]$. This particular representation was discussed earlier in Example 2 of Section 6.2, where we found that the magnitude of the fundamental vector product is $a^2\,|\cos v|$. In this example the density ϕ is constant, say $\phi = c$, and the mass M is $2\pi a^2 c$, the area of S times c. Because of symmetry, the coordinates $\bar{x}$ and $\bar{y}$ of the center of mass are 0. The coordinate $\bar{z}$ is given by

$$\bar{z}M = c \iint\limits_{S} z\,dS = c \iint\limits_{T} a \sin v \cdot a^2\,|\cos v|\,du\,dv$$

$$= 2\pi a^3 c \int_0^{\pi/2} \sin v \cos v\,dv = \pi a^3 c = \frac{a}{2}\,M\,,$$

so $\bar{z} = a/2$.

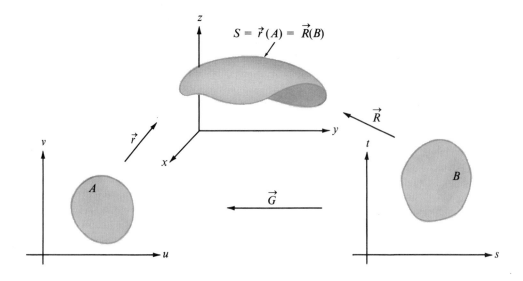

FIGURE 6.13   *Two parametric representations of the same surface.*

6.7 Change of parametric representation

We turn now to a discussion of the independence of surface integrals under a change of parametric representation. Suppose a function $\vec{r}$ maps a region A in the uv-plane onto a parametric surface $\vec{r}(A)$. Suppose also that A is the image of a region B in the st-plane under a one-to-one continuously differentiable mapping $\vec{G}$ given by

$$(6.19) \qquad \vec{G}(s,\, t) = U(s,\, t)\, \vec{i} + V(s,\, t)\, \vec{j} \qquad \text{if} \quad (s,\, t)\, \varepsilon\, B\,.$$

Consider the function $\vec{R}$ defined on B by the equation

$$(6.20) \qquad \vec{R}(s,\, t) = \vec{r}[\vec{G}(s,\, t)]\,.$$

(See Figure 6.13.) Two functions $\vec{r}$ and $\vec{R}$ so related will be called *smoothly equivalent*. Smoothly equivalent functions describe the same surface. That is, $\vec{r}(A)$ and $\vec{R}(B)$ are identical as point sets. (This follows at once from the one-to-one nature of $\vec{G}$.) The next theorem describes the relationship between their fundamental vector products.

6– 1   THEOREM. Let $\vec{r}$ and $\vec{R}$ be smoothly equivalent functions related by Equation (6.20), where $\vec{G} = U\vec{i} + V\vec{j}$ is a one-to-one continuously differentiable mapping of a region B in the st-plane onto a region A in the uv-plane given by Equation (6.19). Then we have

$$(6.21) \qquad \frac{\partial \vec{R}}{\partial s} \times \frac{\partial \vec{R}}{\partial t} = \frac{\partial \vec{r}}{\partial u} \times \frac{\partial \vec{r}}{\partial v} \frac{\partial(U,\, V)}{\partial(s,\, t)}\,,$$

where the partial derivatives $\partial \vec{r}/\partial u$ and $\partial \vec{r}/\partial v$ are to be evaluated at the point $(U(s,\, t),\, V(s,\, t))$. In other words, the fundamental vector product of $\vec{R}$ is equal to that of $\vec{r}$, times the Jacobian of the mapping $\vec{G}$.

Proof. The derivatives $\partial \vec{R}/\partial s$ and $\partial \vec{R}/\partial t$ may be computed by differentiation of Equation (6.20). If we apply the chain rule (Theorem 4–8) to each component of $\vec{R}$ and rearrange terms, we find that

$$\frac{\partial \vec{R}}{\partial s} = \frac{\partial \vec{r}}{\partial u} \frac{\partial U}{\partial s} + \frac{\partial \vec{r}}{\partial v} \frac{\partial V}{\partial s} \qquad \text{and} \qquad \frac{\partial \vec{R}}{\partial t} = \frac{\partial \vec{r}}{\partial u} \frac{\partial U}{\partial t} + \frac{\partial \vec{r}}{\partial v} \frac{\partial V}{\partial t}\,,$$

where the derivatives $\partial \vec{r}/\partial u$ and $\partial \vec{r}/\partial v$ are evaluated at $(U(s,\, t),\, V(s,\, t))$. Now we cross multiply these two equations and, noting the order of the factors, we obtain

$$\frac{\partial \vec{R}}{\partial s} \times \frac{\partial \vec{R}}{\partial t} = \left(\frac{\partial \vec{r}}{\partial u} \times \frac{\partial \vec{r}}{\partial v} \right) \left(\frac{\partial U}{\partial s} \frac{\partial V}{\partial t} - \frac{\partial U}{\partial t} \frac{\partial V}{\partial s} \right) = \frac{\partial \vec{r}}{\partial u} \times \frac{\partial \vec{r}}{\partial v} \frac{\partial(U,\, V)}{\partial(s,\, t)}\,.$$

This completes the proof.

The invariance of surface integrals under smoothly equivalent parametric representations is now an easy consequence of Theorem 6–1.

6– 2   THEOREM. Let $\vec{r}$ and $\vec{R}$ be smoothly equivalent functions, as described in Theorem 6–1. If the surface integral $\iint\limits_{\vec{r}(A)} \phi\ dS$ exists, the surface integral $\iint\limits_{\vec{R}(B)} \phi\ dS$ also exists and we have

$$\iint\limits_{\vec{r}(A)} \phi \; dS = \iint\limits_{\vec{R}(B)} \phi \; dS .$$

Proof. By the definition of a surface integral we have

$$\iint\limits_{\vec{r}(A)} \phi \; dS = \iint\limits_{A} \phi[\vec{r}(u, v)] \left| \frac{\partial \vec{r}}{\partial u} \times \frac{\partial \vec{r}}{\partial v} \right| du \; dv .$$

Now we use the mapping $\vec{G}$ of Theorem 6–1 to transform this into a double integral over the region B in the st-plane. The transformation formula for double integrals states that

$$\iint\limits_{A} \phi[\vec{r}(u, v)] \left| \frac{\partial \vec{r}}{\partial u} \times \frac{\partial \vec{r}}{\partial v} \right| du \; dv = \iint\limits_{B} \phi\{\vec{r}[\vec{G}(s, t)]\} \left| \frac{\partial \vec{r}}{\partial u} \times \frac{\partial \vec{r}}{\partial v} \right| \left| \frac{\partial(U, V)}{\partial(s, t)} \right| ds \; dt ,$$

where the derivatives $\partial \vec{r}/\partial u$ and $\partial \vec{r}/\partial v$ on the right are to be evaluated at $(U(s, t), V(s, t))$. Because of Equation (6.21), the integral over B is equal to

$$\iint\limits_{B} \phi[\vec{R}(s, t)] \left| \frac{\partial \vec{R}}{\partial s} \times \frac{\partial \vec{R}}{\partial t} \right| ds \; dt .$$

This, in turn, is the definition of the surface integral $\iint\limits_{\vec{R}(B)} \phi \; dS$. The proof is now complete.

6.8   Other notations for surface integrals

If $S = \vec{r}(T)$ is a parametric surface, the fundamental vector product $\partial \vec{r}/\partial u \times \partial \vec{r}/\partial v$ is normal to S at each regular point of the surface. At each such point there are *two* unit normals, a unit normal $\vec{n}_1$ which has the same direction as the fundamental vector product, and a unit normal $\vec{n}_2$ which has the opposite direction. Thus,

$$\vec{n}_1 = \frac{\dfrac{\partial \vec{r}}{\partial u} \times \dfrac{\partial \vec{r}}{\partial v}}{\left| \dfrac{\partial \vec{r}}{\partial u} \times \dfrac{\partial \vec{r}}{\partial v} \right|} \quad \text{and} \quad \vec{n}_2 = - \frac{\dfrac{\partial \vec{r}}{\partial u} \times \dfrac{\partial \vec{r}}{\partial v}}{\left| \dfrac{\partial \vec{r}}{\partial u} \times \dfrac{\partial \vec{r}}{\partial v} \right|} .$$

Let $\vec{n}$ be one of the two normals $\vec{n}_1$ or $\vec{n}_2$. Let $\vec{F}$ be a vector field defined on S and assume the surface integral $\iint\limits_{S} \vec{F} \cdot \vec{n} \; dS$ exists. Then we may write

(6.22)
$$\iint\limits_{S} \vec{F} \cdot \vec{n} \; dS = \iint\limits_{T} \vec{F}[\vec{r}(u, v)] \cdot \vec{n}(u, v) \left| \frac{\partial \vec{r}}{\partial u} \times \frac{\partial \vec{r}}{\partial v} \right| du \; dv$$

$$= \pm \iint\limits_{T} \vec{F}[\vec{r}(u, v)] \cdot \frac{\partial \vec{r}}{\partial u} \times \frac{\partial \vec{r}}{\partial v} \; du \; dv ,$$

where the $+$ sign is used if $\vec{n} = \vec{n}_1$ and the $-$ sign is used if $\vec{n} = \vec{n}_2$.

Suppose now we express $\vec{F}$ and $\vec{r}$ in terms of their components, say

$$\vec{F}(x, y, z) = P(x, y, z) \, \vec{i} + Q(x, y, z) \, \vec{j} + R(x, y, z) \vec{k}$$

and

$$\vec{r}(u, v) = X(u, v) \, \vec{i} + Y(u, v) \, \vec{j} + Z(u, v) \vec{k} .$$

Then the fundamental vector product of $\vec{r}$ is given by

$$\frac{\partial \vec{r}}{\partial u} \times \frac{\partial \vec{r}}{\partial v} = \frac{\partial(Y, Z)}{\partial(u, v)} \vec{i} + \frac{\partial(Z, X)}{\partial(u, v)} \vec{j} + \frac{\partial(X, Y)}{\partial(u, v)} \vec{k} .$$

If $\vec{n} = \vec{n}_1$, Equation (6.22) becomes

(6.23) $$\iint\limits_{S} \vec{F} \cdot \vec{n} \, dS = \iint\limits_{T} P[\vec{r}(u, v)] \frac{\partial(Y, Z)}{\partial(u, v)} du \, dv$$

$$+ \iint\limits_{T} Q[\vec{r}(u, v)] \frac{\partial(Z, X)}{\partial(u, v)} du \, dv + \iint\limits_{T} R[\vec{r}(u, v)] \frac{\partial(X, Y)}{\partial(u, v)} du \, dv ;$$

if $\vec{n} = \vec{n}_2$, each double integral on the right must be replaced by its negative. The sum of the double integrals on the right is often written more briefly as

(6.24) $$\iint\limits_{S} P(x, y, z) \, dy \, dz + \iint\limits_{S} Q(x, y, z) \, dz \, dx + \iint\limits_{S} R(x, y, z) \, dx \, dy ,$$

or even more briefly as

(6.25) $$\iint\limits_{S} P \, dy \, dz + Q \, dz \, dx + R \, dx \, dy .$$

The integrals which appear in (6.24) and (6.25) are also referred to as surface integrals. Thus, for example, the surface integral $\iint\limits_{S} P \, dy \, dz$ is defined by the equation

(6.26) $$\iint\limits_{S} P \, dy \, dz = \iint\limits_{T} P[\vec{r}(u, v)] \frac{\partial(Y, Z)}{\partial(u, v)} du \, dv .$$

This notation is suggested by the formula for changing variables in a double integral.

Despite similarity in notation, the integral on the left of (6.26) is *not* a double integral. First of all, P is a function of three variables. Also, we must take into consideration the order in which the symbols dy and dz appear in the surface integral, because

$$\frac{\partial(Y, Z)}{\partial(u, v)} = - \frac{\partial(Z, Y)}{\partial(u, v)}$$

and hence

$$\iint\limits_{S} P \, dy \, dz = - \iint\limits_{S} P \, dz \, dy .$$

In this notation, formula (6.23) becomes

(6.27) $$\iint\limits_{S} \vec{F} \cdot \vec{n} \, dS = \iint\limits_{S} P \, dy \, dz + Q \, dz \, dx + R \, dx \, dy$$

if $\vec{n} = \vec{n}_1$. If $\vec{n} = \vec{n}_2$ the integral on the right must be replaced by its negative. This formula resembles the following formula for line integrals:

$$\int_{C} \vec{F} \cdot d\vec{r} = \int_{C} P \, dx + Q \, dy + R \, dz .$$

The resemblance can be carried one step further if we introduce the symbolic "vector" $d\vec{S} = \vec{n}\,dS$ (sometimes called the vector element of surface area) and write $\iint\limits_{S} \vec{F} \cdot d\vec{S}$ instead of $\iint\limits_{S} \vec{F} \cdot \vec{n}\,dS$.

If the unit normal $\vec{n}$ is expressed in terms of its direction cosines, say

$$\vec{n} = \cos \alpha \,\vec{i} + \cos \beta \,\vec{j} + \cos \gamma \,\vec{k}\,,$$

then $\vec{F} \cdot \vec{n} = P \cos \alpha + Q \cos \beta + R \cos \gamma$, and we may write

$$\iint\limits_{S} \vec{F} \cdot \vec{n}\,dS = \iint\limits_{S} (P \cos \alpha + Q \cos \beta + R \cos \gamma)\,dS\,.$$

This equation holds when $\vec{n}$ is either $\vec{n}_1$ or $\vec{n}_2$. The direction cosines will depend on the choice of the normal. If $\vec{n} = \vec{n}_1$ we may use (6.27) to write

$$(6.28) \qquad \iint\limits_{S} (P \cos \alpha + Q \cos \beta + R \cos \gamma)\,dS = \iint\limits_{S} P\,dy\,dz + Q\,dz\,dx + R\,dx\,dy\,.$$

If $\vec{n} = \vec{n}_2$ we have, instead,

$$(6.29) \qquad \iint\limits_{S} (P \cos \alpha + Q \cos \beta + R \cos \gamma)\,dS = -\iint\limits_{S} P\,dy\,dz + Q\,dz\,dx + R\,dx\,dy\,.$$

6.9 Exercises

1. Let S denote the hemisphere $x^2 + y^2 + z^2 = 1$, $z \geq 0$, and let $\vec{F}(x, y, z) = x\vec{i} + y\vec{j}$. Let $\vec{n}$ be the unit outward normal of S. Compute the value of the surface integral $\iint\limits_{S} \vec{F} \cdot \vec{n}\,dS$, using:

(a) the vector representation

$$\vec{r}(u, v) = \sin u \cos v \,\vec{i} + \sin u \sin v \,\vec{j} + \cos u \,\vec{k}\,,$$

(b) the explicit representation $z = \sqrt{1 - x^2 - y^2}$.

2. Show that the moment of inertia of a homogeneous spherical shell about a diameter is equal to $\frac{2}{3}Ma^2$, where M is the mass of the shell and a is its radius.

3. Find the center of mass of that portion of the homogeneous hemispherical surface $x^2 + y^2 + z^2 = a^2$ lying above the first quadrant in the xy-plane.

4. Let S denote the plane surface whose boundary is the triangle with vertices at $(1, 0, 0)$, $(0, 1, 0)$, and $(0, 0, 1)$, and let $\vec{F}(x, y, z) = x\vec{i} + y\vec{j} + z\vec{k}$. Let $\vec{n}$ denote the unit normal to S having a nonnegative z-component. Evaluate the surface integral $\iint\limits_{S} \vec{F} \cdot \vec{n}\,dS$, using:

(a) the vector representation

$$\vec{r}(u, v) = (u + v)\,\vec{i} + (u - v)\,\vec{j} + (1 - 2u)\,\vec{k}\,,$$

(b) an explicit representation of the form $z = f(x, y)$.

5. Let S be a parametric surface described by the explicit formula $z = f(x, y)$, where (x, y) varies over a plane region T, the projection of S in the xy-plane. Let $\vec{F} = P\vec{i} + Q\vec{j} + R\vec{k}$ and let $\vec{n}$ denote the unit normal to S having a nonnegative z-component. Use the parametric representation $\vec{r}(x, y) = x\vec{i} + y\vec{j} + f(x, y)\,\vec{k}$ and show that

$$\iint\limits_{S} \vec{F} \cdot \vec{n}\,dS = \iint\limits_{T} \left(-P \frac{\partial f}{\partial x} - Q \frac{\partial f}{\partial y} + R \right) dx\,dy\,,$$

where each of P, Q, and R is to be evaluated at $(x, y, f(x, y))$.

6. Let S be as in Exercise 5, and let ϕ be a scalar field. Show that:

(a) $\displaystyle\iint_S \phi(x, y, z)\, dS = \iint_T \phi[x, y, f(x, y)] \sqrt{1 + \left(\frac{\partial f}{\partial x}\right)^2 + \left(\frac{\partial f}{\partial y}\right)^2}\, dx\, dy\,.$

(b) $\displaystyle\iint_S \phi(x, y, z)\, dy\, dz = -\iint_T \phi[x, y, f(x, y)] \frac{\partial f}{\partial x}\, dx\, dy\,.$

(c) $\displaystyle\iint_S \phi(x, y, z)\, dz\, dx = -\iint_T \phi[x, y, f(x, y)] \frac{\partial f}{\partial y}\, dx\, dy\,.$

7. Let S be the hemisphere $x^2 + y^2 + z^2 = 1, z \geq 0$, and let $\vec{n}$ denote the unit normal that points out of the sphere. If $\vec{F}(x, y, z) = (x^2 + xy - z^2)\,\vec{k}$, evaluate the surface integral

$$\iint_S (\operatorname{curl} \vec{F}) \cdot \vec{n}\, dS\,.$$

8. Solve Exercise 7 if S also includes the planar base of the hemisphere. On the lower base the unit normal is $-\vec{k}$.

9. If S is the surface of the sphere $x^2 + y^2 + z^2 = a^2$, compute the value of the surface integral

$$\iint_S xz\, dy\, dz + yz\, dz\, dx + x^2\, dx\, dy\,.$$

Choose a representation for which the fundamental vector product points in the direction of the outward normal.

10. The cylinder $x^2 + y^2 = 2x$ cuts out a portion of a surface S from the upper nappe of the cone $x^2 + y^2 = z^2$. Compute the value of the surface integral

$$\iint_S (x^4 - y^4 + y^2 z^2 - z^2 x^2 + 1)\, dS\,.$$

11. Let S denote the portion of the plane $x + y + z = t$ cut off by the unit sphere $x^2 + y^2 + z^2 = 1$. Let $\phi(x, y, z) = 1 - x^2 - y^2 - z^2$ if (x, y, z) is inside this sphere, and let $\phi(x, y, z)$ be 0 otherwise. Show that

$$\iint_S \phi(x, y, z)\, dS = \begin{cases} \dfrac{\pi}{18}\,(3 - t^2)^2 & \text{if } |t| \leq \sqrt{3}\,, \\[2mm] 0 & \text{if } |t| > \sqrt{3}\,. \end{cases}$$

[*Hint.* Introduce new coordinates (x_1, y_1, z_1) with the z_1-axis normal to the plane $x + y + z = t$. Then use the polar coordinates in the $x_1 y_1$-plane as parameters for S.]

12. A homogeneous spherical shell of radius a is cut by one nappe of a right circular cone whose vertex is at the center of the sphere. If the vertex angle of the cone is α, where $0 < \alpha < \pi$, determine (in terms of a and α) the center of mass of the portion of the spherical shell that lies inside the cone.

6.10 The theorem of Stokes

Green's theorem in the plane asserts that

(6.30) $$\iint_S \left(\frac{\partial Q}{\partial x} - \frac{\partial P}{\partial y}\right) dx\, dy = \oint_C P\, dx + Q\, dy\,,$$

where S is a region bounded by a piecewise smooth simple closed curve C. There are two ways of expressing Green's theorem in vector form. If we introduce the vector field $\vec{F} = P\,\vec{i} + Q\,\vec{j}$ we can write Equation (6.30) in the form

$$\iint\limits_{S} (\operatorname{curl} \vec{F}) \cdot \vec{k}\, dx\, dy = \oint_{C} \vec{F} \cdot d\vec{r}\,.$$

If we let $\vec{V} = Q\,\vec{i} - P\,\vec{j}$ we can write

$$\iint\limits_{S} \operatorname{div} \vec{V}\, dx\, dy = \oint_{C} \vec{V} \cdot \vec{n}\, ds\,,$$

where $\vec{n}$ is the unit outer normal of C and the line integral is taken with respect to arc length. The extensions of these formulas to 3-space are known, respectively, as *Stokes' theorem*† and the *divergence theorem*. Stokes' theorem will be stated and proved in this section. The divergence theorem is discussed in Section 6.14.

6–3   THEOREM. *Stokes' theorem.* Let T be a region in the uv-plane bounded by a piecewise smooth Jordan curve Γ. Let $S = \vec{r}(T)$ be a smooth simple parametric surface described by a one-to-one mapping function $\vec{r}$ whose components have continuous second-order partial derivatives on some open set containing $T \cup \Gamma$. Let Γ be described by a function $\vec{\gamma}$ defined on an interval $[a, b]$. Since $\vec{r}$ is one-to-one, the image of Γ is a simple closed curve C described by the composite function $\vec{\rho}$ given by

$$\vec{\rho}(t) = \vec{r}[\vec{\gamma}(t)] \qquad \text{for} \quad a \le t \le b\,.$$

(See Figure 6.14.) Let $\vec{n}$ be the unit normal vector having the same direction as the fundamental vector product $\partial\vec{r}/\partial u \times \partial\vec{r}/\partial v$, and let $\vec{F}$ be a vector field that is continuously differentiable on S. Then we have the identity

(6.31) $$\iint\limits_{S} (\operatorname{curl} \vec{F}) \cdot \vec{n}\, dS = \pm \oint_{C} \vec{F} \cdot d\vec{\rho}\,,$$

where the $+$ or $-$ sign is used according to whether $\vec{\gamma}$ describes Γ in a positive (counterclockwise) or negative (clockwise) direction.

Note. If we write $\vec{F}(x, y, z) = P(x, y, z)\,\vec{i} + Q(x, y, z)\,\vec{j} + R(x, y, z)\,\vec{k}$, Stokes' theorem takes the form

(6.32) $$\iint\limits_{S} \left(\frac{\partial R}{\partial y} - \frac{\partial Q}{\partial z}\right) dy\, dz + \left(\frac{\partial P}{\partial z} - \frac{\partial R}{\partial x}\right) dz\, dx + \left(\frac{\partial Q}{\partial x} - \frac{\partial P}{\partial y}\right) dx\, dy$$
$$= \pm \oint_{C} P\, dx + Q\, dy + R\, dz\,.$$

The curve C is traversed in the direction inherited from Γ through the mapping function $\vec{r}$.

Proof. To prove the theorem it suffices to establish the three identities

† In honor of G. G. Stokes (1819–1903), an Irish mathematician who made many fundamental contributions to hydrodynamics and optics.

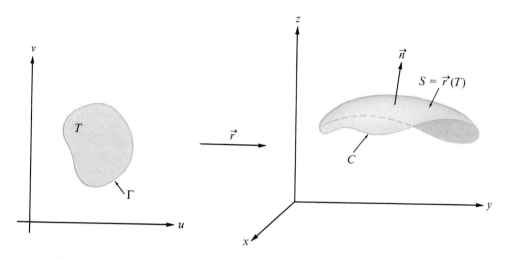

FIGURE 6.14 *An example of a surface to which Stokes' theorem is applicable.*

(6.33) $$\pm \oint_C P\, dx = \iint_S \left(-\frac{\partial P}{\partial y}\, dx\, dy + \frac{\partial P}{\partial z}\, dz\, dx \right),$$

(6.34) $$\pm \oint_C Q\, dy = \iint_S \left(-\frac{\partial Q}{\partial z}\, dy\, dz + \frac{\partial Q}{\partial x}\, dx\, dy \right),$$

(6.35) $$\pm \oint_C R\, dz = \iint_S \left(-\frac{\partial R}{\partial x}\, dz\, dx + \frac{\partial R}{\partial y}\, dy\, dz \right),$$

with the same choice of sign in each formula. Addition of these three equations gives (6.32). In each case the idea of the proof is to express the line integral over C as a line integral over Γ, using the transformation law described in Theorem 5–11 (Section 5.28). Then we apply Green's theorem to the line integral over Γ, expressing it as a double integral over T. Finally, we show that this double integral is the same as that which defines the surface integral over S.

We begin with the line integral in (6.33). If we write

$$\vec{r}(u, v) = X(u, v)\, \vec{i} + Y(u, v)\, \vec{j} + Z(u, v)\, \vec{k}$$

and apply Theorem 5–11 [as extended in Equation (5.74)] we obtain

(6.36) $$\oint_C P\, dx = \oint_\Gamma p\, \frac{\partial X}{\partial u}\, du + p\, \frac{\partial X}{\partial v}\, dv,$$

where p is the composite function given by

(6.37) $$p(u, v) = P[\vec{r}(u, v)] = P[X(u, v), Y(u, v), Z(u, v)].$$

When we apply Green's theorem to the line integral over Γ, we find

$$\oint_\Gamma p \frac{\partial X}{\partial u}\, du + p \frac{\partial X}{\partial v}\, dv \;=\; \pm \iint_T \left\{ \frac{\partial}{\partial u}\left(p \frac{\partial X}{\partial v}\right) - \frac{\partial}{\partial v}\left(p \frac{\partial X}{\partial u}\right) \right\} du\, dv ,$$

where the $+$ or $-$ sign is used according to whether $\vec\gamma$ describes Γ in the positive or negative direction. Combining this equation with (6.36) we find

$$(6.38) \qquad \pm \oint_C P\, dx \;=\; \iint_T \left\{ \frac{\partial}{\partial u}\left(p \frac{\partial X}{\partial v}\right) - \frac{\partial}{\partial v}\left(p \frac{\partial X}{\partial u}\right) \right\} du\, dv .$$

Now we have

$$\frac{\partial}{\partial u}\left(p \frac{\partial X}{\partial v}\right) = \frac{\partial p}{\partial u}\frac{\partial X}{\partial v} + p \frac{\partial^2 X}{\partial u\, \partial v} \qquad \text{and} \qquad \frac{\partial}{\partial v}\left(p \frac{\partial X}{\partial u}\right) = \frac{\partial p}{\partial v}\frac{\partial X}{\partial u} + p \frac{\partial^2 X}{\partial v\, \partial u} .$$

When we subtract these equations the terms involving p cancel and we find

$$(6.39) \qquad \frac{\partial}{\partial u}\left(p \frac{\partial X}{\partial v}\right) - \frac{\partial}{\partial v}\left(p \frac{\partial X}{\partial u}\right) = \frac{\partial p}{\partial u}\frac{\partial X}{\partial v} - \frac{\partial p}{\partial v}\frac{\partial X}{\partial u} .$$

To compute the derivatives $\partial p/\partial u$ and $\partial p/\partial v$ we differentiate Equation (6.37), using the chain rule, and we find

$$\frac{\partial p}{\partial u} = \frac{\partial P}{\partial x}\frac{\partial X}{\partial u} + \frac{\partial P}{\partial y}\frac{\partial Y}{\partial u} + \frac{\partial P}{\partial z}\frac{\partial Z}{\partial u} \qquad \text{and} \qquad \frac{\partial p}{\partial v} = \frac{\partial P}{\partial x}\frac{\partial X}{\partial v} + \frac{\partial P}{\partial y}\frac{\partial Y}{\partial v} + \frac{\partial P}{\partial z}\frac{\partial Z}{\partial v} ,$$

where the derivatives $\partial P/\partial x$, $\partial P/\partial y$, and $\partial P/\partial z$ are to be evaluated at $\vec r(u, v)$. Substituting these equations in (6.39) we obtain

$$\frac{\partial}{\partial u}\left(p \frac{\partial X}{\partial v}\right) - \frac{\partial}{\partial v}\left(p \frac{\partial X}{\partial u}\right) = - \frac{\partial P}{\partial y}\frac{\partial(X, Y)}{\partial(u, v)} + \frac{\partial P}{\partial z}\frac{\partial(Z, X)}{\partial(u, v)} ,$$

and hence Equation (6.38) becomes

$$\pm \oint_C P\, dx \;=\; \iint_T \left\{ - \frac{\partial P}{\partial y}\frac{\partial(X, Y)}{\partial(u, v)} + \frac{\partial P}{\partial z}\frac{\partial(Z, X)}{\partial(u, v)} \right\} du\, dv$$

$$= \iint_S \left(- \frac{\partial P}{\partial y}\, dx\, dy + \frac{\partial P}{\partial z}\, dz\, dx \right).$$

This proves (6.33). The proofs of (6.34) and (6.35) are entirely analogous.

6.11 Applications of Stokes' theorem

We shall use Stokes' theorem to derive a three-dimensional analog of Theorem 5–7 (Section 5.16). We proved there that a two-dimensional continuously differentiable vector field $\vec F = P\vec i + Q\vec j$ is a gradient in an open simply connected set S in the plane if, and only if, $\partial P/\partial y = \partial Q/\partial x$ in S, that is, if and only if curl $\vec F = \vec 0$ in S. We prove now that the theorem extends to 3-space if the set S is convex.

6–4 THEOREM. Let K be an open convex set in 3-space, and let $\vec{F}$ be a vector field that is continuously differentiable on K. Then $\vec{F}$ is a gradient on K if and only if curl $\vec{F} = \vec{0}$.

Proof. If $\vec{F} = \nabla\phi$ for some ϕ, we have curl $\vec{F} = \text{curl}(\nabla\phi) = \vec{0}$, so the condition curl $\vec{F} = \vec{0}$ is necessary for $\vec{F}$ to be a gradient.

To prove that the condition is sufficient, choose a fixed point $\vec{A}$ in K and define a scalar field ϕ on K by the equation

$$\phi(\vec{X}) = \int_{\vec{A}}^{\vec{X}} \vec{F} \cdot d\vec{r},$$

where the integral is taken over the line segment joining $\vec{A}$ to $\vec{X}$. This segment lies in K because K is convex. Now let $\vec{Z}$ be any point in K. We shall prove that

(6.40) $$\phi(\vec{Z}) - \phi(\vec{X}) = \int_{\vec{X}}^{\vec{Z}} \vec{F} \cdot d\vec{r},$$

where the path is again along a line segment. To prove (6.40) we consider the triangle with vertices $\vec{A}$, $\vec{X}$, $\vec{Z}$. Let S be the plane surface bounded by this triangle. Because of the convexity of K, S lies entirely in K, so curl $\vec{F} = \vec{0}$ on S. Therefore $\iint_S (\text{curl } \vec{F}) \cdot \vec{n} \, dS = 0$, where $\vec{n}$ is a unit normal to S. But, by Stokes' theorem, this surface integral is equal to the line integral of $\vec{F}$ around the boundary of S. Hence we have

$$\int_{\vec{A}}^{\vec{X}} \vec{F} \cdot d\vec{r} + \int_{\vec{X}}^{\vec{Z}} \vec{F} \cdot d\vec{r} + \int_{\vec{Z}}^{\vec{A}} \vec{F} \cdot d\vec{r} = 0,$$

where $\vec{r}$ is the function which traces out the triangular boundary. This equation implies

$$\int_{\vec{X}}^{\vec{Z}} \vec{F} \cdot d\vec{r} = \int_{\vec{A}}^{\vec{Z}} \vec{F} \cdot d\vec{r} - \int_{\vec{A}}^{\vec{X}} \vec{F} \cdot d\vec{r} = \phi(\vec{Z}) - \phi(\vec{X}),$$

which proves (6.40).

Now let $N(\vec{X}; r)$ be any neighborhood of $\vec{X}$ of radius r that lies entirely in the set K. If $\vec{Y}$ is a unit coordinate vector, the point $\vec{X} + h\vec{Y}$ lies in K for every real h satisfying $0 < |h| \le r$. For such an h, let $\vec{Z} = \vec{X} + h\vec{Y}$. Then Equation (6.40) becomes

$$\phi(\vec{X} + h\vec{Y}) - \phi(\vec{X}) = \int_{\vec{X}}^{\vec{X}+h\vec{Y}} \vec{F} \cdot d\vec{r},$$

where the path is along the line segment joining $\vec{X}$ to $\vec{X} + h\vec{Y}$. But now we may repeat, word for word, the argument used in the proof of Theorem 5–3 [from Equation (5.23) on] to deduce that ϕ is differentiable at $\vec{X}$ and that $\nabla\phi(\vec{X}) = \vec{F}(\vec{X})$.

In Section 5.25 we proved that a vector field $\vec{V}$ is solenoidal (that is, div $\vec{V} = 0$) on an open rectangular parallelepiped if, and only if, $\vec{V}$ is the curl of another vector field. The following example shows that this statement is not true for *arbitrary* open sets.

Let D be the portion of 3-space between two concentric spheres with center at the origin and radii a and b, where $0 < a < b$. Let $\vec{V} = \vec{r}/r^3$, where $\vec{r} = x\vec{i} + y\vec{j} + z\vec{k}$ and $r = |\vec{r}|$. It is easy to verify that div $\vec{V} = 0$ everywhere in D. In fact, we have the general formula

$$\text{div}(r^n \vec{r}) = (n + 3)r^n,$$

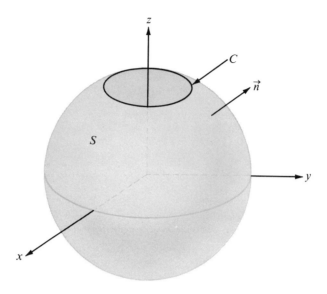

FIGURE 6.15   *The surface S and curve C in Equation (6.41).*

and in this example $n = -3$. We shall use Stokes' theorem to prove that this $\vec{V}$ is *not* a curl in D (although it is a curl on every open rectangular parallelepiped not containing the origin). To do this we assume there is a vector field $\vec{U}$ such that $\vec{V} = \text{curl } \vec{U}$ in D and obtain a contradiction. By Stokes' theorem we may write

(6.41) $$\iint\limits_{S} (\text{curl } \vec{U}) \cdot \vec{n} \, dS = \oint_{C} \vec{U} \cdot d\vec{r} \, ,$$

where S and C are the surface and curve shown in Figure 6.15. To construct S, we take a spherical surface of radius R concentric with the boundaries of D, where $a < R < b$, and we remove a small "polar cap," as indicated in the figure. The portion that remains is the surface S. The curve C is the circular edge shown. Let $\vec{n}$ denote the unit outer normal of S, so that $\vec{n} = \vec{r}/r$. Since curl $\vec{U} = \vec{V} = \vec{r}/r^3$, we have

$$(\text{curl } \vec{U}) \cdot \vec{n} = \frac{\vec{r}}{r^3} \cdot \frac{\vec{r}}{r} = \frac{1}{r^2} \, .$$

On the surface S this dot product has the constant value $1/R^2$. Therefore we have

$$\iint\limits_{S} (\text{curl } \vec{U}) \cdot \vec{n} \, dS = \frac{1}{R^2} \iint\limits_{S} dS = \frac{\text{area of } S}{R^2} \, .$$

When the polar cap shrinks to a point, the area of S approaches $4\pi R^2$ (the area of the whole sphere) and, therefore, the value of the surface integral in (6.41) approaches 4π.

Next we examine the line integral in (6.41). It is easy to prove that for any line integral $\int_{C} \vec{U} \cdot d\vec{r}$ we have the inequality

$$\left| \int_C \vec{U} \cdot d\vec{r} \right| \leq M \cdot (\text{length of } C) \,,$$

where M is a constant depending on $\vec{U}$. (In fact, M can be taken to be the maximum value of $|\vec{U}|$ on C.) Therefore, as we let the polar cap shrink to a point, the length of C and the value of the line integral both approach zero. Thus we have a contradiction; the surface integral in (6.41) can be made arbitrarily close to 4π, and the corresponding line integral to which it is equal can be made arbitrarily close to 0. Therefore a function $\vec{U}$ whose curl is $\vec{V}$ cannot exist in the region D.

The difficulty here is caused by the geometric structure of the region D. Although this region is simply connected (that is, any simple closed curve in D is the edge of a parametric surface lying completely in D) there are closed *surfaces* in D that are not the complete boundaries of solids lying entirely in D. For example, no sphere about the origin is the complete boundary of a solid lying entirely in D. If the region D has the property that *every* closed surface in D is the boundary of a solid lying entirely in D, it can be shown that a vector field $\vec{U}$ exists such that $\vec{V} = \text{curl } \vec{U}$ in D if, and only if, div $\vec{V} = 0$ everywhere in D. The proof of this statement is difficult and will not be given here.

6.12 Exercises

In each of Exercises 1 through 4, transform the surface integral $\iint_S (\text{curl } \vec{F}) \cdot \vec{n} \, dS$ to a line integral by the use of Stokes' theorem, and then evaluate the line integral.

1. $\vec{F}(x, y, z) = y^2 \vec{i} + xy \vec{j} + xz \vec{k}$, where S is the hemisphere $x^2 + y^2 + z^2 = 1$, $z \geq 0$, and $\vec{n}$ is the unit normal with a nonnegative z-component.

2. $\vec{F}(x, y, z) = y \vec{i} + z \vec{j} + x \vec{k}$, where S is the portion of the paraboloid $z = 1 - x^2 - y^2$ with $z \geq 0$, and $\vec{n}$ is the unit normal with a nonnegative z-component.

3. $\vec{F}(x, y, z) = (y - z) \vec{i} + yz \vec{j} - xz \vec{k}$, where S consists of the five faces of the cube $0 \leq x \leq 2$, $0 \leq y \leq 2$, $0 \leq z \leq 2$ not in the xy-plane. The unit normal $\vec{n}$ is the outward normal.

4. $\vec{F}(x, y, z) = xz \vec{i} - y \vec{i} + x^2 y \vec{k}$, where S consists of the three faces not in the xz-plane of the tetrahedron bounded by the three coordinate planes and the plane $3x + y + 3z = 6$. The normal $\vec{n}$ is the unit normal pointing out of the tetrahedron.

In Exercises 5 through 10, use Stokes' theorem to show that the line integrals have the values given. In each case, explain how to traverse C to arrive at the given answer.

5. $\int_C y \, dx + z \, dy + x \, dz = \pi a^2 \sqrt{3}$, where C is the curve of intersection of the sphere $x^2 + y^2 + z^2 = a^2$ and the plane $x + y + z = 0$.

6. $\int_C (y + z) \, dx + (z + x) \, dy + (x + y) \, dz = 0$, where C is the curve of intersection of the cylinder $x^2 + y^2 = 2y$ and the plane $y = z$.

7. $\int_C y^2 \, dx + xy \, dy + xz \, dz = 0$, where C is the curve of Exercise 6.

8. $\int_C (y - z) \, dx + (z - x) \, dy + (x - y) \, dz = 2\pi a(a + b)$, where C is the intersection of the cylinder $x^2 + y^2 = a^2$ and the plane $x/a + z/b = 1$, $a > 0$, $b > 0$.

9. $\int_C (y^2 + z^2) \, dx + (x^2 + z^2) \, dy + (x^2 + y^2) \, dz = 2\pi ab^2$, where C is the intersection of the hemisphere $x^2 + y^2 + z^2 = 2ax$, $z > 0$, and the cylinder $x^2 + y^2 = 2bx$, where $0 < b < a$.

10. $\int (y^2 - z^2)\, dx + (z^2 - x^2)\, dy + (x^2 - y^2)\, dz = 9a^3/2$, where C is the curve cut from the boundary of the cube $0 \leq x \leq a$, $0 \leq y \leq a$, $0 \leq z \leq a$ by the plane $x + y + z = 3a/2$.

11. If $\vec{r} = x\,\vec{i} + y\,\vec{j} + z\,\vec{k}$ and $P\,\vec{i} + Q\,\vec{j} + R\,\vec{k} = \vec{a} \times \vec{r}$, where $\vec{a}$ is a constant vector, show that $\int_C P\, dx + Q\, dy + R\, dz = 2 \iint_S \vec{a} \cdot \vec{n}\, dS$, where C is a curve bounding a parametric surface S and $\vec{n}$ is a suitable normal to S.

12. Let $\vec{F} = P\,\vec{i} + Q\,\vec{j} + R\,\vec{k}$, where $P = -y/(x^2 + y^2)$, $Q = x/(x^2 + y^2)$, $R = z$, and let D be the torus generated by rotating the circle $(x - 2)^2 + z^2 = 1$, $y = 0$, about the z-axis. Show that curl $\vec{F} = \vec{0}$ in D but that $\int_C P\, dx + Q\, dy + R\, dz$ is not zero if the curve C is the circle $x^2 + y^2 = 4$, $z = 0$.

13. Let S be a simple parametric surface of the type described in Stokes' theorem, and let C denote the edge of S. Let f and g be two continuously differentiable scalar fields defined on S, and let $\vec{n}$ denote a choice of a unit normal to S. If ∇f is perpendicular to $\nabla g \times \vec{n}$ everywhere on S, prove that the line integral of $f \nabla g$ around C is zero.

14. Let u and v be scalar fields that are continuously differentiable on an open rectangular parallelepiped R in 3-space.

(a) Show that a vector field $\vec{F}$ exists such that $\nabla u \times \nabla v = $ curl $\vec{F}$ everywhere in R.

(b) Determine whether or not any of the following three vector fields may be used for $\vec{F}$ in part (a): (i) $\nabla(uv)$; (ii) $u\,\nabla v$; (iii) $v\,\nabla u$.

(c) If $u(x, y, z) = x^3 - y^3 + z^2$ and $v(x, y, z) = x + y + z$, evaluate the surface integral

$$\iint_S \nabla u \times \nabla v \cdot \vec{n}\, dS \,,$$

where S is the hemisphere $x^2 + y^2 + z^2 = 1$, $z \geq 0$, and $\vec{n}$ is the unit normal with a nonnegative z-component.

⋆6.13 Extensions of Stokes' theorem

Stokes' theorem can be extended to more general simple smooth surfaces. If T is a multiply connected region like that shown in Figure 6.16 (with a finite number of holes), the one-to-one image $S = \vec{r}(T)$ will contain the same number of holes as T. To extend Stokes' theorem to such surfaces we use exactly the same type of argument as in the foregoing proof, except that we employ Green's theorem for multiply connected regions (Theorem 5–8). In place of the line integral $\oint_C \vec{F} \cdot d\vec{\rho}$ which appears in Equation (6.31) we need a sum of line integrals, with appropriate signs, taken over the images of the curves forming the boundary of T. For example, if T has two holes, as in Figure 6.16, and if the boundary curves Γ, Γ_1, and Γ_2 are traversed in the directions shown, the identity in Stokes' theorem takes the form

$$\iint_S (\text{curl }\vec{F}) \cdot \vec{n}\, dS = \oint_C \vec{F} \cdot d\vec{\rho} + \oint_{C_1} \vec{F} \cdot d\vec{\rho}_1 + \oint_{C_2} \vec{F} \cdot d\vec{\rho}_2 \,,$$

where C, C_1, and C_2 are the images of Γ, Γ_1, and Γ_2, respectively, and $\vec{\rho}$, $\vec{\rho}_1$, and $\vec{\rho}_2$ are the composite functions $\vec{\rho}(t) = \vec{r}[\vec{\gamma}(t)]$, $\vec{\rho}_1(t) = \vec{r}[\vec{\gamma}_1(t)]$, $\vec{\rho}_2(t) = \vec{r}[\vec{\gamma}_2(t)]$. Here $\vec{\gamma}$, $\vec{\gamma}_1$, and $\vec{\gamma}_2$ are the functions that describe Γ, Γ_1, and Γ_2 in the directions shown. The curves C, C_1, and C_2 will be traversed in the directions inherited from Γ, Γ_1, and Γ_2 through the mapping function $\vec{r}$.

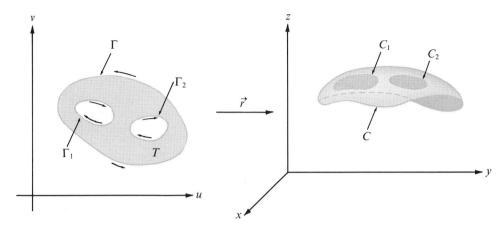

FIGURE 6.16 *Extension of Stokes' theorem to surfaces that are one-to-one images of multiply connected regions.*

Stokes' theorem can also be extended to some (but not all) smooth surfaces that are not simple. We shall illustrate a few of the possibilities with examples.

Consider first the cylinder shown in Figure 6.17. This is the union of two simple smooth parametric surfaces S_1 and S_2, the images of two adjacent rectangles T_1 and T_2, under mappings $\vec{r}_1$ and $\vec{r}_2$, respectively. If $\vec{\gamma}_1$ describes the positively oriented boundary Γ_1 of T_1 and $\vec{\gamma}_2$ describes the positively oriented boundary Γ_2 of T_2, the functions $\vec{\rho}_1$ and $\vec{\rho}_2$ defined by

$$\vec{\rho}_1(t) = \vec{r}_1[\vec{\gamma}_1(t)], \qquad \vec{\rho}_2(t) = \vec{r}_2[\vec{\gamma}_2(t)]$$

describe the images C_1 and C_2 of Γ_1 and Γ_2, respectively. In this example the representations $\vec{r}_1$ and $\vec{r}_2$ can be chosen so that they agree on the intersection $\Gamma_1 \cap \Gamma_2$. If we apply Stokes' theorem to each piece S_1 and S_2 and add the two identities, we obtain

$$(6.42) \qquad \iint\limits_{S_1} (\operatorname{curl} \vec{F}) \cdot \vec{n}_1 \, dS + \iint\limits_{S_2} (\operatorname{curl} \vec{F}) \cdot \vec{n}_2 \, dS = \int_{C_1} \vec{F} \cdot d\vec{\rho}_1 + \int_{C_2} \vec{F} \cdot d\vec{\rho}_2 \,,$$

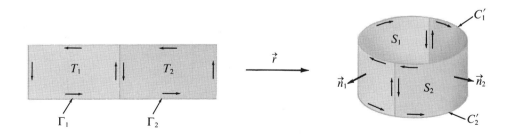

FIGURE 6.17 *Extension of Stokes' theorem to a cylinder.*

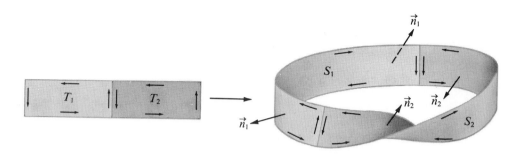

FIGURE 6.18   *A Möbius band considered as the union of two simple parametric surfaces. Stokes'*
theorem does not extend to a Möbius band.

where $\vec{n}_1$ and $\vec{n}_2$ are the normals determined by the fundamental vector products of $\vec{r}_1$
and $\vec{r}_2$, respectively.

Now let $\vec{r}$ denote the mapping of $T_1 \cup T_2$ which agrees with $\vec{r}_1$ on T_1 and with $\vec{r}_2$ on
T_2, and let $\vec{n}$ be the corresponding unit normal determined by the fundamental vector
product of $\vec{r}$. Since the normals $\vec{n}_1$ and $\vec{n}_2$ agree in direction on $S_1 \cap S_2$, the unit normal
$\vec{n}$ is the same as $\vec{n}_1$ on S_1 and the same as $\vec{n}_2$ on S_2. Therefore the sum of the surface
integrals on the left of (6.42) is equal to

$$\iint_{S_1 \cup S_2} (\text{curl } \vec{F}) \cdot \vec{n} \, dS \,.$$

For this example, the representations $\vec{r}_1$ and $\vec{r}_2$ can be chosen so that $\vec{\rho}_1$ and $\vec{\rho}_2$ determine
opposite directions on each arc of the intersection $C_1 \cap C_2$, as indicated by the arrows
in Figure 6.17. The two line integrals on the right of (6.42) may be replaced by a sum
of line integrals along the two circles C_1' and C_2' forming the upper and lower edges of
$S_1 \cup S_2$, since the line integrals along each arc of the intersection $C_1 \cap C_2$ cancel. Therefore, Equation (6.42) may be written as

$$(6.43) \qquad \iint_{S_1 \cup S_2} (\text{curl } \vec{F}) \cdot \vec{n} \, dS = \int_{C_1'} \vec{F} \cdot d\vec{\rho}_1 + \int_{C_2'} \vec{F} \cdot d\vec{\rho}_2 \,,$$

where the line integrals are traversed in the directions inherited from Γ_1 and Γ_2. The two
circles C_1' and C_2' are said to form the complete boundary of $S_1 \cup S_2$. Equation (6.43)
expresses the surface integral of $(\text{curl } \vec{F}) \cdot \vec{n}$ over $S_1 \cup S_2$ as a line integral over the
complete boundary of $S_1 \cup S_2$. This equation is the extension of Stokes' theorem for a
cylinder.

Suppose now we apply the same concepts to the surface shown in Figure 6.18. This
surface is again the union of two smooth simple parametric surfaces S_1 and S_2, the
images of two adjacent rectangles T_1 and T_2. This particular surface is called a *Möbius
band*†; a model can easily be constructed from a long rectangular strip of paper by giving

† After A. F. Möbius (1790–1868), a pupil of Gauss. At the age of 26 he was appointed professor
of astronomy at Leipzig, a position he held until his death. He made many contributions to celestial
mechanics, but his most important researches were in geometry and in the theory of numbers.

one end a half-twist and then fastening the two ends together. We define $\vec{\rho}_1$, $\vec{\rho}_2$, C_1, and C_2 for the Möbius band as we defined them for the cylinder above. The edge of $S_1 \cup S_2$ in this case is one simple closed curve C', rather than two. This curve is called the complete boundary of the Möbius band.

If we apply Stokes' theorem to each piece S_1 and S_2, as we did for the cylinder, we obtain Equation (6.42). But if we try to consolidate the two surface integrals and the two line integrals as we did above, we encounter two difficulties. First, the two normals $\vec{n}_1$ and $\vec{n}_2$ do not agree in direction everywhere on the intersection $C_1 \cap C_2$. (See Figure 6.18.) Therefore we cannot define a normal $\vec{n}$ for the whole surface by taking $\vec{n} = \vec{n}_1$ on S_1 and $\vec{n} = \vec{n}_2$ on S_2, as we did for the cylinder. This is not serious, however, because we can define $\vec{n}$ to be $\vec{n}_1$ on S_1 and on $C_1 \cap C_2$, and then define $\vec{n}$ to be $\vec{n}_2$ everywhere else. This gives a discontinuous normal, but the discontinuities so introduced form a set of measure zero in the uv-plane and do not affect the existence or the value of the surface integral

$$\iint\limits_{S_1 \cup S_2} (\text{curl } \vec{F}) \cdot \vec{n} \, dS \, .$$

A more serious difficulty is encountered when we try to consolidate the line integrals. In this example it is not possible to choose the mappings $\vec{r}_1$ and $\vec{r}_2$ in such a way that $\vec{\rho}_1$ and $\vec{\rho}_2$ determine opposite directions on each arc of the intersection $C_1 \cap C_2$. This is illustrated by the arrows in Figure 6.18; one of these arcs is traced twice in the same direction. On this arc the corresponding line integrals will not necessarily cancel as they did for the cylinder. Therefore the sum of the line integrals in (6.42) is not necessarily equal to the line integral over the complete boundary of $S_1 \cup S_2$, and Stokes' theorem cannot be extended to the Möbius band.

Note. The cylinder and the Mobius band are examples of *orientable* and *nonorientable* surfaces, respectively. We shall not attempt to define these terms precisely, but shall mention some of their differences. For an orientable surface $S_1 \cup S_2$ formed from two smooth simple parametric surfaces as described above, the mappings $\vec{r}_1$ and $\vec{r}_2$ can always be chosen so that $\vec{\rho}_1$ and $\vec{\rho}_2$ determine opposite directions on each arc of the intersection $C_1 \cap C_2$. For a nonorientable surface no such choice is possible. For a smooth orientable surface a unit normal vector can be defined in a continuous fashion over the entire surface. For a nonorientable surface no such definition of a normal is possible. A paper model of an orientable surface always has two sides that can be distinguished by painting them with two different colors. Nonorientable surfaces have only one side. For a rigorous discussion of these and other properties of orientable and nonorientable surfaces, see any book on combinatorial topology. Stokes' theorem can be extended to orientable surfaces by a procedure similar to that outlined above for the cylinder.

Another orientable surface is the sphere shown in Figure 6.19. This surface is the union of two simple parametric surfaces (hemispheres) S_1 and S_2, which we may consider images of a circular disk in the xy-plane under mappings $\vec{r}_1$ and $\vec{r}_2$, respectively. We give $\vec{r}$, $\vec{\rho}_1$, $\vec{\rho}_2$, C_1, C_2 the same meanings as in the above examples. In this case the curves C_1 and C_2 are completely matched by the mapping $\vec{r}$ (they intersect along the equator), and the surface $S_1 \cup S_2$ is said to be *closed*. Moreover, $\vec{r}_1$ and $\vec{r}_2$ can be chosen so that the directions determined by $\vec{\rho}_1$ and $\vec{\rho}_2$ are opposite on C_1 and C_2, as suggested by the arrows in Figure 6.19. (This is why $S_1 \cup S_2$ is orientable.) If we apply Stokes' theorem to each hemisphere and add the results we obtain Equation (6.42), as before.

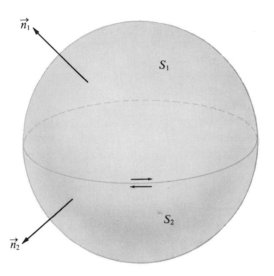

FIGURE 6.19   *Extension of Stokes' theorem to a sphere.*

The normals $\vec{n}_1$ and $\vec{n}_2$ agree on the intersection $C_1 \cap C_2$, and we can consolidate the integrals over S_1 and S_2 into one integral over the whole sphere. The two line integrals on the right of (6.42) cancel completely, leaving us with the formula

$$\iint\limits_{S_1 \cup S_2} (\operatorname{curl} \vec{F}) \cdot \vec{n} \, dS = 0 \, .$$

This holds not only for a sphere, but for any orientable closed surface.

6.14   The divergence theorem (Gauss' theorem)

Stokes' theorem expresses a relationship between an integral extended over a surface and a line integral taken over the one or more curves forming the boundary of this surface. The divergence theorem expresses a relationship between a triple integral extended over a solid and a surface integral taken over the boundary of this solid.

6–5   THEOREM.   *Divergence theorem.* Let V be a solid in 3-space bounded by an orientable closed surface S, and let $\vec{n}$ be the unit outer normal to S. If $\vec{F}$ is a continuously differentiable vector field defined on V, we have

(6.44) $$\iiint\limits_{V} (\operatorname{div} \vec{F}) \, dx \, dy \, dz = \iint\limits_{S} \vec{F} \cdot \vec{n} \, dS \, .$$

Note. If we express $\vec{F}$ and $\vec{n}$ in terms of their components, say

$$\vec{F}(x, y, z) = P(x, y, z)\vec{i} + Q(x, y, z)\vec{j} + R(x, y, z)\vec{k}$$

and

$$\vec{n} = \cos \alpha \, \vec{i} + \cos \beta \, \vec{j} + \cos \gamma \, \vec{k} \, ,$$

then Equation (6.44) can be written as

$$(6.45) \quad \iiint\limits_{V} \left(\frac{\partial P}{\partial x} + \frac{\partial Q}{\partial y} + \frac{\partial R}{\partial z} \right) dx\, dy\, dz = \iint\limits_{S} (P \cos \alpha + Q \cos \beta + R \cos \gamma)\, dS .$$

Proof. It would suffice to establish the three equations

$$\iiint\limits_{V} \frac{\partial P}{\partial x}\, dx\, dy\, dz = \iint\limits_{S} P \cos \alpha\, dS ,$$

$$\iiint\limits_{V} \frac{\partial Q}{\partial y}\, dx\, dy\, dz = \iint\limits_{S} Q \cos \beta\, dS ,$$

$$\iiint\limits_{V} \frac{\partial R}{\partial z}\, dx\, dy\, dz = \iint\limits_{S} R \cos \gamma\, dS ,$$

and add the results to obtain (6.45). We begin with the third of these formulas and prove it for solids of a very special type.

Assume V is a set of points (x, y, z) satisfying a relation of the form

$$g(x, y) \leq z \leq f(x, y) \qquad \text{for} \quad (x, y) \text{ in } T ,$$

where T is a connected region in the xy-plane, and f and g are continuous functions on T, with $g(x, y) \leq f(x, y)$ for each (x, y) in T. Geometrically, this means that T is the projection of V on the xy-plane. Every line through T parallel to the z-axis intersects the solid V along a line segment connecting the surface $z = g(x, y)$ to the surface $z = f(x, y)$. The boundary surface S consists of an upper cap S_1, given by the explicit formula $z = f(x, y)$; a lower part S_2, given by $z = g(x, y)$; and (possibly) a portion S_3 of the cylinder generated by a line moving parallel to the z-axis along the boundary of T. The outer normal to S has a nonnegative z-component on S_1, has a nonpositive component on S_2, and is parallel to the xy-plane on S_3. Solids of this type will be called "xy-projectable." (An example is shown in Figure 6.20.) They include all convex solids (for example, solid spheres, ellipsoids, cubes) and many solids that are not convex (for example, solid tori with axes parallel to the z-axis).

The idea of the proof is quite simple. We express the triple integral as a double integral extended over the projection T. Then we show that this double integral has the same value as the surface integral in question. We begin with the formula

$$\iiint\limits_{V} \frac{\partial R}{\partial z}\, dx\, dy\, dz = \iint\limits_{T} \left[\int_{g(x, y)}^{f(x, y)} \frac{\partial R}{\partial z}\, dz \right] dx\, dy .$$

The one-dimensional integral with respect to z may be evaluated by the second fundamental theorem of calculus, giving us

$$(6.46) \quad \iiint\limits_{V} \frac{\partial R}{\partial z}\, dx\, dy\, dz = \iint\limits_{T} \{ R[x, y, f(x, y)] - R[x, y, g(x, y)] \}\, dx\, dy .$$

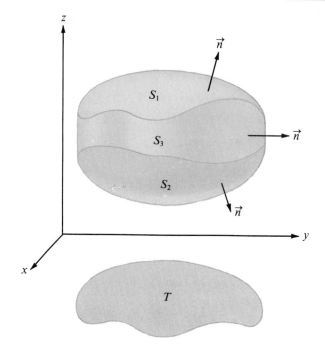

FIGURE 6.20   *An example of a solid that is xy-projectable.*

For the surface integral we may write

$$(6.47) \quad \iint\limits_{S} R \cos \gamma \, dS = \iint\limits_{S_1} R \cos \gamma \, dS + \iint\limits_{S_2} R \cos \gamma \, dS + \iint\limits_{S_3} R \cos \gamma \, dS .$$

On S_3 the normal $\vec{n}$ is parallel to the xy-plane, so $\cos \gamma = 0$ and the integral over S_3 is zero. On the surface S_1 we use the representation

$$\vec{r}(x, y) = x\vec{i} + y\vec{j} + f(x, y)\vec{k} ,$$

and on S_2 we use the representation

$$\vec{r}(x, y) = x\vec{i} + y\vec{j} + g(x, y)\vec{k} .$$

On S_1 the normal $\vec{n}$ has the same direction as the fundamental vector product $\partial \vec{r}/\partial x \times \partial \vec{r}/\partial y$, so we may write [see Equation (6.28)]

$$\iint\limits_{S_1} R \cos \gamma \, dS = \iint\limits_{S_1} R \, dx \, dy = \iint\limits_{T} R[x, y, f(x, y)] \, dx \, dy .$$

On S_2 the normal $\vec{n}$ has the direction opposite to that of $\partial \vec{r}/\partial x \times \partial \vec{r}/\partial y$ so, by Equation (6.29), we have

$$\iint\limits_{S_2} R \cos \gamma \, dS = - \iint\limits_{S_2} R \, dx \, dy = - \iint\limits_{T} R[x, y, g(x, y)] \, dx \, dy .$$

Therefore Equation (6.47) becomes

$$\iint\limits_{S} R \cos \gamma \, dS = \iint\limits_{T} \{R[x, y, f(x, y)] - R[x, y, g(x, y)]\} \, dx \, dy \, .$$

Comparing this with Equation (6.46) we see that

$$\iiint\limits_{V} \frac{\partial R}{\partial z} \, dx \, dy \, dz = \iint\limits_{S} R \cos \gamma \, dS \, .$$

In the foregoing proof the assumption that V is xy-projectable enabled us to express the triple integral over V as a double integral over its projection T in the xy-plane. It is clear that if V is yz-projectable we can use the same type of argument to prove the identity

$$\iiint\limits_{V} \frac{\partial P}{\partial x} \, dx \, dy \, dz = \iint\limits_{S} P \cos \alpha \, dS \, ;$$

and if V is xz-projectable we obtain

$$\iiint\limits_{V} \frac{\partial Q}{\partial y} \, dx \, dy \, dz = \iint\limits_{S} Q \cos \beta \, dS \, .$$

Thus we see that the divergence theorem is valid for all solids projectable on all three coordinate planes. In particular the theorem holds for every convex solid.

A solid torus with its axis parallel to the z-axis is xy-projectable but not xz-projectable or yz-projectable. To extend the divergence theorem to such a solid we cut the torus into four equal parts by planes through its axis parallel to the xz- and yz-planes, respectively, and we apply the divergence theorem to each part. The triple integral over the whole torus is the sum of the triple integrals over the four parts. When we add the surface integrals over the four parts we find that the contributions from the faces common to adjacent parts cancel each other, since the outward normals have opposite directions on two such faces. Therefore the sum of the surface integrals over the four parts is equal to the surface integral over the entire torus. This example illustrates how the divergence theorem can be extended to certain nonconvex solids.

6.15 Applications of the divergence theorem

The concepts of curl and divergence of a vector field $\vec{F} = P\vec{i} + Q\vec{j} + R\vec{k}$ were introduced in Chapter 5 by the formulas

(6.48) $$\operatorname{div} \vec{F} = \frac{\partial P}{\partial x} + \frac{\partial Q}{\partial y} + \frac{\partial R}{\partial z}$$

and

(6.49) $$\operatorname{curl} \vec{F} = \left(\frac{\partial R}{\partial y} - \frac{\partial Q}{\partial z}\right)\vec{i} + \left(\frac{\partial P}{\partial z} - \frac{\partial R}{\partial x}\right)\vec{j} + \left(\frac{\partial Q}{\partial x} - \frac{\partial P}{\partial y}\right)\vec{k} \, .$$

To compute $\operatorname{div} \vec{F}$ and $\operatorname{curl} \vec{F}$ from these formulas requires a knowledge of the components of $\vec{F}$. These components, in turn, depend on the choice of coordinate axes in 3-space. A change in the position of the coordinate axes would mean a change in the components of $\vec{F}$ and, presumably, a corresponding change in the functions div $\vec{F}$ and curl $\vec{F}$. With the help of Stokes' theorem and the divergence theorem we can obtain formulas for the divergence and curl that do not involve the components of $\vec{F}$. These formulas show that the curl and divergence represent intrinsic properties of the vector field $\vec{F}$ and do not depend on the particular choice of coordinate axes. We discuss first the formula for the divergence.

6-6   THEOREM.   Let $V(t)$ be a sphere of radius $t > 0$ with center at a point $\vec{A}$ in 3-space, and let $S(t)$ denote the boundary of $V(t)$. Let $\vec{F}$ be a vector field that is continuously differentiable on $V(t)$. Then if $|V(t)|$ denotes the volume of $V(t)$, and if $\vec{n}$ denotes the unit outer normal to S, we have

(6.50)
$$\text{div } \vec{F}(\vec{A}) = \lim_{t \to 0} \frac{1}{|V(t)|} \iint\limits_{S(t)} \vec{F} \cdot \vec{n} \, dS .$$

Proof. Let $\phi = \text{div } \vec{F}$. If $\epsilon > 0$ is given we must find a $\delta > 0$ such that

(6.51) $\left| \phi(\vec{A}) - \dfrac{1}{|V(t)|} \iint\limits_{S(t)} \vec{F} \cdot \vec{n} \, dS \right| < \epsilon$ whenever $0 < t < \delta$.

Since ϕ is continuous at $\vec{A}$, for the given ϵ there is a neighborhood $N(\vec{A}; h)$ such that

$$|\phi(\vec{X}) - \phi(\vec{A})| < \frac{\epsilon}{2} \qquad \text{whenever} \quad \vec{X} \, \varepsilon \, N(\vec{A}; h) .$$

Therefore, if we write $\phi(\vec{A}) = \phi(\vec{X}) + [\phi(\vec{A}) - \phi(\vec{X})]$ and integrate both sides of this equation over a solid sphere $V(t)$ of radius $t < h$, we find

$$\phi(\vec{A}) \, |V(t)| = \iiint\limits_{V(t)} \phi(\vec{X}) \, dx \, dy \, dz + \iiint\limits_{V(t)} [\phi(\vec{A}) - \phi(\vec{X})] \, dx \, dy \, dz .$$

If we apply the divergence theorem to the first triple integral on the right and then transpose this term to the left, we obtain the relation

$$\left| \phi(\vec{A}) \, |V(t)| - \iint\limits_{S(t)} \vec{F} \cdot \vec{n} \, dS \right| \le \iiint\limits_{V(t)} |\phi(\vec{A}) - \phi(\vec{X})| \, dx \, dy \, dz \le \frac{\epsilon}{2} |V(t)| < \epsilon \, |V(t)| .$$

When we divide this inequality by $|V(t)|$ we see that (6.51) holds with $\delta = h$. This proves the theorem.

In the foregoing proof we made no special use of the fact that $V(t)$ was a sphere. The same theorem holds true if, instead of spheres, we use any set of solids $V(t)$ for which the divergence theorem is valid, provided these solids contain the point $\vec{A}$ and shrink to $\vec{A}$ as $t \to 0$. For example, each $V(t)$ could be a cube inscribed in a sphere of radius t about $\vec{A}$; exactly the same proof would apply.

Theorem 6-6 can also be justified on physical grounds. Suppose $\vec{F}$ represents the flux density vector of a steady flow. Then the surface integral $\iint\limits_{S(t)} \vec{F} \cdot \vec{n} \, dS$ measures the total mass of fluid flowing through S in unit time in the direction of $\vec{n}$. The quotient

$\iint_{S(t)} \vec{F} \cdot \vec{n} \, dS / |V(t)|$ represents the mass per unit volume that flows through S in unit time in the direction of $\vec{n}$. As $t \to 0$, the limit of this quotient is the time rate of change per unit volume at the point $\vec{A}$. As pointed out in Section 5.22, this time rate of change is equal to the divergence of $\vec{F}$ at $\vec{A}$.

In some books on vector analysis, Equation (6.50) is taken as the *definition* of divergence. This makes it possible to assign a physical meaning to the divergence immediately. Also, formula (6.50) does not involve the components of $\vec{F}$. Therefore it holds true in any system of coordinates. If we choose for $V(t)$ a cube with its edges parallel to the xyz-coordinate axes and center at $\vec{A}$, we can use Equation (6.50) to deduce the formula in (6.48) which expresses div $\vec{F}$ in terms of the components of $\vec{F}$. This procedure is outlined in Exercise 14 of Section 6.16.

There is a formula analogous to (6.50) that is sometimes used as an alternative definition of the curl. It states that

$$(6.52) \qquad \text{curl } \vec{F}(\vec{A}) = \lim_{t \to 0} \frac{1}{|V(t)|} \iint_{S(t)} \vec{n} \times \vec{F} \, dS \,,$$

where $V(t)$ and $S(t)$ have the same meanings as in Theorem 6–6. The surface integral that appears on the right has a vector-valued integrand. Such integrals have not been defined in this book, so we shall not attempt to prove (6.52).

There is another formula involving the curl that can be deduced from (6.52) or derived independently. It states that

$$(6.53) \qquad \vec{n} \cdot \text{curl } \vec{F}(\vec{A}) = \lim_{t \to 0} \frac{1}{|S(t)|} \oint_{C(t)} \vec{F} \cdot d\vec{r} \,.$$

In this formula, $S(t)$ is a circular disk of radius t and center at $\vec{A}$, and $|S(t)|$ denotes its area. The vector $\vec{n}$ is a unit normal to $S(t)$, and $\vec{r}$ is the function that traces out $C(t)$ in a direction that appears counterclockwise when viewed from the tip of $\vec{n}$. The vector field $\vec{F}$ is assumed to be continuously differentiable on $S(t)$. A proof of (6.53) can be given by the same method we used to prove (6.50). We let $\phi(\vec{X}) = \vec{n} \cdot \text{curl } \vec{F}(\vec{X})$ and argue as before, except that we use surface integrals instead of triple integrals and Stokes' theorem instead of the divergence theorem.

If $\vec{F}$ is a velocity field, the line integral over $C(t)$ is called the circulation of $\vec{F}$ along $C(t)$; the limit in (6.53) represents the circulation per unit area at the point $\vec{A}$. Thus, $\vec{n} \cdot \text{curl } \vec{F}(\vec{A})$ can be regarded as a "circulation density" of $\vec{F}$ at point $\vec{A}$, with respect to a plane perpendicular to $\vec{n}$ at $\vec{A}$.

When $\vec{n}$ takes the successive values $\vec{i}$, $\vec{j}$, and $\vec{k}$, the dot products $\vec{i} \cdot \text{curl } \vec{F}$, $\vec{j} \cdot \text{curl } \vec{F}$, and $\vec{k} \cdot \text{curl } \vec{F}$ are the components of curl $\vec{F}$ in rectangular coordinates. When Equation (6.52) is taken as the starting point for the definition of curl, the formula in (6.49) for the rectangular components of curl $\vec{F}$ can be deduced from (6.53) in exactly this manner.

6.16 Exercises

1. Let S be the surface of the unit cube, $0 \le x \le 1, 0 \le y \le 1, 0 \le z \le 1$, and let $\vec{n}$ be the unit outer normal to S. If $\vec{F}(x, y, z) = x^2\vec{i} + y^2\vec{j} + z^2\vec{k}$, use the divergence theorem to evaluate the surface integral $\iint_S \vec{F} \cdot \vec{n} \, dS$. Verify the result by evaluating the surface integral directly.

2. The sphere $x^2 + y^2 + z^2 = 25$ is intersected by the plane $z = 3$. The smaller portion forms a solid V bounded by a closed surface S_0 made up of two parts, a spherical part S_1 and a planar part S_2. If the unit outer normal of V is $\cos \alpha \, \vec{i} + \cos \beta \, \vec{j} + \cos \gamma \, \vec{k}$, compute the value of the surface integral

$$\iint_S (xz \cos \alpha + yz \cos \beta + \cos \gamma) \, dS$$

if (a) S is the spherical cap S_1, (b) S is the planar base S_2, (c) S is the complete boundary S_0. Solve part (c) by use of the results of parts (a) and (b), and also by use of the divergence theorem.

3. Let $\vec{n} = \cos \alpha \, \vec{i} + \cos \beta \, \vec{j} + \cos \gamma \, \vec{k}$ be the unit outer normal to a closed surface S which bounds a homogeneous solid V of the type described in the divergence theorem. Assume that the center of mass $(\bar{x}, \bar{y}, \bar{z})$ and the volume $|V|$ of V are known. Evaluate the following surface integrals in terms of $|V|$ and $\bar{x}, \bar{y}, \bar{z}$.

(a) $\iint_S (x \cos \alpha + y \cos \beta + z \cos \gamma) \, dS$.

(b) $\iint_S (xz \cos \alpha + 2yz \cos \beta + 3z^2 \cos \gamma) \, dS$.

(c) $\iint_S (y^2 \cos \alpha + 2xy \cos \beta - xz \cos \gamma) \, dS$.

(d) Express $\iint_S (x^2 + y^2)(x \, \vec{i} + y \, \vec{j}) \cdot \vec{n} \, dS$ in terms of the volume $|V|$ and a moment of inertia of the solid.

In Exercises 4 through 10, $\partial f/\partial n$ and $\partial g/\partial n$ denote directional derivatives of scalar fields f and g in the direction of the unit outer normal $\vec{n}$ to a closed surface S which bounds a solid V of the type described in the divergence theorem. That is, $\partial f/\partial n = \nabla f \cdot \vec{n}$ and $\partial g/\partial n = \nabla g \cdot \vec{n}$. In each of these exercises prove the given statement. You may assume continuity of all derivatives involved.

4. $\displaystyle\iint_S \frac{\partial f}{\partial n} \, dS = \iiint_V \nabla^2 f \, dx \, dy \, dz$.

5. $\displaystyle\iint_S \frac{\partial f}{\partial n} \, dS = 0$ whenever f is harmonic in V.

6. $\displaystyle\iint_S f \frac{\partial g}{\partial n} \, dS = \iiint_V f \nabla^2 g \, dx \, dy \, dz + \iiint_V \nabla f \cdot \nabla g \, dx \, dy \, dz$.

7. $\displaystyle\iint_S \left(f \frac{\partial g}{\partial n} - g \frac{\partial f}{\partial n} \right) dS = \iiint_V (f \nabla^2 g - g \nabla^2 f) \, dx \, dy \, dz$.

8. $\displaystyle\iint_S f \frac{\partial g}{\partial n} \, dS = \iint_S g \frac{\partial f}{\partial n} \, dS$ if both f and g are harmonic in V.

9. $\displaystyle\iint_S f \frac{\partial f}{\partial n} \, dS = \iiint_V |\nabla f|^2 \, dx \, dy \, dz$ if f is harmonic in V.

10. $\nabla^2 f(\vec{A}) = \displaystyle\lim_{t \to 0} \frac{1}{|V(t)|} \iint_{S(t)} \frac{\partial f}{\partial n} \, dS$, where $V(t)$ is a sphere of radius t with center at $\vec{A}$,

$S(t)$ is the surface of $V(t)$, and $|V(t)|$ is the volume of $V(t)$.

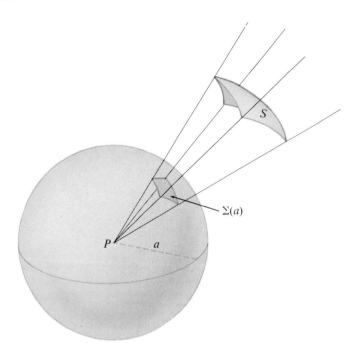

FIGURE 6.21   *The solid angle $\Omega(S)$ with vertex P subtended by a surface S. It is measured by the quotient*

$$|\Omega(S)| = \frac{area\ of\ \Sigma(a)}{a^2}.$$

11. Let V be a convex region in 3-space whose boundary is a closed surface S and let $\vec{n}$ be the unit outer normal to S. Let $\vec{F}$ and $\vec{G}$ be two continuously differentiable vector fields such that

$$\text{curl } \vec{F} = \text{curl } \vec{G} \qquad \text{and} \qquad \text{div } \vec{F} = \text{div } \vec{G} \qquad \text{everywhere in } V,$$

and such that

$$\vec{G} \cdot \vec{n} = \vec{F} \cdot \vec{n} \qquad \text{everywhere on } S.$$

Prove that $\vec{F} = \vec{G}$ everywhere in V [*Hint.* Let $\vec{H} = \vec{F} - \vec{G}$, find a scalar field f such that $\vec{H} = \nabla f$, and use a suitable identity to prove that $\iiint\limits_{V} |\nabla f|^2 \, dx \, dy \, dz = 0$. From this deduce that $\vec{H} = \vec{0}$ in V.]

12. Given a vector field $\vec{G}$ and two scalar fields f and g, each continuously differentiable on a convex solid V bounded by a closed surface S. Let $\vec{n}$ denote the unit outer normal to S. Prove that there is at most one vector field $\vec{F}$ satisfying the following three conditions:

$$\text{curl } \vec{F} = \vec{G} \qquad \text{and} \qquad \text{div } \vec{F} = g \qquad \text{in } V, \qquad \vec{F} \cdot \vec{n} = f \qquad \text{on } S.$$

13. Let S be a smooth parametric surface with the property that each line emanating from a point P intersects S once at most. Let $\Omega(S)$ denote the set of lines emanating from P and passing through S. (See Figure 6.21.) The set $\Omega(S)$ is called the *solid angle* with vertex P subtended by S. Let $\Sigma(a)$ denote the intersection of $\Omega(S)$ with the surface of the sphere of radius a centered at P.

The quotient

$$\frac{\text{area of } \Sigma(a)}{a^2}$$

is denoted by $|\Omega(S)|$ and is used as a measure of the solid angle $\Omega(S)$.

(a) Prove that this quotient is equal to the surface integral

$$\iint\limits_{S} \frac{\vec{r} \cdot \vec{n}}{r^3} \, dS \,,$$

where $\vec{r}$ is the radius vector from P to an arbitrary point of S, and $r = |\vec{r}|$. The vector $\vec{n}$ is the unit normal to S directed away from P. This shows that the quotient for $|\Omega(S)|$ is independent of the radius a. Therefore the solid angle can be measured by the area of the intersection of $\Omega(S)$ and the unit sphere about P. [*Hint.* Apply the divergence theorem to the portion of $\Omega(S)$ lying between S and $\Sigma(a)$.]

(b) Two planes intersect along the diameter of a sphere with center at P. The angle of intersection is θ, where $0 < \theta < \pi$. Let S denote the smaller portion of the surface of the sphere intercepted by the two planes. Show that $|\Omega(S)| = 2\theta$.

14. Let $V(t)$ denote a cube of edge $2t$ and center at $\vec{A}$, and let $S(t)$ denote the boundary of the cube. Let $\vec{n}$ be the unit outer normal of $S(t)$ and let $|V(t)|$ denote the volume of the cube. For a given vector field $\vec{F}$ that is continuously differentiable at $\vec{A}$, assume that the following limit exists:

$$\lim_{t \to 0} \frac{1}{|V(t)|} \iint\limits_{S(t)} \vec{F} \cdot \vec{n} \, dS \,,$$

and use this limit as the definition of the divergence, div $\vec{F}(\vec{A})$. Choose xyz-coordinate axes parallel to the edges of $V(t)$ and let P, Q, and R be the components of $\vec{F}$ relative to this coordinate system. Prove that div $\vec{F}(\vec{A}) = D_1 P(\vec{A}) + D_2 Q(\vec{A}) + D_3 R(\vec{A})$. [*Hint.* Express the surface integral as a sum of six double integrals taken over the faces of the cube. Then show that $1/|V(t)|$ times the sum of the two double integrals over the faces perpendicular to the z-axis approaches the limit $D_3 R(\vec{A})$ as $t \to 0$. Argue in a similar way for the remaining terms.]

15. A scalar field ϕ has the properties

$$|\nabla\phi|^2 = 4\phi \qquad \text{and} \qquad \text{div}(\phi\nabla\phi) = 10\phi \,.$$

Evaluate the surface integral

$$\iint\limits_{S} \frac{\partial\phi}{\partial n} \, dS \,,$$

where S is the surface of a unit sphere with center at the origin, and $\partial\phi/\partial n$ is the directional derivative of ϕ in the direction of the unit outer normal to S.

7

LINEAR DIFFERENTIAL EQUATIONS

7.1 Historical introduction

Differential equations is the one branch of mathematics that, perhaps more than any other, has been directly inspired by mechanics, astronomy, and mathematical physics. Its history began in the 17th century when Newton, Leibniz, and the Bernoullis solved some simple differential equations of the first and second order arising from problems in geometry and mechanics. These early discoveries, beginning about 1690, seemed to suggest that the solutions of all differential equations based on geometric and physical problems could be expressed in terms of the familiar elementary functions of calculus. Therefore, much of the early work was aimed at developing ingenious techniques for solving differential equations by elementary means, that is to say, by addition, subtraction, multiplication, division, composition, and integration, applied only a finite number of times to the familiar functions of calculus.

In the introductory account of differential equations presented in Volume I (Chapter 4) we discussed such particular devices as separation of variables and the use of integrating factors. These and other special methods were devised more or less haphazardly before the end of the 17th century. During the 18th century, more systematic procedures were developed, primarily by Euler, Lagrange, and Laplace. It soon became apparent that relatively few differential equations could be solved by elementary means. Little by little, mathematicians began to realize that it was hopeless to try to discover methods for solving *all* differential equations. Instead, they found it more fruitful to ask whether or not a given differential equation has any solution at all and, when it has, to try to deduce properties of the solution from the differential equation itself. Within this framework, mathematicians began to think of differential equations as new sources of functions.

An important phase in the theory developed early in the 19th century, paralleling the general trend toward a more rigorous approach to the calculus. In the 1820's, Cauchy obtained the first "existence theorem" for differential equations. He proved that every first-order equation of the form

$$y' = f(x, y)$$

has a solution whenever the right member, $f(x, y)$, satisfies certain general conditions. One important example is the so-called *Ricatti equation*

$$(7.1) \qquad y' = P(x)y^2 + Q(x)y + R(x),$$

where P, Q, and R are given functions. Cauchy's work implies the existence of a solution $y = f(x)$ satisfying Equation (7.1) in any open interval $(-r, r)$ about the origin, provided P, Q, and R have power-series expansions in $(-r, r)$. In 1841 Joseph Liouville (1809–1882) showed that in some cases this solution cannot be obtained by elementary means.

Experience has shown that it is difficult to obtain results of much generality about solutions of differential equations, except for a few types. Among these are the so-called *linear* differential equations which occur in a great variety of scientific problems. First-order linear equations were discussed in complete detail in Chapter 4 of Volume I. They have the form

$$(7.2) \qquad y' + P(x)y = Q(x),$$

and their solutions are given by the explicit formula

$$(7.3) \qquad y = e^{-\int P(x)dx}\left[\int Q(x)e^{\int P(x)dx}\,dx + C\right],$$

where C is an arbitrary constant. The Ricatti equation, which is *not* of the form of Equation (7.2) (because of the presence of the term involving y^2), is an example of a first-order *nonlinear* equation.

Linear equations of the second order are those of the form

$$P_0(x)y'' + P_1(x)y' + P_2(x)y = R(x).$$

If P_0, P_1, P_2, and R are continuous on some interval I, and if P_0 is never zero on I, an existence theorem (discussed in Section 7.5) guarantees that solutions always exist over the interval I. Nevertheless, there is no general formula analogous to (7.3) for expressing these solutions in terms of P_0, P_1, P_2, and R. Thus, even in this relatively simple generalization of (7.2), the theory is far from complete, except when P_0, P_1, and P_2 are constants, in which case the solutions can easily be determined by elementary means. (See Sections 7.6 and 7.8.)

Some second-order linear equations occur repeatedly in many applications; special names have been given to the equations and to their solutions. For example, the equation

$$x^2y'' + xy' + (x^2 - \alpha^2)y = 0,$$

where α is a constant, is called the *Bessel equation* of order α. Some of its solutions are known as *Bessel functions*. This equation is used in problems concerning vibrations of membranes, heat flow in cylinders, and propagation of electric currents in cylindrical conductors. It is named after the German astronomer F. W. Bessel (1784–1846), although the equation appeared earlier in the researches of Daniel Bernoulli (1732) and Euler (1764).

Another important example is the *Legendre equation*,

$$(1 - x^2)y'' - 2xy' + \alpha(\alpha + 1)y = 0,$$

where α is a constant. This equation occurs in problems of attraction and in heat-flow problems with spherical symmetry. When α is a positive integer the equation has polynomial solutions called *Legendre polynomials*. The Legendre and Bessel equations will be studied in more detail in Sections 7.17 and 7.19.

7.2 Second-order equations solvable by special methods

This section describes some special methods for transforming certain second-order equations to first-order equations. Although these types of equations are encountered only rarely, some of them do occur naturally in problems in geometry and mechanics, so their study is of practical importance. Moreover, a study of these equations at this stage provides an opportunity to review some of the elementary techniques (discussed in Volume I) for solving first-order equations.

Consider a second-order equation of the form

$$y'' = f(x, y, y') .$$

When the right member does not explicitly contain y, or when it does not explicitly contain x, the substitution $p = y'$ enables us to reduce the order of the equation. The following examples illustrate the technique.

Equations of the form $y'' = f(x, y')$. The substitution $p = y'$ gives us $p' = y''$, and the differential equation becomes $p' = f(x, p)$, a first-order equation for p as a function of x. If a solution of this equation can be expressed in the form $p = F(x, C_1)$, we may integrate to obtain the following solution of the original equation:

$$y = \int F(x, C_1) \, dx + C_2 .$$

Example 1: $xy'' + y' = x$. We write $y' = p$ and $y'' = p'$, and the equation becomes $xp' + p = x$. This can be solved as a first-order equation, linear in p, or we can observe that the left member is the derivative of xp. In any case, integration yields $xp = x^2/2 + C_1$, or

$$p = \frac{x}{2} + \frac{C_1}{x} \qquad \text{if} \quad x \neq 0 .$$

Since $p = dy/dx$ we may integrate this equation at once to obtain

$$y = \frac{x^2}{4} + C_1 \log|x| + C_2 .$$

If $C_1 \neq 0$ the solution is valid if $x \neq 0$. Otherwise it is valid for all x.

Example 2. A plane curve with equation $y = f(x)$ has the property that its curvature at each point is equal to the cosine of the angle θ between the tangent line and the x-axis, where θ is measured so that $0 < \theta < \pi/2$. Find $f(x)$ if the curve passes through $(0, 1)$ with slope 0.

Solution. The vector $\vec{v} = \vec{i} + y' \, \vec{j}$ is tangent to the curve at (x, y), and the cosine of θ is $1/|\vec{v}|$. The curvature at (x, y) is $|y''|/|\vec{v}|^3$. Since $\cos \theta > 0$, the curve satisfies the differential equation

$$\frac{y''}{|\vec{v}|^3} = \frac{1}{|\vec{v}|} , \qquad \text{or} \quad y'' = |\vec{v}|^2 = 1 + (y')^2 .$$

This is a nonlinear differential equation of second order. The substitution $p = y'$ reduces it to a first-order equation for p, namely, $p' = 1 + p^2$. As such, it is separable and may be integrated to give

$$\text{arc tan } p = x + C_1, \quad \text{or} \quad p = \tan(x + C_1).$$

To make $p = 0$ when $x = 0$ we choose $C_1 = 0$. Therefore the first integration yields $y' = \tan x$. Integrating once more we find $y = -\log |\cos x| + C_2$. Since the curve passes through $(0, 1)$, we must have $C_2 = 1$, so the curve we seek has the equation

$$y = 1 - \log |\cos x|.$$

This formula is valid if x is not an odd integer multiple of $\pi/2$.

Equations of the form $y'' = f(y, y')$. An equation of this form can always be reduced to a pair of first-order differential equations. To determine these equations we assume that on some interval I there is a solution, say $y = Y(x)$, with a differentiable inverse ϕ. Then for x in I we may write $x = \phi(y)$ and

$$y' = Y'(x) = Y'[\phi(y)].$$

Therefore the derivative y' can be expressed in terms of y. If we let $P(y) = Y'[\phi(y)]$ we have

(7.4) $$y' = P(y).$$

By the chain rule we obtain

$$y'' = P'(y)y' = P'(y)P(y).$$

The differential equation $y'' = f(y, y')$ now becomes

(7.5) $$P'(y)P(y) = f[y, P(y)].$$

The two equations (7.4) and (7.5) are necessarily satisfied by any solution of the type described.

Now we may turn the argument around to describe a method for solving the original equation. First we try to find a function P satisfying the first-order equation (7.5). If we find such a P we take y as any solution of the first-order equation

$$\frac{dy}{dx} = P(y).$$

This latter equation is separable and can always be integrated. Because of the way P was chosen the resulting function y has the property that $y'' = f(y, y')$.

Example 3. The method works particularly well for the equation of simple harmonic motion, $y'' + k^2 y = 0$, where $k > 0$. In this case Equation (7.5) becomes $P'(y)P(y) = -k^2 y$, or

$$\frac{1}{2} \frac{d}{dy} \left(P^2(y) \right) = -k^2 y.$$

Integrating we obtain $P^2(y) = -k^2 y^2 + C$. Since C is a sum of squares we have $C \geq 0$ and we may write $C = k^2 A^2$, where A is an arbitrary constant. The equation for P becomes $P^2(y) = k^2(A^2 - y^2)$. If we take the positive square root we find

$$P(y) = k \sqrt{A^2 - y^2}.$$

To determine y we solve the first-order equation

$$\frac{dy}{dx} = P(y) = k\sqrt{A^2 - y^2}.$$

Separating the variables and integrating we find

$$\text{arc} \sin \frac{y}{A} = kx + B, \quad \text{or} \quad y = A\sin(kx + B),$$

where B is another arbitrary constant. This particular form of the solution was obtained in Volume I (Section 4.12) by an entirely different method.

Example 4. To solve the nonlinear differential equation

$$y\frac{d^2y}{dx^2} - y^2\frac{dy}{dx} - \left(\frac{dy}{dx}\right)^2 = 0$$

by this method, we write $y' = P(y)$, $y'' = P'(y)P(y)$, and the equation becomes

$$yP(y)P'(y) - y^2P(y) - P^2(y) = 0.$$

One trivial solution is $P(y) = 0$; this leads to $y = C$. If $P(y)$ and y are nonzero we can rewrite the equation in the form

$$P'(y) - \frac{1}{y}P(y) = y,$$

a first-order linear equation for P. It has the solution $P(y) = y(y + C_1)$. To determine y we solve the first-order equation

$$\frac{dy}{dx} = y(y + C_1).$$

Separating the variables and integrating we obtain

$$C_1 x = \log\left|\frac{y}{y + C_1}\right| + C_2,$$

where C_1 and C_2 are arbitrary constants.

Example 5: Motion of a rocket with variable mass. A rocket is propelled by burning fuel in a combustion chamber, allowing the products of combustion to be expelled backward. Designate the position vector of the rocket at time t by $\vec{r}(t)$, the mass of the rocket (including fuel) by $m(t)$, and the velocity of the exhaust matter, relative to the rocket, by $\vec{c}(t)$. We shall prove that these quantities are related by the equation

(7.6) $$m(t)\vec{r}''(t) - m'(t)\vec{c}(t) = \vec{F}(t),$$

where $\vec{F}(t)$ represents the vector sum of all external forces acting on the rocket at time t. In the examples to be considered here, $m(t)$, $\vec{c}(t)$, and $\vec{F}(t)$ are known or can be prescribed in terms of $\vec{r}(t)$ or its derivative $\vec{r}'(t)$ (the velocity of the rocket). Equation (7.6) then becomes a second-order differential equation for the position function $\vec{r}$.

Equation (7.6) can be written in the form

(7.7) $$m(t)\vec{r}''(t) = m'(t)\vec{c}(t) + \vec{F}(t).$$

The term $m'(t)\vec{c}(t)$ is the contribution to the accelerating force on the rocket caused by the thrust developed by the rocket engine; the term $\vec{F}(t)$ is the contribution caused by the external forces. Therefore, to prove (7.7) it suffices to show that *in the absence of external forces* we have

$$(7.8) \qquad\qquad m(t)\vec{r}''(t) = m'(t)\vec{c}(t) .$$

For this purpose we consider first a rocket that fires its exhaust matter intermittently, like bullets from a gun. Specifically, we consider a time interval $[t, t + h]$, where h is a small positive number; we assume that some exhaust matter is expelled at time t, and that no further exhaust matter is expelled in the half-open interval $(t, t + h]$. On the basis of this assumption we obtain a formula whose limit, as $h \to 0$, is Equation (7.8).

Just before the exhaust material is expelled at time t, the rocket has mass $m(t)$ and velocity $\vec{v}(t)$. At the end of the time interval $[t, t + h]$ the rocket has mass $m(t + h)$ and velocity $\vec{v}(t + h)$. The mass of the expelled matter is $m(t) - m(t + h)$ and its velocity during the interval is $\vec{v}(t) + \vec{c}(t)$, since $\vec{c}(t)$ is the velocity of the exhaust relative to the rocket. Just before the exhaust material is expelled at time t, the rocket is a system with momentum $m(t)\vec{v}(t)$. At time $t + h$ this system consists of two parts, a rocket with momentum $m(t + h)\vec{v}(t + h)$ and exhaust matter with momentum $[m(t) - m(t + h)][\vec{v}(t) + \vec{c}(t)]$. The law of conservation of momentum states that the momentum of the new system must be equal to that of the old. Therefore, we have

$$m(t)\vec{v}(t) = m(t + h)\vec{v}(t + h) + [m(t) - m(t + h)][\vec{v}(t) + \vec{c}(t)] ,$$

from which we obtain

$$(7.9) \qquad\qquad m(t + h)[\vec{v}(t + h) - \vec{v}(t)] = [m(t + h) - m(t)]\vec{c}(t) .$$

Dividing by h and letting $h \to 0$ we find

$$(7.10) \qquad\qquad m(t)\vec{v}'(t) = m'(t)\vec{c}(t) ,$$

which is equivalent to Equation (7.8).

Consider a special case in which the rocket starts from rest with an initial weight of w pounds (including b pounds of fuel) and moves vertically upward along a straight line. Assume the fuel is consumed at a constant rate of k pounds per second and that the products of combustion are discharged directly backward with a constant speed of c feet per second relative to the rocket. Assume the only external force acting on the rocket is the earth's gravitational attraction. We want to know how high the rocket will travel before all its fuel is consumed.

Since the motion is along a straight line we need not use vector notation. Let $r(t)$ denote the altitude at time t. Since all the fuel is consumed when $kt = b$, we restrict t to the interval $0 \le t \le b/k$. The only external force acting on the rocket is $-m(t)g$, so Equation (7.6) becomes

$$m(t)r''(t) + m'(t)c = -m(t)g .$$

The weight of the rocket at time t is $w - kt$, and its mass $m(t)$ is $(w - kt)/g$; hence $m'(t) = -k/g$ and we have

$$r''(t) = -g - \frac{m'(t)}{m(t)}\, c = -g + \frac{kc}{w - kt} .$$

Integrating, we find

$$r'(t) = -gt - c \log \frac{w - kt}{w}.$$

A second integration leads to the relation

$$r(t) = -\frac{1}{2}gt^2 + ct + \frac{c(w - kt)}{k} \log \frac{w - kt}{w}.$$

All the fuel is consumed when $t = b/k$. At that instant the altitude is

(7.11)
$$r\left(\frac{b}{k}\right) = -\frac{gb^2}{2k^2} + \frac{cb}{k} + \frac{c(w - b)}{k} \log \frac{w - b}{w}.$$

This formula is valid if $b < w$. For some rockets, the weight of the carrier is negligible compared to the weight of the fuel and it is of interest to consider the limiting case $b = w$. We cannot put $b = w$ in (7.11) because of the presence of the term $\log [(w - b)/w]$. However, if we let $b \to w$ the last term in (7.11) is an indeterminate form with limit 0. Therefore, when $b \to w$ the limiting value of the right member of (7.11) is

$$\lim_{b \to w} r\left(\frac{b}{k}\right) = -\frac{gw^2}{2k^2} + \frac{cw}{k} = -\frac{1}{2}gT^2 + cT,$$

where $T = w/k$ is the time required for the entire weight w to be consumed.

7.3 Exercises

Solve the differential equations in Exercises 1 through 10.

1. $y'' + k^2y^2 = 0,\quad k \neq 0.$

2. $y'' - k^2y^2 = 0,\quad k \neq 0.$

3. $\dfrac{d^2y}{dx^2} + \left(\dfrac{dy}{dx}\right)^2 = 0.$

4. $\dfrac{d^2y}{dx^2} + \left(\dfrac{dy}{dx}\right)^2 = 1.$

5. $y'' + 2y = 2y^3.$

6. $xy'' - (1 + x^2)y' = 4 + 4x^2.$

7. $(1 - x^2)y'' + xy' = x.$

8. $(1 + x^2)\dfrac{d^2y}{dx^2} + \left(\dfrac{dy}{dx}\right)^2 = -1.$

9. $y'' + k^2y^3 = 0,\quad k \neq 0.$

10. $y'' - k^2y^3 = 0,\quad k \neq 0.$

11. If y is a function of x, the change of variable $x = e^t$ transforms y into a function of t. Use the chain rule to show that

$$x\frac{dy}{dx} = \frac{dy}{dt} \quad \text{and} \quad x^2\frac{d^2y}{dx^2} = \frac{d^2y}{dt^2} - \frac{dy}{dt}.$$

Use the change of variable suggested in Exercise 11 to solve the nonlinear differential equations in Exercises 12 through 15.

12. $xy\dfrac{d^2y}{dx^2} + x\left(\dfrac{dy}{dx}\right)^2 - y\dfrac{dy}{dx} = 0.$ [*Hint.* Multiply by x.]

13. $(x^2 + y^2)\left(y - x\dfrac{dy}{dx}\right) + x^2y^2\dfrac{d^2y}{dx^2} = 0.$ [*Hint.* Let $y = vx$.]

14. $x^3 \dfrac{d^2y}{dx^2} = (x^2 - 2xy)\dfrac{dy}{dx} + 2y^2 - xy.$ [*Hint.* Let $y = vx$.]

15. $2x^2y \dfrac{d^2y}{dx^2} + 4y^2 - x^2 \left(\dfrac{dy}{dx}\right)^2 = 2xy \dfrac{dy}{dx}.$ [*Hint.* Let $y = v^2$.]

16. A plane curve with equation $y = f(x)$ has the property that its curvature at each point is equal to the sine of the angle θ between the tangent line and the x-axis, where θ is measured so that $0 < \theta < \pi/2$. Find $f(x)$ if the curve passes through the origin with slope 1.

17. A duck is swimming along a straight line with a constant speed. A dog, initially at a distance a from the duck, swims toward the duck with a constant speed k times that of the duck, where $k > 1$. (The arc length traversed by the dog in unit time is k times that traversed by the duck.) Place the coordinate axes so the dog is initially at the origin and the path of the duck is along the line $x = a$ in the direction of increasing y. Find a Cartesian equation for the curve of pursuit and show that the dog overtakes the duck at the point $(a, ka/(k^2 - 1))$. What is the curve of pursuit when $k = 1$?

18. A spaceship is returning to earth. Assume that the only external force acting on it is the action of gravity, and that it falls along a straight line toward the center of the earth. The effect of gravity is partly overcome by firing a rocket directly downward. The rocket fuel is consumed at a constant rate of k pounds per second and the exhaust material has a constant speed of c feet per second relative to the rocket. Find a formula for the distance the spaceship falls in time t if it starts from rest at time $t = 0$ with an initial weight of w pounds.

19. A rocket of initial weight w pounds starts from rest in free space (no external forces) and moves along a straight line. The fuel is consumed at a constant rate of k pounds per second and the products of combustion are discharged directly backward at a constant speed of c feet per second relative to the rocket. Find the distance traveled at time t.

20. Solve Exercise 19 if the initial speed of the rocket is v_0 and if the products of combustion are fired at such a speed that the discharged material remains at rest in space.

7.4 Linear differential equations

A differential equation of the form

(7.12) $$P_0(x)y^{(n)} + P_1(x)y^{(n-1)} + \cdots + P_n(x)y = R(x)$$

is said to be a *linear equation of order n*. The functions $P_0, P_1, \ldots, P_n$ multiplying the various derivatives of the unknown function y are called the *coefficients* of the equation. In our general discussion of the linear equation we shall assume that all the coefficients are continuous on some interval I. The word "interval" will refer either to a bounded interval of the form $[a, b]$, (a, b), $[a, b)$, or $(a, b]$, with $a < b$, or to an unbounded interval. Unbounded intervals will be denoted by the symbols $(a, +\infty)$, $(-\infty, a)$, $[a, +\infty)$, $(-\infty, a]$. They are defined as follows:

$$(a, +\infty) = \{x \mid x > a\}, \qquad (-\infty, a) = \{x \mid x < a\},$$
$$[a, +\infty) = \{x \mid x \geq a\}, \qquad (-\infty, a] = \{x \mid x \leq a\}.$$

In addition, it is convenient to refer to the collection of *all* real numbers as the interval $(-\infty, +\infty)$. Thus, when we discuss a linear differential equation or its solution over an interval I, it will be understood that I is one of the nine types just described.

In the differential equation (7.12) the leading coefficient P_0 plays a special role, since it determines the order of the equation. Points at which $P_0(x) = 0$ are called *singular points* of the equation. The presence of singular points sometimes introduces complications that require special investigation. To avoid these difficulties we assume that the function P_0 is never zero on I. Then we can divide both sides of Equation (7.12) by P_0 and rewrite the differential equation in a form with leading coefficient 1. Therefore, in our general discussion, we shall assume that the differential equation has the form

$$(7.13) \qquad y^{(n)} + P_1(x)y^{(n-1)} + \cdots + P_n(x)y = R(x) .$$

The discussion of linear equations may be simplified by the use of operator notation. Let $P_1, P_2, \ldots, P_n$ be given functions defined on a common interval I. If f is any function with n derivatives on the interval I we may introduce an operator L which transforms f into another function $L(f)$ defined by the equation

$$L(f) = f^{(n)} + P_1 f^{(n-1)} + \cdots + P_n f .$$

The operator L itself is sometimes written symbolically as

$$L = D^n + P_1 D^{n-1} + \cdots + P_n ,$$

where D^k denotes the kth derivative operator. In operator notation, the differential equation in (7.13) is written as

$$L(y) = R .$$

It is to be understood that the operator L depends on the coefficients $P_1, P_2, \ldots, P_n$.

It is easy to verify that $L(y_1 + y_2) = L(y_1) + L(y_2)$, and that $L(cy) = c\, L(y)$ for every constant c. Therefore, for every pair of constants c_1 and c_2 we have

$$L(c_1 y_1 + c_2 y_2) = c_1\, L(y_1) + c_2\, L(y_2) .$$

Thus we see that L is a *linear* operator. This is why the equation $L(y) = R$ is referred to as a linear equation. The linearity property can be extended by induction to give the formula

$$L\left(\sum_{k=1}^{n} c_k y_k \right) = \sum_{k=1}^{n} c_k L(y_k) .$$

With each linear equation $L(y) = R$ we may associate the equation

$$(7.14) \qquad L(y) = 0 ,$$

in which the right-hand side has been replaced by zero. This is called the *homogeneous* or *reduced* equation corresponding to $L(y) = R$. When R is not identically zero, the equation $L(y) = R$ is called the *nonhomogeneous* or *complete* equation associated with $L(y) = 0$. We shall find that we can always solve the nonhomogeneous equation whenever we can solve the corresponding homogeneous equation. Therefore, we begin our study with the homogeneous equation. Since most of the important features of the theory are exhibited in the study of the second-order equation, we discuss this case first.

7.5 Homogeneous linear equations of second order

We begin our study of linear equations of second order with two simple examples.

Example 1. Consider the equation of simple harmonic motion

(7.15) $$y'' + k^2 y = 0 \,,$$

where k is a nonzero constant. Two particular solutions are $y = \cos kx$ and $y = \sin kx$. By linearity, the combination

(7.16) $$y = c_1 \cos kx + c_2 \sin kx$$

is also a solution for every choice of constants c_1 and c_2. This differential equation was treated in Section 4.12 of Volume I, where we proved that *all* its solutions are given by formula (7.16). The equation was also solved in Section 7.2 of this chapter as an equation with x absent; the solution was expressed in the form $y = A \sin(kx + B)$, where A and B are arbitrary constants. The equivalence of this form of the solution with that in Equation (7.16) was established in Volume I.

In many physical problems it is necessary to select from the family of functions in (7.16) those solutions satisfying one or more additional conditions. These conditions often require the function and its derivative to have prescribed values at a given point. The problem of determining such a solution is called an *initial-value problem*. (This terminology originated in mechanics, where the prescribed values of y and y' represent displacement and velocity at some initial time.) For the differential equation of simple harmonic motion it is easy to verify that every initial-value problem has a solution. That is, for each point x_0 on the real axis and for every choice of real numbers k_0 and k_1, there is a solution $y = f(x)$ satisfying the conditions

(7.17) $$f(x_0) = k_0 \,, \qquad f'(x_0) = k_1 \,.$$

To find such a solution we need only determine constants c_1 and c_2 satisfying the pair of linear algebraic equations

(7.18)
$$c_1 \cos kx_0 + c_2 \sin kx_0 = k_0 \,,$$
$$-kc_1 \sin kx_0 + kc_2 \cos kx_0 = k_1 \,.$$

This system can always be solved for c_1 and c_2 if the determinant of the system is non-zero. The determinant in this case is

$$\begin{vmatrix} \cos kx_0 & \sin kx_0 \\ -k \sin kx_0 & k \cos kx_0 \end{vmatrix} = k(\cos^2 kx_0 + \sin^2 kx_0) = k \neq 0 \,.$$

Therefore c_1 and c_2 satisfying (7.18) always exist. The pair c_1, c_2 is uniquely determined as soon as x_0, k_0, and k_1 are specified, so there is only one solution satisfying the initial conditions (7.17).

Example 2. A related example is the differential equation

(7.19) $$y'' - k^2 y = 0 \,,$$

where k is a nonzero constant. One obvious solution is $y = e^{kx}$, and another is $y = e^{-kx}$. From these we can obtain further solutions by constructing linear combinations of the form

(7.20) $$y = c_1 e^{kx} + c_2 e^{-kx} \,,$$

where c_1 and c_2 are arbitrary constants.† We shall prove now that for each real x_0 a solution $y = f(x)$ exists for which $f(x_0)$ and $f'(x_0)$ have prescribed values. If we want $f(x_0) = k_0$ and $f'(x_0) = k_1$ we must find c_1 and c_2 to satisfy the following pair of linear algebraic equations:

$$c_1 e^{kx_0} + c_2 e^{-kx_0} = k_0,$$
$$kc_1 e^{kx_0} - kc_2 e^{-kx_0} = k_1.$$

Again, this system can always be solved for c_1 and c_2 because the determinant of the system is nonzero; in fact, the determinant is

$$\begin{vmatrix} e^{kx_0} & e^{-kx_0} \\ ke^{kx_0} & -ke^{-kx_0} \end{vmatrix} = -ke^{kx_0} \cdot e^{-kx_0} - ke^{kx_0} \cdot e^{-kx_0} = -2k \neq 0.$$

The pair c_1, c_2 is uniquely determined as soon as x_0, k_0, and k_1 are specified, so there is only one solution of the form (7.20) that satisfies the initial-value problem $L(y) = 0$, $f(x_0) = k_0, f'(x_0) = k_1$.

The foregoing examples illustrate two fundamental theorems in the theory of second-order linear differential equations—an *existence theorem*, which states that every initial-value problem has a solution, and a *uniqueness theorem*, which states that there is at most one solution to every initial-value problem. These theorems may be stated more explicitly as follows:

7–1   THEOREM. *Existence theorem for second-order linear equations.* Let P_1 and P_2 be continuous functions on an open interval I, and let L denote the operator

(7.21) $$L(y) = y'' + P_1 y' + P_2 y.$$

If x_0 is a point in I and if k_0 and k_1 are given real numbers, there exists a function f which is a solution of the differential equation $L(y) = 0$ on I and which satisfies the initial conditions

$$f(x_0) = k_0, \qquad f'(x_0) = k_1.$$

7–2   THEOREM. *Uniqueness theorem for second-order linear equations.* Let L be the linear operator of Theorem 7–1, let f and g be two functions that satisfy the differential equation $L(y) = 0$ on an open interval I, and assume that $f(x_0) = g(x_0)$ and $f'(x_0) = g'(x_0)$ for some x_0 in I. Then $f(x) = g(x)$ for all x in I.

Both these theorems will be deduced in Chapter 9 as corollaries of existence and uniqueness theorems concerning more general differential equations. In this chapter we shall use both the existence and uniqueness theorems to deduce properties of the solutions of linear equations.

The next theorem characterizes the set of solutions of a second-order linear equation.

7–3   THEOREM. Let $L(y) = y'' + P_1 y' + P_2 y$, where P_1 and P_2 are continuous on an open interval I. Let u_1 and u_2 be two nonzero functions satisfying the equation

---

† It will be shown presently (in Theorem 7–3) that all solutions of (7.19) are included in (7.20).

$L(y) = 0$ on I, and assume that the quotient u_2/u_1 is not constant on I. Then for every choice of constants c_1 and c_2, the linear combination $c_1u_1 + c_2u_2$ is a solution of $L(y) = 0$ on I. Conversely, if y is a solution of $L(y) = 0$ on I, there exist constants c_1 and c_2 such that

$$(7.22) \qquad\qquad y = c_1u_1 + c_2u_2.$$

Proof. To verify that $c_1u_1 + c_2u_2$ is a solution for every choice of c_1 and c_2, we note that $L(u_1) = L(u_2) = 0$, so by linearity we have

$$L(c_1u_1 + c_2u_2) = c_1\,L(u_1) + c_2\,L(u_2) = c_1 \cdot 0 + c_2 \cdot 0 = 0.$$

It remains to show that *all* solutions are to be found among those in (7.22). We shall deduce this as a consequence of the uniqueness theorem. The idea of the proof is this: Let f be any solution of $L(y) = 0$. Choose a point x_0 in I and consider $f(x_0)$ and $f'(x_0)$. If we can show that constants c_1 and c_2 exist satisfying the pair of equations

$$(7.23) \qquad \begin{aligned} c_1u_1(x_0) + c_2u_2(x_0) &= f(x_0), \\ c_1u_1'(x_0) + c_2u_2'(x_0) &= f'(x_0), \end{aligned}$$

then both f and $c_1u_1 + c_2u_2$ have the same value and the same derivative at x_0. By the uniqueness theorem it follows that $f = c_1u_1 + c_2u_2$, so f is one of the solutions in (7.22).

To show that the system (7.23) can be solved for c_1 and c_2 it suffices to show that there is an x_0 in I for which the determinant of the system is not zero. This determinant is

$$\begin{vmatrix} u_1(x_0) & u_2(x_0) \\ u_1'(x_0) & u_2'(x_0) \end{vmatrix} = u_1(x_0)\,u_2'(x_0) - u_2(x_0)\,u_1'(x_0).$$

For an arbitrary x in I define $W(x)$ to be the determinant

$$W(x) = \begin{vmatrix} u_1(x) & u_2(x) \\ u_1'(x) & u_2'(x) \end{vmatrix} = u_1(x)u_2'(x) - u_2(x)u_1'(x).$$

The determinant $W(x)$ is called the *Wronskian* of u_1 and u_2, after J. M. H. Wronski (1778–1853). We wish to prove that $W(x_0) \neq 0$ for some x_0 in I. We shall prove this by contradiction. Suppose that $W(x)$ is zero for all x in I. Then the quotient u_2/u_1 must be constant on I because the derivative of this quotient is

$$\left(\frac{u_2}{u_1}\right)' = \frac{u_1u_2' - u_2u_1'}{u_1^2} = \frac{W}{u_1^2} = 0.$$

This contradicts the hypothesis that u_2/u_1 is not a constant. Therefore $W(x_0) \neq 0$ for at least one x_0 in I. As observed earlier, this implies the existence of constants c_1 and c_2 satisfying (7.23). Thus, Theorem 7–3 has been deduced as a consequence of the uniqueness theorem. (We remind the reader once more that we have not yet proved the uniqueness theorem.) The uniqueness theorem can also be deduced as a consequence of Theorem 7–3. That is, if it is known that every solution of the equation has the form $c_1u_1 + c_2u_2$, where u_1 and u_2 have nonconstant ratio on I, it can be shown that every initial-value problem has at most one solution on I. (See Exercise 14 of Section 7.7.)

In the course of the foregoing proof we showed that the Wronskian $W(x)$ is different from 0 for at least one x in I. Actually, it is easy to prove that $W(x) \neq 0$ for *all* x in I. For this purpose we use the formula

$$(7.24) \qquad W(x) = W(c)e^{-\int_c^x P_1(t)\,dt},$$

which is valid for every choice of c in I. [Equation (7.24) is known as Abel's formula for the Wronskian; a proof is outlined in Exercise 13 of Section 7.7.] When we choose c so that $W(c) \neq 0$ we find that $W(x) \neq 0$ for all x in I.

Since all solutions of the differential equation $L(y) = 0$ are contained in formula (7.22), the linear combination $c_1 u_1 + c_2 u_2$, with c_1 and c_2 arbitrary constants, is said to be the *general solution* of the equation. Theorem 7–3 tells us that we can find the general solution as soon as we know two particular nonzero solutions whose ratio is not constant.

If the ratio u_2/u_1 is constant, say $u_2/u_1 = c$, we have $u_2 = cu_1$, or $cu_1 - u_2 = 0$. This is a linear combination $c_1 u_1 + c_2 u_2$ that is identically zero without both c_1 and c_2 being zero. Two functions with this property are said to be *linearly dependent*. More precisely, we have the following definition:

DEFINITION. *Two functions u_1 and u_2 are called linearly dependent on an interval I if there exist constants c_1 and c_2, not both zero, such that $c_1 u_1 + c_2 u_2 = 0$ on I; that is, if*

$$(7.25) \qquad c_1 u_1(x) + c_2 u_2(x) = 0$$

for every x in I. If no such identity holds except when $c_1 = c_2 = 0$, the functions u_1 and u_2 are said to be linearly independent on I.

Note. Two functions u_1 and u_2 cannot be linearly independent if either of them is zero. For example, if $u_1 = 0$ we have $1 \cdot u_1 + 0 \cdot u_2 = 0$ and Equation (7.25) is satisfied with $c_1 = 1$ and $c_2 = 0$.

In the language of linear independence, Theorem 7–3 states that if u_1 and u_2 are two linearly independent solutions of $L(y) = 0$, the general solution is $c_1 u_1 + c_2 u_2$. Thus, the problem of solving a homogeneous second-order linear equation is reduced to that of finding two linearly independent solutions. With the help of the existence theorem we can easily prove that such solutions always exist.

7– 4   THEOREM. *Existence of linearly independent solutions. Let $L(y) = y'' + P_1 y' + P_2 y$, where P_1 and P_2 are continuous on an open interval I. Let u_1 and u_2 be solutions of the equation $L(y) = 0$ on I satisfying the initial conditions*

$$(7.26) \qquad u_1(x_0) = 1, \qquad u_1'(x_0) = 0,$$

and

$$(7.27) \qquad u_2(x_0) = 0, \qquad u_2'(x_0) = 1,$$

for some point x_0 in I. Then the solutions u_1 and u_2 are linearly independent on I.

Note. The existence of solutions u_1 and u_2 satisfying the initial conditions (7.26) and (7.27) is guaranteed by Theorem 7–1.

Proof. Suppose constants c_1 and c_2 exist such that

$$c_1 u_1(x) + c_2 u_2(x) = 0$$

for all x in I. We wish to prove that $c_1 = c_2 = 0$. Differentiation of the last equation gives us

$$c_1 u_1'(x) + c_2 u_2'(x) = 0$$

for all x in I. If we substitute $x = x_0$ in the last two equations and use the initial conditions (7.26) and (7.27) we find that $c_1 = c_2 = 0$. This proves that the solutions u_1 and u_2 are linearly independent on I.

Although a pair of linearly independent solutions always exists, it may not be possible to express these solutions in terms of elementary functions. However, when the coefficients of the equation are *constants*, the solutions can always be expressed in terms of exponential functions, sines, cosines, and polynomials. We turn now to this case.†

7.6 Homogeneous linear equations of second order with constant coefficients

A linear second-order homogeneous equation with constant coefficients can be put in the form

$$(7.28) \qquad y'' + ay' + by = 0 \, ,$$

where a and b are constants. Since the coefficients are continuous everywhere, we seek solutions valid over the entire real axis. In this case we can determine all solutions of the equation without using the existence theorem or the uniqueness theorem stated in Section 7.5. First we shall exhibit two linearly independent solutions u_1 and u_2. Then we prove that every solution of (7.28) can be expressed as a linear combination of these two.

The two examples $y'' + k^2 y = 0$ and $y'' - k^2 y = 0$ treated in the foregoing section are of this type. Their general solutions are

$$y = c_1 \cos kx + c_2 \sin kx \qquad \text{and} \qquad y = c_1 e^{kx} + c_2 e^{-kx} \, ,$$

respectively. These examples suggest that we try to find exponential or trigonometric functions as solutions of the general equation. If we try $y = e^{rx}$, where r is a constant, we have $y' = re^{rx}$, $y'' = r^2 e^{rx}$, so Equation (7.28) becomes

$$e^{rx}(r^2 + ar + b) = 0 \, .$$

Since e^{rx} is never zero, the function $y = e^{rx}$ is a solution if and only if r satisfies the quadratic equation

$$r^2 + ar + b = 0 \, .$$

This is called the *characteristic equation* associated with (7.28). Since it is a quadratic equation it has two roots r_1 and r_2, which may be real or complex,‡ distinct or equal. If we want to confine the discussion to real-valued functions we must distinguish two cases, according to whether the roots r_1 and r_2 are real or complex.

---

† The homogeneous linear equation with constant coefficients was the first differential equation of a general type to be completely solved. A solution was first published by Euler in 1743. Apart from its historical interest, the linear equation with constant coefficients has important practical applications; because of the simplicity of its solution, it is of theoretical interest as well.

‡ To understand the discussion in this section, the reader must have some familiarity with complex numbers. He should know how to solve a quadratic equation when its roots are not real. A brief account of complex numbers is given in a supplement at the end of this chapter.

CASE 1. Real roots r_1 and r_2. If the roots of the characteristic equation are real and distinct, the two functions

$$u_1(x) = e^{r_1 x} \quad \text{and} \quad u_2(x) = e^{r_2 x}$$

are linearly independent because their ratio is not constant.

Example 1. The equation $y'' - k^2 y = 0$, with k a nonzero constant, falls in this category. The characteristic equation is $r^2 - k^2 = 0$; its roots are $r_1 = k$, $r_2 = -k$, so $u_1(x) = e^{kx}$ and $u_2(x) = e^{-kx}$ are two linearly independent solutions.

If $k = 0$, the roots r_1 and r_2 are both equal to zero and the corresponding solutions are $u_1(x) = u_2(x) = e^{0 \cdot x} = 1$. Since u_1 and u_2 are identical they are not independent solutions. However, in this case the differential equation simplifies to $y'' = 0$, and it may be integrated at once to give us the general solution

$$y = c_1 + c_2 x.$$

This has the form

$$y = c_1 v_1(x) + c_2 v_2(x),$$

where $v_1(x) = 1$ and $v_2(x) = x$. The functions v_1 and v_2 are linearly independent solutions. The solution $y = v_1(x)$ originated from the characteristic equation; the second solution $y = v_2(x)$ is simply x times $v_1(x)$.

The foregoing example suggests how to treat the case of equal roots in the general equation (7.28). If $r_1 = r_2 = \alpha$, say, the characteristic equation leads to only one solution, $u_1(x) = e^{\alpha x}$. Guided by the foregoing example, we try to find a second solution by multiplying $u_1(x)$ by x. In this case the differential equation has the form $y'' - 2\alpha y' + \alpha^2 y = 0$; it is easy to verify that the equation is satisfied by $u_2(x) = xe^{\alpha x}$. Since $u_2(x)/u_1(x) = x$, the solutions u_1 and u_2 are independent.

CASE 2. Complex roots r_1 and r_2. For the equation of simple harmonic motion, $y'' + k^2 y = 0$, the characteristic equation $r^2 + k^2 = 0$ has complex roots $r_1 = ik$ and $r_2 = -ik$. For this equation we have seen that the general solution is given by $y = c_1 \cos kx + c_2 \sin kx$. The use of trigonometric functions enables us to treat the general case of complex roots.

We first note that the roots in this case must be complex conjugates. That is, we have

$$r_1 = \alpha + i\beta \quad \text{and} \quad r_2 = \alpha - i\beta,$$

where α and β are real. Since

$$r^2 + ar + b = (r - r_1)(r - r_2) = r^2 - (r_1 + r_2)r + r_1 r_2,$$

the coefficients a and b are related to α and β by the equations

(7.29) $$a = -(r_1 + r_2) = -2\alpha \quad \text{and} \quad b = r_1 r_2 = \alpha^2 + \beta^2.$$

When $\beta = 0$ we know that $y = e^{\alpha x}$ is a solution. When $\alpha = 0$ and $\beta \neq 0$ the equation is that of simple harmonic motion, and two independent solutions are given by $y = \cos \beta x$ and $y = \sin \beta x$. This suggests that for the general case of complex roots we try the functions

(7.30) $\qquad u_1(x) = e^{\alpha x} \cos \beta x \qquad$ and $\qquad u_2(x) = e^{\alpha x} \sin \beta x$.

These are linearly independent because their quotient $u_2(x)/u_1(x) = \tan \beta x$ is not constant. To show that they are indeed solutions we note that

$$u_1'(x) = e^{\alpha x}(-\beta \sin \beta x + \alpha \cos \beta x), \qquad u_1''(x) = e^{\alpha x}[(\alpha^2 - \beta^2) \cos \beta x - 2\alpha\beta \sin \beta x],$$

and hence

$$u_1''(x) + au_1'(x) + bu_1(x) = e^{\alpha x}[(\alpha^2 - \beta^2) + a\alpha + b] \cos \beta x + e^{\alpha x}[-2\alpha\beta - a\beta] \sin \beta x .$$

If we use the relations in (7.29) we see that each square bracket vanishes; hence u_1 is a solution. Similarly, we find that u_2 is a solution. Therefore the two functions in (7.30) are linearly independent solutions.

Example 2. The equation $y'' + 2y' + 5y = 0$ has characteristic equation $r^2 + 2r + 5 = 0$. The roots are

$$r_1 = -1 + 2i, \qquad r_2 = -1 - 2i .$$

Therefore the independent solutions in (7.30) are given by

$$u_1(x) = e^{-x} \cos 2x , \qquad u_2(x) = e^{-x} \sin 2x .$$

The results of this section are summarized in part (a) of the following theorem.

7-5 $\qquad$ THEOREM. (a) *Every homogeneous second-order linear equation*

$$y'' + ay' + by = 0$$

with constant coefficients has linearly independent solutions u_1 *and* u_2 *which may be determined as follows: Let* r_1 *and* r_2 *be the roots of the corresponding characteristic equation*

$$r^2 + ar + b = 0 .$$

If r_1 *and* r_2 *are real and distinct we may take*

(7.31) $\qquad u_1(x) = e^{r_1 x} , \qquad u_2(x) = e^{r_2 x} .$

If the roots are real and equal, say $r_1 = r_2 = \alpha$, *we may take*

$$u_1(x) = e^{\alpha x} , \qquad u_2(x) = xe^{\alpha x} .$$

If the roots are complex, with $r_1 = \alpha + i\beta$ *and* $r_2 = \alpha - i\beta$, *we may take*

(7.32) $\qquad u_1(x) = e^{\alpha x} \cos \beta x , \qquad u_2(x) = e^{\alpha x} \sin \beta x .$

$\qquad$ (b) *Let* u_1 *and* u_2 *be the solutions described in part (a). Then every solution of* $y'' + ay' + by = 0$ *has the form*

$$y = c_1 u_1(x) + c_2 u_2(x)$$

where c_1 *and* c_2 *are constants.*

Proof. Part (a) has already been proved. To prove part (b), let y be any solution of $L(y) = 0$, where $L(y) = y'' + ay' + by$. Let $v = y/u_1$, where u_1 is the solution in part (a). (The function v is defined at those points at which u_1 does not vanish.) Then we have

$$y = u_1 v, \qquad y' = u_1 v' + u_1' v, \qquad y'' = u_1 v'' + 2u_1' v_1' + u_1'' v,$$

and the differential equation $L(y) = 0$ becomes

$$v(u_1'' + au_1' + bu_1) + v'(au_1 + 2u_1') + v''u_1 = 0.$$

The coefficient of v is zero since $L(u_1) = 0$. Therefore v must satisfy the differential equation

$$v'' + v'(a + 2u_1'/u_1) = 0.$$

This is a first-order linear equation for v'; when we solve it we find that v' has the form

$$v'(x) = Ae^{-ax}/[u_1(x)]^2$$

for some constant A. Now $-a = r_1 + r_2$, where r_1 and r_2 are the roots of the characteristic equation $r^2 + ar + b = 0$. Therefore the formula for $v'(x)$ becomes

$$v'(x) = A \frac{e^{(r_1+r_2)x}}{[u_1(x)]^2}.$$

From the formulas for u_1 and u_2 given in part (a) it is easy to verify that

$$\frac{e^{(r_1+r_2)x}}{[u_1(x)]^2} = C \frac{d}{dx}\left(\frac{u_2(x)}{u_1(x)}\right)$$

for some constant C (depending on r_1 and r_2). Therefore we may integrate the formula for $v'(x)$ to obtain

$$v(x) = c_2 \frac{u_2(x)}{u_1(x)} + c_1,$$

where c_1 and c_2 are constants. Multiplying by $u_1(x)$ we find that $y = c_1 u_1(x) + c_2 u_2(x)$, as required. This completes the proof of part (b).

Note. There is a more elegant way to determine the solutions u_1 and u_2 without distinguishing between real and complex roots of the characteristic equation. The definition of the exponential function can be extended so that $e^{r_1 x}$ and $e^{r_2 x}$ are meaningful when r_1 and r_2 are complex numbers. This extension can be made in such a way that the familiar properties of exponentials carry over to the complex case. The analysis given above for real distinct roots r_1 and r_2 remains valid for complex r_1 and r_2 as well. The details of this procedure are outlined in Section 7.24. It is shown there that the definition of the complex exponential function implies the relation

$$e^{(\alpha + i\beta)x} = e^{\alpha x} e^{i\beta x} = e^{\alpha x}(\cos \beta x + i \sin \beta x);$$

this accounts for the appearance of the trigonometric functions in (7.32).

7.7 Exercises

Solve the differential equations in Exercises 1 through 6.

1. $y'' - 2y' + 3y = 0.$
2. $y'' + 2y' - 3y = 0.$
3. $y'' - 2y' + 2y = 0.$

4. $y'' - 2y' + 5y = 0.$
5. $y'' + 2y' + y = 0.$
6. $y'' - 2y' + y = 0.$

In Exercises 7 through 10, find the particular solution satisfying the given initial conditions.

7. $2y'' + 3y' = 0$,   with $y = 1$ and $y' = 1$ when $x = 0$.

8. $y'' + 25y = 0$,   with $y = -1$ and $y' = 0$ when $x = 3$.

9. $y'' - 4y' - y = 0$,   with $y = 2$ and $y' = -1$ when $x = 1$.

10. $y'' + 4y' + 5y = 0$,   with $y = 2$ and $y' = y''$ when $x = 0$.

11. An integral curve $y = u(x)$ of the differential equation $y'' - 3y' - 4y = 0$ intersects an integral curve $y = v(x)$ of the differential equation $y'' + 4y' - 5y = 0$ at the origin. Determine the functions u and v if the two curves have equal slopes at the origin and if

$$\lim_{x \to \infty} \frac{[v(x)]^4}{u(x)} = \frac{5}{6}.$$

12. An integral curve $y = u(x)$ of the differential equation $y'' - 4y' + 29y = 0$ intersects an integral curve $y = v(x)$ of the differential equation $y'' + 4y' + 13y = 0$ at the origin. The two curves have equal slopes at the origin. Determine u and v if $u'(\pi/2) = 1$.

13. Let W denote the Wronskian of two functions u_1 and u_2.

(a) Show that $W' = u_1 u_2'' - u_2 u_1''$.

(b) If u_1 and u_2 are solutions of the differential equation $y'' + P_1 y' + P_2 y = 0$ on an interval I, show that their Wronskian satisfies the first-order equation $W' + P_1 W = 0$. Solve this equation and derive Abel's formula for the Wronskian [Equation (7.24)].

14. Let u_1 and u_2 be linearly independent solutions of the differential equation $y'' + P_1(x)y' + P_2(x)y = 0$ on an interval I. In the proof of Theorem 7–3 we used the uniqueness theorem (Theorem 7–2) to prove that every solution of the equation has the form $y = c_1 u_1 + c_2 u_2$. Prove the converse. That is, assume it is known that every solution of this equation has the form $y = c_1 u_1 + c_2 u_2$, and use this to prove the uniqueness theorem.

15. Given that the differential equation $y'' + 4xy' + Q(x)y = 0$ has two solutions of the form $y_1 = u(x)$ and $y_2 = xu(x)$, where $u(0) = 1$. Determine both $u(x)$ and $Q(x)$ explicitly in terms of x.

16. Find all values of the constant k such that the differential equation $y'' + ky = 0$ has a nonzero solution $y = f_k(x)$ for which $f_k(0) = f_k(1) = 0$. For each permissible value of k, determine the corresponding solution $y = f_k(x)$. Consider both positive and negative values of k.

17. In each case, verify that u_1 and u_2 are linearly independent over every interval I, and find a linear differential equation of second order satisfied by u_1 and u_2.

(a) $u_1(x) = e^x$, $u_2(x) = e^{-x}$.

(b) $u_1(x) = e^{2x}$, $u_2(x) = xe^{2x}$.

(c) $u_1(x) = e^{-x/2} \cos x$, $u_2(x) = e^{-x/2} \sin x$.

(d) $u_1(x) = \sin(2x + 1)$, $u_2(x) = \sin(2x + 2)$.

(e) $u_1(x) = \cosh x$, $u_2(x) = \sinh x$.

18. Let u_1 and u_2 be the linearly independent solutions of the equation $y'' + ay' + by = 0$ given in Theorem 7–5. If r_1 and r_2 are the roots of the characteristic equation $r^2 + ar + b = 0$, show that

$$\frac{e^{(r_1 + r_2)x}}{[u_1(x)]^2} = C \frac{d}{dx}\left(\frac{u_2(x)}{u_1(x)}\right)$$

for some constant C.

7.8   Nonhomogeneous linear equations of second order. Variation of parameters

We turn now to a discussion of nonhomogeneous linear equations of second order. Consider the equation

(7.33) $$y'' + P_1 y' + P_2 y = R,$$

where the functions P_1, P_2, and R are continuous on an interval I. This equation may be written as $L(y) = R$, where $L(y)$ denotes the left member of (7.33). Suppose y_1 and y_2 are any two solutions of this equation. Since $L(y_1) = L(y_2) = R$, linearity gives us

$$L(y_2 - y_1) = L(y_2) - L(y_1) = R - R = 0,$$

so $y_2 - y_1$ is a solution of the homogeneous equation $L(y) = 0$. Therefore, if u_1 and u_2 are two linearly independent solutions of the homogeneous equation, we must have $y_2 - y_1 = c_1 u_1 + c_2 u_2$, or

$$y_2 = c_1 u_1 + c_2 u_2 + y_1$$

for some choice of constants c_1 and c_2. This equation must be satisfied by every pair of solutions y_1 and y_2 of the nonhomogeneous equation (7.33). Therefore, if we can determine *one particular solution* y_1 of the nonhomogeneous equation, *all* solutions are contained in the formula

(7.34) $$y = c_1 u_1 + c_2 u_2 + y_1,$$

where c_1 and c_2 are arbitrary constants. Each such y is clearly a solution of (7.33) because $L(c_1 u_1 + c_2 u_2 + y_1) = L(c_1 u_1 + c_2 u_2) + L(y_1) = 0 + R = R$. Since all solutions of (7.33) are found in Equation (7.34), the linear combination $c_1 u_1 + c_2 u_2 + y_1$ is called the general solution of (7.33). Thus, we have proved the following theorem:

7– 6   THEOREM. *If y_1 is a particular solution of the nonhomogeneous equation $L(y) = R$, the general solution of this equation is obtained by adding to y_1 the general solution of the corresponding homogeneous equation $L(y) = 0$.*

To use this theorem in practice we must solve two problems: (1) Find the general solution of the homogeneous equation $L(y) = 0$, and (2) find a particular solution of the nonhomogeneous equation $L(y) = R$. The next theorem shows that we can always solve problem (2) if we can solve problem (1).

7– 7   THEOREM.   *Let u_1 and u_2 be linearly independent solutions of the homogeneous linear equation $L(y) = 0$ on an interval I, where $L(y) = y'' + P_1 y' + P_2 y$. Let $W(x) = u_1(x) u_2'(x) - u_2(x) u_1'(x)$ be the Wronskian of u_1 and u_2. Then the nonhomogeneous equation $L(y) = R$ has a solution y_1 given by the formula*

(7.35) $$y_1(x) = v_1(x) u_1(x) + v_2(x) u_2(x),$$

where

(7.36) $$v_1(x) = - \int u_2(x) \frac{R(x)}{W(x)} \, dx,$$

and

(7.37) $$v_2(x) = \int u_1(x) \frac{R(x)}{W(x)} \, dx.$$

Proof. Let us try to find functions v_1 and v_2 such that the combination $y_1 = v_1 u_1 + v_2 u_2$ will satisfy the equation $L(y_1) = R$. We have

$$y_1' = v_1 u_1' + v_2 u_2' + (v_1' u_1 + v_2' u_2),$$

$$y_1'' = v_1 u_1'' + v_2 u_2'' + (v_1' u_1' + v_2' u_2') + (v_1' u_1 + v_2' u_2)'.$$

When we form the linear combination $L(y_1) = y_1'' + P_1 y_1' + P_2 y_1$, the terms involving v_1 and v_2 drop out because of the relations $L(u_1) = L(u_2) = 0$. The remaining terms give us the relation

$$L(y_1) = (v_1' u_1' + v_2' u_2') + (v_1' u_1 + v_2' u_2)' + P_1 \cdot (v_1' u_1 + v_2' u_2).$$

We want to choose v_1 and v_2 so that $L(y_1) = R$. We can satisfy this equation if we choose v_1 and v_2 so that

$$v_1' u_1 + v_2' u_2 = 0 \quad \text{and} \quad v_1' u_1' + v_2' u_2' = R.$$

This is a pair of algebraic equations for v_1' and v_2'. The determinant of the system is the Wronskian of u_1 and u_2. Since this is never zero on I, the system has a solution given by

$$v_1' = \frac{\begin{vmatrix} 0 & u_2 \\ R & u_2' \end{vmatrix}}{\begin{vmatrix} u_1 & u_2 \\ u_1' & u_2' \end{vmatrix}} = -u_2 R / W, \quad \text{and} \quad v_2' = \frac{\begin{vmatrix} u_1 & 0 \\ u_1' & R \end{vmatrix}}{\begin{vmatrix} u_1 & u_2 \\ u_1' & u_2' \end{vmatrix}} = u_1 R / W.$$

Integrating these relations we obtain Equations (7.36) and (7.37), respectively, thus completing the proof. The method by which we obtained the solution y_1 is sometimes called *variation of parameters* (or *variation of constants*). It was first used by Johann Bernoulli in 1697 to solve linear equations of first order, and then by Lagrange in 1774 to solve linear equations of second order.

Note. Since the functions v_1 and v_2 in Theorem 7–7 are expressed as indefinite integrals, each of them is determined only to within an additive constant. If we add a constant c_1 to v_1 and a constant c_2 to v_2 we change the function y_1 in (7.35) to a new function $y_2 = y_1 + c_1 u_1 + c_2 u_2$. By linearity, we have

$$L(y_2) = L(y_1) + L(c_1 u_1 + c_2 u_2) = L(y_1),$$

so the new function y_2 is also a particular solution of the nonhomogeneous equation.

Example 1. Find the general solution of the equation

$$y'' + y = \tan x.$$

Solution. We consider an interval in which the right-hand member is continuous, say the interval $[-a, a]$, where $0 < a < \pi/2$. The homogeneous equation has the linearly independent solutions

$$u_1(x) = \cos x, \quad u_2(x) = \sin x.$$

Their Wronskian is

$$W(x) = \begin{vmatrix} \cos x & \sin x \\ -\sin x & \cos x \end{vmatrix} = \cos^2 x + \sin^2 x = 1 \,.$$

Equations (7.36) and (7.37) give us

$$v_1(x) = -\int \sin x \tan x \, dx = \sin x - \log |\sec x + \tan x| \,,$$

and

$$v_2(x) = \int \cos x \tan x \, dx = \int \sin x \, dx = -\cos x \,.$$

Therefore a particular solution of the nonhomogeneous equation is given by

$$y_1 = v_1(x)u_1(x) + v_2(x)u_2(x) = \sin x \cos x - \cos x \log |\sec x + \tan x| - \sin x \cos x$$

$$= -\cos x \log |\sec x + \tan x| \,;$$

by Theorem 7–6, its general solution is

$$y = c_1 \cos x + c_2 \sin x - \cos x \log |\sec x + \tan x| \,.$$

Although Theorem 7–7 provides a general method for determining a particular solution of $L(y) = R$, special methods are available that are often easier to apply when the function R has certain special forms. This is especially true when the differential equation has constant coefficients. For example, suppose the equation is

(7.38)
$$y'' + ay' + by = R \,,$$

where a and b are constants, and suppose R is a polynomial of degree n. Then if $b \neq 0$ we can always find a polynomial of degree n that satisfies this equation.† We try a polynomial of the form

$$y_1(x) = \sum_{k=0}^{n} a_k x^k$$

with undetermined coefficients. Substituting in differential equation (7.38) and equating coefficients of like powers of x, we may determine $a_n, a_{n-1}, \ldots, a_1, a_0$ in succession. The method is illustrated by the following example.

Example 2. Consider the equation

(7.39)
$$y'' + y = x^3 \,.$$

Since the right member is a polynomial of degree 3, and since the coefficient of y is nonzero, we try to find a particular solution of the form $y_1(x) = Ax^3 + Bx^2 + Cx + D$.

---

† If $b = 0$ and $a \neq 0$ the equation cannot be satisfied by a polynomial of degree n, but it can be satisfied by a polynomial of degree $n + 1$. If both a and b are zero, the equation becomes $y'' = R$; its general solution is a polynomial of degree $n + 2$ obtained by two successive integrations.

Differentiating twice, we find $y_1''(x) = 6Ax + 2B$. The differential equation leads to the relation

$$(6Ax + 2B) + (Ax^3 + Bx^2 + Cx + D) = x^3 .$$

Equating coefficients of like powers of x we obtain $A = 1$, $B = 0$, $C = -6$, and $D = 0$, so a particular solution of (7.39) is $y_1(x) = x^3 - 6x$. Since the homogeneous equation is the same as that in Example 1 [with linearly independent solutions $u_1(x) = \cos x$ and $u_2(x) = \sin x$] the general solution of (7.39) is

$$y = c_1 \cos x + c_2 \sin x + x^3 - 6x .$$

It may be of interest to compare this method with variation of parameters. Equations (7.36) and (7.37) give us

$$v_1(x) = - \int x^3 \sin x \, dx = -(3x^3 - 6) \sin x + (x^3 - 6x) \cos x$$

and

$$v_2(x) = \int x^3 \cos x \, dx = (3x^2 - 6) \cos x + (x^3 - 6x) \sin x .$$

When we form the combination $v_1 u_1 + v_2 u_2$ we find the particular solution $y_1(x) = x^3 - 6x$, as before. In this case, the use of variation of parameters required the evaluation of the integrals $\int x^3 \sin x \, dx$ and $\int x^3 \cos x \, dx$. With the method of undetermined coefficients no integration is required.

Similar methods are available when the right-hand member is a finite sum of terms of the form $p(x)e^{\alpha x} \sin \beta x$ or $p(x)e^{\alpha x} \cos \beta x$, where p is a polynomial. Some of the exercises in the next section describe these methods. These equations can also be handled by another method (the method of annihilators) described in Section 7.15.

Example 3. If we express the functions v_1 and v_2 in Theorem 7-7 as definite integrals we may write

$$v_1(x) = - \int_c^x u_2(t) \frac{R(t)}{W(t)} \, dt \quad \text{and} \quad v_2(x) = \int_c^x u_1(t) \frac{R(t)}{W(t)} \, dt ,$$

where c is any fixed number in the interval I. When these equations are substituted in (7.35) the formula for y_1 becomes

$$(7.40) \qquad y_1(x) = \int_c^x [u_1(t)u_2(x) - u_1(x)u_2(t)] \frac{R(t)}{W(t)} \, dt .$$

If the left member of the differential equation has constant coefficients, Equation (7.40) simplifies to an interesting form. Specifically, if the differential equation in question is

$$y'' + ay' + by = R ,$$

where a and b are constants, Equation (7.40) can be written in the form

$$(7.41) \qquad y_1(x) = \int_c^x f(x - t)R(t) \, dt ,$$

where f is that particular solution of the homogeneous equation which satisfies the conditions

$$f(0) = 0 \quad \text{and} \quad f'(0) = 1.$$

We shall deduce (7.41) from (7.40) for the special case in which the characteristic equation $r^2 + ar + b = 0$ has distinct real roots. The proofs for the remaining cases are requested in Exercise 23 of the next section.

If the roots of the characteristic equation are r_1 and r_2, the functions

$$u_1(x) = e^{r_1 x} \quad \text{and} \quad u_2(x) = e^{r_2 x}$$

are linearly independent solutions of the homogeneous equation. The Wronskian of these two solutions is

$$W(x) = \begin{vmatrix} e^{r_1 x} & e^{r_2 x} \\ r_1 e^{r_1 x} & r_2 e^{r_2 x} \end{vmatrix} = (r_2 - r_1)e^{(r_1 + r_2)x}.$$

Substituting these relations in Equation (7.40) we obtain

$$y_1(x) = \int_c^x \frac{e^{r_2(x-t)} - e^{r_1(x-t)}}{r_2 - r_1} R(t)\, dt.$$

This formula has the form of Equation (7.41) with

$$f(t) = \frac{e^{r_2 t} - e^{r_1 t}}{r_2 - r_1}.$$

Since f is a linear combination of u_1 and u_2 it is a particular solution of the homogeneous equation. Moreover, it has the two properties $f(0) = 0$ and $f'(0) = 1$.

Note. Integrals of the form $\int_c^x f(x - t)R(t)\, dt$ occur frequently in the theory of differential equations and elsewhere. They are known as *convolution integrals*.

Example 4. Let $L(y) = y'' + P_1 y' + P_2 y$. To solve the nonhomogeneous equation $L(y) = R$ by variation of parameters, we need to know two linearly independent solutions of the homogeneous equation. This example shows that if *one* solution u_1 of $L(y) = 0$ is known, and if u_1 is never zero on an interval I, a second solution u_2 of the homogeneous equation is given by the formula

$$(7.42) \qquad\qquad u_2(x) = u_1(x) \int_c^x \frac{Q(t)}{[u_1(t)]^2}\, dt,$$

where $Q(x) = e^{-\int P_1(x)\,dx}$, and c is any point in I. These two solutions are linearly independent on I.

It is a straightforward exercise to show that the function u_2 does, indeed, satisfy $L(y) = 0$; we leave this verification to the reader. To prove that u_1 and u_2 are independent we note that $u_2(x)/u_1(x) = \int_c^x Q(t) [u_1(t)]^{-2}\, dt$. The ratio $u_2(x)/u_1(x)$ is not a constant because its derivative, $Q(x) [u_1(x)]^{-2}$, is never zero on I (since Q is an exponential).

It is of interest to know how the formula for u_2 might be discovered. Suppose we try to find a function v such that the product $y = u_1 v$ satisfies $L(y) = 0$. Differentiating, we have

$$y' = u_1 v' + u_1' v , \qquad y'' = u_1 v'' + 2u_1' v' + u_1'' v ,$$

and we find

$$L(y) = u_1 v'' + (2u_1' + P_1 u_1)v' + L(u_1)v$$

Since $L(u_1) = 0$, the function v must satisfy the equation

(7.43) $$u_1 v'' + (2u_1' + P_1 u_1)v' = 0 .$$

This is a first-order differential equation for v'. It may be solved as a first-order linear equation [using Equation (7.3)] or as a separable equation. By either method we obtain

(7.44) $$v'(x) = A \, Q(x)/[u_1(x)]^2 ,$$

where A is an arbitrary constant. Since we seek only a particular solution we may choose $A = 1$. Integration of (7.44) leads to the formula

$$v(x) = \int_c^x \frac{Q(t)}{[u_1(t)]^2} \, dt .$$

Multiplying this by $u_1(x)$ we obtain the solution in (7.42). Knowing the two solutions u_1 and u_2, we can find the general solution of $L(y) = R$ by variation of parameters.

An alternative procedure is to determine v so that the product vu_1 is a solution of the nonhomogeneous equation. Proceeding as above, we find that, in place of (7.43), v must satisfy the equation

(7.45) $$u_1 v'' + (2u_1' + P_1 u_1)v' = R .$$

This may be solved as a first-order linear equation in v'. Knowing v', we integrate to find v. If we use the general solution of (7.45) in determining v, the corresponding product $y = vu_1$ will be the general solution of $L(y) = R$. Specific examples occur in some of the exercises in the next section.

7.9 Exercises

Find the general solution of each of the differential equations in Exercises 1 through 11. If the solution is not valid over the entire real axis, describe an interval over which it is valid.

1. $y'' - y = x$.
2. $y'' - 2y' + 3y = x^3$.
3. $y'' - y' = x^2$.
4. $y'' + y' = x^2 + 2x$.
5. $y'' - 5y' + 4y = x^2 - 2x + 1$.
6. $y'' + y' - 6y = 2x^3 + 5x^2 - 7x + 2$.
7. $y'' + 2y' + y = e^{-x}/x^2$.
8. $y'' + y = \cot^2 x$.
9. $y'' - y = 2/(1 + e^x)$.
10. $y'' + y' - 2y = e^x/(1 + e^x)$.

11. $y'' + 6y' + 9y = f(x)$, where $f(x) = 1$ for $1 \le x \le 2$, and $f(x) = 0$ for all other values of x.

12. Consider the equation $y'' + ay' + by = p(x)e^{mx}$, where a, b, and m are constants, and p is a polynomial of degree n.

(a) Show that the change of variable $y = u(x)e^{mx}$ transforms this equation to

$$u'' + (2m + a)u' + (m^2 + am + b)u = p .$$

(b) Use part (a) to deduce that the equation $y'' + ay' + by = p(x)e^{mx}$ has a solution of the form $y = q(x)e^{mx}$, where q is a polynomial. What is the relation between the degrees of q and of p?

Solve the equations in Exercises 13 through 16 either by variation of parameters or by the method suggested by Exercise 12.

13. $y'' - 4y = e^{2x}$.

14. $y'' + 2y' = 3xe^x$.

15. $y'' + y' - 2y = e^x + e^{2x}$.

16. $y'' - 2y' + y = x + 2xe^x$.

17. Consider the equation $y'' + ay' + by = p(x)e^{\alpha x} \cos \beta x$, where a, b, α, and β are constants, and p is a polynomial.

(a) Show that there is a particular solution of the form

$$y = e^{\alpha x}[q(x) \cos \beta x + r(x) \sin \beta x],$$

where q and r are polynomials. How are the degrees of q and r related to the degree of p?

(b) Discuss, in a similar way, the equation $y'' + ay' + by = p(x)e^{\alpha x} \sin \beta x$.

Solve the equations in Exercises 18 through 21 either by variation of parameters or by the method suggested by Exercise 17.

18. $y'' + 4y = 3x \cos x$.

19. $y'' + y = \sin x$.

20. $y'' - 3y' = 2e^{2x} \sin x$.

21. $y'' + y = e^{2x} \cos 3x$.

22. The current $I(t)$ at time t flowing in an electric circuit obeys the differential equation

$$I''(t) + RI'(t) + I(t) = \sin \omega t,$$

where R and ω are positive constants. The solution can be expressed in the form $I(t) = F(t) + A \sin(\omega t + \alpha)$, where $F(t) \to 0$ as $t \to +\infty$, and A and α are constants depending on R and ω, with $A > 0$. If there is a value of ω which makes A as large as possible, then $\omega/(2\pi)$ is called a *resonance frequency* of the circuit.

(a) Find all resonance frequencies when $R = 1$.

(b) Find those values of R for which the circuit will have a resonance frequency.

23. If $L(y) = y'' + ay' + by$, where a and b are constants, let f be that particular solution of $L(y) = 0$ satisfying the conditions $f(0) = 0$ and $f'(0) = 1$. Show that a particular solution of $L(y) = R$ is given by the formula

$$y_1(x) = \int_c^x f(x - t)R(t)\, dt$$

for any choice of c. In particular, if the roots of the characteristic equation are equal, say $r_1 = r_2 = m$, show that the formula for $y_1(x)$ becomes

$$y_1(x) = e^{mx} \int_c^x (x - t)e^{-mt}R(t)\, dt.$$

24. Find the general solution of the equation

$$xy'' - 2(x + 1)y' + (x + 2)y = x^3 e^{2x}$$

for $x > 0$, given that the homogeneous equation has a solution of the form $y = e^{mx}$.

25. Obtain one nonzero solution by inspection and then find the general solution of the differential equation

$$(y'' - 4y') + x^2(y' - 4y) = 0.$$

26. Find the general solution of the differential equation

$$4x^2y'' + 4xy' - y = 0,$$

given that there is a particular solution of the form $y = x^m$ for $x > 0$.

27. Find a solution of the homogeneous equation by trial, and then find the general solution of the equation

$$x(1 - x)y'' - (1 - 2x)y' + (x^2 - 3x + 1)y = (1 - x)^3.$$

28. Find the general solution of the equation

$$(2x - 3x^3)y'' + 4y' + 6xy = 0,$$

given that it has a solution that is a polynomial in x.

29. Find the general solution of the equation

$$x^2(1 - x)y'' + 2x(2 - x)y' + 2(1 + x)y = x^2,$$

given that the homogeneous equation has a solution of the form $y = x^c$.

30. Let $g(x) = \int_1^x e^t/t \, dt$ if $x > 0$. (Do not attempt to evaluate this integral.) Find all values of the constant a such that the function f defined by

$$f(x) = \frac{1}{x} e^{ag(x)}$$

satisfies the linear differential equation

$$x^2 y'' + (3x - x^2)y' + (1 - x - e^{2x})y = 0.$$

Use this information to determine the general solution of the equation on the interval $(0, + \infty)$.

7.10 Linear equations of order n

The principal results of the theory of linear equations of order two can be extended to linear equations of order n. This section indicates briefly how the extension takes place for the general linear equation. Section 7.12 treats in somewhat more detail the case of constant coefficients. We begin with the statements of the existence and uniqueness theorems.

7–8 THEOREM. *Existence theorem for linear equations of order n.* Let $P_1, P_2, \ldots, P_n$ be continuous functions on an open interval I, and let

$$L(y) = y^{(n)} + P_1 y^{(n-1)} + \cdots + P_n y.$$

If x_0 is a point in I and if $k_0, k_1, \ldots, k_{n-1}$ are n given real numbers, there exists a function f which is a solution of the differential equation $L(y) = 0$ on I and which satisfies the initial conditions

$$f(x_0) = k_0, \qquad f'(x_0) = k_1, \qquad \ldots, \qquad f^{(n-1)}(x_0) = k_{n-1}.$$

7–9 THEOREM. *Uniqueness theorem for linear equations of order n.* Let L be the linear operator of Theorem 7–8, let f and g be two functions that satisfy the differential equation $L(y) = 0$ on an open interval I, and assume that

$$f(x_0) = g(x_0), \qquad f'(x_0) = g'(x_0), \qquad \ldots, \qquad f^{(n-1)}(x_0) = g^{(n-1)}(x_0)$$

for some x_0 in I. Then $f(x) = g(x)$ for all x in I.

Both these theorems will be deduced as corollaries of more general theorems discussed in Chapter 9. We shall use both theorems to deduce properties of solutions of linear equations. As in the second-order case, the concept of linear independence plays a fundamental role. The definition for n functions is as follows:

DEFINITION. *A collection of n functions $u_1, u_2, \ldots, u_n$ is called linearly dependent on an interval I if there exist constants $c_1, c_2, \ldots, c_n$, not all zero, such that*

$$\sum_{i=1}^{n} c_i u_i(x) = 0$$

for every x in I. If no such identity holds except when $c_1 = c_2 = \cdots = c_n = 0$, the functions $u_1, u_2, \ldots, u_n$ are said to be linearly independent on I.

Example 1. Let $u_1(x) = e^{r_1 x}$, $u_2(x) = e^{r_2 x}$, $\ldots$, $u_n(x) = e^{r_n x}$, where $r_1, r_2, \ldots, r_n$ are n distinct real numbers. (Functions of this type occur as solutions of homogeneous linear equations of order n with constant coefficients.) We shall prove that the functions $u_1, u_2, \ldots, u_n$ are linearly independent over every interval I. The method of proof is by induction on the number n.

For $n = 2$ the result is obvious. Assume, then, that it is true for p exponential functions, and consider $p + 1$ functions, say $u_1, u_2, \ldots, u_{p+1}$. Suppose constants $c_1, c_2, \ldots, c_{p+1}$ exist such that

(7.46) $$\sum_{k=1}^{p+1} c_k e^{r_k x} = 0$$

for all x in I. We wish to prove that $c_1 = c_2 = \cdots = c_{p+1} = 0$. If we multiply both sides of (7.46) by $e^{-r_{p+1} x}$ and then differentiate with respect to x, we obtain

$$\sum_{k=1}^{p} c_k (r_k - r_{p+1}) e^{(r_k - r_{p+1})x} = 0.$$

The p numbers $r_1 - r_{p+1}, r_2 - r_{p+1}, \ldots, r_p - r_{p+1}$ are distinct. Therefore, because of the inductive hypothesis, the p exponential functions appearing in this sum are linearly independent on I. Hence we must have

$$c_k (r_k - r_{p+1}) = 0 \qquad \text{for} \quad k = 1, 2, \ldots, p.$$

But since $r_k \neq r_{p+1}$ for each $k \leq p$, it follows that $c_k = 0$ for $k \leq p$. Using this in (7.46) we find also that $c_{p+1} = 0$. This proves, by induction, that the functions $u_1, u_2, \ldots, u_n$ are linearly independent on every interval I.

Example 2. Let $u_1(x) = 1$, $u_2(x) = x$, $\ldots$, $u_n(x) = x^{n-1}$. Then $u_1, u_2, \ldots, u_n$ are linearly independent on every interval I. This is easily proved by induction on n. Details are requested in Exercise 3 of Section 7.11.

Example 3. If r is a constant, the n functions

$$u_1(x) = e^{rx}, \qquad u_2(x) = x e^{rx}, \qquad \ldots, \qquad u_n(x) = x^{n-1} e^{rx}$$

are linearly independent on every interval I. This follows at once from the result of Example 2. If constants $c_1, c_2, \ldots, c_n$ exist such that $\sum c_k u_k = 0$ on I, we must have

$$e^{rx} \sum_{k=1}^{n} c_k x^{k-1} = 0$$

for all x in I. Since e^{rx} is not zero, the polynomial multiplying e^{rx} must be zero for all x in I, and the result of Example 2 shows that $c_1 = c_2 = \cdots = c_n = 0$.

Example 4. Let $r_1, r_2, \ldots, r_n$ be n distinct real numbers, and let $Q_1, Q_2, \ldots, Q_n$ be n polynomials, none of which is identically zero on an interval I. Then the n functions

$$u_1(x) = Q_1(x)e^{r_1x}, \qquad u_2(x) = Q_2(x)e^{r_2x}, \qquad \ldots, \qquad u_n(x) = Q_n(x)e^{r_nx}$$

are linearly independent on I. We can prove this by induction on n. For $n = 1$ or $n = 2$ the result is obvious. Therefore, assume the statement is true for $n = p$ and consider $p + 1$ distinct real numbers $r_1, r_2, \ldots, r_{p+1}$ and $p + 1$ polynomials $Q_1, Q_2, \ldots, Q_{p+1}$, none of which is identically zero on I. Let $c_1, c_2, \ldots, c_{p+1}$ be $p + 1$ constants such that

$$\sum_{k=1}^{p+1} c_k Q_k(x)e^{r_kx} = 0$$

for all x in I. We multiply both sides of this equation by $e^{-r_{p+1}x}$ and rewrite it as

(7.47) $$\sum_{k=1}^{p} c_k Q_k(x)e^{(r_k-r_{p+1})x} + c_{p+1}Q_{p+1}(x) = 0.$$

Differentiation of this relation gives us

$$\sum_{k=1}^{p} c_k[Q_k'(x) + Q_k(x)(r_k - r_{p+1})] \, e^{(r_k-r_{p+1})x} + c_{p+1}Q_{p+1}'(x) = 0.$$

Note that the polynomial multiplying $e^{(r_k-r_{p+1})x}$ has the same degree as Q_k. The degree of this polynomial is preserved under repeated differentiation of the equation. If we differentiate repeatedly until the coefficient of c_{p+1} is identically zero we obtain a relation of the form

$$\sum_{k=1}^{p} c_k P_k(x)e^{(r_k-r_{p+1})x} = 0,$$

where none of the polynomials P_k is identically zero on I. Since the p numbers $r_k - r_{p+1}$ are distinct, we may apply the induction hypothesis to deduce that $c_1 = c_2 = \cdots = c_p = 0$. Substituting these relations in (7.47) and using the fact that Q_{p+1} is not identically zero we see that $c_{p+1} = 0$ as well. This proves, by induction, that the functions $u_1, u_2, \ldots, u_n$ are linearly independent on every interval I.

Example 5. Let $m_1, m_2, \ldots, m_k$ be k positive integers, let $r_1, r_2, \ldots, r_k$ be k distinct real numbers, and let $n = m_1 + \cdots + m_k$. For each pair of integers p, q satisfying $1 \le p \le k, 1 \le q \le m_p$, let

$$u_{q,p}(x) = x^{q-1} e^{r_px}.$$

For example, when $p = 1$ the corresponding functions are

$$u_{1,1}(x) = e^{r_1x}, \qquad u_{2,1}(x) = xe^{r_1x}, \qquad \ldots, \qquad u_{m_1,1}(x) = x^{m_1-1}e^{r_1x}.$$

We shall show that the n functions $u_{q,p}$ so defined are linearly independent over every interval. Consider n constants $c_{q,p}$ such that

(7.48) $$\sum_{p=1}^{k} \sum_{q=1}^{m_p} c_{q,p} \, u_{q,p}(x) = 0$$

for all x on I. We wish to prove that all n constants $c_{q,p}$ are zero. Using the definition of $u_{q,p}(x)$ we may write Equation (7.48) in the form

(7.49) $$\sum_{p=1}^{k} Q_p(x)e^{r_px} = 0,$$

where each Q_p is a polynomial given by

$$Q_p(x) = \sum_{q=1}^{m_p} c_{q,p} \, x^{q-1} .$$

Because of the statement proved in Example 4, Equation (7.49) implies that at least one of these polynomials must be identically zero on I, say the polynomial Q_k. Therefore Equation (7.49) becomes

$$\sum_{p=1}^{k-1} Q_p(x) e^{r_p x} = 0$$

for all x in I. Again, by Example 4, at least one of the polynomials Q_p appearing in this sum must be identically zero on I. Continuing in this way we find that *every* polynomial Q_p is identically zero on I. Hence each coefficient $c_{q,p}$ must be zero.

With the help of the existence theorem we can easily prove that every linear equation of order n with continuous coefficients on an interval I has n linearly independent solutions on I. The proof is similar to that of Theorem 7–4 and is requested in Exercise 7 of Section 7.11. The extension of Theorem 7–3 takes the following form:

7–10 THEOREM. *Let P_1, P_2, ..., P_n be continuous on an open interval I and let $L(y) = y^{(n)} + P_1 y^{(n-1)} + \cdots + P_n y$. If $u_1, u_2, \ldots, u_n$ are n linearly independent solutions of the equation $L(y) = 0$ on the interval I, then every solution of $L(y) = 0$ on I can be expressed in the form*

(7.50)
$$y = \sum_{k=1}^{n} c_k \, u_k(x) ,$$

where $c_1, c_2, \ldots, c_n$ are constants.

Note. Since all solutions of the differential equation are contained in (7.50), the linear combination $\Sigma c_i u_i$ (with arbitrary constants $c_1, c_2, \ldots, c_n$) is called the *general solution* of the equation.

Proof. A proof of this theorem can be given by the same method used to prove Theorem 7–3. We shall carry out the details only for the case $n = 3$; the argument for $n > 3$ is entirely analogous.

In the proof of Theorem 7–3 we used the fact that the Wronskian of two independent solutions of a second-order equation is not identically zero. In this proof we need to know that the Wronskian of u_1, u_2, u_3 is not identically zero on I. The Wronskian of these functions is defined to be the determinant

$$W(x) = \begin{vmatrix} u_1(x) & u_2(x) & u_3(x) \\ u_1'(x) & u_2'(x) & u_3'(x) \\ u_1''(x) & u_2''(x) & u_3''(x) \end{vmatrix} .$$

We wish to prove that $W(x) \neq 0$ for some x in I. We shall do this by contradiction. Suppose $W(x) = 0$ for *all* x in I. For a fixed x in I, say $x = t$, consider the system of linear algebraic equations

$$a_1 u_1(t) + a_2 u_2(t) + a_3 u_3(t) = 0$$
$$a_1 u_1'(t) + a_2 u_2'(t) + a_3 u_3'(t) = 0$$
$$a_1 u_1''(t) + a_2 u_2''(t) + a_3 u_3''(t) = 0 \, ,$$

where a_1, a_2, a_3 are considered as "unknowns." The determinant of this system is the Wronskian $W(t)$. Since this determinant is zero, the system has infinitely many solutions; in particular there is a solution with a_1, a_2, a_3 not all zero. (See Section 5.17 of Volume I.) Choose such a triple of numbers a_1, a_2, a_3, and let g be the function defined by the equation

$$g(x) = a_1 u_1(x) + a_2 u_2(x) + a_3 u_3(x) \, .$$

This g is a solution of the differential equation $L(y) = 0$ such that g and its first two derivatives vanish at the point $x = t$ (because of the way the a's were chosen). By the uniqueness theorem it follows that g must be identically zero on I. Hence we have

$$a_1 u_1(x) + a_2 u_2(x) + a_3 u_3(x) = 0$$

for all x in I, contradicting the fact that u_1, u_2, u_3 are linearly independent on I. This contradiction shows that the Wronskian is not identically zero on I.

Now it is easy to carry out the proof of Theorem 7–10. First we note that, because of linearity, the function given by Equation (7.50) is a solution of the differential equation $L(y) = 0$. Let f be any solution of this equation. Choose a point x_0 in I such that $W(x_0) \neq 0$, and consider $f(x_0)$, $f'(x_0)$, and $f''(x_0)$. Since $W(x_0) \neq 0$, there exist constants c_1, c_2, c_3 satisfying the three linear algebraic equations

$$c_1 u_1(x_0) + c_2 u_2(x_0) + c_3 u_3(x_0) = f(x_0)$$
$$c_1 u_1'(x_0) + c_2 u_2'(x_0) + c_3 u_3'(x_0) = f'(x_0)$$
$$c_1 u_1''(x_0) + c_2 u_2''(x_0) + c_3 u_3''(x_0) = f''(x_0) \, .$$

Therefore both f and $c_1 u_1 + c_2 u_2 + c_3 u_3$ have the same value and the same first and second derivatives at x_0. By the uniqueness theorem the functions must be identical, so $f = c_1 u_1 + c_2 u_2 + c_3 u_3$. This shows that every solution of $L(y) = 0$ is contained in (7.50), completing the proof of Theorem 7–10 when $n = 3$.

Note. In the course of the foregoing proof we also showed that the Wronskian of three linearly independent solutions of a homogeneous linear equation of order three does not vanish identically on I. Actually, it can be shown that the Wronskian *never* vanishes on I. (See Exercise 8 in the next section.)

Let S denote the set of solutions of a linear equation $L(y) = 0$ on an interval I. If $u_1 \in S$ and $u_2 \in S$ then (by linearity) the linear combination $(c_1 u_1 + c_2 u_2) \in S$ for every choice of constants c_1 and c_2. A set of functions with this property is called a *linear space* of functions. Theorem 7–10 tells us that every function in S can be expressed as a linear combination of n linearly independent members of S. This is analogous to the fact that every vector in n-space can be expressed as a linear combination of n linearly independent vectors. Some of the terminology of vector spaces is often used in discussions concerning linear spaces of functions. For example, the functions u_1, u_2, $\ldots$, u_n in Theorem 7–10 are said to form a *basis* for the linear space S; the integer n is called the *dimension* of S.

7.11 Exercises

1. If $u_1, u_2, \ldots, u_n$ are linearly independent functions on an interval I, prove that they are also linearly independent on every subinterval of I.

2. For each of the following statements, either give a proof or provide a counterexample.

(a) If $u_1, u_2, \ldots, u_n$ are linearly independent on an interval I, and if $k < n$, then any k of these functions are linearly independent on I.

(b) If $u_1, u_2, \ldots, u_n$ are linearly dependent on an interval I, and if $k < n$, then any k of these functions are linearly dependent on I.

3. If $u_k(x) = x^{k-1}$, use mathematical induction or some other method to prove that $u_1, u_2, \ldots, u_n$ are linearly independent on every interval.

4. Let $u_k(x) = x^{k-1} f(x)$. Prove that $u_1, u_2, \ldots, u_n$ are linearly independent on an interval I if there are at least n points in I at which the function f is not zero.

5. (a) Prove that any three linear polynomials are linearly dependent on $(-\infty, +\infty)$.

(b) Prove that any four quadratic polynomials are linearly dependent on $(-\infty, +\infty)$.

(c) Generalize to polynomials of degree n.

6. Given n real numbers $r_1 < r_2 < \cdots < r_n$, let $u_k(x) = e^{r_k x}$. In Section 7.10 (Example 1) we used mathematical induction to prove that $u_1, u_2, \ldots, u_n$ are linearly independent on every interval. Give an alternative proof by the following method. If constants $c_1, c_2, \ldots, c_n$ exist such that $\sum c_k e^{r_k x} = 0$ for all real x, multiply this relation by $e^{-r_n x}$ and then let $x \to +\infty$ to deduce that $c_n = 0$. Repeat the process.

7. Let $L(y) = y^{(n)} + P_1 y^{(n-1)} + \cdots + P_n y$, where $P_1, P_2, \ldots, P_n$ are continuous on an interval I. Choose a point x_0 in I. For each $k = 0, 1, 2, \ldots, n - 1$, let u_k be that solution of $L(y) = 0$ satisfying the initial conditions

$$u_k^{(k)}(x_0) = 1, \qquad u_k^{(j)}(x_0) = 0 \qquad \text{for} \quad j \neq k.$$

(a) Prove that the functions $u_0, u_1, \ldots, u_{n-1}$ are linearly independent on I.

(b) Find, in terms of $u_0, u_1, \ldots, u_{n-1}$, that particular solution of $L(y) = 0$ which satisfies the initial conditions

$$f(x_0) = k_0, \quad f'(x_0) = k_1, \ldots, f^{(n-1)}(x_0) = k_{n-1}.$$

8. Let W denote the Wronskian of three functions u_1, u_2, u_3 having third-order derivatives.

(a) Show that the derivative of W is given by the determinant

$$W'(x) = \begin{vmatrix} u_1(x) & u_2(x) & u_3(x) \\ u_1'(x) & u_2'(x) & u_3'(x) \\ u_1'''(x) & u_2'''(x) & u_3'''(x) \end{vmatrix}.$$

In other words, the derivative of W may be obtained by differentiating the elements in the last row of the determinant for W.

(b) If u_1, u_2, u_3 are solutions of the linear equation

$$y''' + P_1 y'' + P_2 y' + P_3 y = 0$$

on an interval I, show that on the interval I the Wronskian satisfies the first-order linear equation $W' + P_1 W = 0$. Solve this equation to derive Abel's formula for the Wronskian,

$$W(x) = W(c) e^{-\int_c^x P_1(t)\, dt},$$

valid for each c in I. If there exists at least one point c such that $W(c) \neq 0$, this formula shows that $W(x) \neq 0$ for all x in I. In particular, such a c exists if u_1, u_2, u_3 are linearly independent solutions. (See the proof of Theorem 7-10.) Therefore, the Wronskian of three linearly independent solutions of a homogeneous linear equation of third order is never zero on I.

7.12   Linear equations of order n with constant coefficients

To solve a homogeneous linear differential equation of order n with constant coefficients, say

$$\text{(7.51)} \qquad y^{(n)} + a_1 y^{(n-1)} + \cdots + a_n y = 0,$$

we try to obtain solutions of the form $y = e^{rx}$. Since $y^{(k)} = r^k e^{rx}$, when we substitute in (7.51) we find that such a function will be a solution if and only if r satisfies the polynomial equation

$$r^n + a_1 r^{n-1} + \cdots + a_n = 0.$$

This is called the *characteristic equation* of (7.51). The fundamental theorem of algebra tells us that this equation has exactly n roots, $r_1, r_2, \ldots, r_n$, where each root is written as often as its multiplicity indicates. The roots may be real or complex. As in the second-order case, the form of the solution depends on the nature of the roots.

Real distinct roots. In this case the corresponding solutions are

$$\text{(7.52)} \qquad u_1(x) = e^{r_1 x}, \qquad u_2(x) = e^{r_2 x}, \qquad \ldots, \qquad u_n(x) = e^{r_n x}.$$

In Example 1 of Section 7.10 we proved that these functions are linearly independent over every interval. Therefore, the general solution of (7.51), valid for all real x, is given by the formula

$$\text{(7.53)} \qquad y = \sum_{k=1}^{n} c_k e^{r_k x}.$$

Example 1. $y''' - 7y' + 6 = 0$. The characteristic equation factors as follows:

$$r^3 - 7r + 6 = (r - 1)(r - 2)(r + 3) = 0.$$

The corresponding roots are $r_1 = 1$, $r_2 = 2$, $r_3 = -3$, so the general solution is

$$y = c_1 e^x + c_2 e^{2x} + c_3 e^{-3x}.$$

Real roots, some of which are repeated. If all the roots are real but not distinct, the functions in (7.52) are not independent and the formula in (7.53) does not give the general solution. If the distinct roots are $r_1, r_2, \ldots, r_k$ and if they occur with respective multiplicities $m_1, m_2, \ldots, m_k$, the part of the solution corresponding to the root m_p is given by the sum

$$\text{(7.54)} \qquad (c_1 + c_2 x + c_3 x^2 + \cdots + c_{m_p} x^{m_p - 1}) e^{r_p x}.$$

For each $p \le k$ and each $q \le m_p$, the function $u_{q,p}(x) = x^{q-1} e^{r_p x}$ is a solution of the differential equation (see Exercise 15 of Section 7.13). In Section 7.10 (Example 5) we proved that the n functions $u_{q,p}$ so obtained are linearly independent on every interval. Therefore the general solution of the equation consists of a sum of k terms of the form (7.54); it is valid for all real x. The following examples illustrate some of the possibilities.

Example 2. $y''' - y'' - 8y' + 12y = 0$. The characteristic equation is

$$r^3 - r^2 - 8r + 12 = (r - 2)^2(r + 3) = 0 .$$

The roots of this equation are 2, 2, -3. The part of the solution corresponding to the double root 2 is $(c_1 + c_2x) e^{2x}$; the part corresponding to the simple root -3 is c_3e^{-3x}. Therefore the general solution is

$$y = (c_1 + c_2x)e^{2x} + c_3e^{-3x} .$$

Example 3. $y^{(6)} + 2y^{(5)} - 2y''' - y'' = 0$. The characteristic equation is

$$r^6 + 2r^5 - 2r^3 - r^2 = r^2(r - 1)(r + 1)^3 = 0 .$$

The roots are 0, 0, 1, -1, -1, -1. The part of the solution corresponding to the double root 0 is $c_1 + c_2x$; the part corresponding to the simple root 1 is c_3e^x; and the part corresponding to the triple root -1 is $(c_4 + c_5x + c_6x^2)e^{-x}$. Therefore the general solution is

$$y = c_1 + c_2x + c_3e^x + (c_4 + c_5x + c_6x^2)e^{-x} .$$

Complex roots. If complex exponentials are used, there is no need to distinguish between real and complex roots of the characteristic equation. If real-valued solutions are desired, we introduce trigonometric functions as in the second-order case. Complex roots occur in conjugate pairs; the part of the solution corresponding to each pair $\alpha + i\beta$, $\alpha - i\beta$ has the form

$$e^{\alpha x}(c_1 \cos \beta x + c_2 \sin \beta x) .$$

If such a pair occurs with multiplicity m, each multiplier c_1 and c_2 must be replaced by a polynomial of degree $m - 1$. The following examples illustrate some of the possibilities.

Example 4. $y''' - 4y'' + 13y' = 0$. The characteristic equation, $r^3 - 4r^2 + 13r = 0$, has the roots 0, $2 \pm 3i$; the general solution is

$$y = c_1 + e^{2x}(c_2 \cos 3x + c_3 \sin 3x) .$$

Example 5. $y''' - 2y'' + 4y' - 8y = 0$. The characteristic equation is

$$r^3 - 2r^2 + 4r - 8 = (r - 2)(r^2 + 4) = 0 ;$$

its roots are 2, $2i$, $-2i$, so the general solution of the differential equation is

$$y = c_1e^{2x} + c_2 \cos 2x + c_3 \sin 2x .$$

Example 6. $y^{(5)} - 9y^{(4)} + 34y''' - 66y'' + 65y' - 25y = 0$. The characteristic equation can be written as

$$(r - 1)(r^2 - 4r + 5)^2 = 0 ;$$

its roots are 1, $2 \pm i$, $2 \pm i$, so the general solution of the differential equation is

$$y = c_1e^x + e^{2x} [(c_2 + c_3x) \cos x + (c_4 + c_5x) \sin x] .$$

7.13 Exercises

Find the general solution of each of the differential equations in Exercises 1 through 12.

1. $y''' - 2y'' - 3y' = 0$.

2. $y''' - y' = 0$.

3. $y''' + 4y'' + 4y' = 0$.

4. $y''' - 3y'' + 3y' - y = 0$.

5. $y^{(4)} + 4y''' + 6y'' + 4y' + y = 0$.

6. $y^{(4)} - 16y = 0$.

7. $y^{(4)} + 16y = 0$.

8. $y''' - y = 0$.

9. $y^{(4)} + 4y''' + 8y'' + 8y' + 4y = 0$.

10. $y^{(4)} + 2y'' + y = 0$.

11. $y^{(6)} + 4y^{(4)} + 4y'' = 0$.

12. $y^{(6)} + 8y^{(4)} + 16y'' = 0$.

13. If m is a positive constant, find that particular solution $y = f(x)$ of the differential equation

$$y''' - my'' + m^2 y' - m^3 = 0$$

which satisfies the conditions $f(0) = f'(0) = 0$, $f''(1) = 1$.

14. A linear differential equation with constant coefficients has characteristic equation $f(r) = 0$. If all the roots of the characteristic equation are negative, prove that every solution of the differential equation approaches zero as $x \to +\infty$. What can you conclude about the behavior of all solutions on the interval $[0, +\infty)$ if all the roots of the characteristic equation are nonpositive?

15. If $L(y) = y^{(n)} + a_1 y^{(n-1)} + \cdots + a_n y$, where the a_i are constants, let $f(r) = r^n + a_1 r^{n-1} + \cdots + a_n$.

  (a) If α is a constant and if u has n derivatives, show that

$$L[e^{\alpha x} u(x)] = e^{\alpha x} \sum_{k=0}^{n} \frac{f^{(k)}(\alpha)}{k!} u^{(k)}(x) .$$

[*Hint.* Use Leibniz's rule for the kth derivative of a product (see page 147 in Volume I).]

  (b) If α is a root of multiplicity m of the characteristic equation $f(r) = 0$, show that $y = e^{\alpha x} u(x)$ will satisfy the differential equation $L(y) = 0$ if u is a polynomial of degree $m - 1$.

16. In each case, find a linear differential equation with constant coefficients satisfied by all the given functions.

  (a) $u_1(x) = e^x$, $u_2(x) = e^{-x}$, $u_3(x) = e^{2x}$, $u_4(x) = e^{-2x}$.

  (b) $u_1(x) = e^{-2x}$, $u_2(x) = xe^{-2x}$, $u_3(x) = x^2 e^{-2x}$.

  (c) $u_1(x) = 1$, $u_2(x) = x$, $u_3(x) = e^x$, $u_4(x) = xe^x$.

  (d) $u_1(x) = x$, $u_2(x) = e^x$, $u_3(x) = xe^x$.

  (e) $u_1(x) = x^2$, $u_2(x) = e^x$, $u_3(x) = xe^x$.

  (f) $u_1(x) = e^{-2x}\cos 3x$, $u_2(x) = e^{-2x}\sin 3x$, $u_3(x) = e^{-2x}$, $u_4(x) = xe^{-2x}$.

  (g) $u_1(x) = \cosh x$, $u_2(x) = \sinh x$, $u_3(x) = x \cosh x$, $u_4(x) = x \sinh x$.

  (h) $u_1(x) = \cosh x \sin x$, $u_2(x) = \sinh x \cos x$, $u_3(x) = x$.

7.14 Nonhomogeneous linear equations of order n

The theory for nonhomogeneous equations is related to that of homogeneous equations exactly as in the second-order case. This relation is provided by the following theorem which extends Theorem 7–6 to nth order equations.

7–11   THEOREM.   Let $P_1, P_2, \ldots, P_n$, and R be functions continuous on an open interval I, and let

$$L(y) = y^{(n)} + P_1 y^{(n-1)} + \cdots + P_n y .$$

If $u_1, u_2, \ldots, u_n$ are n linearly independent solutions of the homogeneous equation $L(y) = 0$ on I, and if y_1 is any particular solution of the nonhomogeneous equation $L(y) = R$, then every solution of the nonhomogeneous equation can be expressed in the form

(7.55)
$$y = y_1 + \sum_{k=1}^{n} c_k u_k ,$$

where $c_1, c_2, \ldots, c_n$ are constants.

Note. For every choice of constants $c_1, c_2, \ldots, c_n$ the function y determined by (7.55) is a solution of $L(y) = R$, since

$$L(y_1 + \sum_{k=1}^{n} c_k u_k) = L(y_1) + \sum_{k=1}^{n} c_k L(u_k) = L(y_1) = R .$$

Since all solutions of $L(y) = R$ are found in (7.55), the sum on the right of (7.55) (with arbitrary constants $c_1, c_2, \ldots, c_n$) is called the *general solution* of the nonhomogeneous equation. Theorem 7–11 states that the general solution of the nonhomogeneous equation is obtained by adding to y_1 the general solution of the homogeneous equation.

Proof. Let y_2 be any solution of $L(y) = R$. Since we also have $L(y_1) = R$, linearity gives us $L(y_2 - y_1) = L(y_2) - L(y_1) = 0$, so $y_2 - y_1$ is a solution of the homogeneous equation. By Theorem 7–10 there exist constants $c_1, c_2, \ldots, c_n$ such that

$$y_2 - y_1 = \sum_{k=1}^{n} c_k u_k .$$

Therefore, y_2 is one of the solutions in Equation (7.55). This completes the proof.

We turn now to the problem of determining one particular solution y_1 of the nonhomogeneous equation. If we know n linearly independent solutions $u_1, u_2, \ldots, u_n$ of the homogeneous equation on an interval I, we can always find a particular solution of the nonhomogeneous equation by an extension of the method of variation of parameters. The method will be described in detail for $n = 3$; its extension to general n will then be clear.

The idea of the method is to determine functions v_1, v_2, v_3 in such a way that the sum

(7.56)
$$y_1 = \sum_{k=1}^{3} u_k v_k$$

will satisfy $L(y) = R$. Differentiating (7.56) we obtain

$$y_1' = \sum_{k=1}^{3} u_k' v_k + \sum_{k=1}^{3} u_k v_k' .$$

We have three v's to determine, so we should be able to put three conditions on them. If we make one condition be that the second sum should vanish in the foregoing equation, the formula for y_1' simplifies to

$$y_1' = \sum_{k=1}^{3} u_k' v_k .$$

Differentiating this relation we find

(7.57)
$$y_1'' = \sum_{k=1}^{3} u_k'' v_k + \sum_{k=1}^{3} u_k' v_k' .$$

If we can choose v_1, v_2, v_3 so as to make the second sum in (7.57) vanish also, the formula for y_1' simplifies to

$$y_1'' = \sum_{k=1}^{3} u_k' v_k .$$

Differentiating once more we obtain

$$y_1''' = \sum_{k=1}^{3} u_k''' v_k + \sum_{k=1}^{3} u_k'' v_k' .$$

In this formula we try to make the second sum equal to R. If we can choose v_1, v_2, v_3 so that all the conditions stated are satisfied, we find

$$L(y_1) = y_1''' + P_1 y_1'' + P_2 y_1' + P_3 y_1$$

$$= \left(\sum_{k=1}^{3} u_k''' v_k + R \right) + P_1 \sum_{k=1}^{3} u_k'' v_k + P_2 \sum_{k=1}^{3} u_k' v_k + P_3 \sum_{k=1}^{3} u_k v_k$$

$$= \sum_{k=1}^{3} (u_k''' + P_1 u_k'' + P_2 u_k' + P_3 u_k) v_k + R = \sum_{k=1}^{3} L(u_k) v_k + R .$$

Since $L(u_1) = L(u_2) = L(u_3) = 0$, the right member of the last equation reduces to R, and we see that y_1 satisfies $L(y_1) = R$.

To complete the proof we must show that v_1, v_2, v_3 can always be chosen so as to satisfy the conditions imposed on them. These conditions may be expressed as a system of linear algebraic equations for the derivatives v_1', v_2', v_3':

(7.58)
$$\sum_{k=1}^{3} u_k v_k' = 0 , \qquad \sum_{k=1}^{3} u_k' v_k' = 0 , \qquad \sum_{k=1}^{3} u_k'' v_k' = R .$$

The determinant of this system is the Wronskian W of u_1, u_2, u_3. Since u_1, u_2, u_3 are linearly independent solutions of $L(y) = 0$, their Wronskian is never zero on I (see Exercise 8 of Section 7.11); hence we can always solve the system (7.58) for v_1', v_2', v_3'. If the solution is obtained by Cramer's rule, it may be put in the form

$$v_1' = W_1/W , \qquad v_2' = W_2/W , \qquad v_3' = W_3/W ,$$

where W_k is the determinant obtained by replacing the kth column of the Wronskian determinant by $(0, 0, R)$. Integrating these relations we obtain v_1, v_2, v_3. Substituting these functions in (7.56) we find that the nonhomogeneous equation $L(y) = R$ has a solution y_1 given by the formula

$$y_1(x) = \sum_{k=1}^{3} u_k(x) \int_{c}^{x} \frac{W_k(t)}{W(t)} \, dt ,$$

where c is any point in I.

7.15 Special methods for determining a particular solution of the nonhomogeneous equation. The algebra of constant-coefficient operators

As in the second-order case, special methods may yield a particular solution y_1 of the nonhomogeneous equation more easily than the method of variation of parameters. For example, if the equation has the form

$$y^{(n)} + a_1 y^{(n-1)} + a_2 y^{(n-2)} + \cdots + a_n y = R\,,$$

where the a_i are constants and R is a polynomial, there always exists a polynomial solution y_1 which we can obtain by the method of undetermined coefficients. If a_n, the coefficient of y, is nonzero, the degree of y_1 is the same as that of R. If the coefficient of $y^{(k)}$ is nonzero but the coefficient of $y^{(j)}$ is zero for each $j < k$, the degree of y_1 exceeds that of R by k.

Example 1. Find a particular solution of the equation $y^{(4)} - 16y = x^4 + x + 1$.

Solution. We seek a polynomial solution y_1 of degree four, so we write

$$16y_1 = ax^4 + bx^3 + cx^2 + dx + e\,.$$

This gives us $16y_1^{(4)} = 24a$, so $y_1^{(4)} = 3a/2$. Substituting in the differential equation we must determine a, b, c, d, e to satisfy

$$\frac{3}{2}a - ax^4 - bx^3 - cx^2 - dx - e = x^4 + x + 1\,.$$

Equating coefficients of like powers of x we obtain

$$a = -1\,, \qquad b = c = 0\,, \qquad d = -1\,, \qquad e = -\frac{5}{2}\,,$$

so the particular solution y_1 is given by

$$y_1 = -\frac{1}{16}x^4 - \frac{1}{16}x - \frac{5}{32}\,.$$

There are other methods for solving nonhomogeneous equations that work especially well when the equation has constant coefficients. Some of these are best described in operator notation. Let A denote the linear operator defined by the equation

$$(7.59) \qquad\qquad A(y) = a_0 y^{(n)} + a_1 y^{(n-1)} + \cdots + a_n y\,,$$

where $a_0, a_1, \ldots, a_n$ are constants. Such an operator is called a *constant-coefficient operator*. If $a_0 \neq 0$ the operator is said to have order n. The function y which appears in this equation may be any real-valued function with n derivatives on some interval. We shall restrict ourselves to functions having derivatives of *every* order on $(-\infty, +\infty)$. The collection of all such functions y will be denoted by $\mathcal{D}$ and will be referred to as the class of infinitely differentiable functions. When we apply an operator A to a function y in $\mathcal{D}$, the result of the operation is another function $A(y)$ in class $\mathcal{D}$. The value of the function $A(y)$ at a point x is $A(y)(x)$, sometimes written as $A[y(x)]$.

Next we develop an algebra of constant-coefficient operators; we discuss addition and multiplication of operators, as well as multiplication of operators by scalars. Let A and B be two constant-coefficient operators, where A is given by (7.59) and B is given by

$$B(y) = b_0 y^{(m)} + b_1 y^{(m-1)} + \cdots + b_m y .$$

Since these operators are functions with domain $\mathfrak{D}$, we have $A = B$ if and only if $A(y) = B(y)$ for every y in $\mathfrak{D}$. The *sum* of A and B is a new operator C defined by the equation

$$C(y) = A(y) + B(y) \qquad \text{for every } y \text{ in } \mathfrak{D} .$$

We write $A + B$ for C. The product of A and B (in that order) is denoted by AB and is the operator defined by the equation

$$(AB)(y) = A[B(y)] \qquad \text{for every } y \text{ in } \mathfrak{D} .$$

If λ is a real number (a scalar) the operator λA is defined by the equation

$$(\lambda A)(y) = \lambda \cdot A(y) \qquad \text{for every } y \text{ in } \mathfrak{D} .$$

It is clear that $A + B$, AB, and λA are also constant-coefficient operators. The definitions of the sum and product of operators may be extended by induction to any finite number of operators. Sums, products, and scalar multiples of operators satisfy the usual laws of algebra, such as the commutative, associative, and distributive laws. We could prove these laws directly from the definitions, but it is simpler and more instructive to proceed in another way.

With each constant-coefficient operator A we associate a polynomial p_A called the *characteristic polynomial* of A. If A is given by (7.59), p_A is that polynomial which has the same coefficients as A. That is, for every real r we have

$$p_A(r) = a_0 r^n + a_1 r^{n-1} + \cdots + a_n .$$

Conversely, given any polynomial p, there is a corresponding operator A whose coefficients are the same as those of p. The next theorem shows that this association between operators and polynomials is a one-to-one correspondence. Moreover, this correspondence associates with sums, products, and scalar multiples of operators the respective sums, products, and scalar multiples of their characteristic polynomials.

7–12   THEOREM.   Let A and B denote constant-coefficient operators with characteristic polynomials p_A and p_B, respectively, and let λ be a real number. Then we have

(a) $A = B$ if, and only if, $p_A = p_B$,
(b) $p_{A+B} = p_A + p_B$,
(c) $p_{AB} = p_A \cdot p_B$,
(d) $p_{\lambda A} = \lambda \cdot p_A$.

Proof. We consider part (a) first. Assume $p_A = p_B$. We wish to prove that $A(y) = B(y)$ for every y in $\mathfrak{D}$. Since $p_A = p_B$, both polynomials have the same degree and the same coefficients. Therefore A and B have the same order and the same coefficients, so $A(y) = B(y)$ for every y in $\mathfrak{D}$.

Next we prove that $A = B$ implies $p_A = p_B$. The relation $A = B$ means that $A(y) = B(y)$ for every y in $\mathfrak{D}$. Take $y = e^{rx}$, where r is a constant. Since $y^{(k)} = r^k e^{rx}$ for every $k \geq 0$, we have

$$A(y) = p_A(r)e^{rx} \qquad \text{and} \qquad B(y) = p_B(r)e^{rx} .$$

The equation $A(y) = B(y)$ implies $p_A(r) = p_B(r)$. Since r is arbitrary we must have $p_A = p_B$. This completes the proof of part (a).

To prove part (b), let $C = A + B$, and let $y = e^{rx}$. Then we have

$$A(y) = p_A(r)e^{rx}, \qquad B(y) = p_B(r)e^{rx}, \qquad \text{and} \qquad C(y) = p_C(r)e^{rx}.$$

Since $C = A + B$ we have $C(y) = A(y) + B(y)$, which gives us

$$p_C(r)e^{rx} = p_A(r)e^{rx} + p_B(r)e^{rx}.$$

Canceling e^{rx} we find $p_C(r) = p_A(r) + p_B(r)$ for every real r. This proves (b); the proofs of (c) and (d) are entirely analogous.

From Theorem 7–12 it follows that every algebraic relation involving sums, products, and scalar multiples of polynomials p_A and p_B also holds for the operators A and B. In particular, we have the *commutative laws*,

$$A + B = B + A, \qquad AB = BA, \qquad \lambda(\mu A) = \mu(\lambda A),$$

the *associative laws*,

$$A + (B + C) = (A + B) + C, \qquad A(BC) = (AB)C, \qquad \lambda(\mu A) = (\lambda\mu)A,$$

and the *distributive laws*,

$$A(B + C) = AB + AC, \qquad \lambda(A + B) = \lambda A + \lambda B, \qquad (\lambda + \mu)A = \lambda A + \mu A.$$

All constant-coefficient operators can be expressed as polynomials in the derivative operator D. If, as usual, we denote by D^k the kth derivative operator defined by $D^k(y) = y^{(k)}$ for every y in $\mathfrak{D}$, Equation (7.59) can be written in the form

$$A(y) = a_0 D^n(y) + a_1 D^{n-1}(y) + \cdots + a_0 y.$$

Therefore, by the definition of equality of operators, we have

$$A = a_0 D^n + a_1 D^{n-1} + \cdots + a_0.$$

If the characteristic polynomial p_A can be factored as a product of two or more polynomials, each factor must be the characteristic polynomial of some constant-coefficient operator, so, by Theorem 7–12, there is a corresponding factorization of the operator A. For example, if $p_A(r) = p_B(r)p_C(r)$, then $A = BC$. If $p_A(r)$ is factored as a product of n linear factors, say

$$p_A(r) = a_0(r - r_1)(r - r_2) \cdots (r - r_n),$$

the corresponding factorization of A takes the form

$$A = a_0(D - r_1)(D - r_2) \cdots (D - r_n).$$

Once we know the zeros of the characteristic polynomial p_A we can determine the general solution of the homogeneous equation $A(y) = 0$ without any integration. Thus, the problem of solving any homogeneous linear differential equation with constant coefficients is a purely algebraic problem.

In some cases, a particular solution of a nonhomogeneous equation $A(y) = R$ can also be obtained by algebraic means. For example, suppose the right-hand member R is itself a solution of a linear differential equation with constant coefficients, say $B(R) = 0$, where B is a constant-coefficient operator. If we apply B to both sides of the equation $A(y) = R$ we find $BA(y) = 0$, so every solution of $A(y) = R$ is also a solution of the linear homogeneous equation $BA(y) = 0$. Since BA is a constant-coefficient operator, we can determine all the solutions of $BA(y) = 0$ by algebraic means. Now the problem remains of choosing from these solutions a particular function y_1 that satisfies $A(y_1) = R$. The following example illustrates how the process may be carried out in practice.

Example 2. Solve the differential equation $y'' - 5y' + 6y = xe^x$.

Solution. The differential equation has the form

$$(7.60) \qquad\qquad\qquad A(y) = R \, ,$$

where $R(x) = xe^x$ and $A = D^2 - 5D + 6$. The corresponding homogeneous equation can be written as

$$(D - 2)(D - 3)y = 0 \, ;$$

it has the linearly independent solutions $u_1(x) = e^{2x}$, $u_2(x) = e^{3x}$. Now we seek a particular solution y_1 of the nonhomogeneous equation. We recognize the function $R(x) = xe^x$ as a solution of the homogeneous equation

$$(D - 1)^2 y = 0 \, .$$

Therefore, if we operate on both sides of (7.60) with the operator $(D - 1)^2$ we find that any function which satisfies (7.60) must also satisfy the equation

$$(D - 1)^2(D - 2)(D - 3)y = 0 \, .$$

This differential equation has the characteristic roots 1, 1, 2, 3, so all its solutions are to be found in the linear combination

$$y = ae^x + bxe^x + ce^{2x} + de^{3x} \, ,$$

where a, b, c, d are constants. We want to choose a, b, c, d so that $A(ae^x + bxe^x + ce^{2x} + de^{3x}) = xe^x$. Since $A(ce^{2x} + de^{3x}) = 0$ for every choice of c and d, we need only choose a and b so that $A(ae^x + bxe^x) = xe^x$. If we put

$$y_1 = ae^x + bxe^x \, ,$$

we have

$$D(y_1) = (a + b)e^x + bxe^x , \qquad D^2(y_1) = (a + 2b)e^x + bxe^x ,$$

so the equation $(D^2 - 5D + 6)y_1 = xe^x$ becomes

$$(2a - 3b)e^x + 2bxe^x = xe^x \, .$$

Canceling e^x and equating coefficients of like powers of x we find $a = \frac{3}{4}$, $b = \frac{1}{2}$. Therefore $y_1 = \frac{3}{4}e^x + \frac{1}{2}xe^x$ and the general solution of $A(y) = R$ is given by the formula

$$y = c_1 e^{2x} + c_2 e^{3x} + \tfrac{3}{4}e^x + \tfrac{1}{2}xe^x \, .$$

The method used in the foregoing example will always work if we can find a constant-coefficient operator B that makes $B(R)$ identically zero. Such an operator is said to *annihilate* R; the method described in the example is called the *annihilator method*. From our knowledge of homogeneous linear differential equations with constant coefficients, we know that the only real-valued functions annihilated by constant-coefficient operators are linear combinations of terms of the form

$$x^{m-1}e^{\alpha x}, \qquad x^{m-1}e^{\alpha x}\cos \beta x, \qquad x^{m-1}e^{\alpha x}\sin \beta x,$$

where m is a positive integer and α and β are real constants. The function $y = x^{m-1}e^{\alpha x}$ is a solution of a differential equation with a characteristic root α having multiplicity m. Therefore, this function has the annihilator $(D - \alpha)^m$. Each of the functions $y = x^{m-1}e^{\alpha x}\cos \beta x$ and $y = x^{m-1}e^{\alpha x}\sin \beta x$ is a solution of a differential equation with complex characteristic roots $\alpha \pm i\beta$, each occurring with multiplicity m, so they are annihilated by the operator $[D^2 - 2\alpha D + (\alpha^2 + \beta^2)]^m$. For ease of reference, we list these annihilators in Table I, along with some of their special cases.

Table I.

Function			Annihilator
$y = x^{m-1}$			D^m
$y = e^{\alpha x}$			$D - \alpha$
$y = x^{m-1}e^{\alpha x}$			$(D - \alpha)^m$
$y = \cos \beta x$	or	$y = \sin \beta x$	$D^2 + \beta^2$
$y = x^{m-1}\cos \beta x$	or	$y = x^{m-1}\sin \beta x$	$(D^2 + \beta^2)^m$
$y = e^{\alpha x}\cos \beta x$	or	$y = e^{\alpha x}\sin \beta x$	$D^2 - 2\alpha D + (\alpha^2 + \beta^2)$
$y = x^{m-1}e^{\alpha x}\cos \beta x$	or	$y = x^{m-1}e^{\alpha x}\sin \beta x$	$[D^2 - 2\alpha D + (\alpha^2 + \beta^2)]^m$

Although the annihilator method is very efficient when applicable, it is limited to equations whose right members R have a constant-coefficient annihilator. If $R(x)$ has the form e^{x^2}, $\log x$, or $\tan x$, the method will not work; we must then use variation of parameters or some other method to find a particular solution. The next example illustrates a method for reducing the equation to a succession of linear equations of first order.

Example 3. Find a particular solution of the equation

$$(D - 1)(D - 2)y = xe^{x+x^2}.$$

Solution. If we write

(7.61) $$(D - 2)y = u,$$

the equation becomes

$$(D - 1)u = xe^{x+x^2}.$$

This is a first-order linear equation in u. As such it can be solved [using Equation (7.3)] to give

$$ue^{-x} = \int xe^{x^2}dx + C = \tfrac{1}{2}e^{x^2} + C.$$

Since we seek only a particular solution we take $C = 0$. This gives us

$$u = \tfrac{1}{2}e^{x+x^2}.$$

Substituting in (7.61) we obtain

$$(D - 2)y = \tfrac{1}{2}e^{x+x^2},$$

a first-order linear equation for y. Solving this by Equation (7.3) we find that a particular solution y_1 is given by

$$y_1 = \tfrac{1}{2}e^{2x} \int e^{x^2-x} \, dx \,.$$

Although the last integral cannot be evaluated in terms of elementary functions we consider the equation as having been solved, since the solution is expressed in terms of integrals of familiar functions.

7.16   Exercises

In each of Exercises 1 through 10, use the annihilator method to find a particular solution.

1. $y'' - y' = x^2$.
2. $y'' - 4y = e^{2x}$.
3. $y'' + 2y' = 3xe^x$.
4. $y'' + 4y = \sin x$.
5. $y'' - 2y' + y = e^x + e^{2x}$.

6. $y''' - y' = e^x$.
7. $y''' - y' = e^x + e^{-x}$.
8. $y''' + 3y'' + 3y' + y = xe^{-x}$.
9. $y'' + y = xe^x \sin 2x$.
10. $y^{(4)} - y = x^2 e^{-x}$.

11. If a constant-coefficient operator A annihilates f and if a constant-coefficient operator B annihilates g, show that the product AB annihilates $f + g$.

12. Let A be a constant-coefficient operator with characteristic polynomial p_A.
(a) Use the annihilator method to prove that the differential equation $A(y) = e^{\alpha x}$ has a particular solution of the form

$$y_1 = \frac{e^{\alpha x}}{p_A(\alpha)}$$

if α is not a zero of the polynomial p_A.
(b) If α is a simple zero of p_A (multiplicity 1), prove that the equation $A(y) = e^{\alpha x}$ has the particular solution

$$y_1 = \frac{xe^{\alpha x}}{p_A'(\alpha)} \,.$$

(c) Generalize the results of (a) and (b) when α is a zero of p_A with multiplicity m.

13. Given two constant-coefficient operators A and B whose characteristic polynomials have no zeros in common. Let $C = AB$.
(a) Prove that every solution of the differential equation $C(y) = 0$ has the form $y = y_1 + y_2$, where $A(y_1) = 0$ and $B(y_2) = 0$.
(b) Prove that the functions y_1 and y_2 in part (a) are uniquely determined. That is, for a given y satisfying $C(y) = 0$ there is only one pair y_1, y_2 with the properties in part (a).

14. Let P and Q denote operators given by

$$P(y) = P_0 y^{(n)} + P_1 y^{(n-1)} + \cdots + P_n y, \quad Q(y) = Q_0 y^{(m)} + Q_1 y^{(m-1)} + \cdots + Q_m y,$$

where $y \in \mathcal{D}$ and the P_i and Q_i are real-valued functions with derivatives of every order on an interval. Define addition $P + Q$ and multiplication PQ by the same formulas used for constant-coefficient operators. Show that, with the exception of the commutative law for multiplication, the algebraic laws for constant-coefficient operators hold also for these more general operators.

15. Let Q be the operator defined by $Q(y)(x) = x \cdot y(x)$ for each y in class $\mathfrak{D}$ and each real x. Let I denote the identity operator, defined by $I(y) = y$ for each y in $\mathfrak{D}$.

(a) Prove that $DQ - QD = I$.

(b) Show that $D^2Q - QD^2$ is a constant-coefficient operator of first order, and determine this operator explicitly as a linear polynomial in D.

(c) Show that $D^3Q - QD^3$ is a constant-coefficient operator of second order, and determine this operator explicitly as a quadratic polynomial in D.

(d) Guess the generalization suggested for the operator $D^nQ - QD^n$, and prove your result by induction.

In each of Exercises 16 through 20, find the general solution of the differential equation in the given interval.

16. $y'' - y = 1/x$, $\quad (0, +\infty)$.

17. $y'' + 4y = \sec 2x$, $\quad \left(-\dfrac{\pi}{4}, \dfrac{\pi}{4}\right)$.

18. $y'' - y = \sec^3 x - \sec x$, $\quad \left(-\dfrac{\pi}{2}, \dfrac{\pi}{2}\right)$.

19. $y'' - 2y' + y = e^{e^x}(e^x - 1)^2$, $\quad (-\infty, +\infty)$.

20. $y''' - 7y'' + 14y' - 8y = \log x$, $\quad (0, +\infty)$.

7.17 The Legendre equation

Linearly independent solutions of a homogeneous linear equation can sometimes be obtained by the use of power series. One method was illustrated in Volume I (Section 9.24), where we solved the equation $(1 - x^2)y'' + 2y = 0$ by the method of undetermined coefficients. In this section we shall use the same method to solve the Legendre equation

$$(7.62) \qquad (1 - x^2)y'' - 2xy' + \alpha(\alpha + 1)y = 0 ,$$

where α is a constant. We try to find a power-series solution of the form

$$y = \sum_{n=0}^{\infty} a_n x^n$$

valid in some open interval $(-r, r)$ about the origin. Differentiating this series term by term we obtain

$$y' = \sum_{n=1}^{\infty} na_n x^{n-1} \quad \text{and} \quad y'' = \sum_{n=2}^{\infty} n(n - 1)a_n x^{n-2} .$$

Therefore we have

$$2xy' = \sum_{n=1}^{\infty} 2na_n x^n = \sum_{n=0}^{\infty} 2na_n x^n ,$$

and

$$(1 - x^2)y'' = \sum_{n=2}^{\infty} n(n - 1)a_n x^{n-2} - \sum_{n=2}^{\infty} n(n - 1)a_n x^n$$

$$= \sum_{n=0}^{\infty} (n + 2)(n + 1)a_{n+2}x^n - \sum_{n=0}^{\infty} n(n - 1)a_n x^n$$

$$= \sum_{n=0}^{\infty} [(n + 2)(n + 1)a_{n+2} - n(n - 1)a_n]x^n .$$

If we substitute these series in the differential equation (7.62), we see that the equation will be satisfied if, and only if, the coefficients satisfy the relation

$$(n + 2)(n + 1)a_{n+2} - n(n - 1)a_n - 2na_n + \alpha(\alpha + 1)a_n = 0$$

for all $n \geq 0$. This equation is the same as

$$(n + 2)(n + 1)a_{n+2} - (n - \alpha)(n + 1 + \alpha)a_n = 0 ,$$

or

(7.63) $$a_{n+2} = - \frac{(\alpha - n)(\alpha + n + 1)}{(n + 1)(n + 2)} a_n .$$

This relation enables us to determine $a_2, a_4, a_6, \ldots$ successively in terms of a_0. Similarly, we can compute $a_3, a_5, a_7, \ldots$ in terms of a_1. For the coefficients with even subscripts we have

$$a_2 = - \frac{\alpha(\alpha + 1)}{1 \cdot 2} a_0 ,$$

$$a_4 = - \frac{(\alpha - 2)(\alpha + 3)}{3 \cdot 4} a_2 = (-1)^2 \frac{\alpha(\alpha - 2)(\alpha + 1)(\alpha + 3)}{4!} a_0 ,$$

and, in general,

(7.64) $$a_{2n} = (-1)^n \frac{\alpha(\alpha - 2) \cdots (\alpha - 2n + 2) \cdot (\alpha + 1)(\alpha + 3) \cdots (\alpha + 2n - 1)}{(2n)!} a_0 .$$

The validity of (7.64) for $n \geq 1$ can be established by induction. For the coefficients with odd subscripts we find

$$a_{2n+1} = (-1)^n \frac{(\alpha - 1)(\alpha - 3) \cdots (\alpha - 2n + 1) \cdot (\alpha + 2)(\alpha + 4) \cdots (\alpha + 2n)}{(2n + 1)!} a_1 .$$

Therefore the series for y can be written as

(7.65) $$y = a_0 u_1(x) + a_1 u_2(x) ,$$

where

(7.66) $u_1(x)$

$$= 1 + \sum_{n=1}^{\infty} (-1)^n \frac{\alpha(\alpha - 2) \cdots (\alpha - 2n + 2) \cdot (\alpha + 1)(\alpha + 3) \cdots (\alpha + 2n - 1)}{(2n)!} x^{2n}$$

and

(7.67) $u_2(x)$

$$= x + \sum_{n=1}^{\infty} (-1)^n \frac{(\alpha - 1)(\alpha - 3) \cdots (\alpha - 2n + 1) \cdot (\alpha + 2)(\alpha + 4) \cdots (\alpha + 2n)}{(2n + 1)!} x^{2n+1} .$$

The ratio test shows that each of these series converges for $|x| < 1$. Also, since the relation (7.63) is satisfied separately by the even and odd coefficients, each of u_1 and u_2 is a solution of the differential equation (7.62). These solutions satisfy the initial conditions

$$u_1(0) = 1, \qquad u_1'(0) = 0, \qquad u_2(0) = 0, \qquad u_2'(0) = 1.$$

Since u_1 and u_2 are linearly independent, the general solution of the Legendre equation (7.62) over the open interval $(-1, 1)$ is given by the linear combination (7.65) with arbitrary constants a_0 and a_1.

When α is 0 or a positive even integer, say $\alpha = 2m$, the series for $u_1(x)$ becomes a polynomial of degree $2m$ containing only even powers of x. Since we have

$$\alpha(\alpha - 2) \cdots (\alpha - 2n + 2) = 2m(2m - 2) \cdots (2m - 2n + 2) = \frac{2^n m!}{(m - n)!}$$

and

$$(\alpha + 1)(\alpha + 3) \cdots (\alpha + 2n - 1) = (2m + 1)(2m + 3) \cdots (2m + 2n - 1)$$

$$= \frac{(2m + 2n)! \, m!}{2^n (2m)! \, (m + n)!}$$

the formula for $u_1(x)$ in this case becomes

(7.68) $$u_1(x) = 1 + \frac{(m!)^2}{(2m!)} \sum_{k=1}^{m} (-1)^k \frac{(2m + 2k)!}{(m - k)! \, (m + k)! \, (2k)!} x^{2k}.$$

For example, when $\alpha = 0, 2, 4, 6$ $(m = 0, 1, 2, 3)$ the corresponding polynomials are

$$u_1(x) = 1, \qquad 1 - 3x^3, \qquad 1 - 10x^2 + \frac{35}{3} x^4, \qquad 1 - 21x^2 + 63x^4 - \frac{231}{5} x^6.$$

The companion series for $u_2(x)$ is not a polynomial when α is even because none of its coefficients are zero.

When α is an *odd* positive integer, the roles of u_1 and u_2 are reversed; the series for $u_2(x)$ becomes a polynomial and the series for $u_1(x)$ is not a polynomial. Specifically, if $\alpha = 2m + 1$ we have

(7.69) $$u_2(x) = x + \frac{(m!)^2}{(2m + 1)!} \sum_{k=1}^{m} (-1)^k \frac{(2m + 2k + 1)!}{(m - k)! \, (m + k)! \, (2k + 1)!} x^{2k+1}.$$

For example, when $\alpha = 1, 3, 5$ $(m = 0, 1, 2)$, the corresponding polynomials are

$$u_2(x) = x, \qquad x - \frac{5}{3} x^3, \qquad x - \frac{14}{3} x^3 + \frac{21}{5} x^5.$$

Some of the polynomial solutions of the Legendre equation have a number of interesting properties which are important in other branches of mathematics. For example, the theory of polynomial approximation considers the problem of approximating a given continuous function f on the interval $[-1, 1]$ by a polynomial p_n of degree $\leq n$ in such a way that the "mean-square error"

$$\int_{-1}^{1} |f(x) - p_n(x)|^2 \, dx$$

will be as small as possible. Polynomial solutions of the Legendre equation play a fundamental role in the solution of this problem. (See Section 8.10.) Some of the properties
of these polynomial solutions can be deduced directly from the differential equation or
from the formulas in (7.68) and (7.69). Others are more easily deduced from an alternative formula for these polynomials which we shall now derive.

First we shall obtain a single formula which contains (aside from constant factors)
both the polynomials in (7.68) and (7.69). Let

$$P_n(x) = \frac{1}{2^n} \sum_{r=0}^{[n/2]} \frac{(-1)^r (2n-2r)!}{r!\,(n-r)!\,(n-2r)!}\, x^{n-2r},$$

where $[n/2]$ denotes the greatest integer $\leq n/2$. This is called the *Legendre polynomial* of
degree n. When n is even, it is a constant multiple of the polynomial $u_1(x)$ in Equation
(7.68); when n is odd, it is a constant multiple of the polynomial $u_2(x)$ in (7.69).† The
first seven Legendre polynomials are given by the formulas

$$P_0(x) = 1, \qquad P_1(x) = x, \qquad P_2(x) = \tfrac{1}{2}(3x^2 - 1), \qquad P_3(x) = \tfrac{1}{2}(5x^3 - 3x),$$
$$P_4(x) = \tfrac{1}{8}(35x^4 - 30x^2 + 3), \qquad P_5(x) = \tfrac{1}{8}(63x^5 - 70x^3 + 15x),$$
$$P_6(x) = \tfrac{1}{16}(231x^6 - 315x^4 + 105x^2 - 5).$$

Figure 7.1 shows the graphs of the first five of these functions over the interval $[-1, 1]$.
In the sum defining $P_n(x)$ we note that

$$\frac{(2n-2r)!}{(n-2r)!}\, x^{n-2r} = \frac{d^n}{dx^n} x^{2n-2r} \qquad \text{and} \qquad \frac{1}{r!\,(n-r)!} = \frac{1}{n!}\binom{n}{r},$$

where $\binom{n}{r}$ is the binomial coefficient, and we write the sum in the form

$$P_n(x) = \frac{1}{2^n n!} \frac{d^n}{dx^n} \sum_{r=0}^{[n/2]} (-1)^r \binom{n}{r} x^{2n-2r}.$$

When $[n/2] < r \leq n$, the term x^{2n-2r} has degree less than n, so its nth derivative is zero.
Therefore we do not alter the sum if we allow r to run from 0 to n. This gives us

$$P_n(x) = \frac{1}{2^n n!} \frac{d^n}{dx^n} \sum_{r=0}^{n} (-1)^r \binom{n}{r} x^{2n-2r}.$$

Now we recognize the sum on the right as the binomial expansion of $(x^2 - 1)^n$. Therefore we have

$$P_n(x) = \frac{1}{2^n n!} \frac{d^n}{dx^n} (x^2 - 1)^n.$$

This is known as *Rodrigues' formula* for the Legendre polynomials.

---

† When n is even, say $n = 2m$, we may replace the index of summation k in Equation (7.68) by
a new index r, where $r = m - k$; we find that the sum in (7.68) is a constant multiple of $P_n(x)$.
Similarly, when n is odd, a change of index transforms the sum in (7.69) to a constant multiple of
$P_n(x)$.

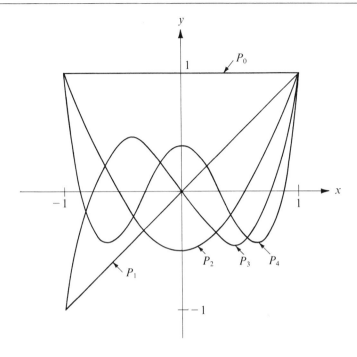

FIGURE 7.1 *Graphs of Legendre polynomials over the interval* [−1, 1].

Using Rodrigues' formula and the differential equation, we can derive a number of important properties of the Legendre polynomials. Some of these properties are listed below. Their proofs are outlined in the next set of exercises.

For each $n \geq 0$ we have

$$P_n(1) = 1 .$$

Moreover, $P_n(x)$ is the only polynomial which satisfies the Legendre equation

$$(1 - x^2) y'' - 2xy' + n(n + 1)y = 0$$

and has the value 1 when $x = 1$.

For each $n \geq 0$ we have

$$P_n(-x) = (-1)^n P_n(x) .$$

This shows that P_n is an even function when n is even, and an odd function when n is odd.

If $m \neq n$ we have

$$\int_{-1}^{1} P_n(x)P_m(x) \, dx = 0 .$$

This is called the *orthogonality relation* for Legendre polynomials. When $m = n$ we have the relation

$$\int_{-1}^{1} [P_n(x)]^2 \, dx = \frac{2}{2n + 1} \, .$$

Every polynomial of degree n can be expressed as a linear combination of the Legendre polynomials $P_0, P_1, \ldots, P_n$. In fact, if f is a polynomial of degree n we have

$$f(x) = \sum_{k=0}^{n} c_k P_k(x) \, ,$$

where

$$c_k = \frac{2k + 1}{2} \int_{-1}^{1} f(x) P_k(x) \, dx \, .$$

From the orthogonality relation it follows that

$$\int_{-1}^{1} g(x) P_n(x) \, dx = 0$$

for every polynomial g of degree less than n. This property can be used to prove that the Legendre polynomial P_n has n distinct real zeros and that they all lie in the open interval $(-1, 1)$.

The method used to solve the Legendre equation can always be applied to every second-order equation of the form

(7.70) $$y'' + P_1 y' + P_2 y = 0$$

if the coefficients P_1 and P_2 have power-series expansions. The theoretical justification for the method is provided by the following theorem.

7–13   THEOREM. *Let P_1 and P_2 be functions having power-series expansions of the form*

$$P_1(x) = \sum_{n=0}^{\infty} b_n(x - x_0)^n \, , \qquad P_2(x) = \sum_{n=0}^{\infty} c_n(x - x_0)^n \, ,$$

valid in some open interval $(x_0 - r, x_0 + r)$. Then the differential equation (7.70) has a power-series solution

(7.71) $$y = \sum_{n=0}^{\infty} a_n(x - x_0)^n$$

convergent in the same interval. Moreover, if k_0 and k_1 are given real numbers, there is exactly one power-series solution $y = f(x)$ satisfying the initial conditions

$$f(x_0) = k_0 \qquad \text{and} \qquad f'(x_0) = k_1 \, .$$

For this solution we have $a_0 = k_0$ and $a_1 = k_1$. The remaining coefficients $a_2, a_3, a_4, \ldots$ can be determined in terms of a_0 and a_1 by the method of undetermined coefficients.

Note. The coefficient of y'' in (7.70) is 1. The Legendre equation

$$(1 - x^2)y'' - 2xy' + \alpha(\alpha + 1)y = 0$$

can be put in this form if we divide through by $1 - x^2$. Thus, for the Legendre equation we have

$$P_1(x) = -\frac{2x}{1 - x^2} \qquad \text{and} \qquad P_2(x) = \frac{\alpha(\alpha + 1)}{1 - x^2}$$

if $x^2 \neq 1$. Since $1/(1 - x^2) = \sum_{n=0}^{\infty} x^{2n}$ for $|x| < 1$, both P_1 and P_2 have power-series expansions in the open interval $(-1, 1)$, so Theorem 7-13 is applicable.

Proof. We shall not present all the details of the proof of Theorem 7-13 but shall merely sketch the principal steps. We substitute the given series for P_1 and P_2 in the differential equation and then try to determine coefficients a_n so that the equation will be satisfied by the series in (7.71). This leads to the recursion formula

$$(n + 2)(n + 1)a_{n+2} = -\sum_{k=0}^{n} [(k + 1)b_{n-k}a_{k+1} + c_{n-k}a_k],$$

expressing a_{n+2} in terms of $a_0, a_1, \ldots, a_{n+1}$. We choose arbitrary values of a_0 and a_1 and use this formula to *define* the numbers $a_2, a_3, \ldots$ in terms of a_0 and a_1. This guarantees that the power series in (7.71) will satisfy the differential equation. To complete the proof it is necessary to show that the series so defined actually converges for every x in the interval $(x_0 - r, x_0 + r)$. This is done by dominating the series in (7.71) by another power series known to converge.

Choose a fixed point $x_1 \neq x_0$ in the interval $(x_0 - r, x_0 + r)$ and let $t = |x_1 - x_0|$. Since the series for P_1 and P_2 converge absolutely for $x = x_1$ the terms of these series are bounded, say

$$|b_k|\, t^k \leq M \qquad \text{and} \qquad |c_k|\, t^k \leq M$$

for some $M > 0$. The recursion formula implies the inequality

$$(n + 2)(n + 1)\, |a_{n+2}| \leq \frac{M}{t^n} \sum_{k=0}^{n} [(k + 1)\, |a_{k+1}| + |a_k|]t^k.$$

Now let $A_0 = |a_0|$, $A_1 = |a_1|$, and define $A_2, A_3, \ldots$ successively by the recursion formula

(7.72) $$(n + 2)(n + 1)A_{n+2} = \frac{M}{t^n} \sum_{k=0}^{n} [(k + 1)A_{k+1} + A_k]t^k + MA_{n+1}t$$

for $n \geq 1$. It follows that $|a_n| \leq A_n$ for all $n \geq 0$, so the series $\sum a_n(x - x_0)^n$ is dominated by the series $\sum A_n|x - x_0|^n$. Now we use the ratio test to show that $\sum A_n|x - x_0|^n$ converges if $|x - x_0| < t$. From (7.72) we can deduce the relation

$$(n + 2)(n + 1)A_{n+2} = \frac{1}{t}[(n + 1)n + M(n + 1)t + Mt^2]A_{n+1}$$

(by induction) and we have

$$\frac{A_{n+2}\, |x - x_0|^{n+2}}{A_{n+1}\, |x - x_0|^{n+1}} = \frac{(n + 1)n + M(n + 1)t + Mt^2}{(n + 2)(n + 1)t}\, |x - x_0| \to \frac{|x - x_0|}{t}$$

as $n \to \infty$. This limit is less than 1 if $|x - x_0| < t$. Hence $\sum a_n (x - x_0)^n$ converges if $|x - x_0| < t$. But since $t = |x_1 - x_0|$ and since x_1 was an arbitrary point in the interval $(x_0 - r, x_0 + r)$, the series $\sum a_n (x - x_0)^n$ must converge for all x in $(x_0 - r, x_0 + r)$.

7.18   Exercises

1. The Legendre equation (7.62) with $\alpha = 0$ has the polynomial solution $u_1(x) = 1$ and a solution u_2, not a polynomial, given by the series in Equation (7.67).

(a) Show that the sum of the series for u_2 is given by

$$u_2(x) = \frac{1}{2} \log \frac{1 + x}{1 - x} \qquad \text{for} \quad |x| < 1 .$$

(b) Verify directly that the function u_2 in part (a) is a solution of the Legendre equation when $\alpha = 0$.

2. Show that the function f defined by the equation

$$f(x) = 1 - \frac{x}{2} \log \frac{1 + x}{1 - x}$$

for $|x| < 1$ satisfies the Legendre equation (7.62) with $\alpha = 1$. Express this function as a linear combination of the solutions u_1 and u_2 given in Equations (7.66) and (7.67).

3. The Legendre equation (7.62) can be written in the form

$$[(x^2 - 1)y']' - \alpha(\alpha + 1)y = 0 .$$

(a) If a, b, c are constants with $a > b$ and $4c + 1 > 0$, show that a differential equation of the type

$$[(x - a)(x - b)y']' - cy = 0$$

can be transformed to a Legendre equation by a change of variable of the form $x = At + B$, with $A > 0$. Determine A and B in terms of a and b.

(b) Use the method suggested in part (a) to transform the equation

$$(x^2 - x)y'' + (2x - 1)y' - 2y = 0$$

to a Legendre equation.

4. Find two linearly independent power-series solutions of the *Hermite equation*

$$y'' - 2xy' + 2\alpha y = 0$$

on an interval of the form $(-r, r)$. Show that one of these solutions is a polynomial when α is a nonnegative integer.

5. Use the method of undetermined coefficients to find a power-series solution of the differential equation

$$xy'' + (3 + x^3)y' + 3x^2 y = 0$$

valid for all x. Find a second solution of the form $y = x^{-2} \sum a_n x^n$ valid for all $x \neq 0$.

6. Find a power-series solution of the differential equation

$$x^2 y'' + x^2 y' - (\alpha x + 2)y = 0$$

valid on an interval of the form $(-r, r)$.

7. This exercise shows how the Legendre equation arises when we seek solutions of Laplace's equation having a special form. Let f be a scalar field satisfying Laplace's equation

$$\frac{\partial^2 f}{\partial x^2} + \frac{\partial^2 f}{\partial y^2} + \frac{\partial^2 f}{\partial z^2} = 0 .$$

The introduction of spherical coordinates

$$x = \rho \cos \theta \sin \phi , \qquad y = \rho \sin \theta \sin \phi , \qquad z = \rho \cos \phi ,$$

transforms $f(x, y, z)$ to $F(\rho, \theta, \phi)$.

(a) Show that F satisfies the partial differential equation

$$\frac{\partial^2 F}{\partial \rho^2} + \frac{2}{\rho} \frac{\partial F}{\partial \rho} + \frac{1}{\rho^2} \frac{\partial^2 F}{\partial \phi^2} + \frac{\cot \phi}{\rho^2} \frac{\partial F}{\partial \phi} + \frac{1}{\rho^2 \sin^2 \phi} \frac{\partial^2 F}{\partial \theta^2} = 0 .$$

(b) Suppose we seek solutions of this equation which are independent of θ and have the form $F(\rho, \theta, \phi) = \rho^n G(\phi)$. Show that the equation in (a) is satisfied if G satisfies the second-order equation

$$\frac{d^2 G}{d\phi^2} + \cot \phi \frac{dG}{d\phi} + n(n + 1)G = 0 .$$

(c) The change of variable $x = \cos \phi$ ($\phi = \arccos x$, $-1 \le x \le 1$) transforms $G(\phi)$ to $g(x)$. Show that g satisfies the Legendre equation

$$(1 - x^2) \frac{d^2 g}{dx^2} - 2x \frac{dg}{dx} + n(n + 1)g = 0 .$$

In Exercises 8 through 14, $P_n(x)$ denotes the Legendre polynomial of degree n. These exercises outline proofs of the properties of the Legendre polynomials described in Section 7.17.

8. (a) Use Rodrigues' formula to show that

$$P_n(x) = \frac{1}{2^n} (x + 1)^n + (x - 1)Q_n(x) ,$$

where $Q_n(x)$ is a polynomial.

(b) Prove that $P_n(1) = 1$ and that $P_n(-1) = (-1)^n$.

(c) Prove that $P_n(x)$ is the only polynomial solution of Legendre's equation (with $\alpha = n$) having the value 1 when $x = 1$.

9. (a) Use the differential equations satisfied by P_n and P_m to show that

$$[(1 - x^2)(P_n P_m' - P_n' P_m)]' = [n(n + 1) - m(m + 1)] P_n P_m .$$

(b) If $m \ne n$, integrate the equation in (a) from -1 to 1 to deduce the relation

$$\int_{-1}^{1} P_n(x) P_m(x) \, dx = 0 .$$

10. (a) Let $f(x) = (x^2 - 1)^n$. Use integration by parts to show that

$$\int_{-1}^{1} f^{(n)}(x) f^{(n)}(x) \, dx = -\int_{-1}^{1} f^{(n+1)}(x) f^{(n-1)}(x) \, dx .$$

Apply this formula repeatedly to deduce that the integral on the left is equal to

$$2(2n)! \int_{0}^{1} (1 - x^2)^n \, dx .$$

(b) The substitution $x = \cos t$ transforms the integral $\int_{0}^{1} (1 - x^2)^n \, dx$ to $\int_{0}^{\pi/2} \sin^{2n+1} t \, dt$. Use the relation

$$\int_{0}^{\pi/2} \sin^{2n+1} t \, dt = \frac{2n(2n - 2) \cdots 2}{(2n + 1)(2n - 1) \cdots 3 \cdot 1}$$

(see Exercise 10 on p. 258 of Volume I) and Rodrigues' formula to obtain

$$\int_{-1}^{1} [P_n(x)]^2 \, dx = \frac{2}{2n + 1} .$$

11. (a) Show that

$$P_n(x) = \frac{(2n)!}{2^n(n!)^2} x^n + Q_n(x),$$

where $Q_n(x)$ is a polynomial of degree less than n.

(b) Express the polynomial $f(x) = x^4$ as a linear combination of P_0, P_1, P_2, P_3, and P_4.

(c) Show that every polynomial f of degree n can be expressed as a linear combination of the Legendre polynomials P_0, P_1, $\ldots$, P_n.

12. If f is a polynomial of degree n, write

$$f(x) = \sum_{k=0}^{n} c_k P_k(x).$$

[This is possible because of Exercise 11(c).] For a fixed m, $0 \le m \le n$, multiply both sides of this equation by $P_m(x)$ and integrate from -1 to 1. Use Exercises 9(b) and 10(b) to deduce the relation

$$c_m = \frac{2m + 1}{2} \int_{-1}^{1} f(x) P_m(x)\, dx.$$

13. Use Exercises 9 and 11 to show that $\int_{-1}^{1} g(x) P_n(x)\, dx = 0$ for every polynomial g of degree less than n.

14. (a) Use Rolle's theorem to show that P_n cannot have any multiple zeros in the open interval $(-1, 1)$. In other words, any zeros of P_n which lie in $(-1, 1)$ must be simple zeros.

(b) Assume P_n has m zeros in the interval $(-1, 1)$. If $m = 0$, let $Q_0(x) = 1$. If $m \ge 1$, let

$$Q_m(x) = (x - x_1)(x - x_2) \cdots (x - x_m),$$

where x_1, x_2, $\ldots$, x_m are the m zeros of P_n in $(-1, 1)$. Show that, at each point x in $(-1, 1)$, $Q_m(x)$ has the same sign as $P_n(x)$.

(c) Use part (b), along with Exercise 13, to show that the inequality $m < n$ leads to a contradiction. This shows that P_n has n distinct real zeros, all of which lie in the open interval $(-1, 1)$.

15. (a) Show that the value of the integral $\int_{-1}^{1} P_n(x) P_{n+1}'(x)\, dx$ is independent of n.

(b) Evaluate the integral $\int_{-1}^{1} x\, P_n(x) P_{n-1}(x)\, dx$.

7.19 The Bessel equation

In Section 7.17 we learned how to find a power-series solution of the differential equation

$$(7.73) \qquad\qquad y'' + P_1 y' + P_2 y = 0$$

near a point x_0 whenever the coefficients P_1 and P_2 have power-series expansions near x_0. If either P_1 or P_2 does not have a power-series expansion near x_0, power-series solutions valid near x_0 may or may not exist. For example, suppose we try to find a power-series solution $y = \sum a_k x^k$ of the differential equation

$$(7.74) \qquad\qquad x^2 y'' - y' - y = 0$$

near $x_0 = 0$. If we use the method of undetermined coefficients we are led to the recursion formula

$$a_{n+1} = \frac{n^2 - n - 1}{n + 1}\, a_n.$$

Although this gives us a power series $y = \sum a_k x^k$ which formally satisfies (7.74), the ratio test shows that this power series converges *only* for $x = 0$. Thus, there is no power-series solution of (7.74) valid in any open interval about $x_0 = 0$. This example does not violate Theorem 7–13 because when we put Equation (7.74) in the form (7.73) we find that the coefficients P_1 and P_2 are given by

$$P_1(x) = -\frac{1}{x^2} \quad \text{and} \quad P_2(x) = -\frac{1}{x^2}.$$

These functions do not have power-series expansions about the origin. The difficulty here is that the coefficient of y'' in (7.74) has the value 0 when $x = 0$; in other words, the differential equation has a singular point at $x = 0$.

A knowledge of the theory of functions of a complex variable is needed to appreciate the difficulties encountered in the investigation of differential equations near a singular point. However, some important special cases of equations with singular points can be treated by elementary methods. For example, suppose the differential equation in (7.73) is equivalent to an equation of the form

(7.75) $$(x - x_0)^2 y'' + (x - x_0)P(x)y' + Q(x)y = 0,$$

where P and Q have power-series expansions in some open interval $(x_0 - r, x_0 + r)$. In this case we say that x_0 is a *regular* singular point of the equation. If we divide both sides of (7.75) by $(x - x_0)^2$ the equation becomes

$$y'' + \frac{P(x)}{x - x_0} y' + \frac{Q(x)}{(x - x_0)^2} y = 0$$

for $x \neq x_0$. If $P(x_0) \neq 0$ or $Q(x_0) \neq 0$, either the coefficient of y' or the coefficient of y will not have a power-series expansion about the point x_0, so Theorem 7–13 will not be applicable. In 1873 the German mathematician Georg Frobenius (1849–1917) developed a useful method for treating such equations. He showed that the differential equation in (7.75) can always be satisfied by a function of the form

(7.76) $$y = |x - x_0|^t \sum_{n=0}^{\infty} a_n(x - x_0)^n$$

for some real exponent t, with $a_0 \neq 0$. The power series which multiplies $|x - x_0|^t$ will converge in the interval $(x_0 - r, x_0 + r)$. If the exponent t is zero or a positive even integer, the formula gives a power-series solution of the differential equation valid everywhere in the interval $(x_0 - r, x_0 + r)$. Otherwise, the solution is not a power series and the solution is valid for all x in the interval $(x_0 - r, x_0 + r)$ with the possible exception of the point x_0 itself.

We shall not discuss the method of Frobenius in all its ramifications but merely show how the method can be applied to solve the Bessel equation

$$x^2 y'' + xy' + (x^2 - \alpha^2)y = 0,$$

where α is a nonnegative constant. This equation has the form (7.75) with $x_0 = 0$, $P(x) = 1$, and $Q(x) = x^2 - \alpha^2$, so the point $x_0 = 0$ is a regular singular point. Since P and Q have power-series expansions over the entire real axis, we try to find a solution of the form

(7.77)
$$y = |x|^t \sum_{n=0}^{\infty} a_n x^n \,,$$

with $a_0 \neq 0$, valid for all real x with the possible exception of $x = 0$.

First we keep $x > 0$, so that $|x|^t = x^t$. Differentiation of (7.77) gives us

$$y' = t x^{t-1} \sum_{n=0}^{\infty} a_n x^n + x^t \sum_{n=0}^{\infty} n a_n x^{n-1} = x^{t-1} \sum_{n=0}^{\infty} (n + t) a_n x^n \,.$$

Similarly, we obtain

$$y'' = x^{t-2} \sum_{n=0}^{\infty} (n + t)(n + t - 1) a_n x^n \,.$$

If $L(y) = x^2 y'' + x y' + (x^2 - \alpha^2) y$, we find

$$L(y) = x^t \sum_{n=0}^{\infty} (n + t)(n + t - 1) a_n x^n + x^t \sum_{n=0}^{\infty} (n + t) a_n x^n$$

$$+ x^t \sum_{n=0}^{\infty} a_n x^{n+2} - x^t \sum_{n=0}^{\infty} \alpha^2 a_n x^n = x^t \sum_{n=0}^{\infty} [(n + t)^2 - \alpha^2] a_n x^n + x^t \sum_{n=0}^{\infty} a_n x^{n+2} \,.$$

Now we put $L(y) = 0$, cancel x^t, and try to determine the a_n so that the coefficient of each power of x will vanish. For the constant term we need $(t^2 - \alpha^2) a_0 = 0$. Since we seek a solution with $a_0 \neq 0$, this requires that

(7.78)
$$t^2 - \alpha^2 = 0 \,.$$

This quadratic equation in t is called the *indicial equation*. Its roots α and $-\alpha$ are the only possible values of t that can give us a solution of the desired type.

Consider first the choice $t = \alpha$. For this t the remaining equations for determining the coefficients become

(7.79) $[(1 + \alpha)^2 - \alpha^2] a_1 = 0$ and $[(n + \alpha)^2 - \alpha^2] a_n + a_{n-2} = 0$

for $n \geq 2$. Since $\alpha \geq 0$, the first of these implies that $a_1 = 0$. The second formula can be written as

(7.80)
$$a_n = - \frac{a_{n-2}}{(n + \alpha)^2 - \alpha^2} = - \frac{a_{n-2}}{n(n + 2\alpha)} \,,$$

so $a_3 = a_5 = a_7 = \cdots = 0$. For the coefficients with even subscripts we have

$$a_2 = \frac{-a_0}{2(2 + 2\alpha)} = \frac{-a_0}{2^2(1 + \alpha)} \,, \qquad a_4 = \frac{-a_2}{4(4 + 2\alpha)} = \frac{(-1)^2 a_0}{2^4 2!(1 + \alpha)(2 + \alpha)} \,,$$

$$a_6 = \frac{-a_4}{6(6 + 2\alpha)} = \frac{(-1)^3 a_0}{2^6 3!(1 + \alpha)(2 + \alpha)(3 + \alpha)} \,,$$

and, in general,

$$a_{2n} = \frac{(-1)^n a_0}{2^{2n} n!(1 + \alpha)(2 + \alpha) \cdots (n + \alpha)} \,.$$

Therefore the choice $t = \alpha$ gives us the solution

$$y = a_0 x^\alpha \left(1 + \sum_{n=1}^{\infty} \frac{(-1)^n x^{2n}}{2^{2n} n! (1 + \alpha)(2 + \alpha) \cdots (n + \alpha)} \right).$$

The ratio test shows that the power series appearing in this formula converges for all real x.

In this discussion we assumed that $x > 0$. If $x < 0$ we can repeat the discussion with x^t replaced by $(-x)^t$. We again find that t must satisfy the equation $t^2 - \alpha^2 = 0$. Taking $t = \alpha$ we then obtain the same solution, except that the outside factor x^α is replaced by $(-x)^\alpha$. Therefore the function f_α given by the equation

$$(7.81) \qquad f_\alpha(x) = a_0 |x|^\alpha \left(1 + \sum_{n=1}^{\infty} \frac{(-1)^n x^{2n}}{2^{2n} n! (1 + \alpha)(2 + \alpha) \cdots (n + \alpha)} \right)$$

is a solution of the Bessel equation valid for all real $x \neq 0$. For those values of α for which $f_\alpha'(0)$ and $f_\alpha''(0)$ exist the solution is also valid for $x = 0$.

Now consider the root $t = -\alpha$ of the indicial equation. We obtain, in place of (7.79), the equations

$$[(1 - \alpha)^2 - \alpha^2] a_1 = 0 \qquad \text{and} \qquad [(n - \alpha)^2 - \alpha^2] a_n + a_{n-2} = 0 \,,$$

which become

$$(1 - 2\alpha) a_1 = 0 \qquad \text{and} \qquad n(n - 2\alpha) a_n + a_{n-2} = 0 \,.$$

If 2α is not an integer these equations give us $a_1 = 0$ and

$$a_n = -\frac{a_{n-2}}{n(n - 2\alpha)}$$

for $n \geq 2$. Since this recursion formula is the same as (7.80), with α replaced by $-\alpha$, we are led to the solution

$$(7.82) \qquad f_{-\alpha}(x) = a_0 |x|^{-\alpha} \left(1 + \sum_{n=1}^{\infty} \frac{(-1)^n x^{2n}}{2^{2n} n! (1 - \alpha)(2 - \alpha) \cdots (n - \alpha)} \right)$$

valid for all real $x \neq 0$.

The solution $f_{-\alpha}$ was obtained under the hypothesis that 2α is not a positive integer. However, the series for $f_{-\alpha}$ is meaningful even if 2α is a positive integer, so long as α is not a positive integer. It can be verified that $f_{-\alpha}$ satisfies the Bessel equation for such α. Therefore, for each $\alpha \geq 0$ we have the series solution f_α, given by Equation (7.81); and if α is not a positive integer we have found another solution $f_{-\alpha}$ given by Equation (7.82). We have not yet shown that the two solutions f_α and $f_{-\alpha}$ are linearly independent. Before we discuss their independence we shall simplify the form of the solutions. To do this we need some properties of Euler's gamma function, and we digress briefly to discuss these properties.

For each real $s > 0$ we define $\Gamma(s)$ by the improper integral

$$\Gamma(s) = \int_{0+}^{\infty} t^{s-1}e^{-t}\, dt\,.$$

It was shown in Volume I (Section 9.28) that this integral converges if $s > 0$ and diverges if $s \leq 0$. Integration by parts leads to the functional equation

(7.83) $$\Gamma(s + 1) = s\,\Gamma(s)\,.$$

This implies that

$$\Gamma(s + 2) = (s + 1)\Gamma(s + 1) = (s + 1)s\,\Gamma(s)\,,$$

$$\Gamma(s + 3) = (s + 2)\Gamma(s + 2) = (s + 2)(s + 1)s\,\Gamma(s)\,,$$

and, in general,

(7.84) $$\Gamma(s + n) = (s + n - 1) \cdots (s + 1)s\,\Gamma(s)$$

for every positive integer n. Since $\Gamma(1) = \int_0^{\infty} e^{-t}\, dt = 1$, when we put $s = 1$ in (7.84) we find

$$\Gamma(n + 1) = n!\,.$$

Thus, the gamma function is an extension of the factorial function from integers to positive real numbers.

The functional equation (7.83) can be used to extend the definition of $\Gamma(s)$ to negative values of s that are not integers. We write (7.83) in the form

(7.85) $$\Gamma(s) = \frac{\Gamma(s + 1)}{s}\,.$$

The right-hand member is meaningful if $s + 1 > 0$ and $s \neq 0$. Therefore, we can use this equation to *define* $\Gamma(s)$ if $-1 < s < 0$. The right-hand member of (7.85) is now meaningful if $s + 2 > 0$, $s \neq -1$, $s \neq 0$, and we can use this equation to define $\Gamma(s)$ for $-2 < s < -1$. Continuing in this manner, we can extend the definition of $\Gamma(s)$ by induction to every open interval of the form $-n < s < -n + 1$, where n is a positive integer. The functional equation (7.83) and its extension in (7.84) are now valid for all real s for which both sides are meaningful.

We return now to the discussion of the Bessel equation. The series for f_α in Equation (7.81) contains the product $(1 + \alpha)(2 + \alpha) \cdots (n + \alpha)$. We can express this product in terms of the gamma function by taking $s = 1 + \alpha$ in (7.84). This gives us

$$(1 + \alpha)(2 + \alpha) \cdots (n + \alpha) = \frac{\Gamma(n + 1 + \alpha)}{\Gamma(1 + \alpha)}\,.$$

Therefore, if we choose $a_0 = 2^{-\alpha}/\Gamma(1 + \alpha)$ in Equation (7.81) and denote the resulting function $f_\alpha(x)$ by $J_\alpha(x)$ when $x > 0$, the solution for $x > 0$ can be written as

(7.86) $$J_\alpha(x) = \left(\frac{x}{2}\right)^\alpha \sum_{n=0}^{\infty} \frac{(-1)^n}{n!\,\Gamma(n + 1 + \alpha)} \left(\frac{x}{2}\right)^{2n}\,.$$

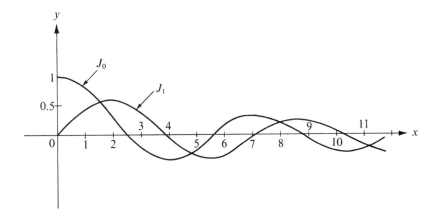

FIGURE 7.2 *Graphs of the Bessel functions J_0 and J_1.*

The function J_α defined by this equation for $x > 0$ and $\alpha \geq 0$ is called the *Bessel function of the first kind of order* α. When α is a nonnegative integer, say $\alpha = p$, the Bessel function J_p is given by the power series

$$J_p(x) = \sum_{n=0}^{\infty} \frac{(-1)^n}{n! \, (n+p)!} \left(\frac{x}{2}\right)^{2n+p} \qquad (p = 0, 1, 2, \ldots).$$

Extensive tables of Bessel functions have been constructed. The graphs of the two functions J_0 and J_1 are shown in Figure 7.2.

We can define a new function $J_{-\alpha}$ by replacing α by $-\alpha$ in Equation (7.86), if α is such that $\Gamma(n+1-\alpha)$ is meaningful; that is, if α is not a positive integer. Therefore, if $x > 0$ and $\alpha > 0$, $\alpha \neq 1, 2, 3, \ldots$, we define

$$J_{-\alpha}(x) = \left(\frac{x}{2}\right)^{-\alpha} \sum_{n=0}^{\infty} \frac{(-1)^n}{n! \, \Gamma(n+1-\alpha)} \left(\frac{x}{2}\right)^{2n}.$$

Taking $s = 1 - \alpha$ in (7.84) we obtain

$$\Gamma(n+1-\alpha) = (1-\alpha)(2-\alpha) \cdots (n-\alpha) \, \Gamma(1-\alpha)$$

and we see that the series for $J_{-\alpha}(x)$ is the same as that for $f_{-\alpha}(x)$ in Equation (7.82) with $a_0 = 2^\alpha / \Gamma(1-\alpha)$, $x > 0$. Therefore, if α is not a positive integer, $J_{-\alpha}$ is a solution of the Bessel equation for $x > 0$.

If α is not an integer, the two solutions $J_\alpha(x)$ and $J_{-\alpha}(x)$ are linearly independent on the positive real axis (since their ratio is not constant) and the general solution of the Bessel equation for $x > 0$ is

$$y = c_1 J_\alpha(x) + c_2 J_{-\alpha}(x).$$

If α is a nonnegative integer, say $\alpha = p$, we have found only the solution J_p and its constant multiples valid for $x > 0$. Another solution, independent of this one, can be found by the method described in Example 4 of Section 7.8. We recall that if u_1 is a solution of $y'' + P_1 y' + P_2 y = 0$ that never vanishes on an interval I, a second solution u_2 independent of u_1 is given by the integral

$$u_2(x) = u_1(x) \int_c^x \frac{Q(t)}{[u_1(t)]^2} \, dt \, ,$$

where $Q(x) = e^{-\int P_1(x) \, dx}$. For the Bessel equation we have $P_1(x) = 1/x$, so $Q(x) = 1/x$ and a second solution u_2 is given by the formula

$$(7.87) \qquad\qquad u_2(x) = J_p(x) \int_c^x \frac{1}{t[J_p(t)]^2} \, dt \, ,$$

if c and x lie in an interval I in which J_p does not vanish.

This second solution can be put in other forms. For example, from Equation (7.86) we may write

$$\frac{1}{[J_p(t)]^2} = \frac{1}{t^{2p}} g_p(t) \, ,$$

where $g_p(0) \neq 0$. In the interval I the function g_p has a power-series expansion

$$g_p(t) = \sum_{n=0}^{\infty} A_n t^n$$

which could be determined by equating coefficients in the identity $g_p(t) \, [J_p(t)]^2 = t^{2p}$. If we assume the existence of such an expansion, the integrand in (7.87) takes the form

$$\frac{1}{t[J_p(t)]^2} = \frac{1}{t^{2p+1}} \sum_{n=0}^{\infty} A_n t^n \, .$$

Integrating this formula term by term from c to x we obtain a logarithmic term $A_{2p} \log x$ (from the power t^{-1}) plus a series of the form $x^{-2p} \sum B_n x^n$. Therefore Equation (7.87) takes the form

$$u_2(x) = A_{2p} J_p(x) \log x + J_p(x) x^{-2p} \sum_{n=0}^{\infty} B_n x^n \, .$$

It can be shown that the coefficient $A_{2p} \neq 0$. If we multiply $u_2(x)$ by $1/A_{2p}$ the resulting solution is denoted by $K_p(x)$ and has the form

$$K_p(x) = J_p(x) \log x + x^{-p} \sum_{n=0}^{\infty} C_n x^n \, .$$

Having arrived at this formula, we can verify that a solution of this form actually exists by substituting the right-hand member in the Bessel equation and determining the coefficients C_n so as to satisfy the equation. The details of this calculation are lengthy and will be omitted. The final result can be expressed as

$$K_p(x) = J_p(x) \log x - \frac{1}{2} \left(\frac{x}{2}\right)^{-p} \sum_{n=0}^{p-1} \frac{(p-n-1)!}{n!} \left(\frac{x}{2}\right)^{2n}$$

$$- \frac{1}{2} \left(\frac{x}{2}\right)^{p} \sum_{n=0}^{\infty} (-1)^n \frac{h_n + h_{n+p}}{n! \, (n+p)!} \left(\frac{x}{2}\right)^{2n} ,$$

where $h_0 = 0$ and $h_n = 1 + 1/2 + \cdots + 1/n$ for $n \geq 1$. The series on the right converges for all real x. The function K_p defined for $x > 0$ by this formula is called the *Bessel function of the second kind of order p*. Since K_p is not a constant multiple of J_p, the general solution of the Bessel equation in this case for $x > 0$ is

$$y = c_1 J_p(x) + c_2 K_p(x) \,.$$

Further properties of the Bessel functions are discussed in the next set of exercises.

7.20 Exercises

1. (a) Let f be any solution of the Bessel equation of order α and let $g(x) = x^{1/2} f(x)$ for $x > 0$. Show that g satisfies the differential equation

$$y'' + \left(1 + \frac{1 - 4\alpha^2}{4x^2}\right) y = 0 \,.$$

(b) When $4\alpha^2 = 1$ the differential equation in (a) becomes $y'' + y = 0$; its general solution is $y = A \cos x + B \sin x$. Use this information and the equation† $\Gamma(\tfrac{1}{2}) = \sqrt{\pi}$ to show that, for $x > 0$,

$$J_{1/2}(x) = \left(\frac{2}{\pi x}\right)^{1/2} \sin x \qquad \text{and} \qquad J_{-1/2}(x) = \left(\frac{2}{\pi x}\right)^{1/2} \cos x \,.$$

(c) Deduce the formulas in part (b) directly from the series for $J_{1/2}(x)$ and $J_{-1/2}(x)$.

2. Use the series representation for Bessel functions to show that

(a) $\dfrac{d}{dx} (x^\alpha J_\alpha(x)) = x^\alpha J_{\alpha-1}(x),$

(b) $\dfrac{d}{dx} (x^{-\alpha} J_\alpha(x)) = -x^{-\alpha} J_{\alpha+1}(x).$

3. Let $F_\alpha(x) = x^\alpha J_\alpha(x)$ and $G_\alpha(x) = x^{-\alpha} J_\alpha(x)$ for $x > 0$. Note that each positive zero of J_α is a zero of F_α and is also a zero of G_α. Use Rolle's theorem and Exercise 2 to prove that the positive zeros of J_α and $J_{\alpha+1}$ interlace. That is, there is a zero of J_α between each pair of positive zeros of $J_{\alpha+1}$, and a zero of $J_{\alpha+1}$ between each pair of positive zeros of J_α. (See Figure 7.2.)

4. (a) From the relations in Exercise 2 deduce the recurrence relations

$$\frac{\alpha}{x} J_\alpha(x) + J_\alpha'(x) = J_{\alpha-1}(x) \qquad \text{and} \qquad \frac{\alpha}{x} J_\alpha(x) - J_\alpha'(x) = J_{\alpha+1}(x) \,.$$

(b) Use the relations in part (a) to deduce the formulas

$$J_{\alpha-1}(x) + J_{\alpha+1}(x) = \frac{2\alpha}{x} J_\alpha(x) \qquad \text{and} \qquad J_{\alpha-1}(x) - J_{\alpha+1}(x) = 2 J_\alpha'(x) \,.$$

---

† The change of variable $t = u^2$ gives us

$$\Gamma(\tfrac{1}{2}) = \int_{0+}^{\infty} t^{-1/2} e^{-t} \, dt = 2 \int_0^{\infty} e^{-u^2} \, du = \sqrt{\pi} \,.$$

(See Exercise 10 of Section 3.8 for a proof that $2 \int_0^\infty e^{-u^2} \, du = \sqrt{\pi}$.)

5. Use Exercise 1(b) and a suitable recurrence formula to show that

$$J_{3/2}(x) = \left(\frac{2}{\pi x}\right)^{1/2}\left(\frac{\sin x}{x} - \cos x\right).$$

Find a similar formula for $J_{-3/2}(x)$.

6. Prove that

$$\frac{1}{2}\frac{d}{dx}\left(J_\alpha^2(x) + J_{\alpha+1}^2(x)\right) = \frac{\alpha}{x}J_\alpha^2(x) - \frac{\alpha+1}{x}J_{\alpha+1}^2(x)$$

and

$$\frac{d}{dx}\left(x\,J_\alpha(x)J_{\alpha+1}(x)\right) = x\left(J_\alpha^2(x) - J_{\alpha+1}^2(x)\right).$$

7. (a) Use the identities in Exercise 6 to show that

$$J_0^2(x) + 2\sum_{n=1}^\infty J_n^2(x) = 1 \qquad \text{and} \qquad \sum_{n=0}^\infty (2n+1)J_n(x)J_{n+1}(x) = \tfrac{1}{2}x.$$

(b) From part (a), deduce that $|J_0(x)| \le 1$ and $|J_n(x)| \le \tfrac{1}{2}\sqrt{2}$ for $n = 1, 2, 3, \ldots$, and all $x \ge 0$.

8. Let $g_\alpha(x) = x^{1/2} f_\alpha(ax^b)$ for $x > 0$, where a and b are nonzero constants. Show that g_α satisfies the differential equation

$$x^2 y'' + (a^2 b^2 x^{2b} + \tfrac{1}{4} - \alpha^2 b^2)y = 0$$

if, and only if, f_α is a solution of the Bessel equation of order α.

9. Use Exercise 8 to express the general solution of each of the following differential equations in terms of Bessel functions for $x > 0$.
(a) $y'' + xy = 0$.
(b) $y'' + x^2 y = 0$.
(c) $y'' + x^m y = 0$.
(d) $x^2 y'' + (x^4 + \tfrac{1}{8})y = 0$.

10. Generalize Exercise 8 when f_α and g_α are related by the equation $g_\alpha(x) = x^c\, f_\alpha(ax^b)$ for $x > 0$. Then find the general solution of each of the following equations in terms of Bessel functions for $x > 0$.
(a) $xy'' + 6y' + y = 0$.
(b) $xy'' + 6y' + xy = 0$.
(c) $xy'' + 6y' + x^4 y = 0$.
(d) $x^2 y'' - xy' + (x+1)y = 0$.

Supplement. Complex numbers

★7.21 Definitions and basic properties

The axioms for the real-number system imply that the square of a real number cannot be negative. (See Theorem 1–20 in Section 1.9, Volume I.) For example, there is no real number whose square is -1, so the quadratic equation $x^2 + 1 = 0$ has no solution among the real numbers. New types of numbers, called *complex numbers*, have been introduced to provide solutions to such equations. In this section we shall define complex numbers and derive their basic properties.

Complex numbers are merely two-dimensional vectors endowed with a new type of multiplication. That is, a complex number is simply an ordered pair (x_1, x_2) of real numbers, with equality, addition, and multiplication by scalars (real numbers) defined as for two-dimensional vectors:

$$(x_1, x_2) = (y_1, y_2) \quad \text{means} \quad x_1 = y_1 \quad \text{and} \quad x_2 = y_2,$$

$$(x_1, x_2) + (y_1, y_2) = (x_1 + y_1, x_2 + y_2),$$

$$a(x_1, x_2) = (ax_1, ax_2) \quad \text{(if } a \text{ is real)}.$$

In addition, we have multiplication of two complex numbers defined by the equation

(7.88) $$(x_1, x_2)(y_1, y_2) = (x_1y_1 - x_2y_2, x_1y_2 + x_2y_1).$$

It is easy to verify that this multiplication is commutative and associative (properties not possessed by the cross product) and that it is distributive with respect to addition. That is, if x, y, z are arbitrary complex numbers we have

$$xy = yx, \qquad x(yz) = (xy)z, \qquad \text{and} \qquad x(y + z) = xy + xz.$$

For example, to prove the associative law we write $x = (x_1, x_2)$, $y = (y_1, y_2)$, $z = (z_1, z_2)$, and note that

$$x(yz) = (x_1, x_2)(y_1z_1 - y_2z_2, y_1z_2 + y_2z_1)$$

$$= (x_1(y_1z_1 - y_2z_2) - x_2(y_1z_2 + y_2z_1), x_1(y_1z_2 + y_2z_1) + x_2(y_1z_1 - y_2z_2))$$

$$= ((x_1y_1 - x_2y_2)z_1 - (x_1y_2 + x_2y_1)z_2, (x_1y_2 + x_2y_1)z_1 + (x_1y_1 - x_2y_2)z_2)$$

$$= (x_1y_1 - x_2y_2, x_1y_2 + x_2y_1)(z_1, z_2) = (xy)z.$$

The commutative and distributive laws may be similarly proved.

The zero complex number $(0, 0)$ is, of course, an identity element for addition. That is, $(x_1, x_2) + (0, 0) = (x_1, x_2)$ for all complex numbers (x_1, x_2). Also, each complex number has a negative, since $(x_1, x_2) + (-x_1, -x_2) = (0, 0)$. We write $-(x_1, x_2)$ for $(-x_1, -x_2)$.

Multiplication also has an identity element. In fact, we have

$$(x_1, x_2)(1, 0) = (x_1, x_2)$$

so the complex number $(1, 0)$ leaves all complex numbers unchanged by multiplication. Each nonzero complex number has a reciprocal relative to this identity element. That is, if $(x_1, x_2) \neq (0, 0)$ there exists a complex number (y_1, y_2) such that

$$(x_1, x_2)(y_1, y_2) = (1, 0).$$

In fact, this equation is equivalent to the pair of equations

$$x_1y_1 - x_2y_2 = 1 \qquad \text{and} \qquad x_1y_2 + x_2y_1 = 0,$$

which has the unique solution

$$y_1 = \frac{x_1}{x_1^2 + x_2^2}, \qquad y_2 = \frac{-x_2}{x_1^2 + x_2^2}.$$

The condition $(x_1, x_2) \neq (0, 0)$ ensures that $x_1^2 + x_2^2 \neq 0$, so the reciprocal is well defined. We write $(x_1, x_2)^{-1}$ or $1/(x_1, x_2)$ for the reciprocal of (x_1, x_2). Thus, we have

(7.89) $$\frac{1}{(x_1, x_2)} = \left(\frac{x_1}{x_1^2 + x_2^2}, \frac{-x_2}{x_1^2 + x_2^2} \right) \qquad \text{if} \quad (x_1, x_2) \neq (0, 0).$$

The foregoing discussion shows that the set of all complex numbers satisfies the *field properties* of the real-number system (Axioms 1 through 6 in Section 1.7 of Volume I). Therefore, all the laws of algebra deducible from the field axioms also hold for complex numbers. For example, we have cancellation laws for addition and multiplication. If we define $x - y$ to mean $x + (-y)$ we have the usual formulas, such as

$$a - b = -(b - a), \qquad a(b - c) = ab - ac, \qquad (-a)b = a(-b) = -(ab).$$

Also, we can define the quotient x/y of two complex numbers to be xy^{-1} (if y is nonzero) and we have algebraic formulas such as

$$(a/b)(c/d) = (ac)/(bd), \qquad (a/b) + (c/d) = (ad + bc)/(ad),$$

whenever the denominators are nonzero.

The first component, x_1, of a complex number (x_1, x_2) is called the *real part* of the complex number; the second component, x_2, is called the *imaginary part*. When we perform algebraic operations on complex numbers with zero imaginary part we find

$$(x_1, 0) + (y_1, 0) = (x_1 + y_1, 0),$$
$$a(x_1, 0) = (ax_1, 0) \qquad (a \text{ real}),$$
$$(x_1, 0)(y_1, 0) = (x_1 y_1, 0),$$
$$(x_1, 0)/(y_1, 0) = (x_1/y_1, 0) \qquad (y_1 \neq 0).$$

This means that we can perform algebraic operations on complex numbers with zero imaginary part by performing the usual real-number operations on the real parts alone. For this reason we ordinarily make no distinction between the real number x and the complex number $(x, 0)$ whose real part is x; we agree to identify x and $(x, 0)$ and we write $x = (x, 0)$. In particular, we have $0 = (0, 0)$, $1 = (1, 0)$, $-1 = (-1, 0)$, and so on. Thus, we can think of the complex-number system as an extension of the real-number system.

Complex numbers have some algebraic properties not possessed by real numbers. For example, the quadratic equation $x^2 + 1 = 0$, which has no solution among the real numbers, can now be solved with the use of complex numbers. In fact, the complex number $(0, 1)$ is a solution, since we have

$$(0, 1)^2 = (0, 1)(0, 1) = (0 \cdot 0 - 1 \cdot 1, 0 \cdot 1 + 1 \cdot 0) = (-1, 0) = -1.$$

The complex number $(0, 1)$ is denoted by i and is called the *imaginary unit*. It has the property that its square is -1, $i^2 = -1$. The reader can easily verify that $(-i)^2 = -1$, so $x = -i$ is another solution of the equation $x^2 + 1 = 0$.

In vector notation we have used the symbols $\vec{i}$ and $\vec{j}$ to represent the unit coordinate vectors $(1, 0)$ and $(0, 1)$, respectively. In terms of these symbols, every vector (a, b) can be expressed in the form $(a, b) = a\vec{i} + b\vec{j}$. In complex notation we use the symbols 1 and i (instead of $\vec{i}$ and $\vec{j}$) to represent the complex numbers $(1, 0)$ and $(0, 1)$, respectively. Since $(a, b) = (a, 0) + b(0, 1)$ we can express every complex number in the form†

$$(a, b) = a + bi.$$

---

† The use of $\vec{i}$ for $(1, 0)$ in vector notation and i for $(0, 1)$ in complex notation should cause no confusion. Some electrical engineers use the symbol j instead of i for the imaginary unit $(0, 1)$, since they wish to reserve i to represent electric current.

The advantage of this notation is that it aids us in algebraic manipulations of formulas involving addition and multiplication. For example, if we multiply $a + bi$ by $c + di$, using the distributive and associative laws, and replace i^2 by -1, we find

$$(a + bi)(c + di) = ac - bd + (ad + bc)i,$$

which, of course, is in agreement with the definition in (7.88). Similarly, to compute the reciprocal of a nonzero complex number $a + bi$ we may write

$$\frac{1}{a + bi} = \frac{a - bi}{(a + bi)(a - bi)} = \frac{a - bi}{a^2 + b^2} = \frac{a}{a^2 + b^2} - \frac{bi}{a^2 + b^2}.$$

This formula is in agreement with that given in (7.89) for the reciprocal of $x_1 + x_2 i$.

By the introduction of complex numbers we have gained much more than the ability to solve the simple quadratic equation $x^2 + 1 = 0$. Consider, for example, the quadratic equation $ax^2 + bx + c = 0$, where a, b, c are real and $a \neq 0$. By completing the square we may write this equation in the form

$$\left(x + \frac{b}{2a}\right)^2 + \frac{4ac - b^2}{4a^2} = 0.$$

If $4ac - b^2 \leq 0$ the equation has the real roots $(-b \pm \sqrt{b^2 - 4ac})/(2a)$. If $4ac - b^2 > 0$, the left member is positive for every real x and the equation has no real roots. In this case however, there are two complex roots, given by the formulas

$$(7.90) \quad r_1 = -\frac{b}{2a} + i\,\frac{\sqrt{4ac - b^2}}{2a} \quad \text{and} \quad r_2 = -\frac{b}{2a} - i\,\frac{\sqrt{4ac - b^2}}{2a}.$$

In 1799, Gauss proved that every polynomial equation of the form

$$a_0 + a_1 x + a_2 x^2 + \cdots + a_n x^n = 0,$$

where $a_0, a_1, \ldots, a_n$ are arbitrary real numbers, with $a_n \neq 0$, has a solution among the complex numbers if $n \geq 1$. Moreover, even if the coefficients $a_0, a_1, \ldots, a_n$ are complex, a solution exists in the complex-number system. This fact is known as the *fundamental theorem of algebra*.† It shows that there is no need to construct numbers more general than complex numbers to solve polynomial equations with complex coefficients.

★7.22 Geometric interpretation. Modulus and argument

Since a complex number (x, y) is an ordered pair of real numbers it may be represented geometrically by a point in the plane, or by an arrow from the origin to the point (x, y), as shown in Figure 7.3. In this context, the xy-plane is often referred to as the complex

---

† A proof of the fundamental theorem of algebra can be found in almost any book on the theory of functions of a complex variable. For example, see K. Knopp, *Theory of Functions*, Dover Publications, New York, 1945, or E. T. Copson, *An Introduction to the Theory of Functions of a Complex Variable*, Oxford Univ. Press, London, 1935. A more elementary proof is given in O. Schreier and E. Sperner, *Introduction to Modern Algebra and Matrix Theory*, Chelsea Publishing Company, New York, 1951.

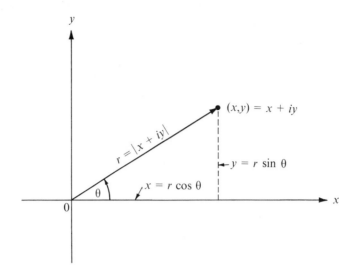

FIGURE 7.3   *Geometric representation of the complex number* $x + iy$.

plane. The x-axis is called the real axis; the y-axis is the imaginary axis. If $(x, y) \neq (0, 0)$ we can express x and y in polar coordinates,

$$x = r \cos \theta , \qquad y = r \sin \theta ,$$

and we obtain

(7.91) $$x + iy = r(\cos \theta + i \sin \theta) .$$

The positive number r, which represents the distance of (x, y) from the origin, is called the *modulus* or *absolute value* of $x + iy$, and is denoted by $|x + iy|$. Thus, we have

$$|x + iy| = \sqrt{x^2 + y^2} .$$

The polar angle θ is called an *argument* of $x + iy$. We say *an* argument rather than *the* argument because for a given point (x, y) the angle θ is determined only up to multiples of 2π. Sometimes it is desirable to assign a unique argument to a complex number. This may be done by restricting θ to lie in a half-open interval of length 2π. The intervals $[0, 2\pi)$ and $(-\pi, \pi]$ are commonly used for this purpose. We shall use the interval $(-\pi, \pi]$ and refer to the corresponding θ as the *principal argument* of $x + iy$; we denote this θ by $\arg(x + iy)$. Thus, if $x + iy \neq 0$ and $r = |x + iy|$ we define $\arg(x + iy)$ to be the unique real θ satisfying the conditions

$$x = r \cos \theta , \qquad y = r \sin \theta , \qquad -\pi < \theta \leq \pi .$$

For the zero complex number we assign the modulus 0 and agree that any real θ may be used as an argument.

Since the absolute value of a complex number z is simply the length of the vector representing z, we have the usual properties of absolute values. For example,

$$|z| > 0 \quad \text{if} \quad z \neq 0, \quad \text{and} \quad |z_1 - z_2| = |z_2 - z_1|.$$

Geometrically, the absolute value $|z_1 - z_2|$ represents the distance between the points z_1 and z_2 in the complex plane. The triangle inequality is also valid,

$$|z_1 + z_2| \leq |z_1| + |z_2|.$$

In addition, we have the following formulas for absolute values of products and quotients of complex numbers:

(7.92) $$|z_1 z_2| = |z_1| \, |z_2|$$

and

$$\left| \frac{z_1}{z_2} \right| = \frac{|z_1|}{|z_2|} \quad \text{if} \quad z_2 \neq 0.$$

If we write $z_1 = a + bi$ and $z_2 = c + di$ we obtain (7.92) at once from the identity

$$(ac - bd)^2 + (bc + ad)^2 = (a^2 + b^2)(c^2 + d^2).$$

The formula for $|z_1/z_2|$ follows from (7.92) if we write z_1 as a product,

$$z_1 = z_2 \frac{z_1}{z_2}.$$

If $z = x + iy$, the *complex conjugate* of z is the complex number $\bar{z} = x - iy$. Geometrically, $\bar{z}$ represents the reflection of z through the real axis. The definition of conjugate implies that

$$\overline{z_1 + z_2} = \bar{z}_1 + \bar{z}_2, \quad \overline{z_1 z_2} = \bar{z}_1 \bar{z}_2, \quad \overline{z_1/z_2} = \bar{z}_1/\bar{z}_2, \quad z\bar{z} = |z|^2.$$

The verification of these properties is left as an exercise for the reader.

If a quadratic equation with real coefficients has no real roots, its complex roots, given by (7.90), are conjugates. Conversely, if r_1 and r_2 are complex conjugates, say $r_1 = \alpha + i\beta$ and $r_2 = \alpha - i\beta$, where α and β are real, then r_1 and r_2 are roots of a quadratic equation with real coefficients. In fact, we have

$$r_1 + r_2 = 2\alpha \quad \text{and} \quad r_1 r_2 = \alpha^2 + \beta^2,$$

so

$$(x - r_1)(x - r_2) = x^2 - (r_1 + r_2)x + r_1 r_2,$$

and the quadratic equation in question is

$$x^2 - 2\alpha x + \alpha^2 + \beta^2 = 0.$$

★7.23 Complex exponentials

We wish now to extend the definition of e^x so that it becomes meaningful when x is replaced by any complex number z. We wish this extension to be such that the law of exponents, $e^a e^b = e^{a+b}$, will be valid for all complex a and b. And, of course, we want e^z to agree with the usual exponential when z is real. There are several equivalent ways to carry out this extension. Probably the simplest is by means of the following definition.

DEFINITION. If $z = x + iy$, we define e^z to be the complex number given by the equation

(7.93) $$e^z = e^x (\cos y + i \sin y).$$

Note that $e^z = e^x$ when $y = 0$, so this exponential agrees with the usual exponential when z is real. To justify this definition we shall use it to deduce the law of exponents.

If $a = x + iy$ and $b = u + iv$, we have

$$e^a = e^x(\cos y + i \sin y), \qquad e^b = e^u(\cos v + i \sin v),$$

so

$$e^a e^b = e^x e^u [\cos y \cos v - \sin y \sin v + i(\cos y \sin v + \sin y \cos v)].$$

Now we use the addition formulas for $\cos (y + v)$ and $\sin (y + v)$ and the law of exponents for real exponentials and we see that the foregoing equation becomes

(7.94) $$e^a e^b = e^{x+u} [\cos (y + v) + i \sin (y + v)].$$

Since $a + b = (x + u) + i (y + v)$, the right member of (7.94) is e^{a+b}. This proves that $e^a e^b = e^{a+b}$ for all complex a and b.

If we take $x = 0$ and $y = \theta$ in (7.93), we obtain the formula

$$e^{i\theta} = \cos \theta + i \sin \theta,$$

valid for every real θ. Comparing this with Equation (7.91), we see that the polar-coordinate form of a complex number can be expressed in terms of complex exponentials. In fact, (7.91) becomes

$$x + iy = re^{i\theta}.$$

This shows that every complex number $x + iy \neq 0$ can be expressed in the form $re^{i\theta}$, with $r = |x + iy|$ and $\theta = \arg(x + iy) + 2n\pi$, n being any integer. This representation of complex numbers is especially useful in connection with multiplication and division of complex numbers. For example, if $z_1 = r_1 e^{i\theta}$ and $z_2 = r_2 e^{i\phi}$, we have

(7.95) $$z_1 z_2 = r_1 e^{i\theta} r_2 e^{i\phi} = r_1 r_2 e^{i(\theta+\phi)}.$$

Therefore the product of the moduli, $r_1 r_2$, is the modulus of the product $z_1 z_2$, in agreement with Equation (7.92), and the sum of the arguments, $\theta + \phi$, is an admissible argument for the product $z_1 z_2$.

When $z = re^{i\theta}$, repeated application of (7.95) gives us the formula

$$z^n = r^n e^{in\theta} = r^n (\cos n\theta + i \sin n\theta),$$

valid for any nonnegative integer n. This formula is also valid for negative integers n if we define z^{-m} to be $(z^{-1})^m$ when m is a positive integer.

Similarly, we have

$$\frac{z_1}{z_2} = \frac{r_1 e^{i\theta}}{r_2 e^{i\phi}} = \frac{r_1}{r_2} e^{i(\theta-\phi)},$$

so the modulus of z_1/z_2 is r_1/r_2 and the difference $\theta - \phi$ is an admissible argument for z_1/z_2.

★7.24   Complex-valued functions

A function f whose values are complex numbers is called a complex-valued function. If the domain of f is a set of real numbers, f is called a complex-valued function of a real variable. If the domain is a set of complex numbers, f is called a complex-valued function of a complex variable, or more simply, a function of a complex variable. An example is the exponential function, defined by the equation

$$f(z) = e^z$$

for all complex z. Most of the familiar elementary functions of calculus, such as the exponential, the logarithm, and the trigonometric functions, can be extended to become functions of a complex variable. (See Exercises 11 and 12 in Section 7.25.) In this more general framework many new properties and interrelationships are often revealed. For example, the complex exponential function is periodic. In fact, if $z = x + iy$ and if n is any integer we have

$$e^{z+2n\pi i} = e^x[\cos(y + 2n\pi) + i\sin(y + 2n\pi)] = e^x(\cos y + i\sin y) = e^z \, .$$

Thus we see that $f(z + 2n\pi i) = f(z)$, so f has the period $2\pi i$. This property of the exponential function is revealed only when we study the exponential as a function of a complex variable.

The first systematic treatment of the differential and integral calculus of functions of a complex variable was given by Cauchy early in the 19th century. Since then the theory has developed into one of the most important and interesting branches of mathematics. It has become an indispensable tool for physicists and engineers and has connections in nearly every branch of pure mathematics. A discussion of this theory will not be given here. We shall discuss only one example of a complex-valued function. This is the function f of a real variable defined for all real x by the equation

$$(7.96) \qquad\qquad f(x) = e^{tx} \, ,$$

where t is a fixed complex number. Functions of this type occur in the study of linear differential equations with constant coefficients. When t is real, the derivative of this function is given by the formula

$$(7.97) \qquad\qquad f'(x) = te^{tx} \, .$$

We will show that, with a natural extension of the definition of derivative, this formula is also valid for complex t.

Suppose f is a complex-valued function defined for all real x in an open interval I. For a fixed x in I and real $h \neq 0$, we form the difference quotient

$$\frac{f(x + h) - f(x)}{h} \, .$$

If there is a complex number z such that

$$\lim_{h \to 0} \left| \frac{f(x + h) - f(x)}{h} - z \right| = 0 \, ,$$

we say that z is the derivative of f at x and we write $z = f'(x)$.

For each x in I, $f(x)$ is a complex number, so we can write

$$f(x) = u(x) + iv(x),$$

where $u(x)$ and $v(x)$ are real. This equation determines two real-valued functions u and v called, respectively, the real and imaginary parts of f. It is easy to prove that $f'(x)$ exists if, and only if, both derivatives $u'(x)$ and $v'(x)$ exist, in which case

$$f'(x) = u'(x) + iv'(x).$$

Let us apply this formula to compute the derivative of the function f given by (7.96). Suppose $t = \alpha + i\beta$, where α and β are real. By the definition of the complex exponential we have

$$f(x) = e^{tx} = e^{\alpha x + i\beta x} = e^{\alpha x}\cos \beta x + i\, e^{\alpha x}\sin \beta x.$$

Therefore the real and imaginary parts of f are given by

(7.98) $u(x) = e^{\alpha x}\cos \beta x$ and $v(x) = e^{\alpha x}\sin \beta x.$

These functions are differentiable for all x and their derivatives are given by the formulas

$$u'(x) = \alpha e^{\alpha x}\cos \beta x - \beta e^{\alpha x}\sin \beta x, \qquad v'(x) = \alpha e^{\alpha x}\sin \beta x + \beta e^{\alpha x}\cos \beta x.$$

Since $f'(x) = u'(x) + iv'(x)$ we have

$$f'(x) = \alpha e^{\alpha x}(\cos \beta x + i \sin \beta x) + i\beta e^{\alpha x}(\cos \beta x + i \sin \beta x)$$

$$= (\alpha + i\beta)e^{(\alpha + i\beta)x} = te^{tx}.$$

Thus we see that the derivative formula (7.97) holds when t is complex. Differentiating once more we find $f''(x) = t^2 e^{tx}$.

Suppose now that t is a root of the quadratic equation

(7.99) $t^2 + at + b = 0.$

Then we have

$$f''(x) + af'(x) + bf(x) = e^{tx}(t^2 + at + b) = 0,$$

so the function f is a complex-valued solution of the differential equation $L(y) = 0$, where

$$L(y) = y'' + ay' + by.$$

If a and b are real numbers, the real and imaginary parts of f will satisfy the differential equation $L(y) = 0$ separately. In fact, if we write $f(x) = u(x) + iv(x)$, then $f'(x) = u'(x) + iv'(x)$ and $f''(x) = u''(x) + iv''(x)$. Substituting $y = f(x)$ in the equation $L(y) = 0$ we find

$$u''(x) + au'(x) + bu(x) + i\,[v''(x) + av'(x) + bv(x)] = 0.$$

Since a complex number can be zero only if both its real and imaginary parts are zero, we see that u and v separately satisfy $L(y) = 0$. This shows that the functions u and v given by (7.98) are solutions of the differential equation $L(y) = 0$ if $\alpha + i\beta$ and $\alpha - i\beta$ are the roots of the quadratic equation (7.99).

★7.25 Exercises

1. Express the following complex numbers in the form $a + bi$.

   (a) $(1 + i)^2$.
   (b) $1/i$.
   (c) $1/(1 + i)$.
   (d) $(2 + 3i)(3 - 4i)$.

   (e) $(1 + i)/(1 - 2i)$.
   (f) $i^5 + i^{16}$.
   (g) $1 + i + i^2 + i^3$.
   (h) $\frac{1}{2}(1 + i)(1 + i^{-8})$.

2. Compute the absolute values of the following complex numbers.

   (a) $1 + i$.
   (b) $3 + 4i$.
   (c) $(1 + i)/(1 - i)$.

   (d) $1 + i + i^2$.
   (e) $i^7 + i^{10}$.
   (f) $2(1 - i) + 3(2 + i)$.

3. Make a sketch showing the set of all z in the complex plane which satisfy each of the following conditions.

   (a) $|z| < 1$.
   (b) $z + \bar{z} = 1$.
   (c) $z - \bar{z} = i$.
   (d) $|z - 1| = |z + 1|$.

   (e) $|z - i| = |z + i|$.
   (f) $|z - 1| + |z + 1| = 2$.
   (g) $|z - 1| - |z + 1| = 2$.
   (h) $z + \bar{z} = |z|^2$.

4. Express in the form $re^{i\theta}$, with $-\pi < \theta \le \pi$.

   (a) $2i$.
   (b) $-3i$.
   (c) -1.
   (d) 1.
   (e) $-3 + \sqrt{3}\,i$.

   (f) $(1 + i)/\sqrt{2}$.
   (g) $(-1 + i)^3$.
   (h) $(-1 - i)^3$.
   (i) $1/(1 + i)$.
   (j) $1/(1 + i)^2$.

5. (a) Given two distinct complex numbers z_1 and z_2 and a positive real number c. Describe the set of all z satisfying

$$|z - z_1| = c\,|z - z_2|$$

for $c = 1$, $c < 1$, and $c > 1$.

   (b) Do the same as in part (a) for the inequality

$$|z - z_1| < c\,|z - z_2|\,.$$

6. Let f be a polynomial with real coefficients.
   (a) Show that $\overline{f(z)} = f(\bar{z})$ for every complex z.
   (b) Use part (a) to deduce that the nonreal zeros of f (if any exist) must occur in pairs of conjugate complex numbers.

7. (a) If θ is real, show that

$$\cos\theta = \frac{e^{i\theta} + e^{-i\theta}}{2} \quad \text{and} \quad \sin\theta = \frac{e^{i\theta} - e^{-i\theta}}{2i}\,.$$

   (b) Use the formulas in (a) to deduce the identities

$$\cos^2\theta = \tfrac{1}{2}(1 + \cos 2\theta)\,, \qquad \sin^2\theta = \tfrac{1}{2}(1 - \cos 2\theta)\,.$$

8. (a) Prove that $e^z \ne 0$ for all complex z.
   (b) Find all complex z such that $e^z = 1$.

9. (a) Prove *DeMoivre's theorem*:

$$(\cos\theta + i\sin\theta)^n = \cos n\theta + i\sin n\theta\,,$$

valid for every real θ and every positive integer n.

(b) Take $n = 3$ in part (a) and deduce the trigonometric identities

$$\sin 3\theta = 3 \cos^2\theta \sin \theta - \sin^3\theta, \qquad \cos 3\theta = \cos^3\theta - 3 \cos \theta \sin^2\theta.$$

10. Given a complex number $z \neq 0$. Write $z = re^{i\theta}$, where $\theta = \arg(z)$. Let $z_1 = Re^{i\alpha}$, where $R = r^{1/n}$ and $\alpha = \theta/n$, and let $\epsilon = e^{2\pi i/n}$, where n is a positive integer.
   (a) Show that $z_1^n = z$. That is, z_1 is an nth root of z.
   (b) Show that z has n distinct nth roots,

$$z_1, \epsilon z_1, \epsilon^2 z_1, \ldots, \epsilon^{n-1} z_1,$$

and no others.
   (c) Determine the three cube roots of i.
   (d) Determine the four fourth roots of i.
   (e) Determine the four fourth roots of $-i$.

11. The definitions of the sine and cosine functions can be extended to the complex plane as follows:

$$\cos z = \frac{e^{iz} + e^{-iz}}{2}, \qquad \sin z = \frac{e^{iz} - e^{-iz}}{2i}.$$

When z is real, these formulas agree with the ordinary sine and cosine functions. (See Exercise 7.) Use these formulas to deduce the following properties of complex sines and cosines. Here u, v, and z denote complex numbers, with $z = x + iy$.
   (a) $\sin (u + v) = \sin u \cos v + \cos u \sin v$.
   (b) $\cos (u + v) = \cos u \cos v - \sin u \sin v$.
   (c) $\sin^2 z + \cos^2 z = 1$.
   (d) $\cos (iy) = \cosh y$, $\quad$ $\sin (iy) = i \sinh y$.
   (e) $\cos z = \cos x \cosh y - i \sin x \sinh y$.
   (f) $\sin z = \sin x \cosh y + i \cos x \sinh y$.

12. If z is a nonzero complex number, we define Log z, the complex logarithm of z, by the equation

$$\text{Log } z = \log |z| + i \arg(z).$$

When z is real and positive this formula agrees with the ordinary logarithm. Use this formula to deduce the following properties of complex logarithms.
   (a) $\text{Log } (-1) = \pi i$, $\quad$ $\text{Log } (i) = \pi i/2$.
   (b) $\text{Log } (z_1 z_2) = \text{Log } z_1 + \text{Log } z_2 + 2n\pi i$, where n is an integer.
   (c) $\text{Log } (z_1/z_2) = \text{Log } z_1 - \text{Log } z_2 + 2n\pi i$, where n is an integer.
   (d) $e^{\text{Log } z} = z$.

8

INTRODUCTION TO NUMERICAL ANALYSIS

8.1 Historical introduction

The planet Uranus was discovered in 1781 by a gifted amateur astronomer, William Herschel (1738–1822), with a homemade 10-ft telescope. With the use of Kepler's laws, the expected orbit of Uranus was quickly calculated from a few widely separated observations. It was found that the mean distance of Uranus from the sun was about twice that of Saturn and that one complete orbit would require 84 years. By 1830 the accumulated empirical data showed deviations from the scheduled orbit that could not be accounted for. Some astronomers felt that Newton's law of universal gravitation might not hold for distances as large as that of Uranus from the sun; others suspected that the perturbations were due to a hitherto undiscovered comet or more distant planet.

An undergraduate student at Cambridge University, John Couch Adams (1819–1892), was intrigued by the possibility of an undiscovered planet. He set himself the difficult task of calculating what the orbit of such a planet must be to account for the observed positions of Uranus, assuming the validity of Newton's law of gravitation. He completed his calculations in 1845 and asked the Royal Observatory at Greenwich to search for the hypothetical planet, but his request was not taken seriously.

A similar calculation was made independently and almost simultaneously by Jean Joseph Leverrier (1811–1877) of Paris, who asked Johann Galle, head of the Berlin Observatory, to confirm his prediction. The same evening that he received Leverrier's letter, Galle found the new planet, *Neptune*, almost exactly in its calculated position. This was another triumph for Newton's law of gravitation, and one of the first major triumphs of *numerical analysis*, the art and science of computation.

The history of numerical analysis goes back to ancient times. As early as 2000 B.C. the Babylonians were compiling mathematical tables. One clay tablet has been found containing the squares of the integers from 1 to 60. The Babylonians worshiped the heavenly bodies and kept elaborate astronomical records. The celebrated Alexandrian astronomer Claudius Ptolemy (circa 150 A.D.) possessed a Babylonian record of eclipses dating from 747 B.C.

In 220 B.C., Archimedes used regular polygons as approximations to a circle and deduced the inequalities $3\frac{10}{71} < \pi < 3\frac{1}{7}$. Numerical work from that time until the 17th century was centered principally around the preparation of astronomical tables. The advent of algebra in the 16th century brought about renewed activity in all branches of mathematics, including numerical analysis. In 1614, Napier published the first table of logarithms. In 1620, the logarithms of the sine and tangent functions were tabulated to seven decimal places. By 1628, fourteen-place tables of the logarithms of the numbers from 1 to 100,000 had been computed.

Computations with infinite series began to flourish near the end of the 17th century, along with the development of the calculus. Early in the 18th century Jacob Stirling and Brook Taylor laid the foundations of the *calculus of finite differences*, which now plays a central role in numerical analysis. With the prediction of the existence and location of the planet Neptune by Adams and Leverrier in 1845, the scientific importance of numerical analysis became established once and for all.

Late in the 19th century the development of automatic calculating machinery further stimulated the growth of numerical analysis. This growth has been explosive since the end of World War II because of the progress in high-speed electronic computing devices. The new machines have made possible a great many outstanding scientific achievements which previously seemed unattainable.

The art of computation (as distinct from the science of computation) lays much stress on the detailed planning required in a particular calculation. It also deals with such matters as precision, accuracy, errors, and checking. This aspect of numerical analysis will not be discussed here; it is best learned by carrying out actual numerical calculations with specific problems. For valuable advice on practical methods and techniques the reader should consult the existing books on numerical analysis, some of which are listed in the bibliography at the end of this chapter. The bibliography also contains some of the standard mathematical tables; many of them also give practical information on how to carry out a specific calculation.

This chapter provides an introduction to the *science* of computation. It contains some of the basic mathematical principles that might be required of almost anyone who uses numerical analysis, whether he works with a desk calculator or with a large-scale high-speed computing machine. Aside from its practical value, the material in this chapter is of interest in its own right, and it is hoped that this brief introduction will stimulate the reader to learn more about this important and fascinating branch of mathematics.

8.2 Approximations by polynomials

A basic idea in numerical analysis is that of using simple functions, usually polynomials, to approximate a given function f. One type of polynomial approximation was discussed in Volume I in connection with Taylor's formula (Section 7.6). The problem there was to find a polynomial P which agrees with a given function f and some of its derivatives at a given point. We proved that if f is a function with a derivative of order n at a point x_0, there is one and only one polynomial P of degree $\leq n$ which satisfies the $n + 1$ relations

$$P(x_0) = f(x_0), \qquad P'(x_0) = f'(x_0), \qquad \ldots, \qquad P^{(n)}(x_0) = f^{(n)}(x_0).$$

The solution is given by the *Taylor polynomial*,

$$P(x) = \sum_{k=0}^{n} \frac{f^{(k)}(x_0)}{k!} (x - x_0)^k.$$

We also discussed the error incurred in approximating $f(x)$ by $P(x)$ at points x other than x_0. This error is defined to be the difference $R(x) = f(x) - P(x)$, so we may write

$$f(x) = \sum_{k=0}^{n} \frac{f^{(k)}(x_0)}{k!} (x - x_0)^k + R(x).$$

To make further statements about the error $R(x)$ we need more information about the function f. For example, suppose we know that f has a derivative of order $n + 1$ everywhere in an open interval (a, b) and that $f^{(n)}$ is continuous on the closed interval $[a, b]$. Then if x and x_0 are distinct points in $[a, b]$ the error term $R(x)$ can be expressed in the form

$$R(x) = (x - x_0)^{n+1} \frac{f^{(n+1)}(c)}{(n + 1)!},$$

where c lies between x and x_0. (See Theorem 7–6 in Volume I.)

There are many other ways to approximate a given function f by polynomials, depending on the use to be made of the approximation. For example, instead of asking for a polynomial that agrees with f and some of its derivatives at a given point, we may ask for a polynomial that takes the same values as f at a number of distinct points. Specifically, if the given distinct points are $x_0, x_1, \ldots, x_n$ we may seek a polynomial P satisfying the conditions

(8.1) $\qquad P(x_0) = f(x_0), \qquad P(x_1) = f(x_1), \qquad \ldots, \qquad P(x_n) = f(x_n).$

Since there are $n + 1$ conditions to be satisfied we try a polynomial of degree $\leq n$, say

$$P(x) = \sum_{k=0}^{n} a_k x^k,$$

with $n + 1$ coefficients $a_0, a_1, \ldots, a_n$ to be determined. The $n + 1$ conditions (8.1) lead to a system of $n + 1$ linear equations for the coefficients. From the theory of linear equations it can be shown that this system has one and only one solution; hence such a polynomial always exists. If the equations are solved by Cramer's rule the coefficients $a_0, a_1, \ldots, a_n$ are expressed as quotients of determinants. In practice, however, the polynomial P is seldom determined in this manner because the calculations are extremely laborious when n is large. Simpler methods have been developed to calculate the polynomial approximation. Some of these will be discussed in later sections. The polynomial which solves the foregoing problem is called an *interpolating polynomial*.

Another common type of polynomial approximation is the so-called *least-square approximation*. Here the given function f is defined and integrable on an interval $[a, b]$ and we seek a polynomial P of degree $\leq n$ such that the mean-square error

(8.2) $$\int_a^b |f(x) - P(x)|^2 \, dx$$

will be as small as possible. In Section 8.10 we shall prove that for a continuous f such a polynomial exists and is uniquely determined. The Legendre polynomials introduced in Section 7.17 play a fundamental role in the solution of this problem.

Least-square approximation can be generalized by considering weighted least-square approximation. Instead of minimizing the integral in (8.2) we try to minimize the integral

(8.3) $$\int_a^b |f(x) - P(x)|^2 \, w(x) \, dx \,,$$

where w is a nonnegative "weight" function. Another generalization may be obtained by using powers other than the second power in (8.2) or (8.3). For example, if p is any real number ≥ 1 we can seek a polynomial P which minimizes the integral

$$\int_a^b |f(x) - P(x)|^p \, dx \,,$$

or, more generally, a polynomial P which minimizes

$$\int_a^b |f(x) - P(x)|^p \, w(x) \, dx$$

with a nonnegative weight function w.

There is another type of polynomial approximation in which we begin with a function f that is continuous on an interval $[a, b]$ and consider the *absolute deviation*

$$A(x) = |f(x) - P(x)| \,,$$

where P is a polynomial of degree n. Since the function A is continuous on $[a, b]$, it attains its absolute maximum value somewhere on $[a, b]$. This maximum value depends on the choice of the polynomial P and we may denote it by $M(P)$. Thus we have

$$M(P) = \max_{a \leq x \leq b} |f(x) - P(x)| \,.$$

Now we can try to choose P so that this maximum will be as small as possible. It can be shown that for each given f such a polynomial P always exists and is uniquely determined. (A special case is considered in Section 8.12.) Some writers refer to this P as the *polynomial of uniform approximation*. It is usually very difficult to actually determine this P once f is given. In fact, no general procedure is known that will always yield P in a finite number of steps.

8.3 Polynomial approximation and normed linear spaces

All the different types of polynomial approximation described in the foregoing section are related by one central idea. To describe this idea we introduce the concept of a linear space of functions.

DEFINITION OF A LINEAR SPACE OF FUNCTIONS. Let S be a nonempty collection of real-valued functions defined on a given interval I. The set S is called a linear space of functions whenever it has the following two properties:

(a) If $f \, \varepsilon \, S$, then $cf \, \varepsilon \, S$ for every real number c.

(b) If $f \, \varepsilon \, S$ and $g \, \varepsilon \, S$, then $f + g \, \varepsilon \, S$.

Linear spaces of functions occur throughout mathematics. For example, in Chapter 7 we showed that the solutions of a homogeneous linear differential equation on an interval I form a linear space. Another example is the linear space consisting of all functions defined and continuous on a given closed bounded interval I. This particular linear space will be denoted by $C(I)$, or simply by C. Much of the theory of polynomial approximation deals with the space C and some of its subspaces.† Among the subspaces of C are (a) the set of all polynomials, (b) the set of all polynomials of degree $\leq n$, (c) the set of all functions differentiable on I, (d) the set of all continuous functions having a derivative of order n at a fixed point x_0 in I, (e) the set of all continuous functions having a power-series expansion in a neighborhood of a point x_0 in I. It is easy to verify that each of these sets of functions is a linear space. Proofs are requested in Exercise 1 of Section 8.4.

When we speak of "approximating" one function f in C by another function g in C, we consider the difference $f - g$, which we call the *error* of the approximation, and then we decide on a way to measure the size of this error. Since the error is a member of C, we need a measure of the "size" of the functions in C. Now the members of a linear space of functions are analogous to vectors. To extend this analogy we shall require the "size" of a function to have the same algebraic properties as the length of a vector. Measures with these properties are called *norms*; they are defined as follows:

DEFINITION OF A NORM. Let S be a linear space of functions. A real-valued function N defined on S is called a norm if it has the following properties:

   (a) $N(f) \geq 0$ for each f in S.
   (b) $N(cf) = |c| N(f)$ for each f in S and each real number c.
   (c) $N(f + g) \leq N(f) + N(g)$ for all f and g in S.
   (d) $N(f) = 0$ implies $f = 0$.

A linear space with a norm assigned to it is called a normed linear space.

The norm of f is sometimes written $\|f\|$ instead of $N(f)$. In this notation, the fundamental properties become:

   (a) $\|f\| \geq 0$,
   (b) $\|cf\| = |c| \, \|f\|$,
   (c) $\|f + g\| \leq \|f\| + \|g\|$,
   (d) $\|f\| = 0$ implies $f = 0$.

These properties are entirely analogous to the corresponding properties of the length of a vector. It is helpful to carry this analogy further and to refer to $\|f - g\|$ as the "distance" between two functions f and g. Thus, when we approximate one function by another, the error in the approximation is measured by the distance between the two functions relative to the chosen norm.

A function N that satisfies properties (a), (b), and (c), but *not* (d), is called a *seminorm*. Some problems in the theory of approximation deal with seminormed linear spaces; others with normed linear spaces. The following examples will be discussed in this chapter.

Example 1: Taylor seminorm. For a fixed integer $n \geq 1$, let S denote the set of all functions having a derivative of order n at a fixed point x_0. The set S is a linear space. If $f \; \varepsilon \; S$, let

---

† A *subspace* of C is a subset of C that is itself a linear space.

$$N(f) = \sum_{k=0}^{n} |f^{(k)}(x_0)| .$$

It is easy to verify that the function N so defined is a seminorm. It is not a norm because $N(f) = 0$ if and only if

$$f(x_0) = f'(x_0) = \cdots = f^{(n)}(x_0) = 0 ,$$

and these equations can be satisfied by a nonzero function. For example, $N(f) = 0$ when $f(x) = (x - x_0)^{n+1}$.

Example 2: Interpolation seminorm. Let S denote the linear space of all real-valued functions defined on an interval $[a, b]$. For a fixed set of $n + 1$ distinct points x_0, x_1, ..., x_n in $[a, b]$, let N be defined by the equation

$$N(f) = \sum_{k=0}^{n} |f(x_k)|$$

if $f \in S$. This function N is a seminorm on S. It is not a norm because $N(f) = 0$ if and only if $f(x_0) = f(x_1) = \cdots = f(x_n) = 0$, and it is clear that these equations can be satisfied by a function f that is not zero everywhere on $[a, b]$.

Example 3: Square norm. Let C denote the linear space of functions continuous on an interval $[a, b]$. If $f \in C$ define

(8.4) $$N(f) = \left(\int_a^b |f(x)|^2 \, dx \right)^{1/2} .$$

The function N is a norm on C. Properties (a) and (b) are clearly satisfied. A proof of property (c) is outlined in Exercise 4 of Section 8.4. To prove that N satisfies property (d), let f be any function in C that is not everywhere zero on $[a, b]$. Then there is at least one point x_0 in $[a, b]$ at which $f(x_0) \neq 0$. By continuity of f, there is a subinterval $[c, d]$ of $[a, b]$ containing x_0 in which $|f(x)| > \frac{1}{2} |f(x_0)|$. Since

$$N(f) = \left(\int_a^b |f(x)|^2 \, dx \right)^{1/2} \geq \left(\int_c^d |f(x)|^2 \, dx \right)^{1/2} > \frac{(d - c)^{1/2} |f(x_0)|}{2} > 0 ,$$

we have $N(f) > 0$. This shows that $N(f) = 0$ only if $f(x) = 0$ for all x in $[a, b]$, so property (d) is satisfied.

Note. Let S denote the set of functions f that are integrable on $[a, b]$. The set S is a linear space, and the function N defined by (8.4) is a seminorm on S. It is not a norm because we can have $N(f) = 0$ without f being identically zero on $[a, b]$.

Example 4: Maximum norm. Let C denote the linear space of functions continuous on an interval $[a, b]$. If $f \in C$, define

$$N(f) = \max_{a \leq x \leq b} |f(x)| ,$$

where the symbol on the right stands for the absolute maximum value of $|f|$ on $[a, b]$. The verification of all four norm properties is requested in Exercise 5 of Section 8.4.

Let C be the space of functions continuous on a given interval $[a, b]$, and let S be a linear subspace of C. For a given integer $n \geq 1$, assume S contains all polynomials of degree $\leq n$. Assume also that a norm or seminorm has been defined on S. Choose a function f in S. If there is a polynomial P of degree $\leq n$ such that

$$\|f - P\| \leq \|f - Q\|$$

for all polynomials Q of degree $\leq n$, we say that P is a *best polynomial approximation* to f with the specified degree. The term "best" is, of course, relative to the given norm (or seminorm). The best polynomial for one choice of norm need not be best for another choice of norm.

Once a norm or seminorm has been chosen, three problems immediately suggest themselves.

(1) *Existence:* Given f in S, is there a best polynomial approximation to f with the specified degree?

(2) *Uniqueness:* If a best polynomial approximation to f exists with the specified degree, is it uniquely determined?

(3) *Construction:* If a best polynomial approximation to f exists with the specified degree, how can it be determined?

There are, of course, many other problems that can be considered. For example, if a unique best polynomial P_n of degree $\leq n$ exists, we may wish to obtain upper bounds for $\|f - P_n\|$ that can be used to satisfy practical requirements. Or we may ask whether $\|f - P_n\| \to 0$ as $n \to \infty$ for the given norm or possibly for some other norm. If so, we say that the polynomial approximations converge to f in this norm. In such a case arbitrarily close approximations exist relative to this norm if n is sufficiently large. These examples illustrate some of the types of problems considered in the general theory of polynomial approximation. In this introductory treatment we restrict our attention primarily to the three problems of existence, uniqueness, and construction, as described above.

For approximation by Taylor polynomials these three problems can be completely solved. If f has a derivative of order n at a point x_0, it is easy to prove that the best polynomial approximation of degree $\leq n$ relative to the Taylor seminorm for this n is the Taylor polynomial

$$(8.5) \qquad\qquad P(x) = \sum_{k=0}^{n} \frac{f^{(k)}(x_0)}{k!} (x - x_0)^k .$$

In fact, for this polynomial we have

$$\|f - P\| = \sum_{k=0}^{n} |f^{(k)}(x_0) - P^{(k)}(x_0)| = 0 ,$$

so the inequality $\|f - P\| \leq \|f - Q\|$ is trivially satisfied for all polynomials Q. Therefore P is a best polynomial approximation relative to this seminorm. To establish uniqueness, we consider any polynomial Q of degree $\leq n$ such that $\|f - Q\| = 0$. This equation implies that

$$Q(x_0) = f(x_0), \qquad Q'(x_0) = f'(x_0), \qquad \dots, \qquad Q^{(n)}(x_0) = f^{(n)}(x_0) .$$

From the discussion in Section 7.6 of Volume I we know that the Taylor polynomial in (8.5) is the only polynomial satisfying all these equations. Therefore $Q = P$. Equation (8.5) also solves the problem of construction.

The corresponding problems for the interpolation seminorm will be treated next in Section 8.5. In later sections we discuss polynomial approximation relative to the square norm and relative to the maximum norm.

8.4 Exercises

1. Prove that each of the following collections of functions is a linear space.
   (a) All polynomials.
   (b) All polynomials of degree $\leq n$.
   (c) All functions continuous on an interval I.
   (d) All functions having a derivative at each point of I.
   (e) All functions having a derivative of order n at each point of I.
   (f) All functions having a derivative of order n at a fixed point x_0.
   (g) All functions having power-series expansions in a neighborhood of a given point x_0.

2. Determine whether or not each of the following collections of real-valued functions is a linear space.
   (a) All polynomials of degree n.
   (b) All functions defined and bounded on an interval $[a, b]$.
   (c) All step functions defined on an interval $[a, b]$.
   (d) All functions monotonic on an interval $[a, b]$.
   (e) All functions integrable on an interval $[a, b]$.
   (f) All functions that are piecewise monotonic on an interval $[a, b]$.
   (g) All functions that can be expressed in the form $f - g$, where f and g are monotonic increasing on an interval $[a, b]$.

3. Let C denote the linear space of real-valued functions continuous on an interval $[a, b]$. A function N is defined on C by the equation given. In each case, determine which of the four properties of a norm are satisfied by N, and determine thereby whether N is a norm, a seminorm, or neither.

(a) $N(f) = f(a)$.

(e) $N(f) = \left| \int_a^b f(x)\, dx \right|$.

(b) $N(f) = |f(a)|$.

(f) $N(f) = \int_a^b |f(x)|\, dx$.

(c) $N(f) = |f(b) - f(a)|$.

(g) $N(f) = \int_a^b |f(x)|^2\, dx$.

(d) $N(f) = \int_a^b f(x)\, dx$.

(h) $N(f) = \left| \int_a^b f(x)\, dx \right|^2$.

4. (a) If f and g are integrable on $[a, b]$, we have

$$\int_a^b [x\, f(t) + g(t)]^2\, dt \geq 0$$

for all real x. This inequality can be written in the form $Ax^2 + 2Bx + C \geq 0$, where

$$A = \int_a^b [f(t)]^2\, dt, \quad B = \int_a^b f(t)g(t)dt, \quad C = \int_a^b [g(t)]^2\, dt.$$

Prove that $B^2 \leq AC$ or, in other words, that

$$\left(\int_a^b f(t)g(t)\, dt \right)^2 \leq \left(\int_a^b [f(t)]^2\, dt \right) \left(\int_a^b [g(t)]^2\, dt \right).$$

This is called the *Cauchy-Schwarz inequality* for integrals.
   (b) Let

$$N(f) = \left(\int_a^b [f(t)]^2 \right)^{1/2}.$$

Show that the Cauchy-Schwarz inequality implies $\int_a^b f(t)g(t)\, dt \leq N(f)N(g)$ and deduce that $N(f + g) \leq N(f) + N(g)$.

   (c) Show that N is a norm for the linear space of all functions continuous on $[a, b]$.

   (d) Show that N is a seminorm for the linear space of all functions integrable on $[a, b]$.

   5. Let C be the linear space of functions continuous on an interval $[a, b]$. If $f \, \varepsilon \, C$, define

$$N(f) = \max_{a \leq x \leq b} |f(x)| .$$

Show that N is a norm for C.

   6. Let B denote the linear space of all real-valued functions that are defined and bounded on an interval $[a, b]$. If $f \, \varepsilon \, B$, define

$$N(f) = \operatorname*{lub}_{a \leq x \leq b} |f(x)| ,$$

where the symbol on the right stands for the least upper bound of the set of all numbers $|f(x)|$ for x in $[a, b]$. Show that N is a norm for B.

   7. Refer to Exercise 3. Determine which of the given functions N have the property that $N(fg) \leq N(f)N(g)$ for all f and g in C.

   8. For a fixed integer $n \geq 1$, let S be the set of all functions having a derivative of order n at a fixed point x_0. If $f \, \varepsilon \, S$, let

$$N(f) = \sum_{k=0}^{n} \frac{1}{k!} |f^{(k)}(x_0)| .$$

   (a) Show that N is a seminorm on S.

   (b) Show that $N(fg) \leq N(f)N(g)$ for all f, g in S. Prove also that the Taylor seminorm does not have this property.

8.5 Interpolating polynomials

   We turn now to approximation by interpolation polynomials. The values of a function f are known at $n + 1$ distinct points $x_0, x_1, \ldots, x_n$ and we seek a polynomial P of degree $\leq n$ that satisfies the conditions

(8.6) $\qquad P(x_0) = f(x_0), \qquad P(x_1) = f(x_1), \qquad \ldots, \qquad P(x_n) = f(x_n) .$

First we prove that if such a polynomial exists it is unique. Then we prove it exists by explicit construction. This polynomial minimizes the distance from f to P, measured in the interpolation seminorm for this n,

$$\|f - P\| = \sum_{k=0}^{n} |f(x_k) - P(x_k)| .$$

Since this distance is 0 if P satisfies (8.6), the interpolating polynomial P is the best approximation relative to this seminorm.

8-1   THEOREM. *Uniqueness theorem. Given $n + 1$ distinct points $x_0, x_1, \ldots, x_n$, let P and Q be two polynomials of degree $\leq n$ such that*

$$P(x_k) = Q(x_k)$$

   for each $k = 0, 1, 2, \ldots, n$. Then $P(x) = Q(x)$ for all x.

Proof. Let $R(x) = P(x) - Q(x)$. The function R is a polynomial of degree $\leq n$ which has $n + 1$ distinct zeros at the points $x_0, x_1, \ldots, x_n$. The only polynomial with this property is the zero polynomial. Therefore $R(x) = 0$ for all x, so $P(x) = Q(x)$ for all x.

The interpolating polynomial P can be constructed in many ways. We describe first a method of Lagrange. Let $A(x)$ be the polynomial given by the equation

$$(8.7) \qquad A(x) = (x - x_0)(x - x_1) \cdots (x - x_n) = \prod_{j=0}^{n} (x - x_j).$$

This polynomial has a simple zero at each of the points x_j. Let $A_k(x)$ denote the polynomial of degree n obtained from $A(x)$ by deleting the factor $x - x_k$. That is, let

$$(8.8) \qquad A_k(x) = \prod_{\substack{j=0 \\ j \neq k}}^{n} (x - x_j).$$

The polynomial $A_k(x)$ has a simple zero at each point $x_j \neq x_k$. At the point x_k itself we have

$$(8.9) \qquad A_k(x_k) = \prod_{\substack{j=0 \\ j \neq k}}^{n} (x_k - x_j).$$

This is nonzero since no factor in the product is zero. Therefore the polynomial $A_k(x)/A_k(x_k)$ has the value 1 when $x = x_k$ and the value 0 when $x = x_j$ for $x_j \neq x_k$. Now let

$$P(x) = \sum_{k=0}^{n} \frac{f(x_k)A_k(x)}{A_k(x_k)}.$$

When $x = x_j$, each term in this sum vanishes except the jth term, which has the value $f(x_j)$. Therefore $P(x_j) = f(x_j)$ for each j. Since each term of this sum is a polynomial of degree n, the sum itself is a polynomial of degree $\leq n$. Thus, we have found a polynomial satisfying the required conditions. These results may be summarized by the following theorem:

8–2   THEOREM.   Given $n + 1$ distinct points $x_0, x_1, \ldots, x_n$ and $n + 1$ real numbers $f(x_0), f(x_1), \ldots, f(x_n)$, not necessarily distinct, there exists one and only one polynomial P of degree $\leq n$ such that $P(x_j) = f(x_j)$ for each $j = 0, 1, 2, \ldots, n$. This polynomial is given by the formula

$$(8.10) \qquad P(x) = \sum_{k=0}^{n} \frac{f(x_k)A_k(x)}{A_k(x_k)},$$

where $A_k(x)$ is the polynomial defined by (8.8).

Formula (8.10) for $P(x)$ is called *Lagrange's interpolation formula*. We may write it in the form

$$P(x) = \sum_{k=0}^{n} f(x_k)L_k(x),$$

where $L_k(x)$ is a polynomial of degree n given by

(8.11)
$$L_k(x) = \frac{A_k(x)}{A_k(x_k)}.$$

Thus, for each fixed x, $P(x)$ is a linear combination of the prescribed values $f(x_0)$, $f(x_1)$, $\ldots$, $f(x_n)$. The multipliers $L_k(x)$ depend only on the points $x_0, x_1, \ldots, x_n$ and not on the prescribed values. They are called *Lagrange interpolation coefficients*. If we use the formulas in (8.8) and (8.9) we may write Equation (8.11) in the form

(8.12)
$$L_k(x) = \prod_{\substack{j=0 \\ j \neq k}}^{n} \frac{x - x_j}{x_k - x_j}.$$

This product formula provides an efficient method for evaluating the number $L_k(x)$ for a given x.

Note. The Lagrange coefficients $L_k(x)$ are often expressed in the form

$$L_k(x) = \frac{A_k(x)}{A'(x_k)},$$

where A' is the derivative of the polynomial in (8.7). To prove this formula it suffices to show that $A'(x_k) = A_k(x_k)$. Differentiating the relation

$$A(x) = (x - x_k)A_k(x)$$

we obtain $A'(x) = (x - x_k)A_k'(x) + A_k(x)$. When $x = x_k$ this gives us $A'(x_k) = A_k(x_k)$.

Example. Determine the polynomial of degree ≤ 3 that takes the values y_0, y_1, y_2, y_3 at the points $-2, -1, 1, 2$, respectively.

Solution. We take $x_0 = -2$, $x_1 = -1$, $x_2 = 1$, $x_3 = 2$. The polynomials $L_k(x)$ in (8.12) are given by the formulas

$$L_0(x) = \frac{(x + 1)(x - 1)(x - 2)}{(-2 + 1)(-2 - 1)(-2 - 2)} = -\frac{1}{12}(x + 1)(x - 1)(x - 2),$$

$$L_1(x) = \frac{(x + 2)(x - 1)(x - 2)}{(-1 + 2)(-1 - 1)(-1 - 2)} = \frac{1}{6}(x + 2)(x - 1)(x - 2),$$

$$L_2(x) = \frac{(x + 2)(x + 1)(x - 2)}{(1 + 2)(1 + 1)(1 - 2)} = -\frac{1}{6}(x + 2)(x + 1)(x - 2),$$

$$L_3(x) = \frac{(x + 2)(x + 1)(x - 1)}{(2 + 2)(2 + 1)(2 - 1)} = \frac{1}{12}(x + 2)(x + 1)(x - 1).$$

Therefore the required polynomial is

$$P(x) = y_0 L_0(x) + y_1 L_1(x) + y_2 L_2(x) + y_3 L_3(x)$$

$$= -\frac{y_0}{12}(x + 1)(x - 1)(x - 2) + \frac{y_1}{6}(x + 2)(x - 1)(x - 2)$$

$$- \frac{y_2}{6}(x + 2)(x + 1)(x - 2) + \frac{y_3}{12}(x + 2)(x + 1)(x - 1).$$

To compute the value of $P(x)$ for a specific x it is usually better to leave the polynomial in this form rather than to rewrite it in increasing powers of x. For example, if $y_0 = -5$, $y_1 = 1$, $y_2 = 1$, and $y_3 = 7$, the value of $P(x)$ for $x = \frac{3}{2}$ is given by

$$P\left(\frac{3}{2}\right) = \frac{5}{12}\left(\frac{5}{2}\right)\left(\frac{1}{2}\right)\left(-\frac{1}{2}\right) + \frac{1}{6}\left(\frac{7}{2}\right)\left(\frac{1}{2}\right)\left(-\frac{1}{2}\right) - \frac{1}{6}\left(\frac{7}{2}\right)\left(\frac{5}{2}\right)\left(-\frac{1}{2}\right) + \frac{7}{12}\left(\frac{7}{2}\right)\left(\frac{5}{2}\right)\left(\frac{1}{2}\right)$$

$$= -\frac{25}{96} - \frac{7}{48} + \frac{35}{48} + \frac{245}{96} = \frac{276}{96} = 2\frac{7}{8}.$$

In the foregoing discussion the interpolation points $x_0, x_1, \ldots, x_n$ were assumed to be distinct but otherwise arbitrary. Now we assume they are equally spaced and show that the Lagrange coefficients $L_k(x)$ can be considerably simplified. Suppose $x_0 < x_1 < x_2 < \cdots < x_n$, and let h denote the distance between adjacent points. Then we may write

$$x_j = x_0 + jh$$

for $j = 0, 1, 2, \ldots, n$. Since $x_k - x_j = (k - j)h$, Equation (8.12) becomes

$$(8.13) \qquad L_k(x) = \prod_{\substack{j=0 \\ j \neq k}}^{n} \frac{x - x_0 - jh}{(k - j)h} = \prod_{\substack{j=0 \\ j \neq k}}^{n} \frac{t - j}{k - j},$$

where

$$t = \frac{x - x_0}{h}.$$

In the last term on the right of (8.13) the product of the factors independent of t is

$$(8.14) \qquad \prod_{\substack{j=0 \\ j \neq k}}^{n} \frac{1}{k - j} = \left(\prod_{j=0}^{k-1} \frac{1}{k - j}\right)\left(\prod_{j=k+1}^{n} \frac{1}{k - j}\right) = \frac{1}{k!}\prod_{j=k+1}^{n} \frac{(-1)}{j - k}$$

$$= \frac{(-1)^{n-k}}{k!\,(n - k)!} = \frac{(-1)^{n-k}}{n!}\binom{n}{k},$$

where $\binom{n}{k}$ is the binomial coefficient. Since $x = x_0 + th$, Equation (8.13) now becomes

$$(8.15) \qquad L_k(x_0 + th) = \frac{(-1)^{n-k}}{n!}\binom{n}{k}\prod_{\substack{j=0 \\ j \neq k}}^{n} (t - j).$$

For each fixed n, the right member of (8.15) is a function of k and t that can be tabulated. Extensive tables of the Lagrangian coefficients for equally spaced interpolation points have been prepared by the National Bureau of Standards. (See Reference 11 in the bibliography at the end of this chapter.) If x and h are chosen so that the number $t = (x - x_0)/h$ is one for which the Lagrangian coefficients $L_k(x_0 + th)$ are tabulated, the actual calculation of $P(x_0 + th)$ is reduced to a multiplication of the $f(x_k)$ by the tabulated $L_k(x_0 + th)$, followed by addition.

8.6   Error analysis in polynomial interpolation

Let f be a function defined on an interval $[a, b]$ containing the $n + 1$ distinct points $x_0, x_1, \ldots, x_n$, and let P be the interpolation polynomial of degree $\leq n$ which agrees with f at these points. If we alter the values of f at points other than the interpolation points we do not alter the polynomial P. This shows that the function f and the polynomial P may differ considerably at points other than the interpolation points. If the given function f has certain qualities of "smoothness" throughout the interval $[a, b]$ we can expect that the interpolating polynomial P will be a good approximation to f at points other than the x_k. The next theorem gives a useful expression that enables us to study the error in polynomial interpolation when the given function has a derivative of order $n + 1$ throughout $[a, b]$.

8–3   THEOREM.   Let $x_0, x_1, \ldots, x_n$ be $n + 1$ distinct points in the domain of a function f, and let P be the interpolation polynomial of degree $\leq n$ that agrees with f at these points. Choose a point x in the domain of f and let $[\alpha, \beta]$ be any closed interval containing the points $x_0, x_1, \ldots, x_n$, and x. If f has a derivative of order $n + 1$ in the interval $[\alpha, \beta]$ there is at least one point c in the open interval (α, β) such that

(8.16)
$$f(x) - P(x) = \frac{A(x)}{(n + 1)!} f^{(n+1)}(c),$$

where

$$A(x) = (x - x_0)(x - x_1) \cdots (x - x_n).$$

Note. Point c depends on both x and n.

Proof. If x is one of the interpolation points x_k, then $A(x_k) = 0$ and Equation (8.16) is trivially satisfied for any choice of c in (α, β). Suppose, then, that x is not one of the interpolation points. Keep x fixed and define a new function F on $[\alpha, \beta]$ by the equation

(8.17) $$F(t) = A(x)[f(t) - P(t)] - A(t)[f(x) - P(x)].$$

The right-hand side of this equation, as a function of t, has a derivative of order $n + 1$; hence the same is true of the left-hand side. Since $P(t)$ is a polynomial in t of degree $\leq n$, its $(n + 1)$st derivative is identically zero. The polynomial $A(t)$ has degree $n + 1$, the term of highest degree being t^{n+1}, and we have $A^{(n+1)}(t) = (n + 1)!$. Therefore, if we differentiate Equation (8.17) $n + 1$ times with respect to t we obtain the formula

(8.18) $$F^{(n+1)}(t) = A(x)f^{(n+1)}(t) - (n + 1)! [f(x) - P(x)].$$

From the definition in Equation (8.17) we see that F has the value zero at the $n + 1$ interpolation points $x_0, x_1, \ldots, x_n$ and *also* at the point x. Therefore $F(t) = 0$ at $n + 2$ distinct points in the interval $[\alpha, \beta]$. These points determine $n + 1$ adjacent subintervals of $[\alpha, \beta]$ and the function F vanishes at both endpoints of each of these subintervals. By Rolle's theorem, the derivative $F'(t)$ must be zero for at least one t interior to each subinterval. If we choose exactly one such t from each subinterval we obtain $n + 1$ distinct points in the open interval (α, β) at which $F'(t) = 0$. These points, in turn, determine n subintervals at whose endpoints we have $F'(t) = 0$. Applying Rolle's theorem to F' we find that the second derivative $F''(t)$ is zero for at least n distinct points in (α, β). After applying Rolle's theorem $n + 1$ times in this manner we finally find that there is at least one point c in (α, β) at which $F^{(n+1)}(c) = 0$. Substituting this value of c in Equation (8.18) we obtain

$$(n + 1)! \, [f(x) - P(x)] = A(x) f^{(n+1)}(c) \, ,$$

which is the same as (8.16). This completes the proof.

It should be noted that, as with approximation by Taylor polynomials, the error term involves the $(n + 1)$st derivative $f^{(n+1)}(c)$ evaluated at an unknown point c. If the extreme values of $f^{(n+1)}$ in $[a, b]$ are known, useful upper and lower bounds for the error can be obtained.

Suppose now that the interpolation points are equally spaced and that $x_0 < x_1 < x_2 < \cdots < x_n$. If h denotes the spacing we may write

$$x_j = x_0 + jh \qquad \text{and} \qquad x = x_0 + th \, ,$$

where $t = (x - x_0)/h$. Since $x - x_j = (t - j)h$, the polynomial $A(x)$ may be written as

$$A(x) = \prod_{j=0}^{n} (x - x_j) = h^{n+1} \prod_{j=0}^{n} (t - j) \, .$$

Formula (8.16) now becomes

(8.19)
$$f(x) - P(x) = \frac{f^{(n+1)}(c)}{(n + 1)!} \, h^{n+1} \prod_{j=0}^{n} (t - j) \, ,$$

with $t = (x - x_0)/h$.

Example: Error in linear interpolation. Suppose a function f with a second derivative is tabulated and we wish to estimate its value at a point x intermediate to two consecutive entries x_0 and $x_0 + h$. If we use linear interpolation we approximate the graph of f over the interval $[x_0, x_0 + h]$ by a straight line, as shown in Figure 8.1. If P denotes the linear interpolating polynomial, the error estimate in (8.19) becomes

(8.20)
$$f(x) - P(x) = \frac{f''(c)}{2!} \, h^2 \, t(t - 1) \, ,$$

where $t = (x - x_0)/h$. When x lies between x_0 and $x_0 + h$ we have $0 < t < 1$ and the maximum value of $|t(t - 1)|$ in this interval is $1/4$. Therefore (8.20) gives us the estimate

$$|f(x) - P(x)| \leq \frac{|f''(c)| \, h^2}{8} \, .$$

The point c is an unknown point in the interval $(x_0, x_0 + h)$. If the second derivative f'' is bounded in this interval, say $|f''(x)| \leq M$, the error estimate becomes

$$|f(x) - P(x)| \leq \frac{Mh^2}{8} \, .$$

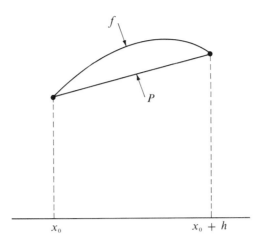

FIGURE 8.1 *Linear interpolation.*

In particular, if f is a sine or cosine, then $|f''(x)| \leq 1$ for all x and we have $|f(x) - P(x)| \leq h^2/8$. If a table of sines or cosines has entries for every degree (one degree $= \pi/180$ radians) we have $h = \pi/180$, so

$$\frac{h^2}{8} = \frac{\pi^2}{8(180)^2} < \frac{10}{259,200} < \frac{1}{25,000} = 0.00004 .$$

Since this error does not exceed $1/2$ in the fourth decimal place, linear interpolation would be satisfactory in a four-place table. The error estimate can be improved in portions of the table where $|f''(c)|$ is considerably less than 1.

8.7 Exercises

1. In each case find the polynomial P of lowest possible degree satisfying the given conditions.
   (a) $P(-1) = 0$, $P(0) = 2$, $P(2) = 7$.
   (b) $P(1) = 1$, $P(2) = 0$, $P(3) = 0$, $P(4) = 1$.
   (c) $P(1) = 1$, $P(2) = 2$, $P(3) = 3$, $P(0) = 1$.
   (d) $P(0) = -2$, $P(1) = 0$, $P(-1) = -2$, $P(2) = 16$.
   (e) $P(-2) = 11$, $P(-1) = -11$, $P(0) = -5$, $P(1) = -1$.

2. Let $f(x) = \cos(\pi x/4)$. Find the polynomial of smallest possible degree that takes the same values as f at the points $-2, -4/3, 0, 4/3, 2$.

3. Let P be a polynomial of degree $\leq n$ and let $A(x) = (x - x_0)(x - x_1) \cdots (x - x_n)$, where $x_0, x_1, \ldots, x_n$ are $n + 1$ distinct points.
   (a) Show that for any polynomial B the polynomial Q given by $Q(x) = P(x) + A(x)B(x)$ agrees with P at the points $x_0, x_1, \ldots, x_n$.
   (b) Prove also the converse. That is, if Q is any polynomial that agrees with P at the points $x_0, x_1, \ldots, x_n$, then $Q(x) = P(x) + A(x)B(x)$ for some polynomial B.

4. (a) Find the polynomial Q of lowest possible degree that satisfies the conditions

$$Q(-2) = -5, \quad Q(-1) = -1, \quad Q(1) = 1, \quad Q'(0) = -1.$$

[*Hint*. First find a polynomial P that takes the prescribed values at $-2, -1, 1$, and then use Exercise 3 to determine Q.]

(b) Find the polynomial Q of lowest possible degree that satisfies the conditions in part (a) with $Q'(0) = -3$ instead of $Q'(0) = -1$.

5. Let $f(x) = \log_4 x$ for $x > 0$. Compute $P(32)$, where P is the polynomial of lowest possible degree that agrees with f at the points:

(a) $x = 1, 64$.   (c) $x = 4, 16, 64$.
(b) $x = 1, 16, 256$.   (d) $x = 1, 4, 16, 64, 256$.

In each case compute the difference $f(32) - P(32)$. These examples show that the accuracy in polynomial interpolation is not necessarily improved by increasing the number of interpolation points.

6. The Lagrange interpolation coefficients $L_k(x)$ given by Equation (8.12) depend not only on x but also on the interpolation points $x_0, x_1, \ldots, x_n$. We can indicate this dependence by writing $L_k(x) = L_k(x; \vec{X})$, where $\vec{X}$ denotes the vector in $(n + 1)$-space given by $\vec{X} = (x_0, x_1, \ldots, x_n)$. For a given real number b, let $\vec{b}$ denote the vector in $(n + 1)$-space all of whose components are equal to b. If $a \neq 0$, show that

$$L_k(ax + b; a\vec{X} + \vec{b}) = L_k(x; \vec{X}).$$

This is called the *invariance property* of the Lagrange interpolation coefficients. The next exercise shows how this property can be used to help simplify calculations in practice.

7. Let P denote the polynomial of degree ≤ 4 that has the values

$$P(2.4) = 72, \quad P(2.5) = 30, \quad P(2.7) = 18, \quad P(2.8) = 24, \quad P(3.0) = 180.$$

(a) Introduce new interpolation points u_j related to the given points x_j by the equation $u_j = 10x_j - 24$. The u_j are integers. For each $k = 0,1,2,3,4$, determine the Lagrange interpolation coefficients $L_k(x)$ in terms of u, where $u = 10x - 24$.

(b) Use the invariance property of Exercise 6 to compute $P(2.6)$.

8. A table of the function $f(x) = \log x$ contains entries for $x = 1$ to $x = 10$ at intervals of 0.001. Values intermediate to each pair of consecutive entries are to be computed by linear interpolation. Assume the entries in the table are exact.

(a) Show that the error in linear interpolation will not exceed $1/8$ in the sixth decimal place.

(b) For what values of x will linear interpolation be satisfactory for a seven-place table?

(c) What should be the spacing of the entries in the interval $1 \leq x \leq 2$ so that linear interpolation will be satisfactory in a seven-place table?

In Exercises 9 through 13, $x_0, x_1, \ldots, x_n$ are distinct points and

$$A(x) = \prod_{j=0}^{n} (x - x_j), \quad A_k(x) = \prod_{\substack{j=0 \\ j \neq k}}^{n} (x - x_j), \quad L_k(x) = \frac{A_k(x)}{A_k(x_k)}.$$

9. Derive the formula

$$A'(x) = \sum_{k=0}^{n} A_k(x)$$

by use of (a) logarithmic differentiation; (b) Lagrange's interpolation formula.

10. Prove each of the following formulas:

(a) $\displaystyle\sum_{k=0}^{n} L_k(x) = 1$ and $\displaystyle\sum_{k=0}^{n} \frac{A'_k(x)}{A'(x_k)} = 0$ for all x.

(b) $\displaystyle\sum_{k=0}^{n} \frac{1}{A'(x_k)} = 0$. [*Hint.* Use part (a) with suitable values of x.]

11. Let P be any polynomial of degree $\leq n$. Show that the coefficient of x^n is equal to

$$\sum_{k=0}^{n} \frac{P(x_k)}{A'(x_k)}.$$

12. Assume $x_0, x_1, \ldots, x_n$ are integers satisfying $x_0 < x_1 < \cdots < x_n$.
(a) Prove that $|A'(x_k)| \geq k! \, (n-k)!$ and deduce that

$$\sum_{k=0}^{n} \frac{1}{|A'(x_k)|} \leq \frac{2^n}{n!}.$$

(b) Let P be any polynomial of degree n, with the term of highest degree equal to x^n. Let M denote the largest of the numbers $|P(x_0)|, |P(x_1)|, \ldots, |P(x_n)|$. Prove that $M \geq n!/2^n$. [*Hint.* Use part (a) and Exercise 11.]

13. Prove the following formulas. In parts (a) and (b), x is any point different from $x_0, x_1, \ldots, x_n$.

(a) $\displaystyle\frac{A'(x)}{A(x)} = \sum_{j=0}^{n} \frac{1}{x - x_j}.$

(b) $\displaystyle\frac{A''(x)}{A'(x)} = \frac{A_k(x)}{A'(x)} \sum_{\substack{j=0 \\ j \neq k}}^{n} \frac{1}{x - x_j} + \sum_{\substack{j=0 \\ j \neq k}}^{n} \frac{1}{x - x_j} - \frac{A(x)}{A'(x)} \sum_{\substack{j=0 \\ j \neq k}}^{n} \frac{1}{(x - x_j)^2}.$

(c) $\displaystyle\frac{A''(x_k)}{A'(x_k)} = 2 \sum_{\substack{j=0 \\ j \neq k}}^{n} \frac{1}{x_k - x_j}.$

14. (a) Given $n+1$ distinct points $x_0, x_1, \ldots, x_n$, let P and Q be two polynomials of degree $\leq n$ satisfying the $n+1$ conditions

$$P(x_0) = Q(x_0), \quad P'(x_1) = Q'(x_1), \quad P''(x_2) = Q''(x_2), \quad \ldots, \quad P^{(n)}(x_n) = Q^{(n)}(x_n).$$

Prove that $P(x) = Q(x)$ for all x.
(b) Let $B_0(x) = 1$, and for $n \geq 1$ define

$$B_n(x) = \frac{x(x - n)^{n-1}}{n!}.$$

Show that $B'_n(x) = B_{n-1}(x - 1)$ for $n \geq 1$ and deduce that

$$B_n(0) = B'_n(1) = B''_n(2) = \cdots = B_n^{(n-1)}(n-1) = 0 \quad \text{and} \quad B_n^{(n)}(n) = 1.$$

(c) Show that the one and only polynomial of degree $\leq n$ satisfying the conditions

$$P(0) = c_0, \quad P'(1) = c_1, \quad P''(2) = c_2, \quad \ldots, \quad P^{(n)}(n) = c_n$$

is given by

$$P(x) = \sum_{k=0}^{n} c_k B_k(x) .$$

(d) If $x_k = x_0 + kh$ for $k = 0,1,2, \ldots, n$, where $h > 0$, generalize the results in (b) and (c).

8.8   Polynomial approximation by least squares

Let C denote the linear space consisting of all functions that are continuous on an interval $[a, b]$. If $f \, \varepsilon \, C$, let $\|f\|$ denote the square norm, defined by

$$\|f\| = \left(\int_a^b [f(x)]^2 \, dx \right)^{1/2} .$$

We wish to consider the problem of best polynomial approximation relative to this norm.

Choose a function f in C and an integer $n \geq 1$ and consider any polynomial T of degree $\leq n$, say

$$T(x) = \sum_{i=0}^{n} a_i x^i .$$

A polynomial that minimizes $\|f - T\|$ also minimizes $\|f - T\|^2$, so we consider

$$\|f - T\|^2 = \int_a^b [f(x) - T(x)]^2 \, dx = \int_a^b \left(f(x) - \sum_{i=0}^{n} a_i x^i \right)^2 dx .$$

The integral on the right is a function of the $n + 1$ coefficients, which we denote as $g(a_0, a_1, \ldots, a_n)$ or as $g(\vec{A})$, where $\vec{A} = (a_0, a_1, \ldots, a_n)$. We seek those points $\vec{A}$ in $(n + 1)$-space at which the scalar field g will have a minimum. If such points exist they must satisfy $\nabla g(\vec{A}) = \vec{0}$. Since

$$g(\vec{A}) = \int_a^b [f(x)]^2 \, dx - 2 \sum_{i=0}^{n} a_i \int_a^b x^i f(x) \, dx + \sum_{i=0}^{n} \sum_{j=0}^{n} a_i a_j \int_a^b x^{i+j} \, dx ,$$

the kth partial derivative $D_k g(\vec{A})$ exists for each $\vec{A}$ and is given by the formula

$$D_k g(\vec{A}) = -2 \int_a^b x^k f(x) \, dx + \sum_{i=0}^{n} a_i \int_a^b x^{i+k} \, dx + \sum_{j=0}^{n} a_j \int_a^b x^{k+j} \, dx$$

$$= -2 \int_a^b x^k f(x) \, dx + 2 \sum_{i=0}^{n} a_i \int_a^b x^{i+k} \, dx .$$

When we put $D_k g(\vec{A}) = 0$ for $k = 0, 1, 2, \ldots, n$ we obtain a system of $n + 1$ linear equations that must be satisfied by the coefficients $a_0, a_1, \ldots, a_n$ of a minimizing polynomial, if it exists. It can be shown that this system always has exactly one solution, and that this solution does, indeed, minimize g. In this way it is possible to establish the existence and uniqueness of the best polynomial approximation relative to the least-square norm. However, because of the labor involved, the coefficients are rarely determined by solving this system of equations.

The problem of least-square polynomial approximation can be expressed in a more general form that is somewhat easier to deal with. Instead of writing the polynomial T

in powers of x, we consider any set of $n + 1$ polynomials $\phi_0(x)$, $\phi_1(x)$, . . . , $\phi_n(x)$, where $\phi_0(x) = 1$ and $\phi_k(x)$ has degree k, and we write T in the form

$$T(x) = \sum_{i=0}^{n} c_i \, \phi_i(x) \, .$$

(For a proof that such a representation is always possible, see Exercise 1 in Section 8.11.) With this representation of T the square of the norm $\|f - T\|$ defines a function of the $n + 1$ coefficients $c_0, c_1, . . . , c_n$, say

$$h(c_0, c_1, . . . , c_n) = \|f - T\|^2 = \int_a^b \left(f(x) - \sum_{i=0}^{n} c_i \phi_i(x) \right)^2 dx \, .$$

Arguing as above, we are led to consider the $n + 1$ equations $D_k h(c_0, c_1, . . . , c_n) = 0$. In this case we have

$$D_k h(c_0, c_1, . . . , c_n) = -2 \int_a^b \phi_k(x) f(x) \, dx + 2 \sum_{j=0}^{n} c_j \int_a^b \phi_j(x) \phi_k(x) \, dx \, ,$$

so the coefficients in question must satisfy the system of $n + 1$ equations

(8.21) $$\sum_{j=0}^{n} c_j \int_a^b \phi_j(x) \phi_k(x) \, dx = \int_a^b \phi_k(x) f(x) \, dx \, , \qquad k = 0, 1, 2, . . . , n \, .$$

Now we choose polynomials ϕ_k which make this system easy to solve. The best choice is that which makes the coefficient of c_k equal to 1 in the kth equation and equal to zero in the remaining equations. This means we wish to choose the polynomials ϕ_k so that

(8.22) $$\int_a^b \phi_j(x) \phi_k(x) \, dx = \begin{cases} 1 & \text{if } \ j = k \, , \\ 0 & \text{if } \ j \neq k \, . \end{cases}$$

If we can do this the kth equation in (8.21) gives us

(8.23) $$c_k = \int_a^b \phi_k(x) f(x) \, dx \, .$$

Any set of polynomials satisfying (8.22) is called an *orthonormal set*. In the next section we show that orthonormal sets of polynomials can always be constructed. Then we prove that in the space of continuous functions the coefficients given by (8.23) lead to the best approximating polynomial relative to the square norm.

8.9 The Gram-Schmidt process

We shall construct an orthonormal set of polynomials by a method known as the *Gram-Schmidt process*. This method is applicable not only to polynomials but, more generally, to any linearly independent set† of continuous functions. It is best described in terms of the *inner product* of two functions, which is defined as follows.

DEFINITION. *Let f and g be two functions that are integrable on an interval* $[a, b]$. *The inner product of f and g, denoted by* (f, g), *is defined by the equation*

† The concept of linear independence was defined in Section 7.10.

(8.24) $$(f, g) = \int_a^b f(x)\, g(x)\, dx\,.$$

Equation (8.24) is analogous to the formula

$$\vec{X} \cdot \vec{Y} = \sum_{k=1}^n x_k y_k$$

for the dot product of two vectors $\vec{X} = (x_1, \ldots, x_n)$ and $\vec{Y} = (y_1, \ldots, y_n)$ in n-space. The inner product of two functions satisfies the same algebraic laws as the dot product of two vectors. It is clearly commutative, $(f, g) = (g, f)$, and it has the following properties which follow at once from the linearity property of the integral:

(8.25) $(cf, g) = (f, cg) = c(f, g)$ for every constant c,

and

(8.26) $(f_1 + f_2, g) = (f_1, g) + (f_2, g)\,,$ $(f, g_1 + g_2) = (f, g_1) + (f, g_2)\,.$

By analogy with vectors we call two functions f and g *orthogonal* on $[a, b]$ if $(f, g) = 0$. If $n + 1$ functions $f_0, f_1, \ldots, f_n$ have the property that

$$(f_i, f_k) = \begin{cases} 0 & \text{if } i \neq k \\ 1 & \text{if } i = k \end{cases}$$

the collection $\{f_0, f_1, \ldots, f_n\}$ is said to be *orthonormal* on $[a, b]$.

The equation

(8.27) $$\|f\| = (f, f)^{1/2} = \left(\int_a^b [f(x)]^2\, dx \right)^{1/2}$$

defines a seminorm on the linear space S of functions that are integrable on $[a, b]$. The collection C of functions continuous on $[a, b]$ is a linear subspace of S and Equation (8.27) defines a norm on C. In the following discussion we need to know that $\|f\| \neq 0$ when $f \neq 0$, so we confine our attention to the space C.

Suppose $g_0, g_1, \ldots, g_n$ are $n + 1$ linearly independent functions in C. From these functions we shall construct an orthonormal set $\{f_0, f_1, \ldots, f_n\}$. The f_k will be constructed in succession so that each is orthogonal to all the earlier f_j. To start the process we choose

$$f_0(x) = c_0 g_0(x)\,.$$

Since $\|f_0\| = |c_0|\,\|g_0\|$ we can satisfy the condition $\|f_0\| = 1$ by choosing $c_0 = \|g_0\|^{-1}$, provided the norm of g_0 is nonzero. However, $g_0 \neq 0$ because g_0 is a member of a linearly independent set of functions. Since g_0 is continuous we have $\|g_0\| \neq 0$, so the specified choice of c_0 is always possible.

Next we wish to choose f_1 so that $\|f_1\| = 1$ and $(f_1, f_0) = 0$. There are two conditions to be satisfied. Therefore, we try a linear combination of g_0 and g_1 with two constants to be determined. Since $f_0 = c_0 g_0$ we may write this combination in the form

(8.28) $$f_1(x) = c_1\, [g_1(x) - a_{1,0} f_0(x)]\,.$$

The inner product of f_1 and f_0 is given by

$$(f_1, f_0) = (c_1\, [g_1 - a_{1,0} f_0], f_0) = c_1\, (g_1 - a_{1,0} f_0, f_0)$$
$$= c_1\, [(g_1, f_0) - a_{1,0}(f_0, f_0)] = c_1\, [(g_1, f_0) - a_{1,0}]\,.$$

The choice $a_{1,0} = (g_1, f_0)$ will make $(f_1, f_0) = 0$. Equation (8.28) now becomes

$$f_1(x) = c_1 [g_1(x) - (g_1, f_0)f_0(x)] .$$

Let $h = g_1 - (g_1, f_0)f_0$. Since h is a linear combination of g_0 and g_1, h is not identically zero (because the coefficient of g_1 is nonzero). Therefore $\|h\| \neq 0$ and the choice $c_1 = \|h\|^{-1}$ will make $\|f_1\| = 1$.

Now suppose we have chosen k functions $f_0, f_1, \ldots, f_{k-1}$ so that each f_j is a linear combination of $g_0, g_1, \ldots, g_j$ and so that $\{f_0, f_1, \ldots, f_{k-1}\}$ is an orthonormal set. To enlarge this to an orthonormal set of $k + 1$ functions $\{f_0, f_1, \ldots, f_k\}$ we consider a linear combination of the form

$$(8.29) \qquad f_k(x) = c_k \left[g_k(x) - \sum_{i=0}^{k-1} a_{k,i} f_i(x) \right] .$$

If $j < k$ the inner product (f_k, f_j) is given by

$$(f_k, f_j) = c_k \left[(g_k, f_j) - \sum_{i=0}^{k-1} a_{k,i} (f_i, f_j) \right] = c_k [(g_k, f_j) - a_{k,j}] .$$

We shall make this zero by choosing

$$(8.30) \qquad a_{k,j} = (g_k, f_j) \qquad \text{for} \quad j = 1, 2, \ldots, k - 1 .$$

The factor which multiplies c_k in (8.29) is not identically zero, so if we choose c_k to be the reciprocal of the norm of this factor we have $\|f_k\| = 1$. Therefore the set $\{f_0, f_1, \ldots, f_k\}$ is orthonormal. This proves, by induction, that the Gram-Schmidt process gives an orthonormal set $\{f_0, f_1, \ldots, f_n\}$, as required.

Note. From Equation (8.29) we see that each function g_k is a linear combination of $f_0, f_1, \ldots, f_k$. Therefore each function f_m with $m > k$ is orthogonal to g_k. Also, if g_k is a polynomial of degree k for $k = 0, 1, 2, \ldots, n$, then f_k has degree k, and the coefficients of x^k in $g_k(x)$ and in $f_k(x)$ have the same sign.

8.10 Orthonormal sets of polynomials

To obtain an orthonormal set $\{f_0, f_1, \ldots, f_n\}$ of $n + 1$ polynomials we may begin with the linearly independent polynomials $g_0, g_1, \ldots, g_n$ given by

$$g_k(x) = x^k \qquad \text{for} \quad k = 0, 1, 2, \ldots, n$$

and use the Gram-Schmidt process. The first polynomial g_0 has norm $\|g_0\| = \sqrt{b - a}$, so we take

$$f_0(x) = \frac{1}{\sqrt{b - a}} .$$

Now we apply Equation (8.29) repeatedly, with $a_{k,j}$ given by (8.30). For $k = 1$ we have

$$a_{1,0} = (g_1, f_0) = \int_a^b x f_0(x) \, dx = \frac{1}{\sqrt{b - a}} \frac{b^2 - a^2}{2} .$$

Equation (8.29) now becomes

$$f_1(x) = c_1 [x - a_{1,0} f_0(x)] = c_1 \left(x - \frac{b + a}{2} \right).$$

To make $\|f_1\| = 1$ we must choose c_1 so that

$$c_1^2 \int_a^b \left(x - \frac{b + a}{2} \right)^2 dx = 1 .$$

The change of variable $t = x - h$, where $h = (b + a)/2$, transforms the integral to

$$\int_{a-h}^{b-h} t^2 \, dt = 2 \int_0^{(b-a)/2} t^2 \, dt = \frac{(b - a)^3}{12} .$$

Therefore, we choose $c_1 = 2 \sqrt{3}(b - a)^{-3/2}$, and we obtain

$$f_1(x) = \frac{2 \sqrt{3}}{(b - a)^{3/2}} \left(x - \frac{a + b}{2} \right).$$

Further polynomials $f_2, f_3, \ldots$ can be determined in the same manner.

The Legendre polynomials, introduced in Section 7.17, satisfy the relation

$$\int_{-1}^1 P_n(x) P_m(x) \, dx = \begin{cases} 0 & \text{if} \quad m \neq n , \\ \dfrac{2}{2n + 1} & \text{if} \quad m = n . \end{cases}$$

Therefore the polynomials $\phi_0, \phi_1, \ldots, \phi_n$ given by

(8.31) $$\phi_k(x) = \sqrt{\frac{2k + 1}{2}} P_k(x)$$

form an orthonormal set on the interval $[-1, 1]$. We can prove that these polynomials are the same as those constructed from $1, x, x^2, \ldots, x^n$ by the Gram-Schmidt process over the interval $[-1, 1]$. This follows at once from the following uniqueness theorem.

8– 4   THEOREM.   Let $\{f_0, f_1, \ldots, f_n\}$ and $\{\phi_0, \phi_1, \ldots, \phi_n\}$ be two sets of polynomials that are orthonormal over an interval $[a, b]$. Assume that f_k and ϕ_k each have degree k. If the coefficients of x^k in $f_k(x)$ and $\phi_k(x)$ have the same sign, then $f_k = \phi_k$.

Proof. We shall prove that $\|f_k - \phi_k\| = 0$. We have

$$\|f_k - \phi_k\|^2 = (f_k - \phi_k, f_k - \phi_k) = (f_k, f_k) - 2(f_k, \phi_k) + (\phi_k, \phi_k) = 2 - 2(f_k, \phi_k) .$$

Therefore the theorem will be proved if we show that $(f_k, \phi_k) = 1$.

Since f_k and ϕ_k each have degree k we may write

$$f_k(x) = a_k x^k + \cdots \qquad \text{and} \qquad \phi_k(x) = b_k x^k + \cdots ,$$

where $a_k \neq 0$, $b_k \neq 0$, and $+ \cdots$ indicates a sum of lower powers of x. Let $g_k(x) = x^k$. The polynomial g_k can be expressed as a linear combination of $f_0, f_1, \ldots, f_k$ and also as a linear combination of $\phi_0, \phi_1, \ldots, \phi_k$. Therefore $(f_k, g_j) = (\phi_k, g_j) = 0$ for each $j < k$.

Since $(f_k, f_k) = 1$ we have

$$1 = \int_a^b [f_k(x)]^2 \, dx = \int_a^b f_k(x) \, (a_k x^k + \cdots) \, dx = a_k \int_a^b f_k(x) x^k \, dx \, ,$$

so

$$\int_a^b f_k(x) x^k \, dx = \frac{1}{a_k} \, .$$

Similarly,

$$\int_a^b \phi_k(x) x^k \, dx = \frac{1}{b_k} \, .$$

Therefore we have

(8.32)
$$(f_k, \phi_k) = \int_a^b f_k(x) \, (b_k x^k + \cdots) \, dx = \frac{b_k}{a_k}$$

and

$$(\phi_k, f_k) = \int_a^b \phi_k(x) \, (a_k x^k + \cdots) \, dx = \frac{a_k}{b_k} \, .$$

Since $(f_k, \phi_k) = (\phi_k, f_k)$ we obtain $b_k/a_k = a_k/b_k$, or $a_k^2 = b_k^2$. But a_k and b_k have the same sign, so they are equal. Therefore (8.32) states that $(f_k, \phi_k) = 1$ and, as we have already noted, this proves that $\|f_k - \phi_k\| = 0$. Since f_k and ϕ_k are continuous we must have $f_k = \phi_k$, as asserted.

We return now to the problem of least-square approximation in the space of continuous functions. Let $\{\phi_0, \phi_1, \ldots, \phi_n\}$ be an orthonormal set of polynomials on $[a, b]$ and let f be any function that is continuous on $[a, b]$. In Section 8.8 we proved that if a polynomial of the form

(8.33)
$$T(x) = \sum_{k=0}^n c_k \, \phi_k(x)$$

minimizes the square norm $\|f - T\|$, the coefficients c_k in (8.33) must necessarily be given by the equations

(8.34)
$$c_k = \int_a^b \phi_k(x) \, f(x) \, dx$$

for $k = 0, 1, 2, \ldots, n$. Therefore, if such a polynomial exists it is unique.

The foregoing discussion suggests a method for establishing the existence of a best T. Choose an orthonormal set of polynomials $\{\phi_0, \phi_1, \ldots, \phi_n\}$ on $[a, b]$ where ϕ_k has degree k. (Except for sign, each ϕ_k is uniquely determined.) If f is given, define numbers c_0, $c_1, \ldots, c_n$ by Equation (8.34), and let T be the polynomial given by (8.33). We shall prove that

(8.35)
$$\|f - T\| \leq \|f - Q\|$$

for all polynomials Q of degree $\leq n$. This will prove that T is, indeed, the best polynomial approximation relative to the square norm.

To prove (8.35) we write Q in the form

$$Q(x) = \sum_{k=0}^{n} b_k \, \phi_k(x)$$

and consider the number

(8.36) $\qquad \|f - Q\|^2 = (f - Q, f - Q) = (f, f) - 2(f, Q) + (Q, Q) \,.$

Since we have

$$(f, Q) = \left(f, \sum_{k=0}^{n} b_k \phi_k\right) = \sum_{k=0}^{n} b_k(f, \phi_k) = \sum_{k=0}^{n} b_k c_k$$

and

$$(Q, Q) = \left(\sum_{k=0}^{n} b_k \phi_k, \sum_{m=0}^{n} b_m \phi_m\right) = \sum_{k=0}^{n} \sum_{m=0}^{n} b_k b_m(\phi_k, \phi_m) = \sum_{k=0}^{n} b_k^2 \,,$$

Equation (8.36) becomes

$$\|f - Q\|^2 = \|f\|^2 - 2\sum_{k=0}^{n} b_k c_k + \sum_{k=0}^{n} b_k^2 = \|f\|^2 - \sum_{k=0}^{n} c_k^2 + \sum_{k=0}^{n} (b_k - c_k)^2 \,.$$

Now it is clear that among all possible choices of coefficients $b_0, b_1, \ldots, b_n$ the choice $b_k = c_k$ for each k makes the sum

$$\sum_{k=0}^{n} (b_k - c_k)^2$$

as small as possible. Therefore $\|f - Q\|$ has its smallest value when $Q = T$. This proves (8.35). Incidentally, we have also shown that for the best polynomial T we have

$$\|f - T\|^2 = \|f\|^2 - \sum_{k=0}^{n} c_k^2 \,.$$

The foregoing discussion is summarized by the following theorem.

8– 5   THEOREM.   Let f be continuous on $[a, b]$ and let $\phi_0, \phi_1, \ldots, \phi_n$ be an orthonormal set of polynomials on $[a, b]$ where ϕ_k has degree k. Define numbers $c_0, c_1, \ldots, c_n$ by the equation

(8.37) $\qquad\qquad\qquad\qquad c_k = \int_a^b \phi_k(x) \, f(x) \, dx \,.$

Then among all polynomials T of degree $\leq n$ there is exactly one that minimizes the square norm $\|f - T\|$, namely

$$T(x) = \sum_{k=0}^{n} c_k \, \phi_k(x) \,.$$

For this T we have

$$\|f - T\|^2 = \|f\|^2 - \sum_{k=0}^{n} c_k^2 \,.$$

Example: Least-square approximation over the interval $[-1, 1]$. Let f be a continuous function on $[-1, 1]$. The polynomial T of degree $\leq n$ that approximates f best over the interval $[-1, 1]$ relative to the square norm can be written in the form

$$(8.38) \qquad T(x) = \sum_{k=0}^{n} a_k \, P_k(x) \, ,$$

where $P_0, P_1, \ldots, P_n$ are the Legendre polynomials. To determine the coefficients we introduce the normalized Legendre polynomials $\phi_k(x) = P_k(x)/\|P_k\|$ of Equation (8.31) and write (8.38) in the form

$$T(x) = \sum_{k=0}^{n} c_k \, \phi_k(x) \, ,$$

where $c_k = \|P_k\| \, a_k$. Since the set $\{\phi_0, \phi_1, \ldots, \phi_n\}$ is orthonormal on $[-1, 1]$ the coefficients c_k are given by Equation (8.37). Hence

$$c_k = \int_{-1}^{1} \phi_k(t) f(t) \, dt = \frac{1}{\|P_k\|} \int_{-1}^{1} P_k(t) \, f(t) \, dt \, .$$

Since $a_k = c_k/\|P_k\|$ the coefficients in (8.38) are given by

$$a_k = \frac{1}{\|P_k\|^2} \int_{-1}^{1} P_k(t) \, f(t) \, dt = \frac{2k+1}{2} \int_{-1}^{1} P_k(t) \, f(t) \, dt \, .$$

The first three coefficients are

$$a_0 = \frac{1}{2} \int_{-1}^{1} f(t) \, dt \, , \qquad a_1 = \frac{3}{2} \int_{-1}^{1} t f(t) \, dt \, , \qquad a_2 = \frac{5}{2} \int_{-1}^{1} \frac{3t^2 - 1}{2} f(t) \, dt \, .$$

8.11 Exercises

1. Let $P_0, P_1, \ldots, P_n$ be $n + 1$ polynomials, where P_k has degree k and $P_0 \neq 0$.
   (a) Prove that $P_0, P_1, \ldots, P_n$ are linearly independent over every interval.
   (b) Prove that every polynomial T of degree $\leq n$ can be expressed in the form

$$T(x) = \sum_{k=0}^{n} c_k P_k(x) \, ,$$

where the c_k are constants. Show also that for a given T the coefficients c_k are unique.

2. Let $\{P_0, P_1, \ldots, P_n\}$ be a set of $n + 1$ polynomials orthonormal on $[a, b]$. Prove that these polynomials are linearly independent over any interval.

3. Let $\{P_0, P_1, \ldots, P_n\}$ be a set of polynomials orthonormal on $[a, b]$, and assume that P_k has degree k.
   (a) If $k \geq 1$ prove that P_k has at least one zero in the interval $[a, b]$. [*Hint.* Use the fact that $(P_0, P_k) = 0$.]
   (b) If $k \geq 1$, let $c_1, c_2, \ldots, c_m$ be the real zeros of P_k of *odd* multiplicity which lie in $[a, b]$, and let $A(x) = (x - c_1) \cdots (x - c_m)$. Show that $(A, P_k) = 0$ if $m < k$. From this relation deduce that $k = m$. This proves that all the zeros of P_k are real and distinct and lie in the interval $[a, b]$.

4. Let $P_0, P_1, \ldots, P_n$ be $n + 1$ polynomials orthonormal on $[a, b]$, and assume that P_k has degree k.

(a) Prove that any three consecutive polynomials in this set are connected by a recurrence relation of the form

$$P_{k+1}(x) = (a_k x + b_k)P_k(x) + c_k P_{k-1}(x)$$

for $1 \leq k \leq n - 1$, where a_k, b_k, c_k are constants.

(b) Determine this recurrence relation explicitly when the polynomials are the orthonormal Legendre polynomials.

5. Refer to Exercise 4, and let p_k denote the coefficient of x^k in $P_k(x)$.

(a) Show that $a_k = p_{k+1}/p_k$.

(b) Use the recurrence relation in Exercise 4 to derive the formula

$$\sum_{k=0}^{m} P_k(x)P_k(y) = \frac{p_m}{p_{m+1}} \frac{P_{m+1}(x)P_m(y) - P_m(x)P_{m+1}(y)}{x - y},$$

valid for $x \neq y$. Discuss also the limiting case $x = y$.

6. Given a function f continuous on $[-1, 1]$. Let T_k denote the polynomial of degree $\leq k$ that minimizes the square norm $\|f - T_k\|$.

(a) Write $T_k(x) = A_0 + A_1 x + \cdots + A_k x^k$ and determine the coefficients explicitly in terms of f when $k = 1, 2, 3$.

(b) Show that

$$\|f - T_1\|^2 = \int_{-1}^{1} [f(t)]^2 \, dt - 2A_0^2 - \tfrac{2}{3} A_1^2 ,$$

and obtain similar formulas for $\|f - T_2\|^2$ and $\|f - T_3\|^2$.

7. Let $f(x) = |x|$ for $-1 \leq x \leq 1$. Find the polynomial of degree ≤ 4 that approximates f best over the interval $[-1, 1]$ relative to the square norm.

8. This exercise shows how to construct a polynomial S_n of degree n such that

(8.39) $$\int_{-1}^{1} S_n(x)Q(x) \, dx = Q(1)$$

for *every* polynomial Q of degree $\leq n$.

(a) Show that there is at most one polynomial S_n with this property. [*Hint.* If T_n is another, consider $\|S_n - T_n\|^2 = (S_n, S_n - T_n) - (T_n, S_n - T_n)$.]

(b) Let P_k denote the Legendre polynomial of degree k. If

$$S_n(x) = \sum_{k=0}^{n} s_k P_k(x) \qquad \text{and} \qquad Q(x) = \sum_{k=0}^{n} q_k P_k(x),$$

show that the relation (8.39) implies

$$\sum_{k=0}^{n} \frac{2}{2k + 1} s_k q_k = \sum_{k=0}^{n} q_k .$$

Use this formula and the uniqueness property in (a) to deduce that the one and only polynomial S_n of degree n that satisfies (8.39) for all Q of degree $\leq n$ is

$$S_n(x) = \sum_{k=0}^{n} \frac{2k + 1}{2} P_k(x) .$$

(c) Let $S_n(x) = c_0 + c_1 x + \cdots + c_n x^n$. Determine the coefficients explicitly when $n = 0, 1, 2, 3$.

9. Refer to Exercise 8. Write

$$(1 - x)S_n(x) = \sum_{k=0}^{n+1} a_k P_k(x)$$

and use the relation (8.39) to prove that

$$(1 - x)S_n(x) = \frac{n+1}{2} \left(P_n(x) - P_{n+1}(x) \right).$$

This implies the relation

$$\sum_{k=0}^{n} \frac{2k+1}{2} P_k(x) = \frac{n+1}{2} \frac{P_n(x) - P_{n+1}(x)}{1 - x}$$

if $x \neq 1$. Show that this formula holds also for $x = 1$.

10. Let w be a nonnegative function that is continuous on $[a, b]$. Let C denote the space of all functions continuous on $[a, b]$. If f and g are in C, define the inner product (f, g) with respect to the weight function w by the equation

$$(f, g) = \int_a^b f(x)g(x)w(x) \, dx .$$

(a) Show that this inner product is commutative and has the linearity properties expressed in (8.25) and (8.26).

(b) If w is never zero on $[a, b]$ show that the equation $\|f\| = (f, f)^{1/2}$ defines a norm on C.

(c) If $n + 1$ functions $f_0, f_1, \ldots, f_n$ satisfy the relations

$$(f_i, f_k) = \begin{cases} 0 & \text{if } i \neq k \\ 1 & \text{if } i = k \end{cases}$$

the set $\{f_0, f_1, \ldots, f_n\}$ is said to be orthonormal on $[a, b]$ relative to w. Prove that, relative to the weight w, a set of $n + 1$ orthonormal polynomials always exists.

(d) Show that for a given function f in C there is one and only one best polynomial approximation to f relative to the norm defined in part (b).

11. Let $f(x) = 1/x$ for $x \neq 0$.

(a) Show that the constant polynomial P that best approximates f over the interval $[1, n]$ relative to the square norm is $P(x) = (\log n)/(n - 1)$. Compute $\|P - f\|^2$ for this P.

(b) Find the linear polynomial P that best approximates f over the interval $[1, n]$ relative to the square norm. Compute $\|P - f\|^2$ for this P when $n = 2$.

12. Let $f(x) = e^x$.

(a) Show that the constant polynomial P that best approximates f over the interval $[0, n]$ relative to the square norm is $P(x) = (e^n - 1)/n$. Compute $\|P - f\|^2$ for this P.

(b) Find the linear polynomial P that best approximates f over the interval $[0, 1]$ relative to the square norm. Compute $\|P - f\|^2$ for this P.

8.12 Polynomial approximation relative to the maximum norm. Chebyshev polynomials

Let C denote the linear space of functions continuous on an interval $[a, b]$. If $f \in C$ let $\|f\|$ denote the maximum norm, defined by

$$\|f\| = \max_{a \leq x \leq b} |f(x)| .$$

The problem of best polynomial approximation relative to this norm is more difficult than in the cases considered up to now. Although it can be shown that for each f in C there exists a unique best polynomial approximation P of degree $\leq n$, the known proofs use more advanced mathematical tools than we have developed in this book and will not be discussed here.[†] In approximation by the Taylor seminorm, the interpolation seminorm, and the least-square norm, we have specific formulas that enable us to construct the optimum polynomial P once f is given. In approximation by the maximum norm no such formulas are known, except when f has certain special forms. In the absence of general formulas the existence of an optimum P is more difficult to establish.

In this section we consider an important special problem in polynomial approximation relative to the maximum norm. This problem arises naturally from the theory of polynomial interpolation. In Theorem 8–3 (Section 8.6) we derived the error formula

$$(8.40) \qquad f(x) - P(x) = \frac{A(x)}{(n+1)!} f^{(n+1)}(c) \,,$$

where

$$A(x) = (x - x_0)(x - x_1) \cdots (x - x_n) \,.$$

Here P is the unique polynomial of degree $\leq n$ that agrees with f at $n+1$ distinct points $x_0, x_1, \ldots, x_n$ in $[a, b]$. The function f is assumed to have a derivative of order $n+1$ on $[a, b]$, and c is an unknown point lying somewhere in $[a, b]$. To estimate the error in (8.40) we need bounds for the $(n+1)$st derivative $f^{(n+1)}$ and for the product $A(x)$. Since A is a polynomial, its absolute value has a maximum, $\|A\|$, somewhere in the interval $[a, b]$. This maximum will depend on the choice of the points $x_0, x_1, \ldots, x_n$, and it is natural to try to choose these points so the norm of A will be as small as possible.

The formula for $A(x)$ may be written as

$$A(x) = g(x) - Q(x) \,,$$

where $g(x) = x^{n+1}$ and $Q(x)$ has degree $\leq n$. Thus, we have $\|A\| = \|g - Q\|$, so $\|A\|$ will be a minimum if and only if Q is the polynomial of degree $\leq n$ which best approximates g. Therefore the problem of minimizing $\|A\|$ is a polynomial approximation problem relative to the maximum norm. The general theory tells us that a unique solution exists. For this special case the optimum A can be constructed explicitly. The problem was first solved by Chebyshev; its solution leads to an interesting class of polynomials that also occur in other connections. We begin the discussion with a brief account of these polynomials and then return to the approximation problem in question.

DEFINITION. *The polynomials* $T_0, T_1, T_2, \ldots$ *defined by the recursion formula*

$$(8.41) \qquad T_{n+1}(x) = 2x\,T_n(x) - T_{n-1}(x) \qquad for \quad n \geq 1 \,,$$

with $T_0(x) = 1$ *and* $T_1(x) = x$, *are called* Chebyshev polynomials of the first kind.

The next four polynomials are

† A proof may be found in John Todd's *Introduction to the Constructive Theory of Functions*, Academic Press, Inc., New York, N.Y., 1963, Chapter 8.

$$T_2(x) = 2x^2 - 1, \qquad T_3(x) = 4x^3 - 3x, \qquad T_4(x) = 8x^4 - 8x^2 + 1,$$

$$T_5(x) = 16x^5 - 20x^3 + 5x.$$

From the recursion formula we see at once that T_n is a polynomial of degree n; the coefficient of x^n is equal to 2^{n-1} if $n \geq 1$.

Further properties of these polynomials are easily deduced from the following theorem.

8–6   THEOREM.   *If* $-1 \leq x \leq 1$ *we have*

(8.42) $$T_n(x) = \cos(n \text{ arc cos } x).$$

Proof. Let $f_n(x) = \cos(n \text{ arc cos } x)$ for $-1 \leq x \leq 1$. Taking $n = 0$ and $n = 1$ we find

$$f_0(x) = \cos 0 = 1 \qquad \text{and} \qquad f_1(x) = \cos(\text{arc cos } x) = x,$$

so Equation (8.42) holds for $n = 0$ and $n = 1$. If we prove that f_n satisfies the recursion formula (8.41) the theorem follows by induction. Using the trigonometric identity

$$\cos(n + 1)\theta + \cos(n - 1)\theta = 2 \cos \theta \cos n\theta$$

with $\theta = $ arc cos x we find $f_{n+1}(x) + f_{n-1}(x) = 2x \, f_n(x)$, which is the same recursion as (8.41). This completes the proof.

———————

The zeros of T_n for $n \geq 1$ are easily determined from the formula in (8.42). Since $\cos n\theta = 0$ only if $n\theta$ is an odd multiple of $\pi/2$, we have $T_n(x) = 0$ for x in $[-1, 1]$ only if n arc cos $x = (2k + 1)\pi/2$ for some integer k. Therefore the zeros of T_n in the interval $[-1, 1]$ are to be found among the numbers

(8.43) $$x_k = \cos \frac{2k + 1}{n} \frac{\pi}{2}, \qquad k = 0, \pm 1, \pm 2, \dots .$$

The values $k = 0, 1, 2, \dots, n - 1$ give n distinct zeros $x_0, x_1, \dots, x_{n-1}$, all lying in the open interval $(-1, 1)$. Since a polynomial of degree n cannot have more than n zeros, these must be *all* the zeros of T_n. The remaining x_k in (8.43) are repetitions of these n. We can now write

$$T_n(x) = 2^{n-1} (x - x_0)(x - x_1) \cdots (x - x_{n-1}) = 2^{n-1} \prod_{k=0}^{n-1} \left(x - \cos \frac{(2k + 1)\pi}{2n} \right).$$

By Rolle's theorem, the relative maxima and minima of T_n must occur between successive zeros; there are $n - 1$ such points in the open interval $(-1, 1)$. From the cosine formula for T_n we see that the extreme values, ± 1, are taken at the $n - 1$ interior points $\cos(k\pi/n)$, $k = 1, 2, \dots, n - 1$, and also at the two endpoints $x = 1$ and $x = -1$. Therefore in the closed interval $[-1, 1]$ the extreme values $+1$ and -1 are taken *alternately* at the $n + 1$ points $t_0, t_1, \dots, t_n$ given by $t_k = \cos(k\pi/n)$ for $k = 0, 1, 2, \dots, n$.

———————

We return now to the problem of finding the polynomial Q of degree $\leq n$ which best approximates $g(x) = x^{n+1}$ relative to the maximum norm. For the interval $[-1, 1]$ this problem is solved by the following theorem.

8– 7   THEOREM.   Let $p_{n+1}(x) = x^{n+1} - Q(x)$, where $Q(x)$ is a polynomial of degree $\leq n$, and let

$$\|p_{n+1}\| = \max_{-1 \leq x \leq 1} |p_{n+1}(x)| .$$

Then we have the inequality

(8.44) $$\|p_{n+1}\| \geq \frac{1}{2^n} .$$

Moreover, $\|p_{n+1}\| = 1/2^n$ if and only if $p_{n+1}(x) = 2^{-n} T_{n+1}(x)$, where T_{n+1} is the Chebyshev polynomial of degree $n + 1$.

Proof. Let $S(x) = 2^{-n} T_{n+1}(x)$. In the interval $[-1, 1]$ the polynomial S takes its extreme values, 2^{-n} and -2^{-n}, alternately at the $n + 2$ distinct points

(8.45) $$t_k = \cos \frac{k\pi}{n + 1} , \qquad k = 0, 1, 2, \ldots , n + 1 .$$

Therefore $\|S\| = 2^{-n}$ and the inequality (8.44) is satisfied (as an equality) when $p_{n+1} = S$. We show next that the inequality

(8.46) $$\|p_{n+1}\| < 2^{-n}$$

leads to a contradiction. Assume, then, that p_{n+1} satisfies (8.46) and consider the difference

$$r(x) = S(x) - p_{n+1}(x) .$$

At the points t_k given by (8.45) we have

$$r(t_k) = (-1)^k 2^{-n} - p_{n+1}(t_k) = (-1)^k [2^{-n} - (-1)^k p_{n+1}(t_k)] .$$

Because of (8.46) the factor in square brackets is always positive. Therefore $r(t_k)$ has alternating signs at the $n + 2$ points $t_0, t_1, \ldots , t_{n+1}$. Since r is continuous it must vanish at least once between consecutive sign changes. Therefore r has at least $n + 1$ distinct zeros. But since r is a polynomial of degree $\leq n$, this means that r is identically zero. Therefore $p_{n+1} = S$, contradicting (8.46).

Thus, we have shown that (8.44) holds for all polynomials p_{n+1} of the specified type. We have also shown that equality holds in (8.44) when $p_{n+1} = S$. Because of the uniqueness theorem, S is the only polynomial that gives equality. (We remind the reader that we have not proved the uniqueness theorem.)

Although Theorem 8–7 refers to the interval $[-1, 1]$ it can be used to deduce a corresponding result for an arbitrary interval $[a, b]$.

8– 8   THEOREM.   Let $p_{n+1}(x) = x^{n+1} - Q(x)$, where Q is a polynomial of degree $\leq n$, and let

$$\|p_{n+1}\| = \max_{a \leq x \leq b} |p_{n+1}(x)| .$$

Then we have the inequality

$$\|p_{n+1}\| \geq \frac{(b-a)^{n+1}}{2^{2n+1}}$$

with equality holding if and only if

$$p_{n+1}(x) = \frac{(b-a)^{n+1}}{2^{2n+1}} T_{n+1}\left(\frac{2x-a-b}{b-a}\right).$$

Proof. Consider the transformation

$$t = \frac{2x-a-b}{b-a}.$$

This maps the interval $a \leq x \leq b$ in a one-to-one fashion onto the interval $-1 \leq t \leq 1$. Since

$$x = \frac{b-a}{2} t + \frac{b+a}{2}$$

we have

$$p_{n+1}(x) = \left(\frac{b-a}{2} t + \frac{b+a}{2}\right)^{n+1} - Q(x) = \left(\frac{b-a}{2}\right)^{n+1} [t^{n+1} - Q^*(t)],$$

where $Q^*(t)$ is a polynomial in t with degree $\leq n$. If we apply Theorem 8–7 to the polynomial $p_{n+1}^*(t) = t^{n+1} - Q^*(t)$ and note that

$$\left(\frac{2}{b-a}\right)^{n+1} p_{n+1}(x) = p_{n+1}^*(t)$$

we immediately obtain Theorem 8–8.

We return now to the error formula (8.40) for polynomial interpolation. If we choose the interpolation points $x_0, x_1, \ldots, x_n$ to be the $n+1$ zeros of the Chebyshev polynomial T_{n+1} we may write (8.40) in the form

$$f(x) - P(x) = \frac{T_{n+1}(x)}{2^n(n+1)!} f^{(n+1)}(c).$$

The points $x_0, x_1, \ldots, x_n$ all lie in the open interval $(-1, 1)$ and are given by

$$x_k = \cos\left(\frac{2k+1}{n+1} \frac{\pi}{2}\right) \quad \text{for} \quad k = 0, 1, 2, \ldots, n.$$

If x is in the interval $[-1, 1]$ we have $|T_{n+1}(x)| \leq 1$ and the error is estimated by the inequality

$$|f(x) - P(x)| \leq \frac{1}{2^n (n+1)!} |f^{(n+1)}(c)|.$$

If the interpolation takes place in an interval $[a, b]$ with the points

$$t_k = \frac{b - a}{2} x_k + \frac{b + a}{2}$$

as interpolation points, the product

$$A(x) = (x - t_0)(x - t_1) \cdots (x - t_n)$$

satisfies the inequality $|A(x)| \leq (b - a)^{n+1}/2^{2n+1}$ for all x in $[a, b]$. The corresponding estimate for $f(x) - P(x)$ is

$$|f(x) - P(x)| \leq \frac{(b - a)^{n+1}}{2^{2n+1}(n + 1)!} |f^{(n+1)}(c)| .$$

*8.13 Error analysis in polynomial approximation relative to the maximum norm

If a function f has a derivative of order $n + 1$ we can obtain an explicit formula for the deviation between f and its polynomial approximations relative to the maximum norm. This formula will be deduced as a consequence of the following theorem.

8–9   THEOREM.   Let f be continuous on $[a, b]$ and assume T is a polynomial of degree $\leq n$ that best approximates f on $[a, b]$ relative to the maximum norm. Let

$$R(x) = f(x) - T(x)$$

denote the error in this approximation, and let $D = \|f - T\|$. Then:
(a) If $D = 0$ the function R is identically zero on $[a, b]$.
(b) If $D > 0$ the function R has at least $n + 1$ sign changes in $[a, b]$.

Proof. For each x in $[a, b]$ we have the inequality

(8.47) $$0 \leq |R(x)| = |f(x) - T(x)| \leq \max_{a \leq x \leq b} |f(x) - T(x)| = D .$$

The statement in part (a) follows at once from this inequality.

To prove part (b) we argue by induction on the number of sign changes of R. First we show that R has at least one sign change in $[a, b]$. Then we prove that if R has k sign changes, where $k \leq n$, it also has $k + 1$ sign changes.

The first step in the induction is proved by contradiction. Assume R has no sign changes in $[a, b]$. Then either $R(x) \geq 0$ for all x in $[a, b]$ or $R(x) \leq 0$ throughout $[a, b]$. Consider first the case $R(x) \geq 0$. Then from (8.47) we have $0 \leq R(x) \leq D$, so that

$$0 \leq |R(x) - \tfrac{1}{2}D| \leq \tfrac{1}{2}D$$

for all x in $[a, b]$. Now let $Q(x) = T(x) + \tfrac{1}{2}D$. This is a polynomial of degree $\leq n$ which differs from f at each point by an amount

$$|f(x) - Q(x)| = |f(x) - T(x) - \tfrac{1}{2}D| = |R(x) - \tfrac{1}{2}D| \leq \tfrac{1}{2}D .$$

Since this is true for all x in $[a, b]$ we also have the inequality

$$\|f - Q\| \leq \tfrac{1}{2}D < D = \|f - T\| ,$$

which contradicts the assumption that T is a best approximation to f. Therefore the assumption that $R(x) \geq 0$ throughout $[a, b]$ leads to a contradiction. In a similar way we can show that we cannot have $R(x) \leq 0$ throughout $[a, b]$. This proves that R has at least one sign change in $[a, b]$.

Now assume that R changes sign at least k times in $[a, b]$, where $k \leq n$. We wish to prove that it changes sign at least $k + 1$ times. To do this we assume R changes sign *exactly* k times and arrive at a contradiction. Since R is a continuous function it must have at least one zero in each interval in which there is a sign change (by Bolzano's theorem). Therefore R has at least k zeros in the open interval (a, b).† From these zeros we can choose k distinct points $x_1 < x_2 < \cdots < x_k$ such that the function R changes its sign in every neighborhood of each x_i. Now let A_k be the polynomial

$$A_k(x) = (x - x_1)(x - x_2) \cdots (x - x_k)$$

and let $F_k(x) = a_k A_k(x)$, where $a_k = \pm 1/\|A_k\|$. The choice of sign will be specified presently. Let S denote the set of points x in $[a, b]$ at which $R(x) \neq 0$. The functions R and F_k have sign changes at the points x_i and *at no other points* in $[a, b]$. Therefore R and F_k have the same sign everywhere in S or the opposite sign everywhere in S. We choose the sign of a_k which will make R and F_k agree in sign everywhere in S.

Now let Q be the polynomial given by

$$Q(x) = T(x) + \frac{D}{2} F_k(x).$$

Since F_k has degree $k \leq n$, the polynomial Q has degree $\leq n$. The difference between f and Q is given by

$$(8.48) \qquad |f(x) - Q(x)| = \left| f(x) - T(x) - \frac{D}{2} F_k(x) \right| = \left| R(x) - \frac{D}{2} F_k(x) \right|.$$

If we can prove that

$$(8.49) \qquad \left| R(x) - \frac{D}{2} F_k(x) \right| < D$$

for all x in $[a, b]$, we will obtain $|f(x) - Q(x)| < D$ from (8.48) and it will follow that

$$\|f - Q\| < D = \|f - T\|.$$

This contradicts the assumption that T is the best approximation to f. The contradiction completes the inductive step needed to prove the theorem.

We still need to prove that (8.49) holds for all x in $[a, b]$. If x is not in S, (8.49) holds trivially, since $R(x) = 0$ and $\|F_k\| = 1$. Therefore, suppose $x \in S$. We know that R and F_k agree in sign everywhere in S. If x is a point at which $F_k(x) > 0$ and $R(x) > 0$, we have

$$R(x) - \frac{D}{2} F_k(x) < R(x) \leq D$$

and

$$R(x) - \frac{D}{2} F_k(x) > - \frac{D}{2} F_k(x) \geq - \frac{D}{2} \|F_k\| = - \frac{D}{2},$$

† The function R may have other zeros, such as double zeros, at which it does not change sign.

so (8.49) holds. On the other hand, if x is a point at which $F_k(x) < 0$ and $R(x) < 0$, we have

$$R(x) - \frac{D}{2} F_k(x) < - \frac{D}{2} F_k(x) = \frac{D}{2} |F_k(x)| \leq \frac{D}{2} \|F_k\| = \frac{D}{2}$$

and

$$R(x) - \frac{D}{2} F_k(x) > R(x) = - |R(x)| \geq - D ,$$

so (8.49) holds for such x as well. Therefore (8.49) holds for all x in $[a, b]$, and the proof is complete.

Now we assume f has a derivative of order $n + 1$ and find an explicit formula for the error.

8–10   THEOREM.   Assume the derivative $f^{(n+1)}$ exists on $[a, b]$ and let T be the polynomial of degree $\leq n$ that best approximates f on $[a, b]$ relative to the maximum norm. Then there are $n + 1$ distinct points $x_0, x_1, \ldots, x_n$ in the open interval (a, b) such that for each x in $[a, b]$ we have

(8.50) $$f(x) - T(x) = \frac{A(x)}{(n + 1)!} f^{(n+1)}(c) ,$$

where

$$A(x) = (x - x_0)(x - x_1) \cdots (x - x_n)$$

and

$$\min\{x_0, x_1, \ldots, x_n, x\} < c < \max\{x_0, x_1, \ldots, x_n, x\} .$$

Proof. Let $R(x) = f(x) - T(x)$. By Theorem 8–9 there are $n + 1$ distinct points x_0, $x_1, \ldots, x_n$ in (a, b) at which R vanishes. At these points the polynomial T agrees with f, so T must be the interpolating polynomial relative to these interpolation points. Applying the error formula in Theorem 8–3 we obtain (8.50).

It should be noted that we cannot use the Lagrange interpolation formula to construct T explicitly in this case because the exact location of the x_i is not known.

8.14 Exercises

In this set of exercises T_n denotes the Chebyshev polynomial of degree n.

1. Prove that $T_n(-x) = (-1)^n T_n(x)$. This shows that T_n is an even function when n is even and an odd function when n is odd.

2. (a) Prove that in the open interval $(-1, 1)$ the derivative T_n' is given by the formula

$$T_n'(x) = \frac{n \sin n\theta}{\sin \theta} , \qquad \text{where} \quad \theta = \text{arc cos } x .$$

(b) Compute $T_n'(1)$ and $T_n'(-1)$.

3. Use the trigonometric identity

$$2 \sin \theta \sin n\theta = \cos (n - 1)\theta - \cos (n + 1)\theta$$

and the result of Exercise 2 to prove that

$$(1 - x^2)T_n'(x) = n\,T_{n-1}(x) - nx\,T_n(x)$$

for $-1 < x < 1$. Then show that the formula holds for all real x.

4. The Chebyshev polynomial T_n satisfies the differential equation

$$(1 - x^2)y'' - xy' + n^2y = 0$$

over the entire real axis. Prove this by each of the following methods:
    (a) Use the result of Exercise 3 and the recursion formula (8.41).
    (b) Introduce the change of variable $x = \cos\theta$ in the differential equation

$$\frac{d^2\,(\cos n\theta)}{d\theta^2} = -n^2\cos n\theta\,.$$

5. The Chebyshev polynomials satisfy the following orthogonality relations:

$$\int_{-1}^{1} \frac{T_n(x)T_m(x)}{\sqrt{1 - x^2}}\,dx = \begin{cases} 0 & \text{if } n \neq m\,, \\ \pi & \text{if } n = m = 0\,, \\ \dfrac{\pi}{2} & \text{if } n = m > 0\,. \end{cases}$$

Prove this by each of the following methods:
    (a) From the differential equation in Exercise 4 deduce that

$$T_m(x)\frac{d}{dx}\left(\sqrt{1 - x^2}\,T_n'(x)\right) + n^2\frac{T_n(x)T_m(x)}{\sqrt{1 - x^2}} = 0\,.$$

    Write a corresponding formula with n and m interchanged, subtract the two equations, and integrate from -1 to 1.
    (b) Use the orthogonality relations

$$\int_{0}^{\pi} \cos m\theta \cos n\theta\,d\theta = \begin{cases} 0 & \text{if } n \neq m\,, \\ \pi & \text{if } n = m = 0\,, \\ \dfrac{\pi}{2} & \text{if } n = m > 0\,, \end{cases}$$

and introduce the change of variable $x = \cos\theta$.

6. Find the polynomial of degree ≤ 4 that best approximates the function $f(x) = x^5$ in the interval $[0, 1]$, relative to the maximum norm.

7. Prove that for $-1 < x < 1$ we have

$$\frac{T_n(x)}{\sqrt{1 - x^2}} = (-1)^n\frac{2^n\,n!}{(2n)!}\frac{d^n}{dx^n}(1 - x^2)^{n-1/2}\,.$$

8. Let $y_1, y_2, \ldots, y_n$ be n real numbers, and let

$$x_k = \cos\frac{(2k - 1)\pi}{2n} \qquad \text{for } k = 1, 2, \ldots, n\,.$$

Let P be the polynomial of degree $\leq n - 1$ that takes the value y_k at x_k for $1 \leq k \leq n$. If x is not one of the x_k show that

$$P(x) = \frac{1}{n}\sum_{k=1}^{n}(-1)^{k-1}\,y_k\,\sqrt{1 - x_k^2}\,\frac{T_n(x)}{x - x_k}\,.$$

9. Let P be a polynomial of degree $\leq n - 1$ such that

$$\sqrt{1 - x^2}\, |P(x)| \leq 1$$

for $-1 \leq x \leq 1$. Prove that $||P|| \leq n$, where $||P||$ is the maximum of $|P|$ on the interval $[-1, 1]$. [*Hint.* Use Exercise 8. Consider three cases: $x_1 \leq x \leq 1$; $-1 \leq x \leq x_n$; $x_n \leq x \leq x_1$; in the first two use Exercise 13(a) of Section 8.7. In the third case note that $\sqrt{1 - x^2} \geq \sin(\pi/2n) > 1/n$.]

10. A polynomial P is called *primary* if the coefficient of the term of highest degree is 1. For a given interval $[a, b]$ let $||P||$ denote the maximum of $|P|$ on $[a, b]$. Prove each of the following statements:

(a) If $b - a < 4$, for every $\epsilon > 0$ there exists a primary polynomial P with $||P|| < \epsilon$.

(b) If for every $\epsilon > 0$ there exists a primary polynomial P with $||P|| < \epsilon$, then $b - a < 4$.

In other words, primary polynomials with arbitrarily small norm exist if, and only if, the interval $[a, b]$ has length less than 4.

In Exercises 11 through 15, $U_n(x) = T'_{n+1}(x)/(n + 1)$ for $n = 0, 1, 2, \ldots$.

11. (a) Prove that $U_n(x) = 2x\, U_{n-1}(x) - U_{n-2}(x)$ for $n \geq 2$.

(b) Determine the explicit form of the polynomials $U_0, U_1, \ldots, U_5$.

(c) Prove that $|U_n(x)| \leq n + 1$ if $-1 \leq x \leq 1$.

12. Show that U_n satisfies the differential equation

$$(1 - x^2)y'' - 3xy' + n(n + 2)y = 0 .$$

13. Derive the orthogonality relations

$$\int_{-1}^{1} \sqrt{1 - x^2}\, U_m(x)\, U_n(x)\, dx = \begin{cases} 0 & \text{if } m \neq n , \\ \dfrac{\pi}{2} & \text{if } m = n . \end{cases}$$

14. Prove that

$$\sqrt{1 - x^2}\, U_n(x) = (-1)^n\, \frac{2^n(n + 1)!}{(2n + 1)!}\, \frac{d^n}{dx^n}\, (1 - x^2)^{n+1/2} .$$

15. Let $y_1, y_2, \ldots, y_n$ be n real numbers and let

$$x_k = \cos\frac{k\pi}{n + 1} \qquad \text{for} \quad k = 1, 2, \ldots, n .$$

Let P be the polynomial of degree $\leq n - 1$ that takes the value y_k at x_k for $1 \leq k \leq n$. If x is not one of the x_k show that

$$P(x) = \frac{1}{n + 1} \sum_{k=1}^{n} (-1)^{k-1} (1 - x_k^2)y_k\, \frac{U_n(x)}{x - x_k} .$$

8.15 Newton's interpolation polynomial with divided differences

Let P_n denote the interpolation polynomial of degree $\leq n$ that agrees with a given function f at $n + 1$ distinct points $x_0, x_1, \ldots, x_n$. Lagrange's interpolation formula tells us that

(8.51)
$$P_n(x) = \sum_{k=0}^{n} L_k(x)f(x_k) ,$$

where $L_k(x)$ is a polynomial of degree n (the Lagrange interpolation coefficient) given by the product formula

$$(8.52) \qquad L_k(x) = \prod_{\substack{j=0 \\ j \neq k}}^{n} \frac{x - x_j}{x_k - x_j}, \qquad \text{for} \quad k = 0, 1, 2, \ldots, n.$$

Suppose we adjoin a new interpolation point x_{n+1} to the given points $x_0, x_1, \ldots, x_n$. To determine the corresponding polynomial P_{n+1} by Lagrange's formula it is necessary to compute a new interpolation coefficient L_{n+1} and to recompute all the earlier coefficients $L_0, L_1, \ldots, L_n$, each of which is now a polynomial of degree $n + 1$. In practice this involves considerable labor. Therefore it is desirable to have another formula for determining P_n that provides an easier transition from P_n to P_{n+1}. One such formula was discovered by Newton; to discuss it we introduce the concept of divided differences.

DEFINITION OF DIVIDED DIFFERENCES. Let $x_0, x_1, \ldots, x_n$ be $n + 1$ distinct points at which a function f is defined. For each x in the domain of f the divided differences of order $1, 2, \ldots, n + 1$ are defined, respectively, by the following formulas:

$$f(x_0, x) = \frac{f(x_0) - f(x)}{x_0 - x} \quad \text{if} \quad x \neq x_0,$$

$$f(x_0, x_1, x) = \frac{f(x_0, x_1) - f(x_0, x)}{x_1 - x} \quad \text{if} \quad x \neq x_0, x \neq x_1,$$

$$\cdot$$
$$\cdot$$
$$\cdot$$

$$f(x_0, x_1, \ldots, x_n, x) = \frac{f(x_0, x_1, \ldots, x_{n-1}, x_n) - f(x_0, x_1, \ldots, x_{n-1}, x)}{x_n - x}$$

$$\text{if} \quad x \neq x_0, x \neq x_1, \ldots, x \neq x_n.$$

Note. The notations $[x_0, x_1, \ldots, x_r, x]$ and $f[x_0, x_1, \ldots, x_r, x]$ are also used for the divided difference of order $r + 1$.

The function value $f(x)$ can be expressed in terms of divided differences. To begin with, the equation for $f(x_0, x)$ may be rewritten as

$$(8.53) \qquad f(x) = f(x_0) + (x - x_0)f(x_0, x) \quad \text{if} \quad x \neq x_0.$$

Also, we may write the equation for $f(x_0, x_1, x)$ in the form

$$f(x_0, x) = f(x_0, x_1) + (x - x_1)f(x_0, x_1, x)$$

and substitute in (8.53) to obtain

$$f(x) = f(x_0) + (x - x_0)f(x_0, x_1) + (x - x_0)(x - x_1)f(x_0, x_1, x) \quad \text{if} \quad x \neq x_0, x \neq x_1.$$

Continuing in this manner we obtain the formula

$$(8.54) \quad f(x) = f(x_0) + \sum_{r=0}^{k-1} (x - x_0) \cdots (x - x_r)f(x_0, x_1, \ldots, x_{r+1})$$

$$+ (x - x_0) \cdots (x - x_k)f(x_0, x_1, \ldots, x_k, x),$$

which is valid if $x \neq x_0, x \neq x_1, \ldots, x \neq x_k$, where $k \leq n$. The first $k + 1$ terms on the right of (8.54) determine a polynomial of degree $\leq k$ which we denote by Q_k. Thus, we may write (8.54) in the form

(8.55) $f(x) = Q_k(x) + (x - x_0) \cdots (x - x_k)f(x_0, x_1, \ldots, x_k, x)$

for $x \neq x_0, \ldots, x \neq x_k$, where

(8.56) $Q_k(x) = f(x_0) + \sum_{r=0}^{k-1} (x - x_0) \cdots (x - x_r)f(x_0, x_1, \ldots, x_{r+1})$.

The polynomial Q_k is called *Newton's divided-difference polynomial*. From (8.56) we see that

(8.57) $Q_k(x) = Q_{k-1}(x) + (x - x_0) \cdots (x - x_{k-1})f(x_0, x_1, \ldots, x_k)$

for every x. This property of the Q_k enables us to prove the following theorem.

8–11   THEOREM.   The Newton divided-difference polynomial Q_n agrees with f at the points $x_0, x_1, \ldots, x_n$. Therefore, Q_n is identical to the Lagrange interpolation polynomial given by (8.51).

Proof. We argue by induction on n. For $n = 0$ we have $Q_0(x) = f(x_0)$; in particular, $Q_0(x_0) = f(x_0)$, so the theorem holds in this case. Assume, therefore, that the theorem has been proved for $n - 1$, and consider the polynomial Q_n. We wish to prove that

(8.58) $Q_n(x_j) = f(x_j)$ for $j = 0, 1, 2, \ldots, n$.

For $j < n$ we use Equation (8.57) to obtain $Q_n(x_j) = Q_{n-1}(x_j)$. By the inductive hypothesis, we have $Q_{n-1}(x_j) = f(x_j)$ for $j < n$, so (8.58) holds for these j. Now we prove that (8.58) also holds for $j = n$. From Equation (8.57) we obtain

(8.59) $Q_n(x_n) = Q_{n-1}(x_n) + (x_n - x_0) \cdots (x_n - x_{n-1})f(x_0, x_1, \ldots, x_n)$.

But if we use (8.55) with $k = n - 1$ and $x = x_n$ we see that the right member of (8.59) is equal to $f(x_n)$. This completes the proof.

Theorem 8–11 gives us a new method for determining the interpolation polynomial P_n. We compute the n divided differences $f(x_0, x_1), f(x_0, x_1, x_2), \ldots, f(x_0, x_1, \ldots, x_n)$ and we have

(8.60) $P_n(x) = f(x_0) + \sum_{r=0}^{n-1} (x - x_0) \cdots (x - x_r)f(x_0, x_1, \ldots, x_{r+1})$.

This is called *Newton's interpolation formula with divided differences*. Since

$$P_{n+1}(x) = P_n(x) + (x - x_0) \cdots (x - x_n)f(x_0, x_1, \ldots, x_{n+1}),$$

we can calculate P_{n+1} simply by adding one new term to P_n. This property of Newton's interpolation formula is not possessed by Lagrange's formula.

The practical usefulness of Newton's formula depends, of course, on the ease with which the divided differences $f(x_0, x_1, \ldots, x_{r+1})$ can be computed. Although it is possible to compute each of these differences directly from its definition, it is preferable to use an alternate method that we shall describe in the next section. The method is based on the following *symmetry property* of divided differences.

8-12   THEOREM.   The divided difference $f(x_0, x_1, \ldots, x_n)$ is a symmetric function of $x_0, x_1, \ldots, x_n$. That is, if k is a one-to-one function whose domain and range is the set of integers $\{0, 1, 2, \ldots, n\}$, we have

$$f(x_0, x_1, \ldots, x_n) = f(x_{k(0)}, x_{k(1)}, \ldots, x_{k(n)}) .$$

Proof. From Equation (8.60) we note that $f(x_0, x_1, \ldots, x_n)$ is the coefficient of x^n in the interpolation polynomial of degree $\leq n$ that agrees with f at the interpolation points $x_0, x_1, \ldots, x_n$. Let $y_j = x_{k(j)}$. Then $f(y_0, y_1, \ldots, y_n)$ is the coefficient of x^n in the interpolation polynomial of degree $\leq n$ that agrees with f at the interpolation points $y_0, y_1, \ldots, y_n$. Since the sets $\{x_0, x_1, \ldots, x_n\}$ and $\{y_0, y_1, \ldots, y_n\}$ are equal the corresponding interpolation polynomials are identical, so the coefficients of x^n must be equal. This proves the theorem.

The symmetric property of divided differences can also be deduced from the following theorem which expresses the nth divided difference as a linear combination of the function values $f(x_0), \ldots, f(x_n)$.

8-13   THEOREM.   If $x_0, x_1, \ldots, x_n$ are distinct, we have

(8.61)
$$f(x_0, x_1, \ldots, x_n) = \sum_{k=0}^{n} \frac{f(x_k)}{A_k(x_k)} ,$$

where

$$A_k(x) = \prod_{\substack{j=0 \\ j \neq k}}^{n} (x - x_j) .$$

Proof. Let P_n be the interpolation polynomial of degree $\leq n$ that agrees with f at $x_0, x_1, \ldots, x_n$. By Lagrange's formula we have

$$P_n(x) = \sum_{k=0}^{n} L_k(x) f(x_k) ,$$

where $L_k(x)$ is the polynomial of degree n given by (8.52). Since the coefficient of x^n in $L_k(x)$ is $1/A_k(x_k)$, the coefficient of x^n in $P_n(x)$ is the sum appearing on the right of (8.61). On the other hand, Newton's formula shows that the coefficient of x^n in $P_n(x)$ is equal to $f(x_0, x_1, \ldots, x_n)$. This completes the proof.

8.16   Divided-difference tables

The symmetry property in Theorem 8–12 leads to an alternative formula for calculating divided differences that is especially useful in connection with tabular data. The formula in question is given by the following theorem.

8-14   THEOREM.   If $x_k, x_{k+1}, \ldots, x_{k+r}$ are distinct, we have

$$f(x_k, x_{k+1}, \ldots, x_{k+r}) = \frac{f(x_k, x_{k+1}, \ldots, x_{k+r-1}) - f(x_{k+1}, x_{k+2}, \ldots, x_{k+r})}{x_k - x_{k+r}} .$$

Proof. Let $y_j = x_{k+j}$. We wish to prove that

$$(8.62) \qquad f(y_0, y_1, \ldots, y_r) = \frac{f(y_0, y_1, \ldots, y_{r-1}) - f(y_1, y_2, \ldots, y_r)}{y_0 - y_r}.$$

From the definition of $f(y_0, y_1, \ldots, y_r)$ we have

$$f(y_0, y_1, \ldots, y_r) = \frac{f(y_0, y_1, \ldots, y_{r-2}, y_{r-1}) - f(y_0, y_1, \ldots, y_{r-2}, y_r)}{y_{r-1} - y_r}.$$

Because of the symmetry property we can interchange y_0 and y_{r-1} without changing the value of $f(y_0, y_1, \ldots, y_r)$. If we make this interchange in the right member, the foregoing equation becomes

$$f(y_0, y_1, \ldots, y_r) = \frac{f(y_{r-1}, y_1, \ldots, y_{r-2}, y_0) - f(y_{r-1}, y_1, \ldots, y_{r-2}, y_r)}{y_0 - y_r}.$$

In the numerator on the right we use the symmetry property in each term and obtain (8.62) at once.

The diagram in Table 8.1, called a *divided-difference table*, shows how divided differences can be systematically calculated from a tabulation of the values of f at the points $x_0, x_1, \ldots, x_n$ by successive applications of Theorem 8–14. For brevity we have written f_i for $f(x_i)$, f_{ij} for $f(x_i, x_j)$, f_{ijk} for $f(x_i, x_j, x_k)$, and so on. The arrows are shown to help indicate how the table is constructed. In each column, the uppermost entry gives the

TABLE 8.1

x	$f(x)$	First divided differences	Second divided differences	Third divided differences	Fourth divided differences
x_0	f_0				
		$\dfrac{f_0 - f_1}{x_0 - x_1} = f_{01}$			
x_1	f_1		$\dfrac{f_{01} - f_{12}}{x_0 - x_2} = f_{012}$		
		$\dfrac{f_1 - f_2}{x_1 - x_2} = f_{12}$		$\dfrac{f_{012} - f_{123}}{x_0 - x_3} = f_{0123}$	
x_2	f_2		$\dfrac{f_{12} - f_{23}}{x_1 - x_3} = f_{123}$		$\dfrac{f_{0123} - f_{1234}}{x_0 - x_4} = f_{01234}$
		$\dfrac{f_2 - f_3}{x_2 - x_3} = f_{23}$		$\dfrac{f_{123} - f_{234}}{x_1 - x_4} = f_{1234}$	
x_3	f_3		$\dfrac{f_{23} - f_{34}}{x_2 - x_4} = f_{234}$		
		$\dfrac{f_3 - f_4}{x_3 - x_4} = f_{34}$			
x_4	f_4				

divided difference required in Newton's formula. This particular table provides the necessary divided differences for the interpolation polynomial of degree ≤ 4. If another interpolation point x_5 is added, the new divided difference f_{012345} can be computed by calculating a new entry at the bottom of each existing column and adding a new column for the fifth-order difference.

Since interpolating polynomials are unique, the error estimates given for Lagrange's formula also apply to Newton's formula. From (8.55) we have

$$(8.63) \qquad f(x) - P_n(x) = (x - x_0) \cdots (x - x_n) f(x_0, x_1, \ldots, x_n, x) .$$

If f has a derivative of order $n + 1$ in an interval $[\alpha, \beta]$ containing the points x_0, x_1, $\ldots$, x_n, x, Theorem 8–3 tells us that

$$f(x) - P_n(x) = (x - x_0) \cdots (x - x_n) \frac{f^{(n+1)}(c)}{(n + 1)!}$$

for some c in (α, β). Comparing this with (8.63) we see that

$$f(x_0, x_1, \ldots, x_n, x) = \frac{f^{(n+1)}(c)}{(n + 1)!} .$$

Therefore, if upper and lower bounds for $f^{(n+1)}$ in (α, β) are known we can obtain corresponding bounds for $f(x_0, x_1, \ldots, x_n, x)$.

8.17 Exercises

1. A function f has the values given in the following table:

x	0	2	3	5
$f(x)$	0.000	20.134	30.452	52.110

Let P be the polynomial of degree ≤ 3 that agrees with f at the tabulated values. Construct a divided-difference table and use Newton's interpolation formula to evaluate $P(2.5)$.

2. A function f has the values given in the following table:

x	-2	0	1	3
$f(x)$	-216	-12	0	-6

(a) Let P be the polynomial of degree ≤ 3 that agrees with f at the tabulated values. Construct a divided-difference table and use Newton's interpolation formula to evaluate $P(2)$.

(b) Let Q be the polynomial of degree ≤ 4 that agrees with f at the tabulated values and assume that $Q(5) = -54$. Extend the difference table in part (a) and compute $Q(2)$.

3. Let $f(x) = c_0 + c_1 x + \cdots + c_n x^n$, where $c_n \neq 0$. If $x_0, x_1, \ldots, x_k$ are $k + 1$ distinct numbers, prove that

$$f(x_0, x_1, \ldots, x_k) = \begin{cases} c_n & \text{if} \quad k = n, \\ 0 & \text{if} \quad k > n. \end{cases}$$

4. Prove each of the following properties of divided differences. In each case assume $x_0 \neq x_1$.
(a) If $f(x) = u(x) + v(x)$, then

$$f(x_0, x_1) = u(x_0, x_1) + v(x_0, x_1).$$

(b) If $f(x) = u(x)v(x)$, then

$$f(x_0, x_1) = u(x_0)v(x_0, x_1) + u(x_0, x_1)v(x_1).$$

(c) If $f(x) = u(x)/v(x)$ whenever $v(x) \neq 0$, then

$$f(x_0, x_1) = \frac{v(x_0)u(x_0, x_1) - u(x_0)v(x_0, x_1)}{v(x_0)v(x_1)},$$

provided $v(x_0) \neq 0$, $v(x_1) \neq 0$.

(d) If $f(x) = u[v(x)]$, then

$$f(x_0, x_1) = u[v(x_0), v(x_1)] \, v(x_0, x_1),$$

provided $v(x_0) \neq v(x_1)$.

5. (a) Show that the relation in Exercise 4(b) generalizes as follows:

$$f(x_0, x_1, x_2) = u(x_0)v(x_0, x_1, x_2) + u(x_0, x_1)v(x_1, x_2) + u(x_0, x_1, x_2)v(x_2).$$

(b) Guess the generalization suggested for $f(x_0, x_1, \ldots, x_n)$ and prove it by induction.

6. Up to now, the divided difference $f(x_0, x)$ has been defined only for $x \neq x_0$. If f has a derivative at x_0, prove that

$$\lim_{x \to x_0} f(x_0, x) = f'(x_0).$$

Because of this relation it is reasonable to define $f(x, x)$ to be $f'(x)$ at those points x for which $f'(x)$ exists. [We do not define $f(x, x)$ at those x for which $f'(x)$ does not exist.]

7. Assume f has a derivative everywhere in an interval (a, b). Choose a fixed x_0 in (a, b) and define a new function g on (a, b) by the equation $g(x) = f(x_0, x)$.

(a) Use Exercise 6 to prove that g is continuous everywhere on (a, b).

(b) If $x \neq x_0$, prove that $g'(x)$ exists and is given by the formula

$$g'(x) = \frac{f'(x) - f(x_0, x)}{x - x_0}.$$

(c) If f'' exists everywhere in (a, b) and if $x \neq x_0$, prove that $g'(x) = \frac{1}{2} f''(c)$ for some c between x and x_0. [*Hint.* Use part (b) and Taylor's formula with remainder.]

(d) If f'' is continuous in (a, b), define $g'(x_0) = \frac{1}{2} f''(x_0)$. Prove that g' is continuous everywhere on (a, b).

8. Let $x_0, x_1, \ldots, x_n, x$ be $n + 2$ distinct points.

(a) Prove that

$$(x - x_0)(x - x_1) \cdots (x - x_n)f(x_0, x_1, \ldots, x_n, x) = \sum_{k=0}^{n} L_k(x)[f(x) - f(x_k)],$$

where $L_k(x)$ is the Lagrange interpolation coefficient given by (8.52). [*Hint.* Use Equation (8.63) and Lagrange's interpolation formula.]

(b) Use part (a) to deduce the formula

(8.64)
$$f(x_0, x_1, \ldots, x_n, x) = \sum_{k=0}^{n} \frac{f(x_k, x)}{A_k(x_k)},$$

where

$$A_k(x_k) = \prod_{\substack{j=0 \\ j \neq k}}^{n} (x_k - x_j).$$

Equation (8.64) expresses a divided difference of order $n + 1$ as a linear combination of divided differences of first order.

9. In Exercise 6 we assigned a meaning to $f(x, x)$ for those x at which $f'(x)$ exists. Therefore, the right member of Equation (8.64) is meaningful if $x = x_j$, provided $f'(x_j)$ exists. If $x_0, x_1, \ldots, x_n$ are distinct, and if $f'(x_j)$ exists, we define $f(x_0, x_1, \ldots, x_n, x_j)$ by Equation (8.64) with $x = x_j$.

(a) Use this definition to prove that

$$f(x_0, x_1, \ldots, x_n, x_j) = \lim_{x \to x_j} f(x_0, x_1, \ldots, x_n, x).$$

(b) Let g be the function defined on (a, b) by the equation $g(x) = f(x_0, x_1, \ldots, x_n, x)$. If f' exists on (a, b) prove that g is continuous everywhere on (a, b).

8.18 Ordinary differences. Equally spaced interpolation points

When the interpolation points $x_0, x_1, \ldots, x_n$ are equally spaced the calculation of divided differences can be considerably simplified. To discuss this case we introduce the so-called *forward difference operator* Δ.

DEFINITION. *Let h be a fixed real number and let f be a given function. The function Δf defined by the equation*

$$\Delta f(x) = f(x + h) - f(x)$$

is called the first forward difference of f. It is defined at those points x for which both x and $x + h$ are in the domain of f. Higher order differences $\Delta^2 f, \Delta^3 f, \ldots$ are defined inductively as follows:

$$\Delta^{k+1} f = \Delta(\Delta^k f) \qquad \text{for} \quad k = 1, 2, 3, \ldots.$$

Note. The notations $\Delta_h f(x)$ and $\Delta f(x; h)$ are also used for $\Delta f(x)$ when it is desirable to indicate the dependence on h. It is convenient to define $\Delta^0 f = f$.

Now suppose f is defined at $n + 1$ equally spaced points $x_0 < x_1 < x_2 < \cdots < x_n$, where $x_j = x_0 + jh$ for $j = 0, 1, 2, \ldots, n$. Here h is a positive number that represents the spacing between adjacent points. The next theorem expresses the divided differences in terms of forward differences.

8–15   THEOREM. *If $h > 0$ and $x_j = x_0 + jh$ for $j = 0, 1, 2, \ldots, n$, we have*

$$f(x_0, x_1, \ldots, x_n) = \frac{\Delta^n f(x_0)}{n! \, h^n}.$$

Proof. The proof proceeds by induction on the number of points. For two points ($n = 1$) we have

$$f(x_0, x_1) = \frac{f(x_1) - f(x_0)}{x_1 - x_0} = \frac{f(x_0 + h) - f(x_0)}{h} = \frac{\Delta f(x_0)}{h},$$

so the theorem holds. Therefore, assume the theorem holds for n points. From Theorem 8–14 we have

$$f(x_0, x_1, \ldots, x_n) = \frac{f(x_0, x_1, \ldots, x_{n-1}) - f(x_1, x_2, \ldots, x_n)}{x_0 - x_n}$$

$$= \frac{f(x_1, x_2, \ldots, x_n) - f(x_0, x_1, \ldots, x_{n-1})}{nh}.$$

From the inductive hypothesis we have

$$f(x_1, x_2, \ldots, x_n) = \frac{\Delta^{n-1}f(x_1)}{(n-1)! \; h^{n-1}} \quad \text{and} \quad f(x_0, x_1, \ldots, x_{n-1}) = \frac{\Delta^{n-1}f(x_0)}{(n-1)! \; h^{n-1}} \; .$$

Since $\Delta^{n-1}f(x_1) = \Delta^{n-1}f(x_0 + h)$, we have

$$f(x_0, x_1, \ldots, x_n) = \frac{\Delta^{n-1}f(x_0 + h) - \Delta^{n-1}f(x_0)}{n! \; h^n} = \frac{\Delta^n f(x_0)}{n! \; h^n} \; .$$

This completes the proof.

Newton's interpolation formula (8.60) now becomes

(8.65)
$$P_n(x) = f(x_0) + \sum_{r=0}^{n-1} \frac{\Delta^{r+1}f(x_0)}{(r+1)! \; h^{r+1}} \prod_{j=0}^{r} (x - x_j) \; .$$

If we write

$$\prod_{j=0}^{r} (x - x_j) = \prod_{j=0}^{r} (x - x_0 - jh) = h^{r+1} \prod_{j=0}^{r} \left(\frac{x - x_0}{h} - j \right) = h^{r+1} \prod_{j=0}^{r} (t - j),$$

where

$$t = \frac{x - x_0}{h},$$

Equation (8.65) becomes

$$P_n(x) = f(x_0) + \sum_{r=0}^{n-1} \frac{\Delta^{r+1}f(x_0)}{(r+1)!} \prod_{j=0}^{r} (t - j) \; .$$

The differences $\Delta^{r+1}f(x_0)$ are easily computed in succession from an ordinary difference table, as illustrated in Table 8.2. Again, we have written f_i for $f(x_i)$.

TABLE 8.2

x	$f(x)$	$\Delta f(x)$	$\Delta^2 f(x)$	$\Delta^3 f(x)$
x_0	f_0			
		$f_1 - f_0 = \Delta f(x_0)$		
x_1	f_1		$\Delta f(x_1) - \Delta f(x_0) = \Delta^2 f(x_0)$	
		$f_2 - f_1 = \Delta f(x_1)$		$\Delta^2 f(x_1) - \Delta^2 f(x_0) = \Delta^3 f(x_0)$
x_2	f_2		$\Delta f(x_2) - \Delta f(x_1) = \Delta^2 f(x_1)$	
		$f_3 - f_2 = \Delta f(x_2)$		
x_3	f_3			

Theorem 8–13 shows that the divided difference $f(x_0, x_1, \ldots, x_n)$ is a linear combination of the function values $f(x_0), \ldots, f(x_n)$, given by

$$(8.66) \qquad f(x_0, x_1, \ldots, x_n) = \sum_{k=0}^{n} \frac{f(x_k)}{A_k(x_k)},$$

where

$$A_k(x_k) = \prod_{\substack{j=0 \\ j \neq k}}^{n} (x_k - x_j).$$

For equally spaced points with $x_k - x_j = h(k - j)$ the product multiplying $f(x_k)$ in (8.66) can be simplified. Using Equation (8.14) (page 398) we obtain

$$(8.67) \qquad \frac{1}{A_k(x_k)} = \prod_{\substack{j=0 \\ j \neq k}}^{n} \frac{1}{x_k - x_j} = \frac{1}{h^n} \prod_{\substack{j=0 \\ j \neq k}}^{n} \frac{1}{k - j} = \frac{(-1)^{n-k}}{n! \, h^n} \binom{n}{k}.$$

Since we also have $\Delta^n f(x_0) = n! \, h^n f(x_0, x_1, \ldots, x_n)$ for equally spaced points, Equations (8.66) and (8.67) give us the formula

$$\Delta^n f(x_0) = \sum_{k=0}^{n} (-1)^{n-k} \binom{n}{k} f(x_k),$$

which expresses the nth order difference $\Delta^n f(x_0)$ as a linear combination of $f(x_0), f(x_1),$ $\ldots, f(x_n)$.

Factorial polynomials. If n is a positive integer, the product $t(t - 1) \cdots (t - n + 1)$ is a polynomial in t of degree n called the nth *factorial polynomial*, or the *factorial nth power* of t. It is denoted by the symbol $t^{(n)}$. Thus, by definition,

$$t^{(n)} = \prod_{j=0}^{n-1} (t - j).$$

We also define $t^{(0)} = 1$. If we consider the forward difference operator Δ with $h = 1$, that is, $\Delta f(x) = f(x + 1) - f(x)$, we find that

$$\Delta t^{(n)} = n t^{(n-1)} \qquad \text{for} \quad n \geq 1.$$

This is analogous to the differentiation formula $D t^n = n t^{n-1}$ for ordinary powers. Thus, the factorial power $t^{(n)}$ is related to differences much in the same way that the ordinary power t^n is related to derivatives.

With the use of factorial polynomials, Newton's interpolation formula (8.65) becomes

$$P_n(x_0 + th) = \sum_{k=0}^{n} \frac{\Delta^k f(x_0)}{k!} t^{(k)}.$$

Expressed in this form, Newton's formula resembles the Taylor formula for the polynomial of degree $\leq n$ that agrees with f and its first n derivatives at x_0. If we write

$$\binom{t}{k} = \frac{t^{(k)}}{k!} = \frac{t(t - 1) \cdots (t - k + 1)}{k!},$$

Newton's formula takes the form

$$P_n(x_0 + th) = \sum_{k=0}^{n} \binom{t}{k} \Delta^k f(x_0) .$$

Further properties of factorial polynomials are developed in the following exercises.

8.19 Exercises

1. Let $\Delta f(x) = f(x + h) - f(x)$. If f is a polynomial of degree n, say

$$f(x) = \sum_{r=0}^{n} a_r x^r$$

with $a_n \neq 0$, show that (a) $\Delta^k f(x)$ is a polynomial of degree $n - k$ if $k \leq n$; (b) $\Delta^n f(x) = n! h^n a_n$; (c) $\Delta^k f(x) = 0$ for $k > n$.

2. Let $\Delta f(x) = f(x + h) - f(x)$. If $f(x) = \sin(ax + b)$, prove that

$$\Delta^n f(x) = \left(2 \sin \frac{ah}{2}\right)^n \sin\left(ax + b + \frac{nah + n\pi}{2}\right).$$

3. Let $\Delta f(x) = f(x + h) - f(x)$.
   (a) If $f(x) = a^x$, where $a > 0$, show that $\Delta^k f(x) = (a^h - 1)^k a^x$.
   (b) If $g(x) = (1 + a)^{x/h}$, where $a > 0$, show that $\Delta^k g(x) = a^k g(x)$.
   (c) Show that the polynomial P_n of degree n that takes the values $P_n(k) = (1 + a)^k$ for $k = 0, 1, 2, \ldots, n$ is given by

$$P_n(x) = \sum_{k=0}^{n} \frac{a^k}{k!} x^{(k)} .$$

4. Let $x^{(n)}$ be the factorial nth power of x. Since $x^{(n)}$ is a polynomial in x of degree n with the value 0 when $x = 0$, we may write

$$x^{(n)} = \sum_{k=1}^{n} S_{k,n} x^k .$$

The numbers $S_{k,n}$ are called *Stirling numbers of the first kind.* From the definition of $x^{(n)}$ it is clear that $S_{n,n} = 1$ for $n \geq 0$.
   (a) Show that $S_{n-1,n} = -n(n - 1)/2$ and that $S_{1,n} = (-1)^{n-1}(n - 1)!$ for $n \geq 1$.
   (b) Prove that $S_{k,n+1} = S_{k-1,n} - n S_{k,n}$. Use this relation to verify the entries in Table 8.3, a table of Stirling numbers of the first kind, and construct the next three rows of the table.

TABLE 8.3

n	$S_{1,n}$	$S_{2,n}$	$S_{3,n}$	$S_{4,n}$	$S_{5,n}$	$S_{6,n}$	$S_{7,n}$
1	1						
2	−1	1					
3	2	−3	1				
4	−6	11	−6	1			
5	24	−50	35	−10	1		
6	−120	274	−225	85	−15	1	
7	720	−1764	1624	−735	175	−21	1

(c) Express the polynomial $x^{(4)} + 3x^{(3)} + 2x^{(1)} + 1$ as a linear combination of powers of x.

5. (a) Prove that

$$x = x^{(1)}, \qquad x^2 = x^{(1)} + x^{(2)}, \qquad x^3 = x^{(1)} + 3x^{(2)} + x^{(3)},$$

and that, in general,

$$x^n = \sum_{k=1}^{n} \frac{\Delta^k f(0)}{k!} x^{(k)},$$

where $f(x) = x^n$ and $\Delta f(x) = f(x+1) - f(x)$. The numbers $T_{k,n} = \Delta^k f(0)/k!$ are called *Stirling numbers of the second kind*.

(b) Prove that

$$\Delta^k x^{n+1} = (x+k)\,\Delta^k x^n + k\,\Delta^{k-1} x^n$$

and use this to deduce that $T_{k,n+1} = T_{k-1,n} + k\,T_{k,n}$.

(c) Use the recursion formula in part (b) to verify the entries in Table 8.4, a table of Stirling numbers of the second kind, and construct the next three rows of the table.

TABLE 8.4

n	$T_{1,n}$	$T_{2,n}$	$T_{3,n}$	$T_{4,n}$	$T_{5,n}$	$T_{6,n}$	$T_{7,n}$
1	1						
2	1	1					
3	1	3	1				
4	1	7	6	1			
5	1	15	25	10	1		
6	1	31	90	65	15	1	
7	1	63	301	350	140	21	1

(d) Express the polynomial $x^4 + 3x^3 + 2x - 1$ as a linear combination of factorial polynomials.

6. (a) If p is a positive integer and if a and b are integers with $a < b$, prove that

$$\sum_{k=a}^{b-1} k^{(p)} = \frac{b^{(p+1)} - a^{(p+1)}}{p+1}.$$

This formula is analogous to the integration formula for $\int_a^b x^p\,dx$. It should be noted, however, that the upper limit in the sum is $b - 1$, not b.

(b) Verify that $k(k+3) = 4k^{(1)} + k^{(2)}$. Then use part (a) to show that

$$\sum_{k=1}^{n} k(k+3) = 4\frac{(n+1)^{(2)}}{2} + \frac{(n+1)^{(3)}}{3} = \frac{n(n+1)(n+5)}{3}.$$

(c) If $f(k)$ is a polynomial in k of degree r, prove that

$$\sum_{k=1}^{n} f(k)$$

is a polynomial in n of degree $r + 1$.

7. Use the method suggested in Exercise 6 to express each of the following sums as a polynomial in n.

(a) $\sum_{k=1}^{n} (4k^2 + 7k + 6)$.

(c) $\sum_{k=1}^{n} k(k + 1)(k + 2)$.

(b) $\sum_{k=1}^{n} k^2(k + 1)$.

(d) $\sum_{k=1}^{n} k^4$.

8. Let A denote the linear operator defined by the equation

$$A(f) = a_0 \Delta^n f + a_1 \Delta^{n-1} f + \cdots + a_{n-1} \Delta f + a_n f,$$

where $a_0, a_1, \ldots, a_n$ are constants. This is called a *constant-coefficient difference operator*. It is analogous to the constant-coefficient derivative operator described in Section 7.15. With each such A we can associate the characteristic polynomial p_A defined by

$$p_A(r) = a_0 r^n + a_1 r^{n-1} + \cdots + a_{n-1} r + a_n.$$

Conversely, with every polynomial p we can associate an operator A having this polynomial as its characteristic polynomial. If A and B are constant-coefficient difference operators and if λ is a real number, define $A + B$, AB, and λA by the same formulas used in Section 7.15 for derivative operators. Then prove that Theorem 7-12 is valid for constant-coefficient difference operators.

8.20 Approximate integration. The trapezoidal rule

Many problems in both pure and applied mathematics lead to new functions whose properties have not been studied or whose values have not been tabulated. To satisfy certain practical needs of applied science it often becomes necessary to obtain quantitative information about such functions, either in graphical or numerical form. Many of these functions occur as integrals of the type

$$F(x) = \int_a^x f(t)\, dt,$$

where the integrand f is given by an explicit analytic formula or is known in part by tabular data. The remainder of this chapter describes some of the most elementary methods for finding numerical approximations to such integrals. The basic idea is very simple. We approximate the integrand f by another function P whose integral is easily computed, and then we use the integral of P as an approximation to the integral of f.

If f is nonnegative the integral $\int_a^b f(x)\, dx$ represents the area of the ordinate set of f over $[a, b]$. This geometric interpretation of the integral immediately suggests certain procedures for approximate integration. Figure 8.2 shows an example of a function f with known values at $n + 1$ equally spaced points $a, a + h, a + 2h, \ldots, a + nh = b$, where $h = (b - a)/n$. Let $x_k = a + kh$. For each $k = 0, 1, 2, \ldots, n - 1$ the graph of f over the interval $[x_k, x_{k+1}]$ has been approximated by a linear function that agrees with f at the endpoints x_k and x_{k+1}. Let P denote the corresponding piecewise linear interpolating function defined over the full interval $[a, b]$. Then we have

$$(8.68) \qquad P(x) = \frac{x_{k+1} - x}{h} f(x_k) + \frac{x - x_k}{h} f(x_{k+1}) \qquad \text{if} \quad x_k \leq x \leq x_{k+1}.$$

Integrating over the interval $[x_k, x_{k+1}]$ we find that

$$\int_{x_k}^{x_{k+1}} P(x)\, dx = h \frac{f(x_k) + f(x_{k+1})}{2}.$$

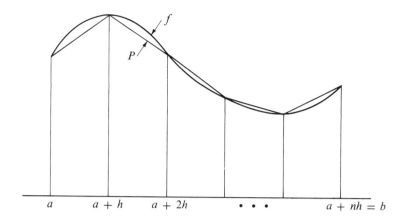

FIGURE 8.2 *The trapezoidal rule obtained by piecewise linear interpolation.*

When f is positive this is the area of the trapezoid determined by the graph of P over $[x_k, x_{k+1}]$. The formula holds, of course, even if f is not positive everywhere. Adding the integrals over all subintervals $[x_k, x_{k+1}]$ we obtain

(8.69)
$$\int_a^b P(x)\,dx = \frac{h}{2}\sum_{k=0}^{n-1}[f(x_k) + f(x_{k+1})]$$

$$= \frac{h}{2}\left(f(a) + 2\sum_{k=1}^{n-1}f(a + kh) + f(b)\right).$$

To use this sum as an approximation to the integral $\int_a^b f(x)\,dx$ we need an estimate for the error, $\int_a^b f(x)\,dx - \int_a^b P(x)\,dx$. If f has a continuous second derivative on $[a, b]$ this error is given by the following theorem.

8–16   THEOREM.   *Trapezoidal rule.* Assume f has a continuous second derivative f'' on $[a, b]$. If n is a positive integer, let $h = (b - a)/n$. Then we have

(8.70)
$$\int_a^b f(x)\,dx = \frac{b - a}{2n}\left(f(a) + 2\sum_{k=1}^{n-1}f(a + kh) + f(b)\right) - \frac{(b - a)^3}{12n^2}f''(c)$$

for some c in $[a, b]$.

Note. Equation (8.70) is known as the *trapezoidal rule.* The term $-f''(c)(b - a)^3/12n^2$ represents the error in approximating $\int_a^b f(x)\,dx$ by $\int_a^b P(x)\,dx$. Once the maximum value of f'' on $[a, b]$ is known we can approximate the integral of f to any desired degree of accuracy by taking n sufficiently large. Note that no knowledge of the interpolating function P is required to use this formula. It is only necessary to know the values of f at the points $a, a + h, \ldots, a + nh$, and to have an esti-mate for $|f''(c)|$.

Proof. Let P be the interpolating function given by (8.68), where $x_k = a + kh$. In each subinterval $[x_k, x_{k+1}]$ we apply the error estimate for linear interpolation given by Theorem 8–3 and we find

(8.71)
$$f(x) - P(x) = (x - x_k)(x - x_{k+1})\frac{f''(c_k)}{2!}$$

for some c_k in (x_k, x_{k+1}). Let M_2 and m_2 denote the maximum and minimum, respectively, of f'' on $[a, b]$, and let

$$B(x) = (x - x_k)(x_{k+1} - x)/2 .$$

Then $B(x) \geq 0$ in the interval $[x_k, x_{k+1}]$, and from (8.71) we obtain the inequalities

$$m_2 B(x) \leq P(x) - f(x) \leq M_2 B(x)$$

in this interval. Integrating, we have

(8.72)
$$m_2 \int_{x_k}^{x_k+h} B(x)\, dx \leq \int_{x_k}^{x_k+h} [P(x) - f(x)]\, dx \leq M_2 \int_{x_k}^{x_k+h} B(x)\, dx .$$

The integral of B is given by

$$\int_{x_k}^{x_k+h} B(x)\, dx = \frac{1}{2}\int_{x_k}^{x_k+h}(x - x_k)(x_{k+1} - x)\, dx = \frac{1}{2}\int_0^h t(h - t)\, dt = \frac{h^3}{12} .$$

Therefore the inequalities (8.72) give us

$$m_2 \leq \frac{12}{h^3}\int_{x_k}^{x_k+h} [P(x) - f(x)]\, dx \leq M_2 .$$

Adding these inequalities for $k = 0, 1, 2, \ldots, n - 1$ and dividing by n, we obtain

$$m_2 \leq \frac{12}{nh^3}\int_a^b [P(x) - f(x)]\, dx \leq M_2 .$$

Since the function f'' is continuous on $[a, b]$, it assumes every value between its minimum m_2 and its maximum M_2 somewhere in $[a, b]$. In particular, we have

$$f''(c) = \frac{12}{nh^3}\int_a^b [P(x) - f(x)]\, dx$$

for some c in $[a, b]$. In other words,

$$\int_a^b f(x)\, dx = \int_a^b P(x)\, dx - \frac{nh^3}{12}f''(c) .$$

Using (8.69) and the relation $h = (b - a)/n$ we obtain (8.70).

To derive the trapezoidal rule we used a linear polynomial to interpolate between each adjacent pair of values of f. More accurate formulas can be obtained by interpolating with polynomials of higher degree. In the next section we consider an important special case that is remarkable for its simplicity and accuracy.

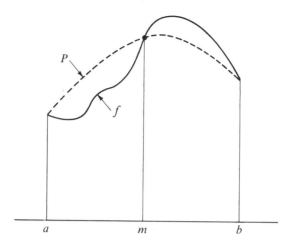

FIGURE 8.3 *Interpolation by a quadratic polynomial P.*

8.21 Simpson's rule

The solid curve in Figure 8.3 is the graph of a function f over an interval $[a, b]$. The mid-point of the interval, $(a + b)/2$, is denoted by m. The dotted curve is the graph of a quadratic polynomial P that agrees with f at the three points a, m, and b. If we use the integral $\int_a^b P(x)\, dx$ as an approximation to $\int_a^b f(x)\, dx$ we are led to an approximate integration formula known as *Simpson's rule.*

Instead of determining P explicitly, we introduce a linear transformation that carries the interval $[a, b]$ onto the interval $[0, 2]$. If we write

$$t = \frac{x - a}{m - a}, \qquad \text{or} \qquad x = a + (m - a)t,$$

we see that t takes the values 0, 1, 2 when x takes the values a, m, b. Now let

$$\phi(t) = P[a + (m - a)t].$$

Then $\phi(t)$ is a quadratic polynomial in t that takes the values $P(a)$, $P(m)$, $P(b)$ at the points $t = 0, 1, 2,$ respectively. Also, we have

$$\int_0^2 \phi(t)\, dt = \int_0^2 P[a + (m - a)t]\, dt = \frac{1}{m - a} \int_a^b P(x)\, dx \;;$$

hence

(8.73) $$\int_a^b P(x)\, dx = (m - a) \int_0^2 \phi(t)\, dt = \frac{b - a}{2} \int_0^2 \phi(t)\, dt \,.$$

Now we use Newton's interpolation formula to construct ϕ. We have

$$\phi(t) = \phi(0) + t \, \Delta\phi(0) + t(t - 1) \frac{\Delta^2\phi(0)}{2!},$$

where $\Delta\phi(t) = \phi(t + 1) - \phi(t)$. Integrating from 0 to 2 we obtain

$$\int_0^2 \phi(t) \, dt = 2 \, \phi(0) + 2 \, \Delta\phi(0) + \frac{1}{3} \Delta^2\phi(0).$$

Since $\Delta\phi(0) = \phi(1) - \phi(0)$ and $\Delta^2\phi(0) = \phi(2) - 2\phi(1) + \phi(0)$, the integral is equal to

$$\int_0^2 \phi(t) \, dt = \frac{1}{3} [\phi(0) + 4 \, \phi(1) + \phi(2)] = \frac{1}{3} [P(a) + 4 \, P(m) + 4 \, P(b)].$$

Using (8.73) and the fact that P agrees with f at a, m, b, we obtain

(8.74) $$\int_a^b P(x) \, dx = \frac{b - a}{6} [f(a) + 4f(m) + f(b)].$$

Therefore, we may write

$$\int_a^b f(x) \, dx = \frac{b - a}{6} [f(a) + 4f(m) + f(b)] + R,$$

where $R = \int_a^b f(x) \, dx - \int_a^b P(x) \, dx$.

If f is a quadratic polynomial, P is identical to f and the error R is zero. It is a remarkable fact that we also have $R = 0$ when f is a *cubic* polynomial. To prove this property we use the error estimate for Lagrange interpolation given by Theorem 8–3, and we write

(8.75) $$f(x) - P(x) = (x - a)(x - m)(x - b)\frac{f'''(c)}{3!},$$

where $c \in (a, b)$. When f is a cubic polynomial the third derivative f''' is constant, say $f'''(x) = C$, and the foregoing formula becomes

$$f(x) - P(x) = \frac{C}{6}(x - a)(x - m)(x - b) = \frac{C}{6}(t + h)t(t - h),$$

where $t = x - m$ and $h = (b - a)/2$. Therefore

$$R = \int_a^b [f(x) - P(x)] \, dx = \frac{C}{6} \int_{-h}^h (t^3 - h^2 t) \, dt = 0,$$

since the last integrand is an odd function. This property is illustrated in Figure 8.4. The dotted curve is the graph of a cubic polynomial f that agrees with P at a, m, b. In this case $R = \int_a^b [f(x) - P(x)] \, dx = A_1 - A_2$, where A_1 and A_2 are the areas of the two shaded regions. Since $R = 0$ the two regions have equal areas.

We have just seen that Equation (8.74) is valid if P is a polynomial of degree ≤ 3 that agrees with f at a, m, and b. By choosing this polynomial carefully we can considerably improve the error estimate in (8.75). We have already imposed three conditions on P, namely, $P(a) = f(a)$, $P(m) = f(m)$, $P(b) = f(b)$. Now we impose a fourth condition, $P'(m) = f'(m)$. This will give P and f the same slope at $(m, f(m))$, and we can hope that this will improve the approximation of f by P throughout $[a, b]$.

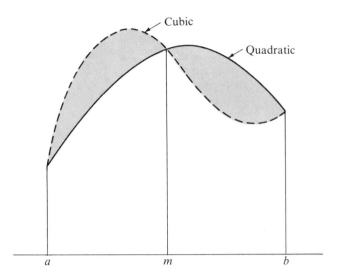

FIGURE 8.4 *The two shaded regions have equal areas for every cubic interpolating polynomial.*

To show that such a P can always be chosen, we let Q be the quadratic polynomial that agrees with f at a, m, b, and we let

$$P(x) = Q(x) + A(x - a)(x - m)(x - b),$$

where A is a constant to be determined. For any choice of A, this cubic polynomial P agrees with Q and hence with f at a, m, b. Now we choose A to make $P'(m) = f'(m)$. Differentiating the formula for $P(x)$ and putting $x = m$ we obtain

$$P'(m) = Q'(m) + A(m - a)(m - b).$$

Therefore if we take $A = [f'(m) - Q'(m)]/[(m - a)(m - b)]$ we also satisfy the condition $P'(m) = f'(m)$.

Next we show that for this choice of P we have

(8.76)
$$f(x) - P(x) = (x - a)(x - m)^2(x - b)\frac{f^{(4)}(z)}{4!}$$

for some z in (a, b), provided that the fourth derivative $f^{(4)}$ exists in $[a, b]$. To prove (8.76) we argue as in the proof of Theorem 8–3. First we note that (8.76) is trivially satisfied for any choice of z if $x = a$, m, or b. Therefore, assume $x \neq a$, $x \neq m$, $x \neq b$, keep x fixed, and introduce a new function F defined on $[a, b]$ by the equation

$$F(t) = A(x)[f(t) - P(t)] - A(t)[f(x) - P(x)],$$

where

$$A(t) = (t - a)(t - m)^2(t - b).$$

Note that $F(t) = 0$ for $t = a, m, b,$ and x. By Rolle's theorem, $F'(t)$ vanishes in each of the three open intervals determined by these four points. In addition, $F'(m) = 0$ because $A'(m) = 0$ and $f'(m) = P'(m)$. Therefore $F'(t) = 0$ for at least four distinct points in (a, b). By Rolle's theorem $F''(t) = 0$ for at least three points, $F'''(t) = 0$ for at least two points, and $F^{(4)}(t) = 0$ for at least one point, say for $t = z$. From the definition of F we find

$$F^{(4)}(t) = A(x) [f^{(4)}(t) - P^{(4)}(t)] - A^{(4)}(t) [f(x) - P(x)]$$
$$= A(x) f^{(4)}(t) - 4! [f(x) - P(x)] .$$

When we substitute $t = z$ in this equation we obtain (8.76).

Now it is a simple matter to prove Simpson's rule in the following form.

8–17   THEOREM. *Simpson's rule.* Assume f has a continuous fourth derivative on $[a, b]$, and let $m = (a + b)/2$. Then we have

(8.77)
$$\int_a^b f(x)\, dx = \frac{b - a}{6} [f(a) + 4f(m) + f(b)] - \frac{(b - a)^5}{2880} f^{(4)}(c)$$

for some c in $[a, b]$.

Proof. Let M_4 and m_4 denote, respectively, the maximum and minimum values of $f^{(4)}$ on $[a, b]$, and let $B(x) = -(x - a)(x - m)^2(x - b)/4!$. Since $B(x) \geq 0$ for each x in $[a, b]$, Equation (8.76) leads to the inequalities

$$m_4 B(x) \leq P(x) - f(x) \leq M_4 B(x) .$$

Integrating, we find

(8.78)
$$m_4 \int_a^b B(x)\, dx \leq \int_a^b [P(x) - f(x)]\, dx \leq M_4 \int_a^b B(x)\, dx .$$

To evaluate the integral $\int_a^b B(x)\, dx$ we let $h = (b - a)/2$ and we have

$$\int_a^b B(x)\, dx = -\frac{1}{4!} \int_a^b (x - a)(x - m)^2(x - b)\, dx = -\frac{1}{4!} \int_{-h}^{h} (t + h) t^2 (t - h)\, dt$$
$$= -\frac{2}{4!} \int_0^h t^2(t^2 - h^2)\, dt = \frac{1}{4!} \frac{4h^5}{15} = \frac{(b - a)^5}{2880} .$$

Therefore the inequalities in (8.78) give us

$$m_4 \leq \frac{2880}{(b - a)^5} \int_a^b [P(x) - f(x)]\, dx \leq M_4 .$$

But since $f^{(4)}$ is continuous on $[a, b]$, it assumes every value between its minimum m_4 and its maximum M_5 somewhere in $[a, b]$. Therefore

$$f^{(4)}(c) = \frac{2880}{(b - a)^5} \int_a^b [P(x) - f(x)]\, dx$$

for some c in $[a, b]$. Since $\int_a^b P(x)\, dx = \frac{1}{6}(b - a)[f(a) + 4f(m) + f(b)]$, this equation gives us (8.77).

Simpson's rule is of special interest because its accuracy is greater than might be expected from a knowledge of the function f at only three points. If the values of f are known at an odd number of equally spaced points, say at $a, a + h, \ldots, a + 2nh$, it is usually simpler to apply Simpson's rule successively to each of the intervals $[a, a + 2h]$, $[a + 2h, a + 4h], \ldots$, rather than to use an interpolating polynomial of degree $\leq 2n$ over the full interval $[a, a + 2nh]$. Applying Simpson's rule in this manner, we obtain the following extension of Theorem 8–17.

8–18   THEOREM. *Extended Simpson's rule.* Assume f has a continuous fourth derivative in $[a, b]$. Let $h = (b - a)/(2n)$ and let $f_k = f(a + kh)$ for $k = 1, 2, \ldots, 2n - 1$. Then we have

$$\int_a^b f(x)\, dx = \frac{b - a}{6n}\left(f(a) + 4\sum_{k=1}^{n} f_{2k-1} + 2\sum_{k=1}^{n-1} f_{2k} + f(b)\right) - \frac{(b - a)^5}{2880n^4} f^{(4)}(\bar{c})$$

for some $\bar{c}$ in $[a, b]$.

The proof of this theorem is requested in Exercise 9 of the next section.

8.22   Exercises

1. (a) Apply the trapezoidal rule with $n = 10$ to estimate the value of the integral

$$\log 2 = \int_1^2 \frac{dx}{x}.$$

Obtain upper and lower bounds for the error. (See Exercise 10(b) to compare the accuracy with that obtained from Simpson's rule.)

     (b) What is the smallest value of n that would ensure six-place accuracy in the calculation of log 2 by this method?

2. (a) Show that there is a positive number c in the interval $[0, 1]$ such that the formula

$$\int_{-1}^{1} f(x)\, dx = f(c) + f(-c)$$

is exact for all polynomials of degree ≤ 3.

     (b) Generalize the result of part (a) for an arbitrary interval. That is, show that constants c_1 and c_2 exist in $[a, b]$ such that the formula

$$\int_a^b f(x)\, dx = \frac{b - a}{2}[f(c_1) + f(c_2)]$$

is exact for all polynomials of degree ≤ 3. Express c_1 and c_2 in terms of a and b.

3. (a) Show that a positive constant c exists such that the formula

$$\int_{-1/2}^{1/2} f(x)\, dx = \tfrac{1}{3}[f(-c) + f(0) + f(c)]$$

is exact for all polynomials of degree ≤ 3.

     (b) Generalize the result of part (a) for an arbitrary interval. That is, show that constants c_1 and c_2 exist in $[a, b]$ such that the formula

$$\int_a^b f(x)\, dx = \frac{b - a}{3}\left[f(c_1) + f\left(\frac{a + b}{2}\right) + f(c_2)\right]$$

is exact for all polynomials of degree ≤ 3. Express c_1 and c_2 in terms of a and b.

4. Show that positive constants a and b exist such that the formula

$$\int_0^\infty e^{-x} f(x) \, dx = \frac{1}{4} [a f(b) + b f(a)]$$

is exact for all polynomials of degree ≤ 3.

5. Show that a positive constant c exists such that the formula

$$\int_{-\infty}^\infty e^{-x^2} f(x) \, dx = \frac{\sqrt{\pi}}{6} [f(-c) + 4f(0) + f(c)]$$

is exact for all polynomials of degree ≤ 5.

6. Let P_n be the interpolation polynomial of degree $\leq n$ that agrees with f at $n + 1$ distinct points $x_0, x_1, \ldots, x_n$.

(a) Show that constants $A_0(n), A_1(n), \ldots, A_n(n)$ exist, depending only on the numbers $x_0, x_1, \ldots, x_n$, a, and b, and not on f, such that

$$\int_a^b P_n(x) \, dx = \sum_{k=0}^n A_k(n) f(x_k) .$$

The numbers $A_k(n)$ are called *weights*. (They are sometimes called Christoffel numbers.)

(b) For a given set of distinct interpolation points and a given interval $[a, b]$, let $W_0(n)$, $W_1(n), \ldots, W_n(n)$ be $n + 1$ constants such that the formula

$$\int_a^b f(x) \, dx = \sum_{k=0}^n W_k(n) f(x_k)$$

is exact for all polynomials of degree $\leq n$. Prove that

$$\sum_{k=0}^n x_k^r W_k(n) = \frac{b^{r+1} - a^{r+1}}{r + 1} \qquad \text{for} \quad r = 0, 1, \ldots, n .$$

This is a system of $n + 1$ linear equations that can be used to determine the weights. It can be shown that this system always has a unique solution. It can also be shown that for a suitable choice of interpolation points it is possible to make all the weights equal. When the weights are all equal the integration formula is called a Chebyshev integration formula. Exercises 2 and 3 give examples of Chebyshev integration formulas. The next exercise shows that for a proper choice of interpolation points the resulting integration formula is exact for all polynomials of degree $\leq 2n + 1$.

7. In this exercise you may use properties of the Legendre polynomials stated in Sections 7.17 and 7.18. Let $x_0, x_1, \ldots, x_n$ be the zeros of the Legendre polynomial $P_{n+1}(x)$. These zeros are distinct and they all lie in the interval $[-1, 1]$. Let $f(x)$ be any polynomial in x of degree $\leq 2n + 1$. Divide $f(x)$ by $P_{n+1}(x)$ and write

$$f(x) = P_{n+1}(x) Q(x) + R(x) ,$$

where the polynomials Q and R have degree $\leq n$.

(a) Show that the polynomial R agrees with f at the zeros of P_{n+1} and that

$$\int_{-1}^1 f(x) \, dx = \int_{-1}^1 R(x) \, dx .$$

(b) Show that $n + 1$ weights $W_0(n), \ldots, W_n(n)$ exist (independent of f) such that

$$\int_{-1}^1 f(x) \, dx = \sum_{k=0}^n W_k(n) f(x_k) .$$

This gives an integration formula with $n + 1$ interpolation points that is exact for all polynomials of degree $\leq 2n + 1$.

(c) Take $n = 2$ and show that the formula in part (b) becomes

$$\int_{-1}^{1} f(x)\,dx = \frac{5}{9}f\left(-\sqrt{\frac{3}{5}}\right) + \frac{8}{9}f(0) + \frac{5}{9}f\left(\sqrt{\frac{3}{5}}\right).$$

This is exact for all polynomials of degree ≤ 5.

(d) Introduce a suitable linear transformation and rewrite the formula in part (c) for an arbitrary interval $[a, b]$.

8. This exercise describes a method of Peano for deriving the error formula in Simpson's rule.

(a) Use integration by parts repeatedly to deduce the relation

$$\int u(t)v'''(t)\,dt = u(t)v''(t) - u'(t)v'(t) + u''(t)v(t) - \int g(t)\,dt,$$

where $g(t) = u'''(t)\,v(t)$.

(b) Assume ϕ has a continuous fourth derivative in the interval $[-1, 1]$. Take

$$v(t) = t(1 - t)^2/6, \qquad u(t) = \phi(t) + \phi(-t),$$

and use part (a) to show that

$$\int_{-1}^{1} \phi(t)\,dt = \frac{1}{3}[\phi(-1) + 4\phi(0) + \phi(1)] - \int_{0}^{1} g(t)\,dt.$$

Then show that $\int_{0}^{1} g(t)\,dt = \phi^{(4)}(c)/90$ for some c in $[-1, 1]$.

(c) Introduce a suitable linear transformation to deduce Theorem 8-17 from the result of part (b).

9. (a) Let $a_1, a_2, \ldots, a_n$ be nonnegative numbers whose sum is 1. Assume ϕ is continuous on an interval $[a, b]$. If $c_1, c_2, \ldots, c_n$ are any n points in $[a, b]$ (not necessarily distinct), prove that there is at least one point c in $[a, b]$ such that

$$\sum_{k=1}^{n} a_k\,\phi(c_k) = \phi(c).$$

[*Hint.* Let M and m denote the maximum and minimum of ϕ on $[a, b]$ and use the inequality $m \leq \phi(c_k) \leq M$.]

(b) Use part (a) and Theorem 8-17 to derive the extended form of Simpson's rule given in Theorem 8-18.

10. Compute $\log 2$ from the formula $\log 2 = \int_{1}^{2} x^{-1}\,dx$ by using the extension of Simpson's rule with (a) $n = 2$; (b) $n = 5$. Give upper and lower bounds for the error in each case.

11. (a) Let $\phi(t)$ be a polynomial in t of degree ≤ 3. Express $\phi(t)$ by Newton's interpolation formula and integrate to deduce the formula

$$\int_{0}^{3} \phi(t)\,dt = \frac{3}{8}[\phi(0) + 3\phi(1) + 3\phi(2) + \phi(3)].$$

(b) Let P be the interpolation polynomial of degree ≤ 3 that agrees with f at the points $a, a + h, a + 2h, a + 3h$, where $h > 0$. Use part (a) to prove that

$$\int_{a}^{a+3h} P(x)\,dx = \frac{3h}{8}[f(a) + 3f(a + h) + 3f(a + 2h) + f(a + 3h)].$$

(c) Assume f has a continuous fourth derivative in $[a, b]$, and let $h = (b - a)/3$. Prove that

$$\int_{a}^{b} f(x)\,dx = \frac{b - a}{8}[f(a) + 3f(a + h) + 3f(a + 2h) + f(b)] - \frac{(b - a)^5}{6480}f^{(4)}(c)$$

for some c in $[a, b]$. This approximate integration formula is called *Cotes' rule*.

(d) Use Cotes' rule to compute $\log 2 = \int_1^2 x^{-1}\, dx$ and give upper and lower bounds for the error.

12. (a) Use the vector equation $\vec{r}(t) = a \sin t\, \vec{i} + b \cos t\, \vec{j}$, where $0 < b < a$, to show that the circumference L of an ellipse is given by the integral

$$L = 4a \int_0^{\pi/2} \sqrt{1 - k^2 \sin^2 t}\, dt\,,$$

where $k = \sqrt{a^2 - b^2}/a$.

(b) Show that Simpson's rule gives the formula

$$L = \frac{\pi}{3}[a + b + \sqrt{8(a^2 + b^2)}] - \frac{a\pi^5}{23040} f^{(4)}(c)$$

for some c in $[0, \pi/2]$, where $f(t) = \sqrt{1 - k^2 \sin^2 t}$.

8.23   The Euler summation formula

The trapezoidal formula, applied to the interval $[0, n]$, where n is a positive integer, becomes

(8.79)
$$\int_0^n f(x)\, dx = \sum_{k=0}^{n-1} f(k) + \frac{1}{2}(f(n) - f(0)) - \frac{f''(c)n}{12}$$

for some c in $[0, n]$. By the mean-value theorem of differential calculus we have $f'(n) - f'(0) = nf''(b)$ for some b in $(0, n)$. Therefore the error term in (8.79) can be written as

$$-\frac{f''(c)n}{12} = -\frac{1}{12}(f'(n) - f'(0)) + \frac{n}{12}(f''(b) - f''(c))\,.$$

When f is a quadratic polynomial, f'' is constant, so $f''(b) = f''(c)$ and the error is exactly $-[f'(n) - f'(0)]/12$. Therefore the formula

(8.80)
$$\int_0^n f(x)\, dx = \sum_{k=0}^{n-1} f(k) + \frac{1}{2}(f(n) - f(0)) - \frac{1}{12}(f'(n) - f'(0))$$

is exact when f is any polynomial of degree ≤ 2. By substituting $f(x) = x^3$ and using the fact that

$$\sum_{k=0}^{n-1} k^3 = \frac{n^4}{4} - \frac{n^3}{2} + \frac{n^2}{4}\,,$$

we see that (8.80) also holds for any polynomial of degree ≤ 3. Euler discovered that if the term $[f'''(n) - f'''(0)]/720$ is added to the right of (8.80) the formula becomes exact for every polynomial of degree ≤ 5. More generally, he found that for every integer p there is a corresponding set of correction terms, depending only on the differences of derivatives of odd order at the end points 0 and n, that make the formula exact for all polynomials of degree $\leq p$. This result is contained in the following theorem.

8–19   THEOREM. *Euler's summation formula for polynomials.* If f is a polynomial of degree $\leq p$ we have

(8.81)
$$\int_0^n f(x)\,dx = \sum_{k=0}^{n-1} f(k) - \sum_{k=1}^{p} \frac{B_k}{k!}\left(f^{(k-1)}(n) - f^{(k-1)}(0)\right),$$

where the numbers $B_1, B_2, B_3, \ldots,$ are rational numbers defined recursively as follows:

(8.82)
$$B_0 = 1, \qquad \sum_{k=0}^{m-1} \binom{m}{k} B_k = 0 \qquad \text{for} \quad m \geq 2.$$

Note. The numbers $B_0, B_1, B_2, \ldots,$ are called *Bernoulli numbers.* They may be easily calculated from the recursion formula (8.82) that defines them. For example, taking $m = 2, 3, 4, 5$, we find

$$2B_1 + B_0 = 0, \qquad B_1 = -\frac{1}{2},$$

$$3B_2 + 3B_1 + B_0 = 0, \qquad B_2 = \frac{1}{6},$$

$$4B_3 + 6B_2 + 4B_1 + B_0 = 0, \qquad B_3 = 0,$$

$$5B_4 + 10B_3 + 10B_2 + 5B_1 + B_0 = 0, \qquad B_4 = -\frac{1}{30}.$$

The next six Bernoulli numbers are

$$B_5 = 0, \quad B_6 = \frac{1}{42}, \quad B_7 = 0, \quad B_8 = -\frac{1}{30}, \quad B_9 = 0, \quad B_{10} = \frac{5}{66}.$$

It can be shown that $B_{2n+1} = 0$ for $n \geq 1$. (See Exercise 2 in the next section.) Therefore the formula in (8.81) contains only derivatives of odd order.

Proof. We use a method of proof that can be modified to give an extension of the theorem applicable to functions more general than polynomials. We begin with Taylor's formula,

$$f(x + h) = f(x) + \sum_{k=1}^{p} \frac{f^{(k)}(x)}{k!} h^k.$$

If we take $h = 1$ and let $\Delta f(x) = f(x + 1) - f(x)$, Taylor's formula becomes

(8.83)
$$\Delta f(x) = \sum_{k=1}^{p} \frac{f^{(k)}(x)}{k!}.$$

This holds for any polynomial of degree p. If we replace p by $p - r$ and replace f by its rth derivative $f^{(r)}$, Equation (8.83) gives us†

(8.84)
$$\Delta f^{(r)}(x) = \sum_{k=1}^{p-r} \frac{f^{(r+k)}(x)}{k!}.$$

† If f is not a polynomial but has a derivative of order $p + 1$, Equation (8.83) holds with an appropriate error term $R_p(f)$ appended on the right. In Equation (8.84) the error term would be $R_{p-r}(f^{(r)})$.

Now we apply Taylor's formula (8.83) once more with p replaced by $p + 1$ and f replaced by g, where

$$g(x) = \int_0^x f(t)\, dt\,.$$

Since $\Delta g(x) = \int_x^{x+1} f(t)\, dt$ and $g^{(k)}(x) = f^{(k-1)}(x)$, Equation (8.83) gives us

$$\int_x^{x+1} f(t)\, dt = \sum_{k=1}^{p+1} \frac{f^{(k-1)}(x)}{k!},$$

or

$$(8.85) \qquad \int_x^{x+1} f(t)\, dt - f(x) = \sum_{m=2}^{p+1} \frac{f^{(m-1)}(x)}{m!}\,.$$

Now let $c_0 = 1$ and let $c_1, c_2, \ldots, c_p$ be p constants to be specified later. Multiply both sides of (8.84) by c_{r+1} and sum for $r = 0, 1, 2, \ldots, p - 1$ to obtain

$$(8.86) \qquad \sum_{r=0}^{p-1} c_{r+1}\, \Delta f^{(r)}(x) = \sum_{r=0}^{p-1} c_{r+1} \sum_{k=1}^{p-r} \frac{f^{(r+k)}(x)}{k!}\,.$$

The sum on the right can be written as

$$\sum_{r=1}^{p} \sum_{k=1}^{p+1-r} \frac{c_r f^{(r-1+k)}(x)}{k!} = \sum_{r=1}^{p} \sum_{m=r+1}^{p+1} \frac{c_r f^{(m-1)}(x)}{(m - r)!}\,,$$

where in the last step we replaced the index of summation k by $m = r + k$. The last sum is extended over all the lattice points in the triangular region shown in Figure 8.5. Therefore if we interchange the order of summation we find

$$\sum_{r=1}^{p} \sum_{m=r+1}^{p+1} \frac{c_r f^{(m-1)}(x)}{(m - r)!} = \sum_{m=2}^{p+1} \sum_{r=1}^{m-1} \frac{c_r f^{(m-1)}(x)}{(m - r)!} = \sum_{m=2}^{p+1} f^{(m-1)}(x) \sum_{r=1}^{m-1} \frac{c_r}{(m - r)!}\,.$$

Equation (8.86) now becomes

$$\sum_{r=0}^{p-1} c_{r+1}\, \Delta f^{(r)}(x) = \sum_{m=2}^{p+1} f^{(m-1)}(x) \sum_{r=1}^{m-1} \frac{c_r}{(m - r)!}\,.$$

If we add this to Equation (8.85) and remember that $c_0 = 1$, we obtain

$$(8.87) \qquad \int_x^{x+1} f(t)\, dt - f(x) + \sum_{r=0}^{p-1} c_{r+1}\, \Delta f^{(r)}(x) = \sum_{m=2}^{p+1} f^{(m-1)}(x) \sum_{r=0}^{m-1} \frac{c_r}{(m - r)!}\,.$$

The sum on the right will vanish identically if we can choose the numbers $c_0, c_1, c_2, \ldots,$ so that

$$(8.88) \qquad \sum_{r=0}^{m-1} \frac{c_r}{(m - r)!} = 0 \qquad \text{for each } \; m \geq 2\,.$$

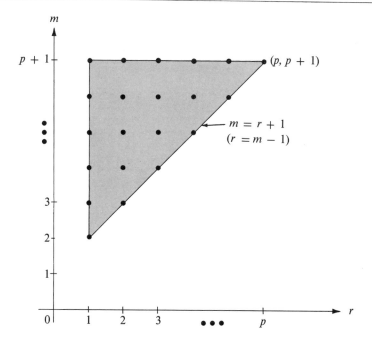

FIGURE 8.5 *A lattice-point diagram illustrating the relation*

$$\sum_{r=1}^{p} \sum_{m=r+1}^{p+1} = \sum_{m=2}^{p+1} \sum_{r=1}^{m-1}.$$

We have already chosen $c_0 = 1$. If we choose $c_r = B_r/r!$, where B_r is the rth Bernoulli number, we have

$$\frac{c_r}{(m-r)!} = \frac{B_r}{r!\,(m-r)!} = \frac{1}{m!}\binom{m}{r}B_r,$$

and Equation (8.88) is equivalent to

$$\sum_{r=0}^{m-1}\binom{m}{r}B_r = 0 \qquad \text{for} \quad m \geq 2.$$

But this is the defining equation for the Bernoulli numbers. Hence the right member of (8.87) vanishes and we obtain

$$(8.89) \qquad \int_{x}^{x+1} f(t)\,dt = f(x) - \sum_{r=0}^{p-1}\frac{B_{r+1}}{(r+1)!}\,\Delta f^{(r)}(x).$$

Taking $x = 0, 1, 2, \ldots, n-1$ and adding, we obtain Equation (8.81).

The foregoing argument can be applied to any function having a continuous derivative of order $p + 1$ in $[0, n]$. In place of (8.83) we use Taylor's formula with remainder,

$$\Delta f(x) = \sum_{k=1}^{p} \frac{f^{(k)}(x)}{k!} + R_p(f) \,,$$

taking the integral form of the remainder (see Exercise 8, Section 7.8, in Volume I),

$$R_p(f) = \frac{1}{p!} \int_x^{x+1} (x + 1 - t)^p f^{(p+1)}(t) \, dt = \frac{1}{p!} \int_0^1 t^p f^{(p+1)}(x + 1 - t) \, dt \,.$$

Corresponding error terms must be added in each of Equations (8.84) and (8.85). The foregoing analysis leads to the following extension of Theorem 8–19.

8–20   THEOREM. *Euler's summation formula with error term.* Assume f has a continuous derivative of order $p + 1$ in $[0, n]$. Then we have

$$\int_0^n f(x) \, dx = \sum_{k=0}^{n-1} f(k) - \sum_{k=1}^{p} \frac{B_k}{k!} (f^{(k-1)}(n) - f^{(k-1)}(0))$$

$$+ \int_0^1 \frac{B_{p+1}(t) - B_{p+1}}{(p + 1)!} \sum_{r=1}^{n} f^{(p+1)}(r - t) \, dt \,,$$

where $B_m(t)$ is the mth Bernoulli polynomial, defined by the equation

$$B_m(t) = \sum_{r=0}^{m} \binom{m}{r} B_r t^{m-r} \,.$$

Proof. The argument given in the proof of Theorem 8–19 leads once more to Equation (8.89), except that on the right we must add a sum of error terms, given by

$$\sum_{r=0}^{p-1} c_{r+1} R_{p-r}(f^{(r)}) + c_0 R_{p+1}(g) = \sum_{r=0}^{p} \frac{c_r}{(p + 1 - r)!} \int_0^1 t^{p+1-r} f^{(p+1)}(x + 1 - t) \, dt$$

$$= \int_0^1 \frac{1}{(p + 1)!} \sum_{r=0}^{p} \binom{p + 1}{r} B_r t^{p+1-r} f^{(p+1)}(x + 1 - t) \, dt \,.$$

Since

$$\sum_{r=0}^{p} \binom{p + 1}{r} B_r \, t^{p+1-r} = B_{p+1}(t) - B_{p+1} \,,$$

Equation (8.89) becomes

$$\int_x^{x+1} f(t) \, dt = f(x) - \sum_{r=0}^{p-1} \frac{B_{r+1}}{(r + 1)!} \Delta f^{(r)}(x) + \int_0^1 \frac{B_{p+1}(t) - B_{p+1}}{(p + 1)!} f^{(p+1)}(x + 1 - t) \, dt \,.$$

Summing for $x = 0, 1, \ldots, n - 1$ we obtain Theorem 8–20.

The error term in Theorem 8–20 is not easy to estimate. If p is *odd* and if $f^{(p+3)}$ is continuous and has the same sign as $f^{(p+1)}$ on $[0, n]$, it can be shown that the error term can be written as

$$- \theta \frac{B_{p+1}}{(p + 1)!} (f^{(p)}(n) - f^{(p)}(0)),$$

where $0 \leq \theta \leq 1$. In other words, under the conditions stated, the absolute value of the error term does not exceed that of the next "correction term" which would normally be added if Theorem 8–20 were used with p replaced by $p + 1$.

Although Euler's formula can be used to approximate integrals by sums, it is more often used to evaluate or estimate sums in terms of integrals. This is why it is usually referred to as a "summation" formula rather than an integration formula. For example, if we take $f(x) = x^4$ in Equation (8.81) we obtain

$$\sum_{k=0}^{n-1} k^4 = \int_0^n x^4 \, dx + B_1 n^4 + \frac{B_2}{2!} 4n^3 + \frac{B_3}{3!} 12n^2 + \frac{B_4}{4!} 24n = \frac{n^5}{5} - \frac{n^4}{2} + \frac{n^3}{3} - \frac{n}{30}.$$

Euler's summation formula can be expressed in an alternate form that is exact for functions with a continuous first derivative. Because of its importance we discuss this case in detail.

8–21   THEOREM.   Assume f has a continuous derivative on $[0, n]$. Then we have

(8.90) $$\sum_{k=0}^n f(k) = \int_0^n f(x) \, dx + \int_0^n \left(x - [x] - \frac{1}{2}\right) f'(x) \, dx + \frac{f(0) + f(n)}{2},$$

where $[x]$ denotes the greatest integer $\leq x$.

Proof. Integration by parts gives us

(8.91) $$\int_0^n (x - \tfrac{1}{2}) f'(x) \, dx = (n - \tfrac{1}{2}) f(n) + \tfrac{1}{2} f(0) - \int_0^n f(x) \, dx.$$

Now we consider the integral $\int_0^n [x] f'(x) dx$ and write it as a sum of integrals in each of which $[x]$ has a fixed value. Thus, we have

$$\int_0^n [x] f'(x) \, dx = \sum_{r=0}^{n-1} \int_r^{r+1} [x] f'(x) \, dx = \sum_{r=0}^{n-1} r \int_r^{r+1} f'(x) \, dx$$

$$= \sum_{r=0}^{n-1} r(f(r + 1) - f(r)) = \sum_{r=0}^{n-1} rf(r + 1) - \sum_{r=0}^{n-1} rf(r)$$

$$= -\sum_{r=0}^{n-1} f(r + 1) + \sum_{r=0}^{n-1} (r + 1)f(r + 1) - \sum_{r=0}^{n-1} rf(r)$$

$$= -\sum_{k=1}^n f(k) + nf(n) = -\sum_{k=0}^n f(k) + f(0) + nf(n).$$

Subtracting this from Equation (8.91) we obtain

$$\int_0^n \left(x - [x] - \frac{1}{2}\right) f'(x) \, dx = \sum_{k=0}^n f(k) - \frac{f(0) + f(n)}{2} - \int_0^n f(x) \, dx,$$

which is equivalent to (8.90).

We now show how Euler's summation formula can be used to derive Stirling's formula for estimating $n!$.

8-22   THEOREM. *Stirling's formula.* If n is a positive integer we have

$$\sqrt{2\pi}\; n^{n+1/2}\, e^{-n} < n! < \sqrt{2\pi}\; n^{n+1/2}\, e^{-n}\left(1 + \frac{1}{4n}\right).$$

Proof. The proof will make use of some simple properties of functions ϕ_1 and ϕ_2, defined as follows:

$$\phi_1(x) = \begin{cases} x - [x] - \frac{1}{2} & \text{if } x \text{ is not an integer,} \\ 0 & \text{if } x \text{ is an integer,} \end{cases} \qquad \phi_2(x) = \int_0^x \phi_1(t)\, dt\, .$$

First we note that $\phi_1(x + 1) = \phi_1(x)$, which means that ϕ_1 is periodic with period 1. Also, if $0 < x < 1$ we have $\phi_1(x) = x - \frac{1}{2}$, so $\int_0^1 \phi_1(t)\, dt = 0$. This implies that ϕ_2 is also periodic with period 1, since

$$\phi_2(x + 1) = \int_0^{x+1} \phi_1(t)\, dt = \int_0^1 \phi_1(t)\, dt + \int_1^{x+1} \phi_1(t)\, dt$$

$$= \int_1^{x+1} \phi_1(t)\, dt = \int_1^{x+1} \phi_1(t - 1)\, dt = \int_0^x \phi_1(u)\, du = \phi_2(x)\, .$$

Now $\phi_2(0) = 0$ so, by periodicity, $\phi_2(n) = 0$ for every integer n. Also, when $0 \leq x \leq 1$ we have $\phi_2(x) = \int_0^x (t - \frac{1}{2})\, dt = x(x - 1)/2$, which shows that $-\frac{1}{8} \leq \phi_2(x) \leq 0$ for all x. The graphs of ϕ_1 and ϕ_2 are shown in Figure 8.6. Note that the strict inequalities $-\frac{1}{8} < \phi_2(x) < 0$ hold except when x is an integer or half an integer.

The error term $\int_0^n (x - [x] - \frac{1}{2})f'(x)\, dx$ in Euler's summation formula can now be written as $\int_0^n \phi_1(x) f'(x)\, dx$. Applying the formula with $f(x) = \log(x + 1)$ and n replaced by $n - 1$ we obtain

$$\sum_{k=0}^{n-1} \log(k + 1) = \int_0^{n-1} \log(x + 1)\, dx + \int_0^{n-1} \frac{\phi_1(x)}{x + 1}\, dx + \frac{1}{2} \log n\, .$$

Since $\int \log t\, dt = t \log t - t$ the foregoing equation becomes

$$\log n! = n \log n - n + 1 + \int_1^n \frac{\phi_1(t - 1)}{t}\, dt + \frac{1}{2} \log n\, ,$$

or

(8.92) $$\log n! = \left(n + \frac{1}{2}\right) \log n - n + 1 + \int_1^n \frac{\phi_1(t)}{t}\, dt\, .$$

Integrating by parts we obtain

$$\int_1^n \frac{\phi_1(t)}{t}\, dt = \int_1^n \frac{\phi_2'(t)}{t}\, dt = \frac{\phi_2(t)}{t}\bigg|_1^n + \int_1^n \frac{\phi_2(t)}{t^2}\, dt = \int_1^n \frac{\phi_2(t)}{t^2}\, dt\, ,$$

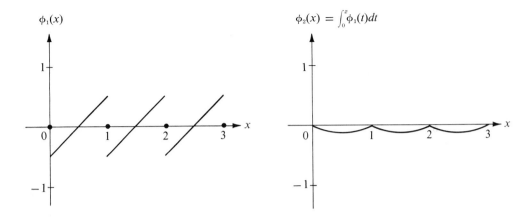

FIGURE 8.6 *Graphs of the periodic functions ϕ_1 and ϕ_2.*

since $\phi_2(n) = \phi_2(1) = 0$. Since $|\phi_2(t)| \leq \frac{1}{8}$ the improper integral $\int_1^\infty t^{-2}\phi_2(t)\,dt$ converges absolutely and we may write

$$\int_1^n \frac{\phi_2(t)}{t^2}\,dt = \int_1^\infty \frac{\phi_2(t)}{t^2}\,dt - \int_n^\infty \frac{\phi_2(t)}{t^2}\,dt\,.$$

Therefore Equation (8.92) becomes

(8.93)
$$\log n! = \left(n + \frac{1}{2}\right)\log n - n + C - \int_n^\infty \frac{\phi_2(t)}{t^2}\,dt\,,$$

where $C = 1 + \int_1^\infty t^{-2}\phi_2(t)\,dt$. Since we have $-\frac{1}{8} < \phi_2(t) < 0$ except when t is an integer or half an integer, we obtain

$$0 < -\int_n^\infty \frac{\phi_2(t)}{t^2}\,dt < \frac{1}{8n}\,,$$

and Equation (8.93) gives us the inequalities

$$\exp((n + \tfrac{1}{2})\log n - n + C) < n! < \exp\left((n + \tfrac{1}{2})\log n - n + C + \frac{1}{8n}\right),$$

where $\exp(t) = e^t$. Using the relation $e^x < 1 + 2x$, with $x = 1/(8n)$, we may rewrite these inequalities as

(8.94)
$$A\, n^{n+1/2}e^{-n} < n! < A\, n^{n+1/2}e^{-n}\left(1 + \frac{1}{4n}\right).$$

where $A = e^C$. To complete the proof we need to show that $A = \sqrt{2\pi}$.

We shall deduce this from the inequality

(8.95)
$$\pi n < \left(\frac{2^{2n}(n!)^2}{(2n)!}\right)^2 < \frac{\pi(2n+1)}{2},$$

discovered by John Wallis (1616–1703). First we show how Wallis' inequality implies $A = \sqrt{2\pi}$; then we discuss the proof of (8.95).

If we let

$$A_n = \frac{n!}{n^{n+1/2}\,e^{-n}}$$

the inequality in (8.94) becomes

$$A < A_n < A\left(1 + \frac{1}{4n}\right).$$

This shows that $A_n \to A$ as $n \to \infty$. In (8.95) we write $n! = n^{n+1/2}e^{-n}A_n$ to obtain

$$\pi n < \left(\frac{2^{2n}\,n^{2n+1}\,e^{-2n}\,A_n^2}{(2n)^{2n+1/2}\,e^{-2n}\,A_{2n}}\right)^2 < \frac{\pi(2n+1)}{2},$$

which is equivalent to

$$\pi < \frac{A_n^4}{2A_{2n}^2} < \pi\,\frac{2n+1}{2n}.$$

Letting $n \to \infty$ in this last inequality we obtain

$$\pi \leq \frac{A^4}{2A^2} \leq \pi.$$

This shows that $A^2 = 2\pi$. Since $A > 0$ we have $A = \sqrt{2\pi}$, as asserted.

It remains to prove Wallis' inequality (8.95). For this purpose we introduce the numbers

$$I_n = \int_0^{\pi/2} \sin^n t\,dt,$$

where n is any nonnegative integer. We note that $I_0 = \pi/2$ and $I_1 = 1$. For $0 \leq t \leq \pi/2$ we have $0 \leq \sin t \leq 1$; hence $0 \leq \sin^{n+1} t \leq \sin^n t$. This shows that the sequence $\{I_n\}$ is monotonic decreasing. Therefore we may write

(8.96)
$$\frac{1}{I_{2n}\,I_{2n-1}} \leq \frac{1}{I_{2n}^2} \leq \frac{1}{I_{2n}\,I_{2n+1}}.$$

Now we shall evaluate each member of this inequality; this will lead at once to Wallis' inequality.

Integration of the identity

$$\frac{d}{dt}(\cos t\,\sin^{n+1} t) = (n+1)\sin^n t - (n+2)\sin^{n+2} t$$

over the interval $[0, \pi/2]$ gives us

$$0 = (n+1)I_n - (n+2)I_{n+2},$$

or

(8.97)
$$I_{n+2} = \frac{n+1}{n+2} I_n .$$

Using this recursion formula with n replaced by $2k - 2$ we find

$$\frac{I_{2k}}{I_{2k-2}} = \frac{2k-1}{2k} = \frac{2k(2k-1)}{(2k)^2} .$$

Multiplying these equations for $k = 1, 2, \ldots, n$ we find

$$\prod_{k=1}^{n} \frac{I_{2k}}{I_{2k-2}} = \prod_{k=1}^{n} \frac{2k(2k-1)}{(2k)^2} = \frac{(2n)!}{2^{2n} (n!)^2} .$$

The product on the left telescopes to I_{2n}/I_0. Since $I_0 = \pi/2$ we obtain

(8.98)
$$I_{2n} = \frac{(2n)!}{2^{2n} (n!)^2} \cdot \frac{\pi}{2} .$$

In a similar way we apply the recursion formula (8.97) with n replaced by $2k - 1$ and multiply the resulting equations for $k = 1, 2, \ldots, n$ to obtain

$$\prod_{k=1}^{n} \frac{I_{2k+1}}{I_{2k-1}} = \prod_{k=1}^{n} \frac{(2k)^2}{2k(2k+1)} = \frac{2^{2n} (n!)^2}{(2n+1)!} = \frac{1}{2n+1} \cdot \frac{\pi}{2} \cdot \frac{1}{I_{2n}} .$$

The product on the left telescopes to $I_{2n+1}/I_1 = I_{2n+1}$, so we get

(8.99)
$$I_{2n} I_{2n+1} = \frac{\pi}{2(2n+1)} .$$

Since $I_{2n+1} = 2n I_{2n-1}/(2n+1)$, Equation (8.99) implies

$$I_{2n} I_{2n-1} = \frac{\pi}{4n} .$$

We use this in (8.96), together with the two relations (8.98) and (8.99). Then we multiply by $\pi^2/4$ to obtain Wallis' inequality (8.95).

8.24 Exercises

1. In Theorem 8-20 we defined the pth Bernoulli polynomial by the equation

$$B_p(t) = \sum_{r=0}^{p} \binom{p}{r} B_r t^{p-r} ,$$

where B_r is the rth Bernoulli number. The first few Bernoulli polynomials are

$$B_0(t) = 1, \quad B_1(t) = t - \tfrac{1}{2}, \quad B_2(t) = t^2 - t + \tfrac{1}{6}, \quad B_3(t) = t^3 - \tfrac{3}{2}t^2 + \tfrac{1}{2}t .$$

Prove the following properties of Bernoulli polynomials:

   (a) $B_p(1) = B_p(0) = B_p$ if $p \geq 2$.
   (b) $B_p'(t) = p B_{p-1}(t)$ if $p \geq 1$.

(c) $\displaystyle\int_a^b B_p(t)\,dt \;=\; \frac{B_{p+1}(b) - B_{p+1}(a)}{p+1}$ if $p \geq 0$.

(d) $\displaystyle\int_0^1 B_p(t)\,dt \;=\; 0$ if $p \geq 1$.

(e) $B_p^{(k)}(x) \;=\; k!\,\dbinom{p}{k} B_{p-k}(x)$ if $p \geq 1$, $0 \leq k \leq p$.

2. (a) Use Euler's summation formula for polynomials to prove that

$$\sum_{k=0}^{n-1} k^p \;=\; \frac{B_{p+1}(n) - B_{p+1}}{p+1}\qquad \text{for}\ \ p \geq 1\,.$$

(b) Use part (a) to prove that for every integer $n \geq 2$ we have

$$B_p(n+1) - B_p(n) \;=\; p\,n^{p-1}\qquad \text{if}\ \ p \geq 0\,.$$

(c) Use part (b) to show that for every real x we have

$$B_p(x+1) - B_p(x) \;=\; p\,x^{p-1}\qquad \text{if}\ \ p \geq 1\,.$$

[*Hint.* A polynomial with infinitely many zeros is identically zero.]

(d) Let $\Delta f(x) = f(x+1) - f(x)$. Use part (c) to show that

$$\Delta B_{2k}(1 - x) \;=\; \Delta B_{2k}(x)$$

for every real x and every integer $k \geq 1$. Sum both sides for $x = 0, 1, 2, \ldots, n$ and deduce that

$$B_{2k}(1 - n) \;=\; B_{2k}(n)$$

for every integer $n \geq 0$.

(e) From the result of part (d) deduce that $B_{2k}(1 - x) = B_{2k}(x)$ for every real x. Then use this to deduce that

$$B_p(1 - x) \;=\; (-1)^p B_p(x)\qquad \text{if}\ \ p \geq 1\,.$$

(f) Use part (e) to show that $B_{2n+1} = 0$ for $n \geq 1$.

3. Use Taylor's formula to show that

$$B_p(x+h) \;=\; \sum_{r=0}^{p} \binom{p}{r} B_r(x) h^{p-r}\qquad \text{if}\ \ p \geq 0\,.$$

4. Prove Raabe's multiplication theorem:

$$B_p(mx) \;=\; m^{p-1} \sum_{r=0}^{m-1} B_p\!\left(x + \frac{r}{m}\right).$$

5. Evaluate the integral $\int_0^1 x\,B_p(x)\,dx$ in two ways and thereby prove that

$$\sum_{r=0}^{p} \binom{p}{r} \frac{B_r}{p+2-r} \;=\; \frac{B_{p+1}}{p+1}\,.$$

6. If we use the binomial theorem to expand $(B + x)^p$ we obtain

$$(B + x)^p \;=\; \sum_{r=0}^{p} \binom{p}{r} B^r x^{p-r}\,.$$

If we replace each power B^r by the Bernoulli number B_r, the right member becomes $B_p(x)$. This means that the definition of the Bernoulli polynomial $B_p(x)$ can be written symbolically as

$$B_p(x) = (B + x)^p,$$

with the understanding that after expanding the right member we replace each power B^r by B_r. In the same way, the recursion formula that we used to define Bernoulli numbers can be written symbolically as

$$(B + 1)^m - B^m = 0.$$

Express each of the following symbolic formulas as a relation involving Bernoulli polynomials and then prove that the formula is correct.

(a) $f(B + x + 1) - f(B + x) = f'(x)$, where f is a polynomial.
(b) If f is a polynomial and if $F'(x) = f(x)$, then

$$\sum_{k=1}^{n} f(k) = F(B + n + 1) - F(B + 1).$$

7. Euler's constant C is defined by the limit formula

$$C = \lim_{n \to \infty} \left(\sum_{k=1}^{n} \frac{1}{k} - \log n \right).$$

(See Section 9.6 in Volume I.) Use Euler's summation formula to prove that

$$\sum_{k=1}^{n} \frac{1}{k} = \log n + C + \frac{1}{2n} - \frac{E(n)}{n^2},$$

where $0 \le E(n) \le \frac{1}{8}$. Also, show that

$$C = 1 - \int_{1}^{\infty} \frac{t - [t]}{t^2} \, dt.$$

8. (a) If $s > 0$, $s \ne 1$, use Euler's summation formula to prove that

$$\sum_{k=1}^{n} \frac{1}{k^s} = \frac{n^{1-s}}{1-s} + C(s) + s \int_{n}^{\infty} \frac{t - [t]}{t^{s+1}} \, dt,$$

where

$$C(s) = 1 + \frac{1}{s-1} - s \int_{1}^{\infty} \frac{t - [t]}{t^{s+1}} \, dt.$$

(b) If $s > 1$, show that $C(s) = \zeta(s)$, where ζ is the Riemann zeta function defined for $s > 1$ by the series

$$\zeta(s) = \sum_{k=1}^{\infty} \frac{1}{k^s}.$$

The series for $\zeta(s)$ diverges for $s \le 1$. However, since the formula for $C(s)$ in part (a) is meaningful for $0 < s < 1$, it may be used to extend the definition of $\zeta(s)$ to the open interval $0 < s < 1$. Thus, for $s > 0$ and $s \ne 1$ we have the formula

$$\zeta(s) = 1 + \frac{1}{s-1} - s \int_{1}^{\infty} \frac{t - [t]}{t^{s+1}} \, dt.$$

9. Use Euler's summation formula to derive the following relations, where A and B are constants.

(a) $\displaystyle\sum_{k=1}^{n} \frac{\log k}{k} = \frac{(\log n)^2}{2} + A + O\left(\frac{\log n}{n}\right)$ for $n > 1$.

(b) $\displaystyle\sum_{k=2}^{n} \frac{1}{k \log k} = \log (\log n) + B + O\left(\frac{1}{n \log n}\right)$ for $n > 2$.

10. Deduce the following limit relations with the aid of Stirling's formula and/or Wallis' inequality.

(a) $\displaystyle\lim_{n \to \infty} \frac{n}{(n!)^{1/n}} = e.$

(b) $\displaystyle\lim_{n \to \infty} \frac{(n!)^2 2^{2n}}{(2n)! \sqrt{n}} = \sqrt{\pi}.$

(c) $\displaystyle\lim_{n \to \infty} (-1)^n \binom{-\frac{1}{2}}{n} n = \frac{1}{\sqrt{\pi}}.$

SUGGESTED REFERENCES

This small list contains only a few books suggested for further reading on the general principles of numerical analysis. All these books contain further references to works of a more special nature. The list of tables given in Todd's survey (reference 7 below) is especially recommended.

Books

1. A. D. Booth, *Numerical Methods*, Academic Press, New York, 1958.

2. D. R. Hartree, *Numerical Analysis*, Oxford Univ. Press (Clarendon), London and New York, 1958.

3. F. B. Hildebrand, *Introduction to Numerical Analysis*, McGraw-Hill, New York, 1956.

4. A. S. Householder, *Principles of Numerical Analysis*, McGraw-Hill, New York, 1953.

5. W. E. Milne, *Numerical Calculus*, Princeton Univ. Press, Princeton, N. J. 1950.

6. J. B. Scarborough, *Numerical Mathematical Analysis*, Johns Hopkins Press, Baltimore, Maryland, 1958.

7. J. Todd (ed.), *Survey of Numerical Analysis*, McGraw-Hill, New York, 1962.

Tables

8. L. J. Comrie (ed.), *Chambers' Six-figure Mathematical Tables*, W. & R. Chambers, London and Edinburgh, 1949.

9. L. J. Comrie, "Interpolation and Allied Tables," 2nd rev. reprint from *Nautical Almanac* for 1937, H. M. Stationery Office, London, 1948.

10. A. J. Fletcher, J. C. P. Miller, and L. Rosenhead, *Index of Mathematical Tables*, McGraw-Hill, New York, 1946.

11. *Tables of Lagrangian Interpolation Coefficients*, Natl. Bur. Standards Columbia Press Series, Vol. 4., Columbia Univ. Press, New York, 1944.

9

EXISTENCE THEOREMS FOR DIFFERENTIAL EQUATIONS

9.1 Introduction

Although the study of differential equations began in the 17th century, it was not until the 19th century that mathematicians realized that relatively few differential equations could be solved by elementary means. The work of Cauchy, Liouville, and others showed the importance of establishing general theorems to guarantee the existence of solutions to certain specific classes of differential equations. Chapter 7 illustrated the use of both existence and uniqueness theorems in the study of linear differential equations. This chapter is concerned with the proofs of these theorems and related theorems.

To begin with, we consider first-order equations of the type

$$(9.1) \qquad\qquad y' = f(x, y).$$

When the right-hand member, $f(x, y)$, has certain special forms the differential equation can be solved by elementary means. For example, if

$$f(x, y) = -P(x)y + Q(x),$$

where P and Q are continuous on some interval I, the differential equation in (9.1) is a first-order *linear* equation; its general solution is

$$y = e^{-\int P(x)dx} \left[\int Q(x)\, e^{\int P(x)dx}\, dx + C \right],$$

where C is an arbitrary constant. The differential equation can also be solved easily when $f(x, y)$ has the form $A(x)/B(y)$, where A and B are continuous functions. In this case the variables are separable and a solution can be found by elementary means. (See Section 4.6 in Volume I.) In Section 9.6 we shall prove that if the right-hand member $f(x, y)$ satisfies certain general conditions a solution of Equation (9.1) always exists, even though it may not be possible to express the solution in terms of the familiar functions of elementary calculus.

Existence theory for differential equations of higher order can be reduced to the first-order case by the introduction of *systems* of equations. For example, suppose we have a second-order equation of the form

$$(9.2) \qquad\qquad y'' = f(x, y, y').$$

If we let $y_1 = y$ and $y_2 = y'$, this equation becomes $y_2' = f(x, y_1, y_2)$. The *pair* of equations

(9.3) $$y_1' = y_2, \qquad y_2' = f(x, y_1, y_2),$$

is an example of a system of two first-order equations for two unknown functions y_1 and y_2. Every function y_1 that satisfies (9.2) gives rise to a pair of functions y_1, y_2 satisfying (9.3); conversely, if a pair of functions y_1, y_2 satisfies (9.3), the function y_1 is a solution of (9.2). In the same way, a third-order differential equation of the form

$$y''' = f(x, y, y', y'')$$

is equivalent to a system of three first-order equations for three unknown functions y_1, y_2, y_3, namely,

$$y_1' = y_2, \qquad y_2' = y_3, \qquad y_3' = f(x, y_1, y_2, y_3).$$

More generally, any nth order equation of the form

$$y^{(n)} = f(x, y, y', y'', \ldots, y^{(n-1)})$$

is equivalent to a system of n first-order equations given by

$$y_1' = y_2, \qquad y_2' = y_3, \qquad \ldots, y_{n-1}' = y_n, \qquad y_n' = f(x, y_1, y_2, \ldots, y_n).$$

Consider next a more general system of n first-order differential equations, say

(9.4) $$y_1' = f_1(x, y_1, \ldots, y_n), \qquad y_2' = f_2(x, y_1, \ldots, y_n), \ldots,$$

$$y_n' = f_n(x, y_1, \ldots, y_n).$$

A solution of such a system on an interval I is any n-tuple of functions $y_1, y_2, \ldots, y_n$ that satisfy all the equations in (9.4) simultaneously on I. The study of such a system can be simplified considerably with the use of vector notation. We introduce a vector-valued function $\vec{y}$ defined on I by the equation

$$\vec{y}(x) = (y_1(x), y_2(x), \ldots, y_n(x));$$

then we write $f_i(x, \vec{y})$ for $f_i(x, y_1, y_2, \ldots, y_n)$. The system in (9.4) can now be written as

(9.5) $$\vec{y}' = \vec{f}(x, \vec{y}),$$

where

$$\vec{y}' = (y_1', y_2', \ldots, y_n') \qquad \text{and} \qquad \vec{f} = (f_1, f_2, \ldots, f_n).$$

Equation (9.5) is called a first-order vector differential equation. We note that it has exactly the same form as Equation (9.1), except that it involves vector-valued functions. The existence and uniqueness theorems that we shall prove for Equation (9.1) have direct extensions for the first-order equation in (9.5). These extended theorems, in turn, give us existence and uniqueness theorems for systems and hence for nth-order equations of the form $y^{(n)} = f(x, y, y', \ldots, y^{(n-1)})$. These include, in particular, the existence and uniqueness theorems for nth-order linear equations which we used in Chapter 7. Since the entire theory rests on a discussion of the first-order equation in (9.1) we turn now to this case.

★9.2   Uniqueness theorem for the differential equation $y' = f(x, y)$

In 1820 Cauchy proved the first existence and uniqueness theorems for the differential equation

$$(9.6) \qquad\qquad y' = f(x, y) .$$

His original proof was unnecessarily complicated and required severe restrictions on the right-hand member $f(x, y)$. For example, it required f to have partial derivatives of every order with respect to x and y. Rudolf Lipschitz (1832–1903), Guiseppe Peano (1858–1932), and others made significant improvements in Cauchy's work. For example, Peano showed in 1890 that if f is merely continuous on a closed rectangle R, then for each point (x_0, y_0) interior to R there is at least one integral curve of (9.6) passing through (x_0, y_0). That is, there is at least one function $y = Y(x)$ with $Y(x_0) = y_0$ that satisfies (9.6) on some interval $(x_0 - c, x_0 + c)$. Moreover, he gave examples of equations having more than one integral curve passing through a given point. The equation

$$(9.7) \qquad\qquad y' = 3y^{2/3}$$

has this property. Two distinct solutions passing through the origin are $Y_1(x) = 0$ and $Y_2(x) = x^3$. Since the right-hand member of (9.7) is continuous everywhere in the xy-plane, this example shows that some condition other than the continuity of f is needed to ensure the uniqueness of the solution through a given point. In 1898 W. F. Osgood (1864–1943) proved that if f is continuous in a neighborhood of (x_0, y_0) there may be a whole family of integral curves of (9.6) passing through (x_0, y_0), with all these curves lying within a region bounded by the graphs of two extremal solutions Y_1 and Y_2; hence there is a unique solution through (x_0, y_0) if and only if these extremal solutions are identical. Osgood also proved that there is a unique solution through each interior point (x_0, y_0) of a rectangle R if f satisfies a condition of the form

$$(9.8) \qquad\qquad |f(x, y) - f(x, z)| \leq \phi(|y - z|)$$

for every pair of points (x, y) and (x, z) in R with the same x-coordinate. Here ϕ is a function that is positive and continuous on the half-open interval $(0, a]$, where a denotes the altitude of the rectangle R. Also, as $t \to 0+$, $\phi(t)$ must approach 0 in such a way that the improper integral $\int_{0+}^{a} \phi(t)^{-1}\, dt$ diverges. That is, ϕ must satisfy the relation

$$\lim_{h \to 0+} \int_{h}^{a} \frac{1}{\phi(t)}\, dt = \infty .$$

For example, this condition is satisfied when $\phi(t) = t$ but not when $\phi(t) = t^{1/2}$. Further examples of permissible functions ϕ are $\phi(t) = Kt$ for $t > 0$, $\phi(t) = Kt|\log t|$ for $0 < t < 1$, $\phi(t) = Kt|\log|\log t||$ for $0 < t < 1/e$, and so on, where K is a positive constant. When $\phi(t) = Kt$, Osgood's condition (9.8) becomes

$$(9.9) \qquad\qquad |f(x, y) - f(x, z)| \leq K|y - z| .$$

This is called a *Lipschitz condition* in honor of Rudolf Lipschitz, who first introduced it in 1876. The constant K is called a Lipschitz constant. A Lipschitz condition does not restrict a function very seriously. For example, if f has a bounded partial derivative $D_2 f$ on R, say $|D_2 f(x, y)| \leq M$ for all (x, y) in R, it is easy to show that (9.9) is automatically satisfied with the constant M as Lipschitz constant. In fact, from the mean-value theorem for derivatives we have

$$f(x, y) - f(x, z) = D_2 f(x, c)(y - z),$$

where c lies between y and z. From this we find that

$$|f(x, y) - f(x, z)| \le M |y - z|,$$

which is a Lipschitz condition. A Lipschitz condition can be satisfied by a discontinuous function. For example, let $f(x, y) = y \sin(1/x)$ if $x \ne 0$, and let $f(0, y) = 0$. This function is discontinuous at each point of the y-axis (except at the origin), yet it satisfies a Lipschitz condition on every rectangle R, with Lipschitz constant $K = 1$.

In this section we show how a Lipschitz condition implies a uniqueness theorem for Equation (9.6). The modifications needed to prove Osgood's more general uniqueness theorem are outlined in Exercise 10 of the next section. In Section 9.6 we assume both a Lipschitz condition and continuity of f to deduce an existence theorem.

9–1   THEOREM.   *Uniqueness theorem.* Assume f satisfies a Lipschitz condition

$$|f(x, y) - f(x, z)| \le K |y - z|$$

on a rectangle R. Let (x_0, y_0) be any point interior to R. Then there is at most one function $y = Y(x)$ with $Y(x_0) = y_0$ that satisfies the differential equation

$$y' = f(x, y)$$

on an interval $I = (x_0 - c, x_0 + c)$, with the graph of Y over I lying in R.

Proof. Choose a point (x_0, y_0) interior to R, and let Y_1 and Y_2 be two functions that satisfy the differential equation $y' = f(x, y)$ on some interval $I = (x_0 - c, x_0 + c)$. Assume that the graphs of Y_1 and Y_2 over I lie in the rectangle R and that $Y_1(x_0) = Y_2(x_0) = y_0$. We shall assume that Y_1 and Y_2 do not agree everywhere on I and show that this leads to a contradiction.

If Y_1 and Y_2 do not agree everywhere on I there is at least one point x_1 in I at which $Y_1(x_1) \ne Y_2(x_1)$. Let us label the functions Y_1 and Y_2 so that $Y_2(x_1) < Y_1(x_1)$. Also, suppose that $x_0 < x_1$. (The argument is entirely analogous if $x_1 < x_0$.) If $x \, \varepsilon \, I$ let $g(x) = Y_1(x) - Y_2(x)$. At the point x_1 we have $g(x_1) > 0$. Now both Y_1 and Y_2 are solutions of the differential equation $y' = f(x, y)$, so we have

$$g'(x) = Y_1'(x) - Y_2'(x) = f[x, Y_1(x)] - f[x, Y_2(x)]$$

for each x in I. Since the points $(x, Y_1(x))$ and $(x, Y_2(x))$ are in R we may apply the Lipschitz condition to obtain the inequality

$$g'(x) \le K |Y_1(x) - Y_2(x)| = K |g(x)|$$

for each x in I. From this we see that

(9.10) $g'(x) < (K + 1) |g(x)|$ whenever $g(x) \ne 0$.

In particular, we have

(9.11) $g'(x_1) < (K + 1) g(x_1)$.

Now let h be the function defined on I by the equation

(9.12) $$h(x) = g(x_1)e^{(K+1)(x-x_1)} .$$

We note that $h(x) > 0$ for each x in I because $g(x_1) > 0$. Since $h(x_1) = g(x_1)$ and $h'(x) = (K+1)h(x)$, we see that

(9.13) $$h'(x_1) = (K+1)h(x_1) = (K+1)g(x_1) > g'(x_1) ,$$

because of (9.11). Now let

$$k(x) = h(x) - g(x)$$

for each x in I. The inequality in (9.13) tells us that $k'(x_1) > 0$. Therefore, by Theorem 8–3 of Volume I, there is a $\delta > 0$ such that

$$k(x) < k(x_1) \qquad \text{if} \quad x_1 - \delta < x < x_1 .$$

Since $k(x_1) = h(x_1) - g(x_1) = 0$, this inequality tells us that

(9.14) $$k(x) < 0 \qquad \text{if} \quad x_1 - \delta < x < x_1 .$$

Now $k(x_0) = h(x_0) - g(x_0) = h(x_0) > 0$, so any δ for which (9.14) holds cannot exceed $x_1 - x_0$. Therefore the set of δ for which (9.14) holds is a nonempty set bounded above by $x_1 - x_0$. Let α be the least upper bound of all such δ, and let $x_2 = x_1 - \alpha$. Then x_2 satisfies $x_0 \leq x_2 \leq x_1$, and we have $k(x) < 0$ in the open interval (x_2, x_1). Since k is continuous on I we must have $k(x_2) \leq 0$. We cannot have $k(x_2) < 0$; otherwise there would be an open interval about x_2 in which $k(x) < 0$, contradicting the definition of α. Therefore $k(x_2) = 0$. Since $k(x) < k(x_2)$ if $x_2 < x < x_1$, we must have $k'(x_2) \leq 0$. In other words, $h'(x_2) \leq g'(x_2)$, or

$$(K+1)h(x_2) \leq g'(x_2) .$$

But since $h(x_2) = g(x_2)$ this gives us

$$(K+1)g(x_2) \leq g'(x_2) ,$$

which contradicts (9.10), since $g(x_2) \neq 0$. This contradiction completes the proof.

★9.3 Exercises

1. A function f is said to satisfy a Lipschitz condition on a plane set S if (9.9) holds for every pair of points (x, y) and (x, z) in S. The constant K is called a Lipschitz constant for S. Show that each of the following functions satisfies a Lipschitz condition on the given set. In each case determine a Lipschitz constant for the set.

    (a) $f(x, y) = xy^2$; $S = \{(x, y) \mid -1 \leq x \leq 1, \quad -1 \leq y \leq 1\}$.

    (b) $f(x, y) = y^{2/3}$; $S = \{(x, y) \mid -1 \leq x \leq 1, \quad 1 \leq y \leq 2\}$.

    (c) $f(x, y) = e^{\sin(x+y)}$; $S = $ the xy-plane.

    (d) $f(x, y) = x^2 \arctan y + e^x$; $S = \{(x, y) \mid |x| \leq 2, \quad y \text{ arbitrary}\}$.

    (e) $f(x, y) = \begin{cases} y(1 - 2x) & \text{if } x \geq 0, \\ y(2x - 1) & \text{if } x < 0; \end{cases}$ $S = \{(x, y) \mid |x| \leq 1, \ y \text{ arbitrary}\}$.

    (f) $f(x, y) = P(x)y^2 + Q(x)y + R(x)$, where P, Q, and R are continuous on an interval $[a, b]$; $S = \{(x, y) \mid a \leq x \leq b, \ c \leq y \leq d\}$.

2. Consider the differential equation $y' = xy^2$. Find a solution $y = Y(x)$ defined for all real x and satisfying the initial condition stated. In each case prove that there is only one solution satisfying this initial condition.

(a) $Y(0) = 0$.   (d) $Y(0) = 1$.
(b) $Y(1) = 0$.   (e) $Y(1) = 1$.
(c) $Y(9) = 0$.   (f) $Y(2) = -1$.

3. Consider the differential equation $y' = f(x, y)$, where f is the function defined in Exercise 1(e). Find a function $y = Y(x)$ which satisfies the differential equation for all $x \neq 0$ and which also satisfies the initial condition $Y(1) = 1$. Show that this solution is unique.

4. Show that none of the following functions satisfies a Lipschitz condition on the given set.

(a) $f(x, y) = xy^2$; $S = \{(x, y) \mid -1 \le x \le 1, \; y \text{ arbitrary}\}$.
(b) $f(x, y) = y^{2/3}$; $S = \{(x, y) \mid -1 \le x \le 1, \; -1 \le y \le 1\}$.

(c) $f(x, y) = \begin{cases} \dfrac{4xy}{x^2 + y^2} & \text{if } (x, y) \neq (0, 0), \\ 0 & \text{if } (x, y) = (0, 0); \end{cases}$ $S = \{(x, y) \mid |x| \le 1, \; |y| \le 1\}$.

[*Hint.* Consider the difference $f(x, y) - f(x, z)$ when $y = ax$, $z = bx$.]

5. Let f be the function defined in Exercise 4(c). Find an infinite set of integral curves of the differential equation $y' = f(x, y)$ passing through the origin.

6. (a) Assume that f satisfies the condition

$$|f(x, y) - f(x, z)| \le K |y - z|^\alpha$$

on a rectangle R, where K and α are constants, $K > 0$, $\alpha > 1$. Prove that $f(x, y)$ is independent of y. That is, $f(x, y) = f(x, z)$ for each pair of points (x, y) and (x, z) in R.

(b) Show that the same conclusion holds if f satisfies a condition of the form

$$|f(x, y) - f(x, z)| \le \phi(|y - z|),$$

where $\phi(0) = \phi'(0) = 0$.

7. Let ϕ be a positive function defined and continuous on $[0, a]$ for some $a > 0$. Assume that $\phi(0) = 0$ and that $\phi'(0)$ exists. Prove that the improper integral $\int_{0+}^{a} \phi(t)^{-1} \, dt$ diverges. [*Hint.* The existence of $\phi'(0)$ implies that $\phi(t)/t$ approaches a finite limit as $t \to 0$. Compare the integral with $\int_{0+}^{a} t^{-1} \, dt$.]

8. Consider the differential equation

$$\text{(9.15)} \qquad \qquad \frac{dy}{dx} = F(y),$$

where F is continuous and nonzero in an open interval (c, d). Prove that for every point (x_0, y_0) with $c < y_0 < d$ there is one and only one integral curve of (9.15) given by an equation of the form $x = X(y)$ with $X(y_0) = x_0$. Also, if $c < y_1 < d$, show that the integral curve through (x_1, y_1) may be obtained from that through (x_0, y_0) by a horizontal translation. Illustrate with $F(y) = e^{-y}$, $(c, d) = (-1, 1)$.

9. (a) Let F be continuous everywhere in (c, d), and assume that F is nonzero everywhere in (c, d) except at one point p. Choose a point y_0 in (c, d), $y_0 \neq p$, and assume that

$$\lim_{y \to p} \int_{y_0}^{y} \frac{dt}{F(t)} = \infty \; .$$

Prove that there is one and only one integral curve of the differential equation

$$\frac{dy}{dx} = F(y)$$

passing through each point (x_0, y_0) with $c < y_0 < d$. When $y_0 = p$ the integral curve is the line $y = p$. Show that all other integral curves have this line as an asymptote. Illustrate with $F(y) = y$, $(c, d) = (-1, 1)$.

(b) Assume F is positive and continuous on (c, d), choose y_0 in (c, d), and assume the improper integral $\int_{c+}^{y_0} F(t)^{-1}\, dt$ diverges. Show that the differential equation (9.16) has a unique integral curve through each point (x_0, y_0) and that the line $y = c$ is an asymptote of this curve.

10. This exercise describes the modifications needed to extend the proof of Theorem 9-1 so that it applies to functions satisfying Osgood's condition,

$$|f(x, y) - f(x, z)| \leq \phi(|y - z|),$$

for every pair of points (x, y) and (x, z) in a rectangle R. Here ϕ is a function that is positive and continuous on the half-open interval $(0, a]$ and satisfies the limit relation

(9.17) $$\lim_{h \to 0+} \int_h^a \frac{dt}{\phi(t)} = \infty,$$

where a denotes the altitude of the rectangle R.

(a) Let Y_1 and Y_2 be two solutions of $y' = f(x, y)$ whose graphs lie in R and intersect at the point (x_0, y_0) interior to R. If Y_1 and Y_2 do not agree everywhere on an open interval $I = (x_0 - c, x_0 + c)$, show that a point x_1 in I can be chosen for which $0 < |Y_1(x_1) - Y_2(x_1)| < a$. Label the functions so that $Y_1(x_1) > Y_2(x_1)$.

(b) Define g as in the proof of Theorem 9-1 and show that

$$g'(x) < 2\phi(|g(x)|) \qquad \text{if} \quad g(x) \neq 0.$$

(c) Instead of the definition given in Equation (9.12), define h to be that solution of the differential equation

$$\frac{dy}{dx} = 2\phi(y)$$

that takes the value $g(x_1)$ when $x = x_1$. Such a solution exists because of Exercise 9(b). [The condition (9.17) is used at this stage.] The graph of h has the line $y = 0$ as an asymptote. Therefore $h(x) > 0$ for all x since $h(x_1) = g(x_1) > 0$. Show that $h'(x_1) > g'(x_1)$. Then verify that the rest of the proof of Theorem 9-1 can be carried out with only trivial modifications.

9.4 The method of successive approximations

Consider the differential equation $y' = f(x, y)$, where the function f is continuous and bounded† on a closed rectangle R with center at (x_0, y_0) and edges parallel to the coordinate axes. We wish to find a function $y = Y(x)$ that satisfies the initial-value problem

(9.18) $$y' = f(x, y), \qquad Y(x_0) = y_0$$

on some interval I containing x_0, with the graph of Y over I lying in R.

There are several methods available for demonstrating the existence of such a function Y. We shall use the so-called *method of successive approximations* which also has applications in many other problems. This method was first published by Liouville in 1838 in connection with the study of linear differential equations of second order. It was later extended by J. Caqué in 1864, L. Fuchs in 1870, and G. Peano in 1888 to the study of linear equations of order n. In 1890 Émile Picard (1856–1941) developed the method in

---

† It can be shown that continuity of f on R implies boundedness. See Theorem 4–20 of the author's *Mathematical Analysis*, Addison-Wesley Publishing Co., Reading, Massachusetts, 1957.

its most general form. In recognition of his fundamental contributions, some writers refer to the method as *Picard's method*. The method is not only of theoretical interest but can also be used to obtain numerical approximations to solutions in some cases.

The method of successive approximations begins with an initial guess at a solution of the initial-value problem (9.18). We choose any continuous function Y_0 whose graph over some interval about x_0 lies in the rectangle R. For example, we can always choose $Y_0(x) = y_0$, although this is not essential. We then substitute this guess in the right-hand member of the differential equation in (9.18), and we obtain a new differential equation,

$$y' = f[x, Y_0(x)],$$

whose right-hand member is now a continuous function of x. This equation has a unique solution Y_1 passing through the point (x_0, y_0); it is given by the equation

$$Y_1(x) = y_0 + \int_{x_0}^{x} f[t, Y_0(t)]\, dt.$$

We shall prove later (in Theorem 9–2) that the graph of Y_1 over some interval containing x_0 lies entirely in R. Now we repeat the process, using Y_1 in place of Y_0. That is, we replace y by Y_1 in the right-hand member of the differential equation in (9.18) to obtain a new differential equation

$$y' = f[x, Y_1(x)].$$

This equation has a unique solution Y_2 passing through (x_0, y_0), namely,

$$Y_2(x) = y_0 + \int_{x_0}^{x} f[t, Y_1(t)]\, dt.$$

Now we substitute Y_2 in the right-hand member of (9.18) and solve the resulting equation to determine Y_3, and so on. This process generates a sequence of continuous functions $Y_0, Y_1, Y_2, \ldots, Y_n, \ldots$, where Y_{n+1} is determined from Y_n by the recursion formula

$$(9.19) \qquad Y_{n+1}(x) = y_0 + \int_{x_0}^{x} f[t, Y_n(t)]\, dt \qquad \text{for} \quad n = 0, 1, 2, \ldots.$$

For this formula to be meaningful the graph of Y_n over some interval containing x_0 must lie in R. We shall prove later in this section that such an interval always exists. In Section 9.6 we shall prove that if f satisfies a Lipschitz condition on R the sequence of functions defined by (9.19) will converge to a continuous limit function Y given by

$$Y(x) = \lim_{n \to \infty} Y_n(x),$$

and that this limit function Y is a solution of the initial-value problem (9.18). The functions $Y_0, Y_1, Y_2, \ldots$ defined by (9.19) are called *successive approximations* to Y. Before we investigate the convergence of the process we discuss some examples.

Example 1. Consider the initial-value problem $y' = 2xy$ with $y = 1$ when $x = 0$. This equation is easily solved as a separable equation or as a linear equation; it has the solution

$$y = e^{x^2}.$$

We shall show how this solution can be obtained by the method of successive approximations.

For the initial guess Y_0 we take $Y_0(x) = 1$. The recursion formula (9.19) now gives us

$$Y_1(x) = 1 + \int_0^x 2t Y_0(t)\, dt = 1 + \int_0^x 2t\, dt = 1 + x^2\,,$$

$$Y_2(x) = 1 + \int_0^x 2t Y_1(t)\, dt = 1 + 2 \int_0^x (t + t^3)\, dt = 1 + x^2 + \frac{x^4}{2}\,,$$

$$Y_3(x) = 1 + \int_0^x 2t Y_2(t)\, dt = 1 + 2 \int_0^x \left(t + t^3 + \frac{t^5}{2}\right) dt = 1 + x^2 + \frac{x^4}{2!} + \frac{x^6}{3!}\,.$$

Using induction we may easily show that

$$Y_n(x) = \sum_{k=0}^{n} \frac{x^{2k}}{k!}\,.$$

The polynomial $Y_n(x)$ is a partial sum of the power-series expansion for e^{x^2}. Since this series converges for all real x we have

$$\lim_{n \to \infty} Y_n(x) = \sum_{k=0}^{\infty} \frac{x^{2k}}{k!} = e^{x^2}$$

for all x. Thus, in this example we are able to show directly that the successive approximations converge to a solution of the initial-value problem.

The foregoing example is simpler than most. The next example gives a more realistic idea of the labor encountered in computing the successive approximations.

Example 2. Consider the initial-value problem $y' = x^2 + y^2$ with $y = 0$ when $x = 0$. This is a nonlinear equation that does not fall under the scope of the special methods discussed in Chapter 7. We shall compute a few approximations to the solution. We choose $Y_0(x) = 0$ and determine the next three approximations as follows:

$$Y_1(x) = \int_0^x t^2\, dt = \frac{x^3}{3}\,,$$

$$Y_2(x) = \int_0^x [t^2 + Y_1^2(t)]\, dt = \int_0^x \left(t^2 + \frac{t^6}{9}\right) dt = \frac{x^3}{3} + \frac{x^7}{63}\,,$$

$$Y_3(x) = \int_0^x \left[t^2 + \left(\frac{t^3}{3} + \frac{t^7}{63}\right)^2\right] dt = \frac{x^3}{3} + \frac{x^7}{63} + \frac{2x^{11}}{2079} + \frac{x^{15}}{59535}\,.$$

It is now apparent that a great deal of labor will be needed to compute further approximations. For example, the next two approximations Y_4 and Y_5 will be polynomials of degrees 31 and 63, respectively.

The next example exhibits a further difficulty that can arise in the computation of the successive approximations.

Example 3. Consider the initial-value problem $y' = 2x + e^y$, with $y = 0$ when $x = 0$. We begin with the initial guess $Y_0(x) = 0$ and we find

$$Y_1(x) = \int_0^x (2t + 1) \, dt = x^2 + x,$$

$$Y_2(x) = \int_0^x (2t + e^{t^2+t}) \, dt = x^2 + \int_0^x e^{t^2+t} \, dt \,.$$

Here further progress is impeded by the fact that the last integral cannot be evaluated in terms of elementary functions. However, for a given x it is possible to calculate a numerical approximation to the integral by one of the methods described in Chapter 8 and thereby obtain an approximation to $Y_2(x)$.

Because of the difficulties displayed in the last two examples, the method of successive approximations is sometimes not very useful for the explicit determination of solutions in practice. The real value of the method is its use in establishing existence theorems.

We have already pointed out that the graph of the nth approximating function Y_n over some interval I about x_0 should lie in the rectangle R in order for the recursion formula (9.19) to be meaningful. The next theorem exhibits such an interval.

9–2   THEOREM.   Let R be the rectangle with center at (x_0, y_0) given by

$$R = \{(x, y) \mid |x - x_0| \le a, |y - y_0| \le b\} \,.$$

Let f be continuous on R and assume that

$$|f(x, y)| \le M$$

for all (x, y) in R, where $M > 0$. Let $I = (x_0 - c, x_0 + c)$, where $c = \min \{a, b/M\}$. If the graph of Y_n over I lies in R, and if Y_{n+1} is defined on I by the recursion formula

(9.20)
$$Y_{n+1}(x) = y_0 + \int_{x_0}^x f[t, Y_n(t)] \, dt \,,$$

then the graph of Y_{n+1} over I also lies in R. Moreover, we have

(9.21)
$$|Y_{n+1}(x) - y_0| \le M \, |x - x_0|$$

for every x in I.

Proof. The set $B = \{(x, y) \mid |x - x_0| \le c, |y - y_0| \le M \, |x - x_0|\}$ is a "butterfly-shaped" region bounded by the two parallel lines $x = x_0 \pm c$ and the two lines $y = y_0 \pm M(x - x_0)$, which intersect at (x_0, y_0). Examples are shown in Figure 9.1. In Figure 9.1(a) we have $M < b/a$, so $a < b/M$ and $c = a$. In Figure 9.1(b) we have $M > b/a$, so $c = b/M$. If $M = b/a$ the lines of slope $\pm M$ through (x_0, y_0) coincide with the diagonals of R. If we prove (9.21) it follows that the point $(x, Y_{n+1}(x))$ lies in B (and hence in R) for each x in I.

The proof of (9.21) is immediate. From Equation (9.20) we obtain

$$|Y_{n+1}(x) - y_0| = \left| \int_{x_0}^x f[t, Y_n(t)] \, dt \right| \le \left| \int_{x_0}^x |f[t, Y_n(t)]| \, dt \right| \,.$$

Since $|f(x, y)| \le M$ for all (x, y) in R and since $(t, Y_n(t))$ is in R, the last integral is bounded by $M \, |x - x_0|$. This proves (9.21).

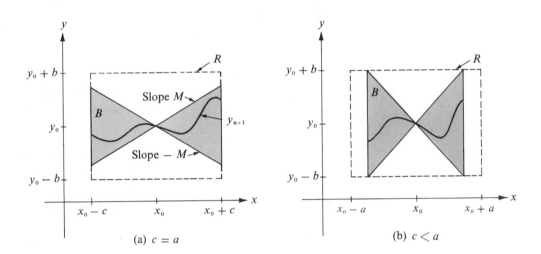

(a) $c = a$

(b) $c < a$

FIGURE 9.1 *The region* $B = \{(x, y) \mid |x - x_0| \leq c, |y - y_0| \leq M \, |x - x_0|\}$.

Note. Let I be the interval of Theorem 9-2. If the initial guess Y_0 is such that its graph over I lies in R we may use induction, along with Theorem 9-2, to deduce that the graphs of *all* approximating functions Y_n over I also lie in R.

9.5 Exercises

1. Consider the initial-value problem

$$y' + y = 2e^x, \qquad \text{with} \quad y = 1 \text{ when } x = 0.$$

(a) Find the exact solution Y of this problem.

(b) Apply the method of successive approximations, starting with the initial guess $Y_0(x) = 1$. Determine $Y_n(x)$ explicitly and show that

$$\lim_{n \to \infty} Y_n(x) = Y(x)$$

for all real x.

2. Apply the method of successive approximations to the initial-value problem

$$y' = x + y^2, \qquad \text{with} \quad y = 0 \text{ when } x = 0.$$

Take $Y_0(x) = 0$ as the initial guess and compute $Y_3(x)$.

3. Apply the method of successive approximations to the initial-value problem

$$y' = 1 + xy^2, \qquad \text{with} \quad y = 0 \text{ when } x = 0.$$

Take $Y_0(x) = 0$ as the initial guess and compute $Y_3(x)$.

4. Apply the method of successive approximations to the initial-value problem

$$y' = x^2 + y^2, \qquad \text{with} \quad y = 0 \text{ when } x = 0.$$

Start with the "bad" initial guess $Y_0(x) = 1$, compute $Y_3(x)$, and compare with the results of Example 2 in Section 9.4.

5. Consider the initial-value problem

$$y' = x^2 + y^2, \qquad \text{with} \quad y = 1 \text{ when } x = 0.$$

(a) Apply the method of successive approximations, starting with the initial guess $Y_0(x) = 1$, and compute $Y_2(x)$.

(b) Let $R = [-1, 1] \times [-1, 1]$. Find the smallest M such that $|f(x, y)| \leq M$ on R. Find an interval $I = (-c, c)$ such that the graph of every approximating function Y_n over I will lie in R.

(c) Assume the solution $y = Y(x)$ has a power-series expansion in a neighborhood of the origin. Determine the first six nonzero terms of this expansion and compare with the result of part (a).

6. Consider the initial-value problem

$$y' = 1 + y^2, \qquad \text{with} \quad y = 0 \text{ when } x = 0.$$

(a) Apply the method of successive approximations, starting with the initial guess $Y_0(x) = 0$, and compute $Y_4(x)$.

(b) Prove that every approximating function Y_n is defined on the entire real axis.

(c) Use Theorem 9-1 to show that the initial-value problem has at most one solution in any interval of the form $(-h, h)$.

(d) Solve the differential equation by separation of variables and thereby show that there is exactly one solution Y of the initial-value problem on the interval $(-\pi/2, \pi/2)$ and no solution on any larger interval. In this example, the successive approximations are defined on the entire real axis, but they converge to a limit function only on the interval $(-\pi/2, \pi/2)$.

7. We seek two functions $y = Y(x)$ and $z = Z(x)$ that simultaneously satisfy the system of equations

$$y' = z, \quad z' = x^3(y + z)$$

with initial conditions $y = 1$ and $z = 1/2$ when $x = 0$. Start with the initial guesses $Y_0(x) = 1$, $Z_0(x) = 1/2$, and use an appropriate modification of the method of successive approximations to obtain the approximating functions

$$Y_3(x) = 1 + \frac{x}{2} + \frac{3x^5}{40} + \frac{x^6}{60} + \frac{x^9}{192},$$

$$Z_3(x) = \frac{1}{2} + \frac{3x^4}{8} + \frac{x^5}{10} + \frac{3x^8}{64} + \frac{7x^9}{360} + \frac{x^{12}}{256}.$$

8. Consider the system of equations

$$y' = 2x + z, \quad z' = 3xy + x^2z,$$

with initial conditions $y = 2$ and $z = 0$ when $x = 0$. Start with the initial guesses $Y_0(x) = 2$, $Z_0(x) = 0$, use an appropriate modification of the method of successive approximations, and determine $Y_3(x)$ and $Z_3(x)$.

9. Consider the initial-value problem

$$y'' = x^2y' + x^4y, \qquad \text{with} \quad y = 5 \text{ and } y' = 1 \text{ when } x = 0.$$

Change this problem to an equivalent problem involving a system of two equations for two unknown functions $y = Y(x)$ and $z = Z(x)$, where $z = y'$. Then use an appropriate modification of the method of successive approximations, starting with initial guesses $Y_0(x) = 5$ and $Z_0(x) = 1$, and determine $Y_3(x)$ and $Z_3(x)$.

10. Let f be defined on the rectangle $R = [-1, 1] \times [-1, 1]$ as follows:

$$f(x, y) = \begin{cases} 0 & \text{if } x = 0, \\ 2y/x & \text{if } x \neq 0 \text{ and } |y| \leq x^2, \\ 2x & \text{if } x \neq 0 \text{ and } y > x^2, \\ -2x & \text{if } x \neq 0 \text{ and } y < -x^2. \end{cases}$$

(a) Prove that f is continuous on R.

(b) Prove that $|f(x, y)| \le 2$ for all (x, y) in R.

(c) Show that f does not satisfy a Lipschitz condition on R.

(d) For each constant C satisfying $|C| \le 1$, show that $y = Cx^2$ is a solution of the initial-value problem $y' = f(x, y)$, with $y = 0$ when $x = 0$. Show also that the graph of each of these solutions over $(-1, 1)$ lies in R.

(e) Apply the method of successive approximations to this initial-value problem, starting with initial guess $Y_0(x) = 0$. Determine $Y_n(x)$ and show that the approximations converge to a solution of the problem on the interval $(-1, 1)$.

(f) Repeat part (e), starting with initial guess $Y_0(x) = x$. Determine $Y_n(x)$ and show that the approximating functions converge to a solution different from any of those in part (d).

(g) Repeat part (e), starting with the initial guess $Y_0(x) = x^3$.

(h) Repeat part (e), starting with the initial guess $Y_0(x) = x^{1/3}$.

9.6 Existence theorem for the differential equation $y' = f(x, y)$

In this section we shall establish an existence theorem for the initial-value problem

$$(9.22) \qquad y' = f(x, y), \qquad \text{with} \quad y = y_0 \text{ when } x = x_0.$$

The most satisfactory theorem of this type was first proved by Peano, who showed that if f is continuous on a closed rectangle R containing (x_0, y_0) there is at least one solution to (9.22). We shall not discuss Peano's proof here because it requires methods from advanced analysis. Instead, we shall impose a Lipschitz condition on f and give a simple proof of the following weaker version of Peano's theorem.

9–3   THEOREM. *Existence theorem.* Assume that f is continuous on the rectangle

$$R = [x_0 - a, x_0 + a] \times [y_0 - b, y_0 + b]$$

with center at (x_0, y_0). Assume also that $|f(x, y)| \le M$ on R, where $M > 0$, and let $I = (x_0 - c, x_0 + c)$, where $c = \min \{a, b/M\}$. If $x \in I$, let $Y_0(x) = y_0$ and define

$$(9.23) \qquad Y_{n+1}(x) = y_0 + \int_{x_0}^{x} f[t, Y_n(t)] \, dt \qquad \text{for} \quad n = 0, 1, 2, \dots \, .$$

Finally, assume f satisfies a Lipschitz condition on R, say

$$|f(x, y) - f(x, z)| \le K |y - z|$$

for each pair of points (x, y), (x, z) in R. Then:

(i) The sequence $\{Y_n(x)\}$ converges for each x in I.

(ii) If we let

$$(9.24) \qquad Y(x) = \lim_{n \to \infty} Y_n(x)$$

for each x in I, the function Y so defined is a solution of the initial-value problem (9.22) on the interval I.

Proof. To prove (i) we shall show that the series

$$(9.25) \qquad Y_0(x) + \sum_{m=0}^{\infty} [Y_{m+1}(x) - Y_m(x)]$$

converges for each x in I. This is equivalent to (i) because the partial sums of this series are given by

$$Y_0(x) + \sum_{m=0}^{n-1} [Y_{m+1}(x) - Y_m(x)] = Y_n(x).$$

To prove that the series in (9.25) converges we compare it with the convergent series

$$M \sum_{m=0}^{\infty} \frac{K^m c^{m+1}}{(m+1)!} = \frac{M}{K} \sum_{m=0}^{\infty} \frac{(Kc)^{m+1}}{(m+1)!} = \frac{M}{K} (e^{Kc} - 1).$$

The comparison is provided by the inequality

(9.26) $$|Y_{m+1}(x) - Y_m(x)| \le \frac{MK^m |x - x_0|^{m+1}}{(m+1)!} \le \frac{MK^m c^{m+1}}{(m+1)!},$$

which is valid for each $m \ge 1$ and each x in I. We shall prove (9.26) by induction. For $m = 1$ we use (9.23) to obtain

$$Y_2(x) - Y_1(x) = \int_{x_0}^{x} \{f[t, Y_1(t)] - f[t, y_0]\} \, dt.$$

Using the Lipschitz condition we obtain

(9.27) $$|Y_2(x) - Y_1(x)| \le \left| \int_{x_0}^{x} |f[t, Y_1(t)] - f[t, y_0]| \, dt \right| \le K \left| \int_{x_0}^{x} |Y_1(t) - y_0| \, dt \right|.$$

Now by (9.21) in Theorem 9–2 we have

$$|Y_1(t) - y_0| \le M |t - x_0|.$$

Therefore, if $x \ge x_0$ we have $|t - x_0| = t - x_0$ for each t in $[x_0, x]$, and the inequality in (9.27) becomes

$$|Y_2(x) - Y_1(x)| \le MK \int_{x_0}^{x} (t - x_0) \, dt = MK \frac{(x - x_0)^2}{2}.$$

If $x \le x_0$, we have $|t - x_0| = x_0 - t$ for each t in $[x, x_0]$, and the inequality in (9.27) becomes

$$|Y_2(x) - Y_1(x)| \le MK \int_{x}^{x_0} (x_0 - t) \, dt = MK \int_{x_0}^{x} (t - x_0) \, dt = MK \frac{(x - x_0)^2}{2}.$$

Therefore for every x in I we have

$$|Y_2(x) - Y_1(x)| \le MK \frac{|x - x_0|^2}{2!} \le \frac{MKc^2}{2!},$$

which proves (9.26) for $m = 1$.

Now we assume that (9.26) holds for $m = n - 1$. To prove that it holds for $m = n$ we use (9.23) again to write

$$|Y_{n+1}(x) - Y_n(x)| = \left| \int_{x_0}^{x} |f[t, Y_n(t)] - f[t, Y_{n-1}(t)]| \, dt \right| \le K \left| \int_{x_0}^{x} |Y_n(t) - Y_{n-1}(t)| \, dt \right|$$

$$\leq K \left| \int_{x_0}^{x} MK^{n-1} \frac{|t - x_0|^n}{n!} dt \right| = \frac{MK^n}{n!} \left| \int_{x_0}^{x} |t - x_0|^n dt \right|$$

$$= \frac{MK^n |x - x_0|^{n+1}}{(n+1)!} \leq \frac{MK^n c^{n+1}}{(n+1)!} \, .$$

This proves (9.26) for all $m \geq 1$. Therefore statement (i) is proved.

Now we define Y by Equation (9.24). Since $Y_n(x_0) = y_0$ for each n we also have $Y(x_0) = y_0$. We prove next that Y is continuous on I and that the graph of Y over I lies in R. Then we shall prove that Y satisfies the "integral equation"

(9.28) $$Y(x) = y_0 + \int_{x_0}^{x} f[t, Y(t)] \, dt \, .$$

The continuity of Y implies continuity of the integrand in (9.28). This, in turn, enables us to differentiate the integral by the first fundamental theorem of calculus to obtain

$$Y'(x) = f[x, Y(x)] \, ,$$

which shows that Y is a solution of the differential equation in (9.22).

To prove that Y is continuous on I, we use the relation (9.23) to obtain

$$Y_{n+1}(x) - Y_{n+1}(x_1) = \int_{x_1}^{x} f[t, Y_n(t)] \, dt$$

for every choice of x and x_1 in I. This implies that

$$|Y_{n+1}(x) - Y_{n+1}(x_1)| \leq M |x - x_1| \, .$$

Letting $n \to \infty$ we obtain the inequality

(9.29) $$|Y(x) - Y(x_1)| \leq M |x - x_1| \, .$$

Letting $x \to x_1$ in this inequality we find

$$\lim_{x \to x_1} Y(x) = Y(x_1) \, .$$

Since this is true for every point x_1 in I, it follows that Y is continuous on I. When $x_1 = x_0$, inequality (9.29) gives us

$$|Y(x) - y_0| \leq M |x - x_0| \, .$$

If x is in I we have $M|x - x_0| < Mc \leq b$, so $|Y(x) - y_0| \leq b$, which shows that the point $(x, Y(x))$ is in R for each x in I.

It remains to prove that Y satisfies the integral equation in (9.28). From Equation (9.24) and the definition of Y_{n+1} we have

$$Y(x) = \lim_{n \to \infty} Y_{n+1}(x) = y_0 + \lim_{n \to \infty} \int_{x_0}^{x} f[t, Y_n(t)] \, dt \, .$$

The proof will be complete if we show that

(9.30) $$\lim_{n \to \infty} \int_{x_0}^{x} f[t, Y_n(t)] \, dt = \int_{x_0}^{x} f[t, Y(t)] \, dt \, .$$

For this purpose we examine the difference

$$d_n = \int_{x_0}^x f[t, Y(t)] \, dt - \int_{x_0}^x f[t, Y_n(t)] \, dt = \int_{x_0}^x \{f[t, Y(t)] - f[t, Y_n(t)]\} \, dt .$$

We wish to prove that $d_n \to 0$ as $n \to \infty$. Using the Lipschitz condition we see that

(9.31) $$|d_n| \le K \left| \int_{x_0}^x |Y(t) - Y_n(t)| \, dt \right| .$$

Since we have

$$Y_n(t) = Y_0(t) + \sum_{m=0}^{n-1} [Y_{m+1}(t) - Y_m(t)]$$

and

$$Y(t) = \lim_{n \to \infty} Y_n(t) = Y_0(t) + \sum_{m=0}^{\infty} [Y_{m+1}(t) - Y_m(t)]$$

we may write

$$|Y(t) - Y_n(t)| \le \sum_{m=n}^{\infty} |Y_{m+1}(t) - Y_m(t)| \le M \sum_{m=n}^{\infty} \frac{K^m c^{m+1}}{(m+1)!} ,$$

where we have used (9.26). This inequality may be written as

$$|Y(t) - Y_n(t)| \le MA_n ,$$

where

$$A_n = \sum_{m=n}^{\infty} \frac{K^m c^{m+1}}{(m+1)!} .$$

Inequality (9.31) now becomes

(9.32) $$|d_n| \le \left| \int_{x_0}^x KMA_n \, dt \right| = KMA_n |x - x_0| = M|x - x_0| \sum_{m=n}^{\infty} \frac{(Kc)^{m+1}}{(m+1)!} .$$

Since the series

$$\sum_{m=0}^{\infty} \frac{(Kc)^{m+1}}{(m+1)!}$$

converges, the right-hand member of (9.32) approaches 0 as $n \to \infty$. Therefore $d_n \to 0$ as $n \to \infty$, which proves (9.30). The proof of Theorem 9–3 is now complete in all details.

Note. In the foregoing proof we established the existence of an integral curve passing through the *center* (x_0, y_0) of the rectangle R. There is no difficulty in extending this theorem to find an integral curve passing through any interior point (x_1, y_1) of R. In fact, every such point (x_1, y_1) is the center of some rectangle R_1 lying in R. If f satisfies the hypotheses of Theorem 9–3 in R, then f also satisfies these hypotheses on R_1, so there exists an integral curve in R_1 passing through (x_1, y_1). The solution will be defined on some interval of the form $(x_1 - c_1, x_1 + c_1)$.

9.7 An extension of the existence theorem

If, in Theorem 9–3, we have $M > b/a$, then $c < a$ and the interval $(x_0 - c, x_0 + c)$ in which a solution exists will be a proper subinterval of $(x_0 - a, x_0 + a)$. It is natural to ask whether further restrictions on f will ensure the existence of a solution over the full interval $(x_0 - a, x_0 + a)$. The next theorem provides an answer to this question.

9– 4   THEOREM.   Let f be defined and continuous on a rectangular strip R' of the form

$$R' = \{(x, y) \mid x_0 - a_1 \leq x \leq x_0 + a_2, y \text{ arbitrary}\},$$

where $a_1 > 0$ and $a_2 > 0$. Assume that f satisfies a Lipschitz condition on R', say

$$|f(x, y) - f(x, z)| \leq K |y - z|$$

for all points (x, y) and (x, z) in R'. Assume also that f is bounded on every rectangle R_b of the form

$$R_b = \{(x, y) \mid x_0 - a_1 \leq x \leq x_0 + a_2, |y - y_0| \leq b\};$$

that is, assume that for every $b > 0$ there is a constant $M_b > 0$ such that

(9.33)
$$|f(x, y)| \leq M_b$$

for all (x, y) in R_b. Then there is a function $y = Y(x)$ defined on the interval $J = (x_0 - a_1, x_0 + a_2)$ such that $Y(x_0) = y_0$ and $Y'(x) = f[x, Y(x)]$ for every x in J.

Proof. As in the proof of Theorem 9–3 we obtain a solution by the method of successive approximations. Certain modifications of the proof are needed to show that the approximations converge on the full interval $(x_0 - a_1, x_0 + a_2)$.

For each x in J we define the sequence $\{Y_n(x)\}$ by the recursion formula

(9.34)
$$Y_0(x) = y_0, \quad Y_{m+1}(x) = y_0 + \int_{x_0}^{x} f[t, Y_m(t)] \, dt,$$

for $m = 0, 1, 2, \ldots$. By induction we see that each function Y_m is continuous on J.

Let M_0 denote the maximum value of $|f(x, y_0)|$ for x in J, and let $a = \max \{a_1, a_2\}$. We show next that the inequality

(9.35)
$$|Y_{m+1}(x) - Y_m(x)| \leq \frac{M_0 K^m |x - x_0|^{m+1}}{(m + 1)!} \leq \frac{M_0 K^m a^{m+1}}{(m + 1)!}$$

is valid for each x in J and each $m \geq 0$. Inequality (9.35) is easily proved by induction. For $m = 0$ we have

$$|Y_1(x) - Y_0(x)| = \left| \int_{x_0}^{x} f(t, y_0) \, dt \right| \leq M_0 |x - x_0| \leq M_0 a.$$

The inductive step from m to $m + 1$ may now be carried out exactly as in the proof of (9.26). Once we have (9.35) the convergence of the sequence $\{Y_n(x)\}$ for each x in J follows exactly as in the proof of Theorem 9–3.

Next we wish to show that the limit function Y defined on J by the equation

$$Y(x) = \lim_{n \to \infty} Y_n(x)$$

is continuous on J and satisfies the integral equation

(9.36) $$Y(x) = y_0 + \int_{x_0}^{x} f[t, Y(t)] \, dt \, .$$

First we prove that there is a constant $B > 0$ such that

(9.37) $$|Y_m(x) - y_0| \le B$$

for each x in J and each $m \ge 1$. This inequality shows that the graph of each approximating function Y_m over J lies in the rectangle R_B given by

$$R_B = \{(x, y) \mid |x - x_0| \le a, |y - y_0| \le B\} \, .$$

To prove (9.37) we begin with the telescoping formula

$$Y_m(x) - y_0 = \sum_{r=0}^{m-1} [Y_{r+1}(x) - Y_r(x)]$$

and use (9.35) in each term on the right to obtain

$$|Y_m(x) - y_0| \le \sum_{r=0}^{m-1} \frac{M_0 K^r a^{r+1}}{(r+1)!} \le \frac{M_0}{K} \sum_{r=0}^{\infty} \frac{(Ka)^{r+1}}{(r+1)!} = \frac{M_0}{K} (e^{Ka} - 1) \, .$$

This shows that (9.37) holds with

(9.38) $$B = \frac{M_0}{K} (e^{Ka} - 1) \, .$$

Letting $m \to \infty$ in (9.37) we find that $|Y(x) - y_0| \le B$, so the graph of Y over J also lies in R_B.

The function f satisfies a Lipschitz condition on the rectangle R_B and is bounded on R_B. In fact, by (9.33) we have

(9.39) $$|f(x, y)| \le M_B$$

for all (x, y) in R_B. We now complete the proof by the same type of argument as that used in the proof of Theorem 9–3. First we note that (9.34) and (9.39) give us the inequality

$$|Y_{m+1}(x) - Y_{m+1}(x_1)| = \left| \int_{x_1}^{x} f[t, Y_m(t)] \, dt \right| \le M_B |x - x_1|$$

for any two points x and x_1 in J. Letting $m \to \infty$ we obtain

$$|Y(x) - Y(x_1)| \le M_B |x - x_1| \, .$$

Letting $x \to x_1$ we find that Y is continuous at each point x_1 in J. Now we let $m \to \infty$ in the recursion formula (9.34) to obtain

$$Y(x) = y_0 + \lim_{m \to \infty} \int_{x_0}^{x} f[t, Y_m(t)] \, dt \, .$$

By exactly the same argument as that used in the proof of Theorem 9–3 we deduce that

$$\lim_{m \to \infty} \int_{x_0}^{x} f[t, Y_m(t)] \, dt = \int_{x_0}^{x} f[t, Y(t)] \, dt$$

for each x in J. This shows that Y satisfies the integral equation in (9.36) everywhere on J. From this we see that $Y(x_0) = y_0$ and that $Y'(x) = f[x, Y(x)]$ for each x in J.

9.8   Another proof of the uniqueness theorem

The method of successive approximations can also be used to give a short proof of the uniqueness theorem (Theorem 9–1) if we assume that f is continuous on R. Consider the initial-value problem

$$(9.40) \qquad y' = f(x, y), \qquad \text{with} \quad y = y_0 \text{ when } x = x_0.$$

Let Y be the solution constructed in Theorem 9–3 and let Z be any solution whose graph over the interval I lies in the rectangle R. (The notation is that of Theorem 9–3.) Then Z also satisfies the integral equation

$$(9.41) \qquad Z(x) = y_0 + \int_{x_0}^{x} f[t, Z(t)] \, dt$$

for every x in I. Using Equations (9.41) and (9.23) we may write

$$|Z(x) - Y_{m+1}(x)| \leq \left| \int_{x_0}^{x} |f[t, Z(t)] - f[t, Y_m(t)]| \, dt \right|.$$

Since both points $(t, Z(t))$ and $(t, Y_m(t))$ lie in R, we may apply the Lipschitz condition to write

$$(9.42) \qquad |Z(x) - Y_{m+1}(x)| \leq K \left| \int_{x_0}^{x} |Z(t) - Y_m(t)| \, dt \right|.$$

When $m = 0$ this inequality becomes

$$|Z(x) - Y_1(x)| \leq K \left| \int_{x_0}^{x} |Z(t) - y_0| \, dt \right| \leq bK |x - x_0|.$$

Using this in (9.42) with $m = 1$ we obtain

$$|Z(x) - Y_2(x)| \leq K \left| \int_{x_0}^{x} |Z(t) - Y_1(t)| \, dt \right| \leq bK^2 \left| \int_{x_0}^{x} |t - x_0| \, dt \right| = bK^2 \frac{|x - x_0|^2}{2}.$$

By induction we find

$$(9.43) \qquad |Z(x) - Y_m(x)| \leq \frac{bK^m |x - x_0|^m}{m!} \leq \frac{bK^m c^m}{m!}$$

for each x in I and every $m \geq 1$. When $m \to \infty$ the right-hand member of (9.43) approaches 0 [since $(Kc)^m/m!$ is the general term of the convergent series for e^{Kc}] and we see that

$$\lim_{m \to \infty} Y_m(x) = Z(x)$$

for each x in I. This proves that $Z(x) = Y(x)$ for each x in I.

If f satisfies the hypotheses of Theorem 9–4 we may use the same type of argument to prove the following extension of the uniqueness theorem.

9– 5   THEOREM. *Extension of the uniqueness theorem.* Assume f satisfies the hypotheses of Theorem 9–4. Let Z be any solution of the initial-value problem (9.40) on J and assume that Z is bounded on J. Then $Z(x) = Y(x)$ for each x in J, where Y is the solution given by Theorem 9–4.

Proof. Since Z is bounded on J, its graph over J lies in a rectangle of the form

$$R_A = \{(x, y) \mid x_0 - a_1 \leq x \leq x_0 + a_2, |y - y_0| \leq A\}.$$

Let $C = \max\{A, B\}$, where B is given by (9.38). Then both rectangles R_A and R_B are contained in R_C. Now we may use exactly the same argument given in the foregoing proof of Theorem 9–1, with the rectangle R replaced by R_C, to prove that $Z(x) = Y(x)$ for every x in J.

9.9 Existence and uniqueness theorems for systems of first-order differential equations

In Section 9.1 we showed that a system of first-order equations

$$y_1' = f_1(x, y_1, \ldots, y_n), \qquad y_2' = f_2(x, y_1, \ldots, y_n), \qquad \ldots, y_n' = f_n(x, y_1, \ldots, y_n)$$

can be expressed more briefly as a first-order vector differential equation of the form

$$\vec{y}' = \vec{f}(x, \vec{y}),$$

where $\vec{y}$ is the vector-valued function defined on an interval I by the equation

$$\vec{y}(x) = (y_1(x), y_2(x), \ldots, y_n(x)),$$

and

$$\vec{f}(x, \vec{y}) = (f_1(x, \vec{y}), f_2(x, \vec{y}), \ldots, f_n(x, \vec{y})),$$

where

$$f_i(x, \vec{y}) = f_i(x, y_1, y_2, \ldots, y_n).$$

The derivative $\vec{y}'$ is defined by the equation

$$\vec{y}'(x) = (y_1'(x), y_2'(x), \ldots, y_n'(x)).$$

In this section we shall extend the method of successive approximations and use it to prove an existence theorem and a uniqueness theorem for the initial-value problem

(9.44) $$\vec{y}' = \vec{f}(x, \vec{y}), \qquad \text{with} \quad \vec{y} = \vec{y}_0 \text{ when } x = x_0.$$

In the one-dimensional case ($n = 1$) we assumed that f was continuous and satisfied a Lipschitz condition on a rectangle R of the form

$$R = \{(x, y) \mid |x - x_0| \leq a, |y - y_0| \leq b\}.$$

In the more general case we consider, instead of a rectangle R, a set S in $(n + 1)$-space given by

$$S = \{(x, \vec{y}) \mid |x - x_0| \leq a, \|\vec{y} - \vec{y}_0\| \leq b\},$$

where the symbol $\|\vec{z}\|$ is defined for any vector $\vec{z} = (z_1, z_2, \ldots, z_n)$ in n-space by the equation

(9.45) $$\|\vec{z}\| = \sum_{k=1}^{n} |z_k|.$$

The use of $\|\vec{z}\|$ in place of the more usual Euclidean length, $|\vec{z}| = (z_1^2 + z_2^2 + \cdots + z_n^2)^{1/2}$, helps to simplify much of the discussion. The reader may easily verify that $\|\vec{z}\|$ has the fundamental "norm" properties:

(a) $\|\vec{z}\| \geq 0$ for every vector $\vec{z}$,
(b) $\|\alpha\vec{z}\| = |\alpha| \, \|\vec{z}\|$ for every vector $\vec{z}$ and every scalar α,
(c) $\|\vec{y} + \vec{z}\| \leq \|\vec{y}\| + \|\vec{z}\|$ for every pair of vectors $\vec{y}$ and $\vec{z}$,
(d) $\|\vec{z}\| = 0$ implies $\vec{z} = \vec{0}$.

These properties enable us to extend all the inequalities relating absolute values that were used in the proofs in Sections 9.6 and 9.8. An existence and uniqueness theorem for (9.44) may now be stated as follows:

9–6   THEOREM. *Existence and uniqueness of solutions to first-order vector differential equations.* Assume that each of the n components of $\vec{f}$ is continuous on the set

$$S = \{(x, \vec{y}) \mid |x - x_0| \leq a, \, \|\vec{y} - \vec{y}_0\| \leq b\},$$

where $a > 0, b > 0$. Assume $\vec{f}$ is bounded on S; that is, assume there is a positive constant M such that

(9.46) $\|\vec{f}(x, \vec{y})\| \leq M$

for all $(x, \vec{y})$ in S. Also, assume $\vec{f}$ satisfies a Lipschitz condition on S, say

$$\|\vec{f}(x, \vec{y}) - \vec{f}(x, \vec{z})\| \leq K \, \|\vec{y} - \vec{z}\|$$

for every pair of points $(x, \vec{y})$ and $(x, \vec{z})$ in S. Let $I = (x_0 - c, x_0 + c)$, where $c = \min\{a, b/M\}$. Then there is one and only one function $\vec{Y}$ defined on I, with $\vec{Y}(x_0) = \vec{y}_0$, such that $(x, \vec{Y}(x)) \, \varepsilon \, S$ and $\vec{Y}'(x) = \vec{f}[x, \vec{Y}(x)]$ for every x in I.

Proof. Since the proof is entirely analogous to the one-dimensional case we sketch only the principal steps. Let $\vec{Y}_0(x) = \vec{y}_0$ for each x in I, and define vector-valued functions $\vec{Y}_1, \vec{Y}_2, \ldots$ on I by the recursion formula

(9.47) $\vec{Y}_{m+1}(x) = \vec{y}_0 + \displaystyle\int_{x_0}^{x} \vec{f}[t, \vec{Y}_m(t)] \, dt$ for $m = 0, 1, 2, \ldots$.

In formulas such as this one the integral is an n-dimensional vector obtained by integrating component by component. Thus, if $\vec{F}(t) = (F_1(t), F_2(t), \ldots, F_n(t))$, we define

$$\int_{x_0}^{x} \vec{F}(t) \, dt = \left(\int_{x_0}^{x} F_1(t) \, dt, \int_{x_0}^{x} F_2(t) \, dt, \ldots, \int_{x_0}^{x} F_n(t) \, dt\right).$$

From this definition and Equation (9.45) it is easy to verify the relation

(9.48) $\left\|\displaystyle\int_{x_0}^{x} \vec{F}(t) \, dt\right\| \leq \left|\displaystyle\int_{x_0}^{x} \|\vec{F}(t)\| \, dt\right|.$

For the recursion formula (9.47) to be meaningful we need to know that $(x, \vec{Y}_m(x)) \, \varepsilon \, S$ for each x in I. This can easily be proved by induction, with the use of (9.48). When $m = 0$ we have $(x, \vec{Y}_0(x)) = (x, \vec{y}_0)$, which is in S. Assume, then, that $(x, \vec{Y}_m(x)) \, \varepsilon \, S$ for some m and each x in I. Using (9.47) and (9.46) we obtain

$$\|\vec{Y}_{m+1}(x) - \vec{y}_0\| \leq \left|\int_{x_0}^{x} \|\vec{f}[t, \vec{Y}_m(t)]\| \, dt\right| \leq M \left|\int_{x_0}^{x} dt\right| = M \, |x - x_0|.$$

Since $|x - x_0| \leq c$ for x in I, this implies that

$$\|\vec{Y}_{m+1}(x) - \vec{y}_0\| \leq Mc \leq b,$$

which shows that $(x, \vec{Y}_{m+1}(x)) \in S$ for each x in I. Therefore the recursion formula is meaningful for every $m \geq 0$ and every x in I.

The convergence of the sequence $\{\vec{Y}_n(x)\}$ is now established exactly as in the proof of Theorem 9–3, where limits are defined component by component. In place of inequality (9.26) we use

$$\|\vec{Y}_{m+1}(x) - \vec{Y}_m(x)\| \leq \frac{MK^m |x - x_0|^{m+1}}{(m+1)!} \leq \frac{MK^m c^{m+1}}{(m+1)!}.$$

This is proved by induction in exactly the same way we proved (9.26). We then define the limit function $\vec{Y}$ by the equation

$$\vec{Y}(x) = \lim_{m \to \infty} \vec{Y}_m(x)$$

for each x in I, and verify that it satisfies the integral equation

$$\vec{Y}(x) = \vec{y}_0 + \int_{x_0}^x \vec{f}[t, \vec{Y}(t)] \, dt$$

exactly as in the one-dimensional case. This proves the existence theorem. The uniqueness theorem may then be proved by the same method used in Section 9.8. Instead of (9.43) we use the inequality

$$\|\vec{Z}(x) - \vec{Y}_m(x)\| \leq \frac{bK^m |x - x_0|^m}{m!} \leq \frac{bK^m c^m}{m!},$$

which is easily verified by induction.

There is, of course, a corresponding extension of Theorem 9–4, which may be stated as follows:

9–7   THEOREM.   Assume the components of $\vec{f}$ are continuous on a set S' in $(n + 1)$-space of the form

$$S' = \{(x, \vec{y}) \mid x_0 - a_1 \leq x \leq x_0 + a_2, \vec{y} \text{ arbitrary}\}.$$

Assume that $\vec{f}$ satisfies a Lipschitz condition on S' and that $\vec{f}$ is bounded on every subset S_b of S' of the form

$$S_b = \{(x, \vec{y}) \mid x_0 - a_1 \leq x \leq x_0 + a_2, \|\vec{y} - \vec{y}_0\| \leq b\}.$$

Then there exists a function $\vec{y} = \vec{Y}(x)$ defined on the open interval $J = (x_0 - a_1, x_0 + a_2)$ which satisfies the differential equation $\vec{y}' = \vec{f}(x, \vec{y})$ on J with $\vec{Y}(x_0) = \vec{y}_0$. Moreover, there is exactly one such solution whose graph over J lies in a set of the type S_C for some $C > 0$.

The proof of Theorem 9–4 may easily be adapted to prove Theorem 9–7. Details are left to the reader.

9.10   Existence and uniqueness theorems for linear equations of order n

Consider a linear differential equation of order n,

(9.49) $y^{(n)} + P_1(x)y^{(n-1)} + \cdots + P_n(x)y = R(x)$,

where the functions $P_1, P_2, \ldots, P_n$, and R are continuous on an open interval I, which may be finite or infinite. Let x_0 be a point in I and let $k_0, k_1, \ldots, k_{n-1}$ be n given real numbers. We wish to prove that there is one and only one function $y = \phi(x)$ which is a solution of (9.49) on I and which satisfies the initial conditions

(9.50) $\phi(x_0) = k_0, \qquad \phi'(x_0) = k_1, \qquad \ldots, \phi^{(n-1)}(x_0) = k_{n-1}$.

The differential equation in (9.49) is equivalent to the system

(9.51) $y_1' = y_2, \qquad y_2' = y_3, \qquad \ldots, y_{n-1}' = y_n, \qquad y_n' = R(x) - L(y_1, y_2, \ldots, y_n)$,

where

$$L(y_1, y_2, \ldots, y_n) = P_n(x)y_1 + P_{n-1}(x)y_2 + \cdots + P_1(x)y_n .$$

We may express this as a first-order vector differential equation,

(9.52) $\vec{y}' = \vec{f}(x, \vec{y})$,

by writing $\vec{y} = (y_1, y_2, \ldots, y_n)$ and

$$\vec{f}(x, \vec{y}) = (y_2, y_3, \ldots, y_n, R(x) - L(y_1, y_2, \ldots, y_n)) .$$

Let $J_0 = [x_0 - a_1, x_0 + a_2]$ be any finite closed subinterval of I containing the point x_0. Let S be the set in $(n + 1)$-space given by

$$S = \{(x, \vec{y}) \mid x \, \varepsilon \, J_0, \vec{y} \text{ arbitrary}\} .$$

Each component of $\vec{f}$ is continuous on S. We show next that $\vec{f}$ satisfies a Lipschitz condition on S. For any two points $(x, \vec{y})$ and $(x, \vec{z})$ in S we have

$$\vec{f}(x, \vec{y}) - \vec{f}(x, \vec{z}) = (y_2 - z_2, \ldots, y_n - z_n, -P_n(x)(y_1 - z_1) - \cdots - P_1(x)(y_n - z_n)) .$$

Therefore

$$\|\vec{f}(x, \vec{y}) - \vec{f}(x, \vec{z})\| \leq |y_2 - z_2| + \cdots + |y_n - z_n| + |P_n(x)| \, |y_1 - z_1|$$
$$+ \cdots + |P_1(x)| \, |y_n - z_n| .$$

Now each of the functions $P_1, P_2, \ldots, P_n$ is continuous on J_0. Since J_0 is a finite closed interval, each P_k is bounded on J_0, say

$$|P_k(x)| \leq A_k$$

for all x in J_0. If $A = \max \{A_1, A_2, \ldots, A_n\}$, the inequality for $\|\vec{f}(x, \vec{y}) - \vec{f}(x, \vec{z})\|$ becomes

$$\|\vec{f}(x, \vec{y}) - \vec{f}(x, \vec{z})\| \leq A \, |y_1 - z_1| + (A + 1) \, |y_2 - z_2| + \cdots + (A + 1) \, |y_n - z_n|$$
$$\leq (A + 1) \, \|\vec{y} - \vec{z}\| .$$

Therefore $\vec{f}$ satisfies a Lipschitz condition on S, with Lipschitz constant $A + 1$.

Next we show that $\vec{f}$ is bounded on every subset S_b of S of the form

$$S_b = \{(x, \vec{y}) \mid x \in J_0,\ \|\vec{y} - \vec{y}_0\| \le b\},$$

where $\vec{y}_0 = (k_0, k_1, \ldots, k_{n-1})$. For any point $(x, \vec{y})$ in S_b we have

$$\|\vec{f}(x, \vec{y})\| \le |y_2| + \cdots + |y_n| + |R(x)| + |P_n(x)|\,|y_1| + \cdots + |P_1(x)|\,|y_n|$$
$$\le |R(x)| + (A + 1)\,(|y_1| + \cdots + |y_n|) = |R(x)| + (A + 1)\,\|\vec{y}\|.$$

Now $\|\vec{y}\| = \|\vec{y} - \vec{y}_0 + \vec{y}_0\| \le \|\vec{y} - \vec{y}_0\| + \|\vec{y}_0\| \le b + \|\vec{y}_0\|$, since $(x, \vec{y}) \in S$. Therefore, if M_R denotes the maximum value of $|R(x)|$ for x in J_0, the foregoing inequality for $\|\vec{f}(x, \vec{y})\|$ gives us

$$\|\vec{f}(x, \vec{y})\| \le M_R + (A + 1)\,(b + \|\vec{y}_0\|).$$

This shows that $\vec{f}$ is bounded on S_b. Thus, $\vec{f}$ satisfies all the hypotheses of Theorem 9–7. Consequently, a solution $\vec{y} = \vec{Y}(x)$ of the initial-value problem

$$\vec{y}' = \vec{f}(x, \vec{y}), \qquad \text{with} \quad \vec{Y}(x_0) = \vec{y}_0,$$

exists on the open interval $J = (x_0 - a_1, x_0 + a_2)$. Moreover, there is at most one such solution whose graph over J lies in a set of the form S_C for some $C > 0$. If we denote the first component of $\vec{Y}$ by ϕ_0 and use the fact that the differential equation in (9.52) is equivalent to the system in (9.51), we see that ϕ_0 is a solution of the linear equation (9.49) on J which satisfies the initial conditions (9.50). Theorem 9–7 implies that there is at most one such solution ϕ_0 that is bounded on J.

Now we must show that a solution ϕ exists over the full interval I. Choose any point x_1 in I and let $J_0 = [x_0 - a_1, x_0 + a_2]$ be any finite closed subinterval of I containing both x_0 and x_1 as interior points. We have just shown that a solution ϕ_0 exists on the open interval $J = (x_0 - a_1, x_0 + a_2)$. We now define $\phi(x_1) = \phi_0(x_1)$. For $\phi(x_1)$ to be well defined we must know that $\phi(x_1)$ depends only on x_1 and not on the choice of the interval J_0. Let J_1 be any other finite closed interval containing both x_0 and x_1 as interior points, and let ϕ_1 be the corresponding solution defined on the interior of J_1. Then there is a finite closed interval J_2 containing both x_0 and x_1 as interior points and lying in the interior of both J_0 and J_1. On J_2 both solutions ϕ_0 and ϕ_1 are bounded. Therefore, by the uniqueness theorem, they must be identical on J_2. In particular, $\phi_0(x_1) = \phi_1(x_1)$. This shows that $\phi(x_1)$ depends only on x_1 and not on the choice of the interval J_0. Since x_1 is an arbitrary point of I we have defined the function ϕ everywhere on I. This ϕ clearly satisfies the differential equation (9.49) on I and the initial conditions (9.50). Moreover, it is unique, because any other solution ψ on I must agree with ϕ_0 on any finite closed subinterval of I and therefore must agree with ϕ on such a subinterval. Therefore ψ agrees with ϕ everywhere on I.

9.11 Contraction operators

The basic idea underlying the method of successive approximations can be used not only to establish existence theorems for solutions of differential equations but also to solve many other important problems in analysis. In this section we show how the method of successive approximations can be reformulated in a more general setting that greatly increases the scope of its applications. The use of the method in other problems is illustrated in Section 9.12.

We have seen that the method of successive approximations involves the construction of a sequence of functions $\{Y_n\}$, defined and continuous on some interval I, according to the recursion formula

(9.53) $$Y_{n+1}(x) = y_0 + \int_{x_0}^{x} f[t, Y_n(t)] \, dt$$

for $n = 0, 1, 2, \ldots$, with $Y_0(x) = y_0$. The integral which appears in this formula can be used to define an operator A which converts certain functions ϕ defined on I into new functions $A(\phi)$ defined on I by the equation

$$A(\phi)(x) = y_0 + \int_{x_0}^{x} f[t, \phi(t)] \, dt \, .$$

In operator notation, the recursion formula (9.53) becomes simply

$$Y_{n+1} = A(Y_n) \, .$$

In the proof of Theorem 9–3 we found that the solution Y of the initial-value problem $y' = f(x, y)$, with $Y(x_0) = y_0$, satisfies the integral equation

$$Y(x) = y_0 + \int_{x_0}^{x} f[t, Y(t)] \, dt \, .$$

In operator notation this states that $Y = A(Y)$. In other words, the solution Y remains unaltered by the operator A. Such a function Y is called a *fixed point* of the operator A. Many important problems in analysis can be formulated so their solution depends on the existence of a fixed point for some operator. Therefore, it is worth while to try to discover properties of operators that guarantee the existence of a fixed point. We turn now to a systematic treatment of this problem.

   The discussion is considerably simplified by the notation and terminology of function spaces. We begin with the collection C of all real-valued functions defined and continuous on a finite closed interval $[a, b]$. (Although the discussion may easily be extended to more general collections of functions defined on more general sets, we shall discuss only the space C.) The set C is a linear space. That is, if $\phi \, \varepsilon \, C$ and $\psi \, \varepsilon \, C$, then $(\phi + \psi) \, \varepsilon \, C$ and $c\phi \, \varepsilon \, C$ for every constant c. The space becomes a normed linear space if we define $\|\phi\|$ for each ϕ in C by the equation

$$\|\phi\| = \max_{a \leq x \leq b} |\phi(x)| \, ,$$

where the symbol on the right stands for the maximum value of $|\phi(x)|$ for x in $[a, b]$. This is the maximum norm discussed in Chapter 8 in connection with polynomial approximation. It has the fundamental properties

   (a) $\|\phi\| \geq 0$ for every ϕ in C,
   (b) $\|c\phi\| = |c| \, \|\phi\|$ for each ϕ in C and each real number c,
   (c) $\|\phi + \psi\| \leq \|\phi\| + \|\psi\|$ for all ϕ and ψ in C,
   (d) $\|\phi\| = 0$ implies $\phi = 0$.

If ϕ and ψ are in C we shall refer to $\|\phi - \psi\|$ as the *distance* between ϕ and ψ.
   We consider now an operator A whose domain and range are both equal to the space C. That is, if $\phi \, \varepsilon \, C$ then $A(\phi)$ is again a function in C. There are many operators of this

kind that can be defined on C. The following formulas illustrate a few simple examples. In each case ϕ is an arbitrary function in C and $A(\phi)(x)$ is defined for each x in $[a, b]$ by the formula given:

$$A(\phi)(x) = \lambda\phi(x), \qquad \text{where } \lambda \text{ is a fixed real number,}$$

$$A(\phi)(x) = \int_{x_0}^{x} \phi(t) \, dt, \qquad \text{where } x_0 \text{ is a fixed point in } [a, b],$$

(9.54) $$A(\phi)(x) = y_0 + \int_{x_0}^{x} f[t, \phi(t)] \, dt,$$

(9.55) $$A(\phi)(x) = \psi(x) + \lambda \int_{a}^{b} K(x, t) \, \phi(t) \, dt.$$

In Equation (9.54), y_0 is a constant and the function f is assumed to be defined and continuous on the rectangular strip $[a, b] \times (-\infty, +\infty)$. This ensures that $A(\phi) \, \mathcal{E} \, C$ for each ϕ in C. In Equation (9.55), ψ is a fixed function in C and the function K is defined and continuous on the square $S = [a, b] \times [a, b]$. It can be shown that $A(\phi) \, \mathcal{E} \, C$ whenever $\phi \, \mathcal{E} \, C$.

Now let A be any operator such that $A(\phi) \, \mathcal{E} \, C$ whenever $\phi \, \mathcal{E} \, C$. We shall be interested in those operators A for which the distance $\|A(\phi) - A(\psi)\|$ is less than a fixed constant multiple of $\|\phi - \psi\|$. These are called *contraction operators*; they are defined as follows:

DEFINITION OF A CONTRACTION OPERATOR. An operator A is called a contraction operator if there is a constant α satisfying $0 \leq \alpha < 1$ such that for every pair of functions ϕ and ψ in C we have

(9.56) $$\|A(\phi) - A(\psi)\| \leq \alpha \|\phi - \psi\|.$$

The constant α is called a *contraction constant* for A.

Note. The inequality (9.56) holds if, and only if, we have

$$|A(\phi)(x) - A(\psi)(x)| \leq \alpha \|\phi - \psi\|$$

for every x in $[a, b]$.

Example 1. Let A be the operator defined on C by the equation $A(\phi)(x) = \lambda\phi(x)$ for each x in $[a, b]$, where λ is a constant. Since

$$|A(\phi)(x) - A(\psi)(x)| = |\lambda| \, |\phi(x) - \psi(x)|$$

we have $\|A(\phi) - A(\psi)\| = |\lambda| \, \|\phi - \psi\|$. Therefore this operator is a contraction operator if, and only if, $|\lambda| < 1$, in which case $|\lambda|$ may be used as a contraction constant.

Example 2. Let A be the operator defined by (9.54), and assume that f satisfies a Lipschitz condition of the form

$$|f(x, y) - f(x, z)| \leq K \, |y - z|$$

on the rectangular strip $[a, b] \times (-\infty, +\infty)$. If $K(b - a) < 1$ we can easily show that A is a contraction operator with contraction constant $\alpha = K(b - a)$. In fact, for every x in $[a, b]$ we have

$$|A(\phi)(x) - A(\psi)(x)| = \left|\int_{x_0}^{x} \{f[t, \phi(t)] - f[t, \psi(t)]\}\, dt\right| \leq K \left|\int_{x_0}^{x} |\phi(t) - \psi(t)|\, dt\right|$$

$$\leq K \|\phi - \psi\| \left|\int_{x_0}^{x} dt\right| \leq K(b - a) \|\phi - \psi\|\,.$$

This shows that A is a contraction operator with contraction constant $\alpha = K(b - a)$.

The operator A of Example 2 was used in the method of successive approximations to construct a solution Y of the initial-value problem $y' = f(x, y)$, with $y = y_0$ when $x = x_0$. We have already pointed out that this solution is a fixed point of the operator A. The next theorem shows that every contraction operator has a fixed point.

9–7   THEOREM.   *Fixed-point theorem for contraction operators*. Let A be a contraction operator defined on the space C of continuous functions on $[a, b]$. Then there exists one and only one function ϕ in C such that

$$(9.57) \qquad\qquad\qquad\qquad A(\phi) = \phi\,.$$

Proof. Let ϕ_0 be any function in C and define a sequence of functions $\{\phi_n\}$ by the recursion formula

$$\phi_{n+1} = A(\phi_n) \qquad \text{for} \quad n = 0, 1, 2, \ldots\,.$$

We shall imitate the method of successive approximations and show that the series

$$(9.58) \qquad\qquad\qquad \phi_0(x) + \sum_{k=0}^{\infty} [\phi_{k+1}(x) - \phi_k(x)]$$

converges for each x in $[a, b]$. Then we shall prove that the sum of this series defines a function ϕ in C satisfying (9.57).

The convergence of the series in (9.58) will be established by comparing it with the convergent geometric series

$$M \sum_{k=0}^{\infty} \alpha^k\,,$$

where $M = \|\phi_0\| + \|\phi_1\|$, and α is a contraction constant for A. The comparison is provided by the inequality

$$(9.59) \qquad\qquad\qquad |\phi_{k+1}(x) - \phi_k(x)| \leq M\alpha^k$$

which holds for every x in $[a, b]$ and every $k \geq 1$. To prove (9.59) we note that

$$|\phi_{k+1}(x) - \phi_k(x)| = |A(\phi_k)(x) - A(\phi_{k-1})(x)| \leq \alpha \|\phi_k - \phi_{k-1}\|\,.$$

Therefore the inequality in (9.59) will be proved if we show that

$$(9.60) \qquad\qquad\qquad \|\phi_k - \phi_{k-1}\| \leq M\alpha^{k-1}$$

for every $k \geq 1$. We now prove (9.60) by induction. For $k = 1$ we have

$$\|\phi_0 - \phi_1\| \leq \|\phi_0\| + \|\phi_1\| = M\,,$$

which is the same as (9.60). To prove that (9.60) holds for $k + 1$ if it holds for k we note that

$$|\phi_{k+1}(x) - \phi_k(x)| = |A(\phi_k)(x) - A(\phi_{k-1})(x)| \le \alpha \, \|\phi_k - \phi_{k-1}\| \le M\alpha^k \, .$$

Since this is valid for each x in $[a, b]$ we must also have

$$\|\phi_{k+1} - \phi_k\| \le M\alpha^k \, .$$

This proves (9.60) by induction. Therefore the series in (9.58) converges for each x in $[a, b]$. If we let $\phi(x)$ denote its sum we have

$$\phi(x) = \lim_{n \to \infty} \phi_n(x)$$

where

$$\phi_n(x) = \phi_0(x) + \sum_{k=0}^{n-1} [\phi_{k+1}(x) - \phi_k(x)] \, .$$

Now we must show that $\phi \in C$ and that $A(\phi) = \phi$.

To show that ϕ is continuous on $[a, b]$ we choose an arbitrary point x_1 in $[a, b]$ and show that ϕ is continuous at x_1. For this purpose we let ϵ be a given positive number and show that there is a neighborhood $N(x_1)$ such that

(9.61) $\qquad |\phi(x) - \phi(x_1)| < \epsilon \qquad$ whenever $\quad x \in N(x_1) \cap [a, b] \, .$

The idea of the proof is to choose a suitable approximating function ϕ_N and write

$$\phi(x) - \phi(x_1) = \phi(x) - \phi_N(x) + \phi_N(x) - \phi_N(x_1) + \phi_N(x_1) - \phi(x_1) \, .$$

This gives us the inequality

(9.62) $\quad |\phi(x) - \phi(x_1)| \le |\phi(x) - \phi_N(x)| + |\phi_N(x) - \phi_N(x_1)| + |\phi_N(x_1) - \phi(x_1)| \, .$

We show next that ϕ_N can be chosen so that each term on the right is less than $\epsilon/3$ if x is sufficiently close to x_1.

First we note that for every x in $[a, b]$ we have

$$\phi(x) - \phi_n(x) = \sum_{k=n}^{\infty} [\phi_{k+1}(x) - \phi_k(x)] \, .$$

Therefore, by (9.59), we have the inequality

(9.63) $\qquad |\phi(x) - \phi_n(x)| \le \sum_{k=n}^{\infty} |\phi_{k+1}(x) - \phi_k(x)| \le M \sum_{k=n}^{\infty} \alpha^k \, .$

Since the series $\Sigma \, \alpha^k$ converges, for the given ϵ there is an N (depending only on ϵ) such that

$$M \sum_{k=n}^{\infty} \alpha^k < \frac{\epsilon}{3} \qquad \text{whenever} \quad n \ge N \, .$$

Therefore (9.63) shows that $|\phi(x) - \phi_n(x)| < \epsilon/3$ for *every* x in $[a, b]$, provided only that $n \ge N$. In particular, if we take $n = N$ we see that the first and third terms on the right of (9.62) have a sum less than $2\epsilon/3$ for any choice of x in $[a, b]$, so (9.62) becomes

(9.64) $\qquad |\phi(x) - \phi(x_1)| < \dfrac{2\epsilon}{3} + |\phi_N(x) - \phi_N(x_1)| \, .$

Now we invoke the continuity of ϕ_N at x_1 to find a neighborhood $N(x_1)$ such that

$$|\phi_N(x) - \phi_N(x_1)| < \frac{\epsilon}{3} \qquad \text{whenever} \quad x \; \varepsilon \; N(x_1) \cap [a, b] \, .$$

Using this inequality along with (9.64) we see that (9.61) is satisfied for this choice of $N(x_1)$. This proves that $\phi \; \varepsilon \; C$.

Next we prove that $A(\phi) = \phi$. From the contraction property of A we have

(9.65) $$|A(\phi)(x) - \phi_{n+1}(x)| = |A(\phi)(x) - A(\phi_n)(x)| \leq \alpha \, \|\phi - \phi_n\|$$

for each x in $[a, b]$. The inequality in (9.63) shows that

$$\|\phi - \phi_n\| \leq M \sum_{k=n}^{\infty} \alpha^k \, .$$

Therefore $\|\phi - \phi_n\| \to 0$ as $n \to \infty$. Letting $n \to \infty$ in (9.65) we obtain

$$\lim_{n \to \infty} |A(\phi)(x) - \phi_{n+1}(x)| = 0 \, .$$

That is, we have

$$A(\phi)(x) = \lim_{n \to \infty} \phi_{n+1}(x) = \phi(x)$$

for every x in $[a, b]$. But this means that $A(\phi) = \phi$.

Finally, we prove that the fixed point ϕ is unique. Suppose ψ is another function in C such that $A(\psi) = \psi$. Then we have

$$\|\phi - \psi\| = \|A(\phi) - A(\psi)\| \leq \alpha \, \|\phi - \psi\| \, .$$

This gives us $(1 - \alpha) \, \|\phi - \psi\| \leq 0$. Since $\alpha < 1$ we may divide by $1 - \alpha$ to obtain the inequality $\|\phi - \psi\| \leq 0$. But since we also have $\|\phi - \psi\| \geq 0$ this means that $\|\phi - \psi\| = 0$, and hence $\phi - \psi = 0$. The proof of the fixed-point theorem is now complete.

9.12 Applications of the fixed-point theorem

In this section we discuss two important applications of the fixed-point theorem for contraction mappings. First we show how it can be used to give a simple proof of a special case of the implicit-function theorem referred to in Chapter 4 (Section 4.16).

9–8   THEOREM. *An implicit-function theorem.* Let f be defined and continuous on a rectangular strip of the form

$$R = [a, b] \times (-\infty, +\infty) \, .$$

Assume that the partial derivative $D_2 f(x, y)$ exists and satisfies a relation of the form

(9.66) $$0 < m \leq D_2 f(x, y) \leq M$$

for all (x, y) in R, where m and M are constants with $m \leq M$. Then there exists one and only one function $y = Y(x)$, continuous on $[a, b]$, such that

(9.67) $$f[x, Y(x)] = 0$$

for all x in $[a, b]$. In other words, the equation $f(x, y) = 0$ serves to define y implicitly as a function of x on $[a, b]$.

Proof. Let C be the space of continuous functions on $[a, b]$, and let A denote the operator defined on C by the equation

$$A(\phi)(x) = \phi(x) - \frac{1}{M} f[x, \phi(x)]$$

for each x in $[a, b]$. Here M is the positive constant in (9.66). The function $A(\phi)$ ε C whenever ϕ ε C. We shall prove that A is a contraction mapping. Once we know this it follows that there is a unique fixed point Y in C. For this function Y we have

$$Y(x) = Y(x) - \frac{1}{M} f[x, Y(x)]$$

for every x in $[a, b]$, which is the same as (9.67).

To show that A is a contraction mapping we consider the difference

$$(9.68) \qquad A(\phi)(x) - A(\psi)(x) = \phi(x) - \psi(x) - \frac{f[x, \phi(x)] - f[x, \psi(x)]}{M}.$$

By the mean-value theorem for derivatives we have

$$f[x, \phi(x)] - f[x, \psi(x)] = D_2 f[x, z(x)] [\phi(x) - \psi(x)],$$

where $z(x)$ lies between $\phi(x)$ and $\psi(x)$. Therefore (9.68) gives us

$$(9.69) \qquad A(\phi)(x) - A(\psi)(x) = [\phi(x) - \psi(x)] \left(1 - \frac{D_2 f[x, z(x)]}{M}\right).$$

The hypothesis (9.66) implies that

$$0 \le 1 - \frac{D_2 f[x, z(x)]}{M} \le 1 - \frac{m}{M}.$$

Therefore (9.69) gives us the inequality

$$(9.70) \qquad |A(\phi)(x) - A(\psi)(x)| \le |\phi(x) - \psi(x)| \left(1 - \frac{m}{M}\right) \le \alpha \|\phi - \psi\|,$$

where $\alpha = 1 - m/M$. Since $0 < m \le M$, we have $0 \le \alpha < 1$. Inequality (9.70) is valid for every x in $[a, b]$. Hence A is a contraction mapping. This completes the proof.

The next application of the fixed-point theorem establishes an existence theorem for the integral equation

$$(9.71) \qquad \phi(x) = \psi(x) + \lambda \int_a^b K(x, t)\phi(t) \, dt.$$

Here K is a function defined and continuous on the square $[a, b] \times [a, b]$; ψ is a fixed function, continuous on $[a, b]$; and λ is a constant. The functions K and ψ are assumed to be known and the function ϕ is unknown. A solution of the integral equation is any continuous function ϕ that satisfies the equation on $[a, b]$.

9– 9   THEOREM.   *An existence theorem for integral equations.* Let K be continuous on the square $S = [a, b] \times [a, b]$, and assume that

(9.72) $$|K(x, y)| \leq M$$

for all (x, y) in S, where $M > 0$. Let ψ be a given function, continuous on $[a, b]$, and let λ be a real number satisfying the inequality

(9.73) $$|\lambda| < \frac{1}{M(b - a)} \, .$$

Then there exists one and only one function ϕ, continuous on $[a, b]$, that satisfies the integral equation (9.71).

Proof. Let C be the space of continuous functions on $[a, b]$, and define an operator A on C by the equation

$$A(\phi)(x) = \psi(x) + \lambda \int_a^b K(x, t) \, \phi(t) \, dt \, .$$

It can be shown† that $A(\phi) \, \varepsilon \, C$ whenever $\phi \, \varepsilon \, C$, We shall prove that A is a contraction mapping.

Take any two functions ϕ_1 and ϕ_2 in C and consider the difference

$$A(\phi_1)(x) - A(\phi_2)(x) = \lambda \int_a^b K(x, t) \, [\phi_1(t) - \phi_2(t)] \, dt \, .$$

Using the inequality (9.72) we may write

$$|A(\phi_1)(x) - A(\phi_2)(x)| \leq |\lambda| \, M(b - a) \, \|\phi_1 - \phi_2\| = \alpha \, \|\phi_1 - \phi_2\| \, ,$$

where $\alpha = |\lambda| \, M(b - a)$. Because of (9.73) we have $0 \leq \alpha < 1$, so A is a contraction mapping with contraction constant α. Therefore A has a unique fixed point ϕ in C. This function ϕ satisfies (9.71).

---

† See Theorem 9–35 of the author's *Mathematical Analysis*, Addison-Wesley Publishing Co., Reading, Massachusetts, 1957.

ANSWERS TO EXERCISES

Chapter 1

1.4 Exercises (page 4)

1. $A = \{1\}$; $B = \{1, 2, 3, 4, \ldots\}$; $C = \{2, 4, 6, 8, \ldots\}$; $D = \{1\}$; $E = \{1, -17\}$; $F = \{1, -17, -8 + \sqrt{47}, -8 - \sqrt{47}\}$

2. $A \subseteq A$; $A \subseteq B$; $A \subseteq D$; $A \subseteq E$; $A \subseteq F$; $B \subseteq B$; $C \subseteq B$; $C \subseteq C$; $D \subseteq A$; $D \subseteq B$; $D \subseteq D$; $D \subseteq E$; $D \subseteq F$; $E \subseteq E$; $E \subseteq F$; $F \subseteq F$. (Not counting "proper" inclusions)

5. (c) $A \subset C$
   (d) Yes
   (e) No

7. (a) False
   (b) True
   (c) True
   (d) False
   (e) True
   (f) False

8. ϕ, $\{1\}$, $\{2\}$, $\{3\}$, $\{4\}$, $\{1, 2\}$, $\{1, 3\}$, $\{1, 4\}$, $\{2, 3\}$, $\{2, 4\}$, $\{3, 4\}$, $\{1, 2, 3\}$, $\{1, 2, 4\}$, $\{1, 3, 4\}$, $\{2, 3, 4\}$, S

10. (a) False
    (b) False
    (c) False
    (d) False
    (e) True
    (f) False
    (g) True
    (h) False
    (i) True
    (j) False

1.6 Exercises (page 7)

18. $A = X \cap Y' \cap Z'$, $B = X \cap Y \cap Z'$, $D = X' \cap Y \cap Z'$, $E = X' \cap Y \cap Z$, $F = X' \cap Y' \cap Z$

19. (a) (ii) is right
    (b) $C \subseteq A$

21. ϕ, $\{3\}$, $\{1, 3\}$, $\{2, 3\}$, S

22. (a) Yes
    (b) $\{2, 3\}$, S

1.8   Exercises (page 10)

5. $A_1 \cup A_2 \cup A_3 = (A_1 \cap A_2' \cap A_3') \cup (A_2 \cap A_3') \cup A_3$; $\displaystyle\bigcup_{k=1}^{n} A_k = \bigcup_{k=1}^{n-1} \left(A_k \cap \bigcap_{j=k+1}^{n} A_j'\right) \cup A_n$

6.

	(i)	(ii)	(iii)	(iv)	(v)
(a) $A' \cap B'$	$A \cap B'$	$A \cup B$	$(A \cap B') \cup (A' \cap B)$	$A' \cup B'$
(b) 500	200	500	300	800

1.10   Exercises (page 15)

2. $\mathfrak{R} = \{\phi, A_1, A_2, A_1 \cup A_2\}$
   $\mathfrak{B} = \{\phi, A_1, A_2, A_1 \cup A_2, A_1', A_2', A_1' \cap A_2', S\}$

3. $\mathfrak{R} = \{\phi, A_1, A_2, A_3, A_1 \cup A_2, A_2 \cup A_3, A_1 \cup A_3, A_1 \cup A_2 \cup A_3\}$
   $\mathfrak{B} = \{\phi, A_1, A_2, A_3, A_1 \cup A_2, A_2 \cup A_3, A_1 \cup A_3, A_1 \cup A_2 \cup A_3, A_1', A_2', A_3', A_1' \cap A_2',$
   $A_2' \cap A_3', A_1' \cap A_3', A_1' \cap A_2' \cap A_3', S\}$ (if $n > 3$)

1.13   Exercises (page 21)

1. $\{(1, 2), (1, 3), (2, 1), (2, 3), (3, 1), (3, 2)\}$
2. 1326
3. 54
4. $\{H, T\} \times \{H, T\} \times \{1, 2, 3, 4, 5, 6\}$; 24 outcomes
5. $52!/(13!)^4$
6. 36
   (a) 18
   (b) 12
   (c) 24
7. (a) $13 \cdot 12 \cdot 11 \cdot 72 = 123552$ (not including triplets or quadruplets)
   (b) 5148
   (c) 36 (not including $10JQKA$)
   (d) 4
8. (a) $\dfrac{2 \cdot 98!}{(49!)^2}$
   (b) $\dfrac{98!}{48! \cdot 50!}$
9. 16
10. n^k

1.15   Exercises (page 25)

1. (a) $f(k) = 2k$
   (b) $f(k) = 3^k$
   (c) $f(k) = p_k$, where p_k is the kth prime ≥ 2
   (d) one such function is $f(k) = (g(k), h(k))$, where
   $$g(k) = \frac{m^2(k) + 3m(k)}{2} - k + 2, \quad h(k) = k - \frac{m^2(k) + m(k)}{2},$$
   and
   $$m(k) = \left[\frac{\sqrt{8k - 7} - 1}{2}\right]$$
   where $[x]$ denotes the greatest integer $\leq x$
   (e) $f(k) = 2^{g(k)} 3^{h(k)}$, where $g(k)$ and $h(k)$ are as defined in part (d)

1.18 Exercises (page 30)

1. $A \subseteq B'$
2. $x \,\varepsilon\, A' \cap B' \cap C'$
3. $x \,\varepsilon\, A \cap B' \cap C'$
4. $x \,\varepsilon\, A \cup B \cup C$
5. $x \,\varepsilon\, (A \cap B' \cap C') \cup (A' \cap B \cap C') \cup (A' \cap B' \cap C)$
6. $x \,\varepsilon\, (A' \cap B') \cup (B' \cap C') \cup (A' \cap C')$
7. $x \,\varepsilon\, (A \cap B) \cup (A \cap C) \cup (B \cap C)$
8. $x \,\varepsilon\, (A \cap B \cap C') \cup (A \cap B' \cap C) \cup (A' \cap B \cap C)$
9. $x \,\varepsilon\, (A \cap B \cap C)'$
10. $x \,\varepsilon\, A \cap C \cap B'$
11. $x \,\varepsilon\, A \cap B \cap C$
12. $x \,\varepsilon\, A \cup B \cup C$
15. (a) $1 - a$
   (b) $1 - b$
   (c) $a + b - c$
   (d) $1 - c$
   (e) $1 - a + c$
   (f) $a - c$

1.20 Exercises (page 34)

2. (a) 5/14
   (b) 45/91
   (c) 10/91
   (d) 36/91
3. (a) 23/36
   (b) 1/6
   (c) 1/3
   (d) 5/36
   (e) 13/36
   (f) 2/3
4. 1/4
5. (a) $4\binom{13}{5} \Big/ \binom{52}{5}$
   (b) $40 \Big/ \binom{52}{5}$
   (c) $4 \Big/ \binom{52}{5}$
6. 9/47
7. 8/47
8. 4/47
9. 1/3
11. $P_0 = 1 - P(A) - P(B) + P(A \cap B)$, $P_1 = P(A) + P(B) - 2P(A \cap B)$, $P_2 = P(A \cap B)$
13. (a) 5 to 9
   (b) 45 to 46
   (c) 10 to 81
   (d) 36 to 55

1.23 Exercises (page 39)

2. (a) $P(A) = \dfrac{3}{10}$; $P(B|A) = \dfrac{6}{11}$; $P(A \cap B) = \dfrac{9}{55}$

4. $\binom{98}{48} \Big/ \left[\binom{100}{50} - \binom{98}{50} \right]$

5. 4/11

6. (a) $1 - \dfrac{26! \cdot 34!}{21! \cdot 39!} = 1 - \dfrac{\binom{34}{13}}{\binom{39}{13}} = 1 - \dfrac{\binom{26}{5}}{\binom{39}{5}}$

   (b) $1 - \dfrac{\binom{34}{13} + 5\binom{34}{12}}{\binom{39}{13}}$

   (c) $3\binom{26}{5} \Big/ \binom{39}{5}\binom{39}{13}$

9. 1/2

15. (a) $P(A) = P(B) = P(C) = \frac{1}{2}$; $P(A \cap B) = P(A \cap C) = P(B \cap C) = \frac{1}{4}$; $P(A \cap B \cap C) = 0$

1.26 Exercises (page 45)

1. (a) $P(H, H) = p_1 p_2$; $P(H, T) = p_1(1 - p_2)$; $P(T, H) = (1 - p_1)p_2$; $P(T, T) = (1 - p_1)(1 - p_2)$
   (b) Yes
   (c) No
   (d) H_1 and H_2, H_1 and T_2, H_2 and T_1, T_1 and T_2

2. (a) 319/512
   (b) 11/1024
   (c) 6

3. $\binom{10}{3} 5^7/6^{10} = \dfrac{390625}{2519424}$

4. (a) 5/16
   (b) 1/2
   (c) 3/16

5. (a) $(5!)^2/10! = 1/252$
   (b) 1/2

6. (a) $36p^{10} - 80p^9 + 45p^8$
   (b) 7/128

7. It is advantageous to bet even money

8. $\binom{n}{k} \dfrac{w^k b^{n-k}}{(w+b)^n}$

9. $\binom{8}{3} 17^5/18^8 = \dfrac{9938999}{1377495072}$

10. 193/512

11. $1 - (19/20)^{10} = 0.4013$

12. 193/512

1.27 Miscellaneous exercises on probability (page 47)

1. 1/6

2. (a) 2/19
   (b) 1/10

3. (a) 1/4
   (b) 7/12

4. (a) 15/34
   (b) 13/51
   (c) 13/165

5. (a) 5/9
   (b) 2/9
   (c) 2/9
   (d) No

6. $p^3 + 6p\left(\dfrac{1-p}{2}\right)^2$

7. $np(1-p)^{n-1} + np^{n-1}(1-p)$

8. $\dfrac{n}{2^{n-1}}\left(1 - \dfrac{n}{2^{n-1}}\right)^{m-1}$

Chapter 2

2.9   Exercises (page 63)

1. 1/3

2. $2\sqrt{3} - \dfrac{38}{3}$

3. $\pi^2/4$

4. 2π

5. 6

6. $t^{-3}(e^{t^2} - e^t) + t^{-2} - t^{-1}$

8. 1/6

9. $\pi/2$

10. $(\log 2)/6$

2.13   Exercises (page 76)

1. $-3\pi/2$

2. $\dfrac{3}{2} + \cos 1 + \sin 1 - \cos 2 - 2\sin 2$

3. $e - \dfrac{1}{e}$

4. $\dfrac{7}{3}\log 2$

5. $\pi^2 - \dfrac{40}{9}$

6. 6

7. 80/3

8. (a) 8/3
   (b) 2
   (c) 320π

9. $\displaystyle\int_0^1 \left[\int_x^1 f(x, y)\, dy\right] dx$

10. $\displaystyle\int_0^4 \left[\int_{x/2}^{\sqrt{x}} f(x, y)\, dy\right] dx$

11. $\displaystyle\int_1^2 \left[\int_1^{y^2} f(x, y)\, dx\right] dy$

12. $\displaystyle\int_0^1 \left[\int_{2-y}^{1+\sqrt{1-y^2}} f(x, y)\, dx\right] dy$

13. $\int_{-1}^{0}\left[\int_{-\sqrt{4y+4}}^{\sqrt{4y+4}} f(x, y)\, dx\right] dy + \int_{0}^{8}\left[\int_{-\sqrt{4y+4}}^{2-y} f(x, y)\, dx\right] dy$

14. $\int_{0}^{1}\left[\int_{e^y}^{e} f(x, y)\, dx\right] dy$

15. $\int_{-1}^{0}\left[\int_{-\sqrt{1-y^2}}^{\sqrt{1-y^2}} f(x, y)\, dx\right] dy + \int_{0}^{1}\left[\int_{-\sqrt{1-y}}^{\sqrt{1-y}} f(x, y)\, dx\right] dy$

16. $\int_{0}^{1}\left[\int_{y^{1/2}}^{y^{1/3}} f(x, y)\, dx\right] dy$

17. $\int_{-1}^{0}\left[\int_{-2\mathrm{arc\,sin}\,y}^{\pi} f(x, y)\, dx\right] dy + \int_{0}^{1}\left[\int_{\mathrm{arc\,sin}\,y}^{\pi-\mathrm{arc\,sin}\,y} f(x, y)\, dx\right] dy$

18. $\int_{-2}^{0}\left[\int_{2x+4}^{4-x^2} f(x, y)\, dy\right] dx$

19. $\int_{0}^{1}\left[\int_{x}^{2-x} (x^2 + y^2)\, dy\right] dx = \frac{4}{3}$

20. $y = 0,\ y = x \tan c,\ x^2 + y^2 = a^2,\ x^2 + y^2 = b^2$

21. (a) $\int_{1}^{8}\left[\int_{y^{1/3}}^{y} f(x, y)\, dx\right] dy$

    (b) $4e^8 + 2e/3$

22. $m = 2;\, n = 1$

2.15   Exercises (page 81)

1. $\bar{x} = -\frac{1}{2},\, \bar{y} = \frac{8}{5}$

2. $\bar{x} = 1,\, \bar{y} = 0$

3. $\bar{x} = \frac{18}{13},\, \bar{y} = \frac{50}{39}$

4. $\bar{x} = \pi/2,\, \bar{y} = \pi/8$

5. $\bar{x} = (\sqrt{2} + 1)\left(\dfrac{\pi\sqrt{2}}{4} - 1\right) = \dfrac{\pi}{2} + \dfrac{\pi\sqrt{2}}{4} - 1 - \sqrt{2},\, \bar{y} = \dfrac{\sqrt{2}+1}{4}$

6. $\bar{x} = \dfrac{2a^2 \log a - a^2 + 1}{4(a \log a - a + 1)},\, \bar{y} = \dfrac{a(\log a)^2}{2(a \log a - a + 1)} - 1$

7. $\bar{x} = \bar{y} = 1/5$

8. $\bar{x} = \bar{y} = 256/(315\pi)$

9. $\frac{26}{3} - \frac{15}{2} \log 3$

10. $\bar{x} = \frac{2}{3}\,|\overrightarrow{AB}|,\, \bar{y} = \frac{2}{3}\,|\overrightarrow{AD}|$; assuming the x- and y-axes are chosen along sides AB and AD, respectively

11. $I_x = \dfrac{5\pi}{12},\, I_y = \dfrac{2\pi^3}{3} - \pi$

12. $I_x = \frac{1}{12} b^3(a - c),\, I_y = \frac{1}{12} b(a^3 - c^3)$

13. $I_x = I_y = (1 - 5\pi/16)\, r^4$

14. $I_x = I_y = 9/8$

15. $I_x = \frac{1}{64}[(4a - 1)\, e^{4a} - 1],\, I_y = \frac{1}{32}[(a^3 - 3a^2 + 6a - 6)\, e^{2a} + 6]$

16. $I_x = 72/105,\, I_y = 148/45$

19. $\frac{1}{3} h\, [\sqrt{2} + \log(1 + \sqrt{2})]$

20. $h^2 + \frac{1}{4} r^2$

21. (a) $(\frac{13}{6}, 1)$

    (b) $(\frac{7}{3}, \frac{9}{2})$

    (c) $(\frac{11}{4}, \frac{11}{4})$

    (d) $(\frac{19}{8}, \frac{13}{8})$

22. $h = 2\sqrt{3}$

2.18   Exercises (page 89)

1. $\int_0^{2\pi}\left[\int_0^a f(r\cos\theta, r\sin\theta)\, r\, dr\right] d\theta$

2. $\int_{-\pi/2}^{\pi/2}\left[\int_0^{2\cos\theta} f(r\cos\theta, r\sin\theta)\, r\, dr\right] d\theta$

3. $\int_0^{2\pi}\left[\int_a^b f(r\cos\theta, r\sin\theta)\, r\, dr\right] d\theta$

4. $\int_0^{\pi/2}\left[\int_0^{g(\theta)} f(r\cos\theta, r\sin\theta)\, r\, dr\right] d\theta,$ where $g(\theta) = 1/(\cos\theta + \sin\theta)$

5. $\int_0^{\pi/4}\left[\int_0^{\tan\theta\sec\theta} f(r\cos\theta, r\sin\theta)\, r\, dr\right] d\theta + \int_{\pi/4}^{3\pi/4}\left[\int_0^{\csc\theta} f(r\cos\theta, r\sin\theta)\, r\, dr\right] d\theta$
   $+ \int_{3\pi/4}^{\pi}\left[\int_0^{\tan\theta\sec\theta} f(r\cos\theta, r\sin\theta)\, r\, dr\right] d\theta$

6. $\frac{3}{4}\pi a^4$

7. $\frac{1}{6}a^3[\sqrt 2 + \log(1 + \sqrt 2)]$

8. $\sqrt 2 - 1$

9. $\pi a^4/8$

10. $\int_0^{\pi/4}\left[\int_0^{\sec\theta} f(r\cos\theta, r\sin\theta)\, r\, dr\right] d\theta + \int_{\pi/4}^{\pi/2}\left[\int_0^{\csc\theta} f(r\cos\theta, r\sin\theta)\, r\, dr\right] d\theta$

11. $\int_{\pi/4}^{\pi/3}\left[\int_0^{2\sec\theta} f(r)\, r\, dr\right] d\theta$

12. $\int_0^{\pi/2}\left[\int_{g(\theta)}^1 f(r\cos\theta, r\sin\theta)\, r\, dr\right] d\theta,$ where $g(\theta) = 1/(\cos\theta + \sin\theta)$

13. $\int_0^{\pi/4}\left[\int_{\tan\theta\sec\theta}^{\sec\theta} f(r\cos\theta, r\sin\theta)\, r\, dr\right] d\theta$

14. $\pi^4/3$

15. (a) $1 + 2u$
    (c) $14/3$
    (d) $2 + \dfrac{2}{\sqrt 3}\left(\arctan\dfrac{1}{\sqrt 3} - \arctan\dfrac{5}{\sqrt 3}\right)$

16. (a) $4(u^2 + v^2)$
    (c) 0

17. $\dfrac{\pi}{1 - p}[(p^2 + r^2)^{1-p} - p^{2(1-p)}]$ if $p \neq 1$; $\pi\log(1 + r^2)$ if $p = 1$.
    $I(p, r)$ tends to a finite limit when $p > 1$

2.20   Exercises (page 96)

1. $1/364$
2. $\log\sqrt 2 - \frac{5}{16}$
3. $1/48$
4. $\frac{4}{5}\pi abc$
5. $\pi/6$
6. $\int_0^1\left\{\int_0^x\left[\int_0^{1-x} f(x, y, z)\, dy\right] dz + \int_x^1\left[\int_{z-x}^{1-x} f(x, y, z)\, dy\right] dz\right\} dx$
7. $\int_0^1\left\{\int_{-z}^z\left[\int_{-\sqrt{z^2-x^2}}^{\sqrt{z^2-x^2}} f(x, y, z)\, dy\right] dx\right\} dz$
8. $\int_0^1\left\{\int_0^{x^2}\left[\int_0^1 f(x, y, z)\, dy\right] dz + \int_{x^2}^{1+x^2}\left[\int_{\sqrt{z-x^2}}^1 f(x, y, z)\, dy\right] dz\right\} dx$
10. $16\pi/3$
11. $1/6$
12. $\frac{1}{60}\pi a^2 h(3a^2 + 2h^2)$

13. $\frac{4}{3}\pi a^3$

14. $\frac{4}{3}\pi(b^3 - a^3)$

15 $\frac{4}{3}\pi R^3(a^2 + b^2 + c^2)^{-1/2}$

18. $\frac{2}{3}\pi(5\sqrt{5} - 4)$

19. 32/9

20. $\frac{4}{3}\pi(b^5 - a^5)$

21. On the axis at distance $\frac{2}{3}h$ from the base

22. On the axis at distance $\frac{1}{5}h$ from the base

23. On the axis of symmetry at distance $\dfrac{3}{8} \cdot \dfrac{b^4 - a^4}{b^3 - a^3}$ from the "cutting plane" of the hemispheres

24. $\bar{x} = \bar{y} = \bar{z} = \frac{7}{12}h$ (assuming the specified corner is at the origin)

25. $\frac{3}{20}M(a^2 + 4h^2)$

26. $\frac{2}{5}MR^2$

27. $\frac{3}{5}Ma^2$

28. $2^{1/4}$

30. (a) $\dfrac{4}{3} \cdot \dfrac{a^2b^2}{a + b}$

Chapter 3

3.3 Exercises (page 106)

1. (b) $X \leq b$.

2. (a) $\{\omega \mid X(\omega) \, \varepsilon \, (a, b], \quad Y(\omega) \, \varepsilon \, (c, d]\}$

   (c) $X \leq a, Y \leq d$

   (d) $P(a < X \leq b, c < Y \leq d) = P(X \leq b, Y \leq d) - P(X \leq a, Y \leq d) - P(X \leq b, Y \leq c)$
   $+ P(X \leq a, Y \leq c)$

3. (a) $\{(1, 6), (2, 5), (3, 4), (4, 3), (5, 2), (6, 1)\}, \{(5, 6), (6, 5)\}, \{(1, 6), (2, 5), (3, 4), (4, 3), (5, 2),$
   $(6, 1), (5, 6), (6, 5)\}$

   (b) $P(X = 7) = \frac{1}{6}; \; P(X = 11) = \frac{1}{18}; \; P(X = 7 \text{ or } X = 11) = \frac{2}{9}$

4. $Y = X_1 + X_2 + X_3 + X_4; \; P(Y = 0) = \frac{1}{16}; \; P(Y = 1) = \frac{1}{4}; \; P(Y \leq 1) = \frac{5}{16}$

5. $Y = 7X \quad$ if $\; 0 \leq X \leq 100; \quad Y = 10X - 300 \quad$ if $\; X > 100$

6. (a) $Z = Y - 1$

   (b) $U = Y_1 + Y_2 - 1$

3.6 Exercises (page 118)

2.

t	2	3	4	5	6	7	8	9	10	11	12
$p_x(t)$	$\frac{1}{36}$	$\frac{1}{18}$	$\frac{1}{12}$	$\frac{1}{9}$	$\frac{5}{36}$	$\frac{1}{6}$	$\frac{5}{36}$	$\frac{1}{9}$	$\frac{1}{12}$	$\frac{1}{18}$	$\frac{1}{36}$

3. (b) $p(-2) = \frac{1}{2}, \; p(0) = p(2) = \frac{1}{4}$

   (c) $0, \frac{3}{4}, \frac{3}{4}, \frac{1}{4}, 1, 0, \frac{1}{4}, \frac{1}{4}$

5. (a) $c = 1/3$

   (b) $1/9, 1/3, 2/3, 8/9$

   (c) $F(t) = 0$ for $t < 0$, $F(t) = 1/9$ for $0 \leq t < 1$, $F(t) = 1/3$ for $1 \leq t < 2$, $F(t) = 1$ for $t \geq 2$

   (d) No such t

   (e) $t = 2$

6. (a)

k	0	1	2	3	4
$p(k)$	$\frac{16}{81}$	$\frac{32}{81}$	$\frac{8}{27}$	$\frac{8}{81}$	$\frac{1}{81}$

$p(t) = 0$ for $t \neq 0, 1, 2, 3, 4$

(b) $F(t) = 0$ for $t < 0$, $F(t) = 16/81$ on $[0, 1)$, $F(t) = 16/27$ on $[1, 2)$, $F(t) = 8/9$ on $[2, 3)$, $F(t) = 80/81$ on $[3, 4)$, $F(t) = 1$ for $t \geq 4$

(c) $8/27$, $56/81$

7. (b) $P(X = 0) = (1 - p)^2$; $P(X = 1) = 2p(1 - p)$

8. $p_X(k) = \dfrac{2k}{n(n + 1)}$; $F_X(t) = \dfrac{[t] \, ([t] + 1)}{n(n + 1)}$ for $0 \leq t \leq n$,   where $[t]$ denotes the greatest integer $\leq t$; $F_X(t) = 0$ for $t < 0$; $F_X(t) = 1$ for $t > n$

9. $p(k) = e^{-c} \dfrac{c^k}{k!}$; $k = 0, 1, 2, 3, \ldots$; $c \geq 0$

$p(t) = 0$ for $t \neq 0, 1, 2, 3, \ldots$

10. (a) $p_X(t) = \frac{1}{2}$ at $t = -1$ and $t = +1$; $p_X(t) = 0$ elsewhere

$F_X(t) = 0$ for $t < -1$; $F_X(t) = \frac{1}{2}$ for $-1 \leq t < 1$; $F_X(t) = 1$ for $t \geq 1$

11. $P(A) = 2/3$; $P(B) = 2/3$; $P(A \cap B) = 1/3$; $P(B|A) = 1/2$; $P(A \cup B) = 1$

3.8 Exercises (page 128)

1. (a) $c = 1$; $f(t) = 1$ if $0 \leq t \leq 1$; $f(t) = 0$ otherwise

(b) 0, $1/3$, $1/3$

2. $c = \frac{1}{2}$; $F(t) = 0$ if $t < -\pi/2$; $F(t) = \frac{1}{2} \cos t$ if $-\pi/2 \leq t < 0$; $F(t) = 1 - \frac{1}{2} \cos t$ if $0 \leq t < \pi/2$; $F(t) = 1$ if $t \geq \pi/2$

3. (a) $f(t) = 0$ if $t < \frac{1}{4}$; $f(t) = 8t - 1$ if $\frac{1}{4} \leq t < \frac{1}{2}$; $f(t) = 7 - 8t$ if $\frac{1}{2} \leq t < \frac{3}{4}$; $f(t) = 0$ if $t \geq \frac{3}{4}$

(b) $F(t) = 0$ if $t < \frac{1}{4}$; $F(t) = 4t^2 - t$ if $\frac{1}{4} \leq t < \frac{1}{2}$; $F(t) = -4t^2 + 7t - 2$ if $\frac{1}{2} \leq t < \frac{3}{4}$; $F(t) = 1$ if $t \geq \frac{3}{4}$

(c) 1, 1, $1/2$, 0, $5/16$

4. (a) 0, $5/6$, $2/3$, $1/2$

(b) $t = 1$

5. (a)

k	5	10	15	20	25	30
$P(X \geq k)$	$\frac{5}{6}$	$\frac{2}{3}$	$\frac{1}{2}$	$\frac{1}{3}$	$\frac{1}{6}$	0

(b) Let each Styx train arrive 5 minutes before a Lethe train

7. Same as in Exercise 6

8. $1/2$; 0

12. $F_Y(t) = 0$ if $t < 0$; $f_Y(t) = 0$ if $t \leq 0$; $f_Y(t) = e^{-t/2}/\sqrt{2\pi t}$ if $t > 0$

3.11 Exercises (page 134)

2. (a) $P(X = x_1) = P(X = x_2) = P(Y = y_1) = P(Y = y_2) = \frac{1}{2}(p + q)$

(b) $p = q = \frac{1}{2}$

3. (a) $F(x, y) = \left(\dfrac{x - a}{b - a}\right)\left(\dfrac{y - c}{d - c}\right)$ if $a \leq x \leq b$ and $c \leq y \leq d$,

$F(x, y) = \dfrac{x - a}{b - a}$ if $a \leq x \leq b$ and $y > d$, $F(x, y) = \dfrac{y - c}{d - c}$ if $x > b$ and $c \leq y \leq d$,

$F(x, y) = 1$ if $x > b$ and $y > d$, $F(x, y) = 0$ otherwise

(b) $F_X(x) = (x - a)/(b - a)$ if $a \leq x \leq b$; $F_X(x) = 0$ if $x < a$; $F_X(x) = 1$ if $x > b$.
$F_Y(y) = (y - c)/(d - c)$ if $c \leq y \leq d$; $F_Y(y) = 0$ if $y < c$; $F_Y(y) = 1$ if $y > d$

(c) X and Y are independent

5. $P(Y = 0) = \frac{1}{2}$; $P(Y = 1) = P(Y = 2) = \frac{1}{4}$

7. 1/5, 4/5

8. 1/3

9. (b) $f(x, y) = \frac{1}{2}$ if $(x, y) \in Q$; $f(x, y) = 0$ if $(x, y) \notin Q$;
   $f_X(x) = 1 - |x|$ if $|x| \le 1$; $f_X(x) = 0$ if $|x| > 1$;
   $f_Y(y) = 1 - |y|$ if $|y| \le 1$, $f_Y(y) = 0$ if $|y| > 1$.
   X and Y are not independent

10. $g(u, v) = f(u + a, v + b)$

3.13   Exercises (page 140)

1. (a) $F_Y(t) = 0$ if $t < 1$; $F_Y(t) = (t - 1)/3$ if $1 \le t \le 4$; $F_Y(t) = 1$ if $t > 4$; $f_Y(t) = 1/3$ if $1 \le t \le 4$; $f_Y(t) = 0$ otherwise

   (b) $F_Y(t) = 0$ if $t < -2$; $F_Y(t) = (t + 2)/3$ if $-2 \le t \le 1$; $F_Y(t) = 1$ if $t > 1$; $f_Y(t) = 1/3$ if $-2 \le t \le 1$; $f_Y(t) = 0$ otherwise

   (c) $F_Y(t) = 0$ if $t < 0$; $F_Y(t) = t^{1/2}$ if $0 \le t \le 1$; $F_Y(t) = 1$ if $t > 1$; $f_Y(t) = (2t)^{-1/2}$ if $0 \le t \le 1$; $f_Y(t) = 0$ otherwise

   (d) $F_Y(t) = e^t$ if $t \le 0$; $F_Y(t) = 1$ if $t > 0$; $f_Y(t) = e^t$ if $t \le 0$; $f_Y(t) = 0$ if $t > 0$

   (e) $F_Y(t) = e^{t/2}$ if $t \le 0$; $F_Y(t) = 1$ if $t > 0$; $f_Y(t) = \frac{1}{2} e^{t/2}$ if $t \le 0$; $f_Y(t) = 0$ if $t > 0$

   (f) $F_Y(t) = 0$ if $t < 1$; $F_Y(t) = \log t$ if $1 \le t \le e$; $F_Y(t) = 1$ if $t > e$; $f_Y(t) = 1/t$ if $1 \le t \le e$; $f_Y(t) = 0$ otherwise

2. Let ψ be the inverse of ϕ, defined on the open interval (a, b).
   Then $F_Y(t) = 0$ if $t \le a$; $F_Y(t) = F_X[\psi(t)]$ if $a < t < b$; $F_Y(t) = 1$ if $t \ge b$; $f_Y(t) = f_X[\psi(t)] \psi'(t)$ if $a < t < b$; $f_Y(t) = 0$ otherwise

3. (a) $f_Y(t) = 0$ if $t \le 0$; $f_Y(t) = (2\pi t)^{-1/2} e^{-t/2}$ if $t > 0$

   (b) $f_Y(t) = 0$ if $t < 0$; $f_Y(t) = 4t(2\pi)^{-1/2} e^{-t^4/2}$ if $t \ge 0$

   (c) $f_Y(t) = 0$ if $t \le 0$; $f_Y(t) = (2\pi t^2)^{-1/2} e^{-(\log t)^2/2}$ if $t > 0$

   (d) $f_Y(t) = (2\pi)^{-1/2} \sec^2 t\, e^{-(\tan^2 t)/2}$ if $|t| < \pi/2$; $f_Y(t) = 0$ if $|t| \ge \pi/2$

4. (a) $f(x, y) = 1$ if $(x, y) \in [0, 1] \times [0, 1]$, $f(x, y) = 0$ otherwise

   (e) $f_V(v) = 1 + v$ if $-1 \le v < 0$; $f_V(v) = 1 - v$ if $0 \le v \le 1$; $f_V(v) = 0$ if $|v| > 1$

   (f) U and V are not independent

5. (a) $f(x, y) = e^{-(x+y)}$ if $x > 0, y > 0$; $f(x, y) = 0$ otherwise

   (c) $g(u, v) = ue^{-u}$ if $u > 0, 0 < v < 1$; $g(u, v) = 0$ otherwise

   (d) $f_U(u) = ue^{-u}$ if $u > 0$; $f_U(u) = 0$ if $u \le 0$

   (e) $f_V(v) = 1$ if $0 < v < 1$; $f_V(v) = 0$ otherwise

6. (b) $g(u, v) = (v/2\pi)e^{-(1+u^2)v^2/2}$ if $v \ge 0$

   (c) $f_U(u) = [\pi(1 + u^2)]^{-1}$

7. $f_Z(t) = \pi^{-1/2} e^{-t^2}$

3.15   Exercises (page 146)

1. $E(X) = 7/2$, $\text{Var}(X) = 35/12$

7. (a) $E(X) = \text{Var}(X) = \lambda$

   (b) None

   (c) $E(X) = 1/\lambda$, $\text{Var}(X) = 1/\lambda^2$

   (d) $E(X) = m$, $\text{Var}(X) = \sigma^2$

8. (a) $C(r) = (r - 1)/2$

   (b) $F_X(t) = \frac{1}{2} |t|^{1-r}$ if $t < -1$; $F_X(t) = 1/2$ if $-1 \le t \le 1$; $F_X(t) = 1 - \frac{1}{2}t^{1-r}$ if $t > 1$

   (c) $P(X < 5) = 1 - 5^{r-1}/2$; $P(5 < X < 10) = (5^{1-r} - 10^{1-r})/2$

   (d) X has a finite expectation when $r > 2$; $E(X) = 0$

   (e) Variance is finite for $r > 3$; $\text{Var}(X) = (r - 1)/(r - 3)$

9. $E(X) = E(Y) = -1/37$; $E(Z) = -1767/50653$; $E(X + Y + Z) = -4505/50653$
10. $E(X) \to \infty$ as $n \to \infty$
12. (a) $(2/\pi)^{1/2}$
    (b) $e^{1/2}$
    (c) $e^2 - e$
    (d) $(\pi/2)^{1/2}$

3.19 Exercises (page 154)

4. 251
5. 0
6. Chebyshev's inequality gives $1/9$; tables give 0.0027
8. (b) 0.6826
9. (b) 0.0796
10. (a) 0.0090
    (b) 0.0179

Chapter 4

4.3 Exercises (page 158)

2. All open except (d), (e), (h), and (j)
3. All open except (d)
5. (e) One example is the collection of all neighborhoods $N(\vec{0}; 1/k)$, where $k = 1, 2, 3, \ldots$
6. (a) Both
   (b) Both
   (c) Closed
   (d) Open
   (e) Closed
   (f) Neither
   (g) Closed
   (h) Neither
   (i) Closed
   (j) Closed
   (k) Neither
   (l) Closed
8. (e) One example is the collection of all sets of the form $S_k = \{\vec{X} \mid |\vec{X}| \leq 1 - 1/k\}$ for $k = 1, 2, 3, \ldots$. Their union is the open set $N(\vec{0}; 1)$

4.5 Exercises (page 164)

1. $f'(\vec{X}; \vec{Y}) = 4|\vec{X}|^2 \, \vec{X} \cdot \vec{Y}$
2. (a) All points on the straight line $2x + 3y = 3/26$
   (b) All points on the two lines $x^2 - 3y^2 = 0$
7. $(1 - m^2)/(1 + m^2)$; No
9. $f(0, 0) = 1$
11. (a) Continuous for all (x, y); $\dfrac{\partial f}{\partial x} = 4x^3 - 8xy^2$; $\dfrac{\partial f}{\partial y} = 4y^3 - 8x^2y$

    (b) Continuous for $(x, y) \neq (0, 0)$; $\dfrac{\partial f}{\partial x} = \dfrac{2x}{x^2 + y^2}$; $\dfrac{\partial f}{\partial y} = \dfrac{2y}{x^2 + y^2}$

(c) Continuous whenever $y \neq 0$; $\dfrac{\partial f}{\partial x} = -\dfrac{2x}{y}\sin(x^2)$; $\dfrac{\partial f}{\partial y} = -\dfrac{1}{y^2}\cos(x^2)$

(d) Continuous whenever $y \neq 0$ and $\dfrac{x^2}{y} \neq \dfrac{\pi}{2} + \pi k$ $(k = 0, 1, 2, \ldots)$; $\dfrac{\partial f}{\partial x} = \dfrac{2x}{y}\sec^2\dfrac{x^2}{y}$;

$\dfrac{\partial f}{\partial y} = -\dfrac{x^2}{y^2}\sec^2\dfrac{x^2}{y}$

(e) Continuous whenever $x \neq 0$; $\dfrac{\partial f}{\partial x} = -\dfrac{y}{x^2 + y^2}$; $\dfrac{\partial f}{\partial y} = \dfrac{1}{x^2 + y^2}$

(f) Continuous for $(x, y) \neq (0, 0)$; $\dfrac{\partial f}{\partial x} = \dfrac{|y|}{x^2 + y^2}$; $\dfrac{\partial f}{\partial y} = -\dfrac{x^2}{|y|(x^2 + y^2)}$

(g) Continuous whenever $xy \neq 1$; $\dfrac{\partial f}{\partial x} = \dfrac{1 + y^2}{1 + x^2 + y^2 + x^2 y^2}$; $\dfrac{\partial f}{\partial x} = \dfrac{1 + x^2}{1 + x^2 + y^2 + x^2 y^2}$

(h) Continuous whenever $(x, y) \neq (0, 0)$; $\partial f/\partial x = y^2/(x^2 + y^2)^{3/2}$; $\partial f/\partial y = -xy/(x^2 + y^2)^{3/2}$

(i) Continuous whenever $(x, y) \neq (0, 0)$; $\partial f/\partial x = y^2 x^{y^2 - 1}$; $\partial f/\partial y = 2yxy^2 \log x$

(j) Continuous whenever $y \neq 0$, and $0 \leq x \leq y$ or $y \leq x \leq 0$; $\dfrac{\partial f}{\partial x} = -\dfrac{1}{\sqrt{x(y - x)}}$;

$\dfrac{\partial f}{\partial y} = \dfrac{\sqrt{x}}{2y\sqrt{y - x}}$

12. $n = -3/2$

13. $a = b = 1$

4.7 Exercises (page 167)

1. (c) $f'(\vec{X}; \vec{Y}) = 2(x_1 y_1 + x_2 y_2 + \cdots + x_n y_n)$; $\vec{Z} = \vec{X} + \frac{1}{2}\vec{Y}$

3. One example is $S = N(\vec{0}; 1) \cup N(3\vec{i}; 1)$, with $f = 0$ on $N(\vec{0}; 1)$, $f = 1$ on $N(3\vec{i}; 1)$

4. One example is $f(\vec{X}) = \vec{X} \cdot \vec{Y}$, where $\vec{Y}$ is a fixed vector

4.10 Exercises (page 172)

1. (a) $(2x + y^3 \cos xy)\vec{i} + (2y \sin xy + xy^2 \cos xy)\vec{j}$

(b) $e^x \cos y\,\vec{i} - e^x \sin y\,\vec{j}$

(c) $2xy^3 z^4\,\vec{i} + 3x^2 y^2 z^4\,\vec{j} + 4x^2 y^3 z^3\vec{k}$

(d) $2x\,\vec{i} - 2y\,\vec{j} + 4z\,\vec{k}$

(e) $\dfrac{2x}{x^2 + 2y^2 - 3z^2}\,\vec{i} + \dfrac{4y}{x^2 + 2y^2 - 3z^2}\,\vec{j} - \dfrac{6z}{x^2 + 2y^2 - 3z^2}\,\vec{k}$

(f) $y^z x^{y^z - 1}\,\vec{i} + zy^{z-1}\,x^{y^z} \log x\,\vec{j} + y^z\,x^{y^z} \log x \log y\,\vec{k}$

2. (a) $-2/\sqrt{6}$

(b) $1/\sqrt{6}$

3. $(1, 0)$, in the direction of $\vec{i}$; $(-1, 0)$, in the direction of $-\vec{i}$

4. $2\vec{i} + 2\vec{j}$; $14/5$

5. $(a, b, c) = (6, 24, -8)$ or $(-6, -24, 8)$

6. The set of points (x, y) on the line $5x - 3y = 6$; $\nabla f(\vec{X}) = 5\vec{i} - 3\vec{j}$

4.13 Exercises (page 179)

1. (a) $-2/3$

(b) $x^2 - y^2$

(c) 0

2. (a) $(1 + 3x^2 + 3y^2)(x\vec{i} + y\vec{j}) - (x^2 + y^2)^{1/2}\,\vec{k}$, or any scalar multiple thereof

(b) $\cos \theta = -[1 + (1 + 3(x^2 + y^2))^2]^{-1/2}$; $\cos \theta \to -\frac{1}{2}\sqrt{2}$ as $(x, y, z) \to (0, 0, 0)$

3. $U(x, y) = \frac{1}{2}\log(x^2 + y^2)$; $V(x, y) = \arctan(y/x)$
4. (b) No
6. $x/x_0 + y/y_0 + z/z_0 = 3$
7. $x + y + 2z = 4$, $x - y - z = -1$
8. $c = \pm 3$
11. (b) $F''(t) = \dfrac{\partial^2 f}{\partial x^2}[X'(t)]^2 + 2\dfrac{\partial^2 f}{\partial x \partial y}X'(t)Y'(t) + \dfrac{\partial^2 f}{\partial y^2}[Y'(t)]^2 + \dfrac{\partial f}{\partial x}X''(t) + \dfrac{\partial f}{\partial y}Y''(t)$
12. (a) $F'(t) = 4t^3 + 2t$; $F''(t) = 12t^2 + 2$
   (b) $F'(t) = (2\cos^2 t - 1)e^{\cos t \sin t}\cos(\cos t \sin^2 t) + (3\sin^3 t - 2\sin t)e^{\cos t \sin t}\sin(\cos t \sin^2 t)$;
   $F''(t) \doteq (5\cos^6 t - 3\cos^4 t - 4\cos^3 t - \cos^2 t - 4\cos t)e^{\cos t \sin t}\cos(\cos t \sin^2 t)$
   $\quad + (14\sin^3 t - 12\sin^5 t - 4\sin t + 7\cos t - 9\cos^3 t)e^{\cos t \sin t}\sin(\cos t \sin^2 t)$
   (c) $F'(t) = \dfrac{2e^{2t}\exp(e^{2t})}{1 + \exp(e^{2t})} + \dfrac{2e^{-2t}\exp(e^{-2t})}{1 + \exp(e^{-2t})}$, where $\exp(u) = e^u$;
   $F''(t) = \dfrac{4[1 + e^{2t} + \exp(e^{2t})]e^{2t}\exp(e^{2t})}{[1 + \exp(e^{2t})]^2} - \dfrac{4[1 + e^{-2t} + \exp(e^{-2t})]e^{-2t}\exp(e^{-2t})}{[1 + \exp(e^{-2t})]^2}$

4.15 Exercises (page 185)

1. (b) $\dfrac{\partial f}{\partial x} = -2x\sin(x^2 + y^2)\cos[\cos(x^2 + y^2)]e^{\sin[\cos(x^2+y^2)]}$
2. $G(x, y) = x - y$
4. (a) $\dfrac{\partial F}{\partial s} = \dfrac{\partial f}{\partial x}\dfrac{\partial X}{\partial s} + \dfrac{\partial f}{\partial y}\dfrac{\partial Y}{\partial s}$; $\dfrac{\partial F}{\partial t} = \dfrac{\partial f}{\partial x}\dfrac{\partial X}{\partial t} + \dfrac{\partial f}{\partial y}\dfrac{\partial Y}{\partial t}$
   (c) $\dfrac{\partial^2 F}{\partial s \partial t} = \dfrac{\partial^2 f}{\partial x^2}\dfrac{\partial X}{\partial s}\dfrac{\partial X}{\partial t} + \dfrac{\partial^2 f}{\partial x \partial y}\left(\dfrac{\partial X}{\partial s}\dfrac{\partial Y}{\partial t} + \dfrac{\partial X}{\partial t}\dfrac{\partial Y}{\partial s}\right) + \dfrac{\partial^2 f}{\partial y^2}\dfrac{\partial Y}{\partial s}\dfrac{\partial Y}{\partial t} + \dfrac{\partial f}{\partial x}\dfrac{\partial^2 X}{\partial s \partial t} + \dfrac{\partial f}{\partial y}\dfrac{\partial^2 Y}{\partial s \partial t}$
5. (a) $\dfrac{\partial F}{\partial s} = \dfrac{\partial f}{\partial x} + t\dfrac{\partial f}{\partial y}$; $\dfrac{\partial F}{\partial t} = \dfrac{\partial f}{\partial x} + s\dfrac{\partial f}{\partial y}$; $\dfrac{\partial^2 F}{\partial s^2} = \dfrac{\partial^2 f}{\partial x^2} + 2t\dfrac{\partial^2 f}{\partial x \partial y} + t^2\dfrac{\partial^2 f}{\partial y^2}$;
   $\dfrac{\partial^2 F}{\partial t^2} = \dfrac{\partial^2 f}{\partial x^2} + 2s\dfrac{\partial^2 f}{\partial x \partial y} + s^2\dfrac{\partial^2 f}{\partial y^2}$; $\dfrac{\partial^2 F}{\partial s \partial t} = \dfrac{\partial^2 f}{\partial x^2} + (s + t)\dfrac{\partial^2 f}{\partial x \partial y} + st\dfrac{\partial^2 f}{\partial y^2} + \dfrac{\partial f}{\partial y}$
   (b) $\dfrac{\partial F}{\partial s} = t\dfrac{\partial f}{\partial x} + \dfrac{1}{t}\dfrac{\partial f}{\partial y}$; $\dfrac{\partial F}{\partial t} = s\dfrac{\partial f}{\partial x} - \dfrac{s}{t^2}\dfrac{\partial f}{\partial y}$; $\dfrac{\partial^2 F}{\partial s^2} = t^2\dfrac{\partial^2 f}{\partial x^2} + 2\dfrac{\partial^2 f}{\partial x \partial y} + \dfrac{1}{t^2}\dfrac{\partial^2 f}{\partial y^2}$;
   $\dfrac{\partial^2 F}{\partial t^2} = s^2\dfrac{\partial^2 f}{\partial x^2} - 2\dfrac{s^2}{t^2}\dfrac{\partial^2 f}{\partial x \partial y} + \dfrac{s^2}{t^4}\dfrac{\partial^2 f}{\partial y^2} + \dfrac{2s}{t^3}\dfrac{\partial f}{\partial y}$; $\dfrac{\partial^2 F}{\partial s \partial t} = st\dfrac{\partial^2 f}{\partial x^2} - \dfrac{s}{t^3}\dfrac{\partial^2 f}{\partial y^2} + \dfrac{\partial f}{\partial x} - \dfrac{1}{t^2}\dfrac{\partial f}{\partial y}$
   (c) $\dfrac{\partial F}{\partial s} = \dfrac{1}{2}\dfrac{\partial f}{\partial x} + \dfrac{1}{2}\dfrac{\partial f}{\partial y}$; $\dfrac{\partial F}{\partial t} = -\dfrac{1}{2}\dfrac{\partial f}{\partial x} + \dfrac{1}{2}\dfrac{\partial f}{\partial y}$; $\dfrac{\partial^2 F}{\partial s \partial t} = -\dfrac{1}{4}\dfrac{\partial^2 f}{\partial x^2} + \dfrac{1}{4}\dfrac{\partial^2 f}{\partial y^2}$;
   $\dfrac{\partial^2 F}{\partial s^2} = \dfrac{1}{4}\dfrac{\partial^2 f}{\partial x^2} + \dfrac{1}{2}\dfrac{\partial^2 f}{\partial x \partial y} + \dfrac{1}{4}\dfrac{\partial^2 f}{\partial y^2}$; $\dfrac{\partial^2 F}{\partial t^2} = \dfrac{1}{4}\dfrac{\partial^2 f}{\partial x^2} - \dfrac{1}{2}\dfrac{\partial^2 f}{\partial x \partial y} + \dfrac{1}{4}\dfrac{\partial^2 f}{\partial y^2}$
6. $a = b = 1$; $c = d = 0$
7. $\dfrac{\partial F}{\partial x} = \dfrac{1}{2}\dfrac{\partial f}{\partial u} + \dfrac{1}{2}\dfrac{\partial f}{\partial v}$; $\dfrac{\partial F}{\partial y} = -\dfrac{1}{2}\dfrac{\partial f}{\partial u} + \dfrac{1}{2}\dfrac{\partial f}{\partial v}$
8. $\dfrac{\partial^2 \phi}{\partial r^2} = \cos^2\theta\dfrac{\partial^2 f}{\partial x^2} + \cos\theta\sin\theta\left(\dfrac{\partial^2 f}{\partial x \partial y} + \dfrac{\partial^2 f}{\partial y \partial x}\right) + \sin^2\theta\dfrac{\partial^2 f}{\partial y^2}$;
   $\dfrac{\partial^2 \phi}{\partial r \partial\theta} = -r\cos\theta\sin\theta\dfrac{\partial^2 f}{\partial x^2} + r\cos^2\theta\dfrac{\partial^2 f}{\partial x \partial y} - r\sin^2\theta\dfrac{\partial^2 f}{\partial y \partial x} + r\cos\theta\sin\theta\dfrac{\partial^2 f}{\partial y^2}$
   $\quad - \sin\theta\dfrac{\partial f}{\partial x} + \cos\theta\dfrac{\partial f}{\partial y}$;
9. $\dfrac{\partial F}{\partial r} = \dfrac{\partial f}{\partial x}\dfrac{\partial X}{\partial r} + \dfrac{\partial f}{\partial y}\dfrac{\partial Y}{\partial r} + \dfrac{\partial f}{\partial z}\dfrac{\partial Z}{\partial r}$; $\dfrac{\partial F}{\partial s} = \dfrac{\partial f}{\partial x}\dfrac{\partial X}{\partial s} + \dfrac{\partial f}{\partial y}\dfrac{\partial Y}{\partial s} + \dfrac{\partial f}{\partial z}\dfrac{\partial Z}{\partial s}$;
   $\dfrac{\partial F}{\partial t} = \dfrac{\partial f}{\partial x}\dfrac{\partial X}{\partial t} + \dfrac{\partial f}{\partial y}\dfrac{\partial Y}{\partial t} + \dfrac{\partial f}{\partial z}\dfrac{\partial Z}{\partial t}$

10. (a) $\dfrac{\partial F}{\partial r} = \dfrac{\partial f}{\partial x} + \dfrac{\partial f}{\partial y} + 2\dfrac{\partial f}{\partial z}$; $\dfrac{\partial F}{\partial s} = \dfrac{\partial f}{\partial x} - 2\dfrac{\partial f}{\partial y} + \dfrac{\partial f}{\partial z}$; $\dfrac{\partial F}{\partial t} = \dfrac{\partial f}{\partial x} + 3\dfrac{\partial f}{\partial y} - \dfrac{\partial f}{\partial z}$

  (b) $\dfrac{\partial F}{\partial r} = 2r\left(\dfrac{\partial f}{\partial x} + \dfrac{\partial f}{\partial y} + \dfrac{\partial f}{\partial z}\right)$; $\dfrac{\partial F}{\partial s} = 2s\left(\dfrac{\partial f}{\partial x} - \dfrac{\partial f}{\partial y} - \dfrac{\partial f}{\partial z}\right)$; $\dfrac{\partial F}{\partial t} = 2t\left(\dfrac{\partial f}{\partial x} - \dfrac{\partial f}{\partial y} + \dfrac{\partial f}{\partial z}\right)$

11. $\dfrac{\partial F}{\partial s} = \dfrac{\partial f}{\partial x}\dfrac{\partial X}{\partial s} + \dfrac{\partial f}{\partial y}\dfrac{\partial Y}{\partial s} + \dfrac{\partial f}{\partial z}\dfrac{\partial Z}{\partial s}$; $\dfrac{\partial F}{\partial t} = \dfrac{\partial f}{\partial x}\dfrac{\partial X}{\partial t} + \dfrac{\partial f}{\partial y}\dfrac{\partial Y}{\partial t} + \dfrac{\partial f}{\partial z}\dfrac{\partial Z}{\partial t}$

12. (a) $\dfrac{\partial F}{\partial s} = 2s\dfrac{\partial f}{\partial x} + 2s\dfrac{\partial f}{\partial y} + 2t\dfrac{\partial f}{\partial z}$; $\dfrac{\partial F}{\partial t} = 2t\dfrac{\partial f}{\partial x} - 2t\dfrac{\partial f}{\partial y} + 2s\dfrac{\partial f}{\partial z}$

  (b) $\dfrac{\partial F}{\partial s} = \dfrac{\partial f}{\partial x} + \dfrac{\partial f}{\partial y} + t\dfrac{\partial f}{\partial z}$; $\dfrac{\partial F}{\partial t} = \dfrac{\partial f}{\partial x} - \dfrac{\partial f}{\partial y} + s\dfrac{\partial f}{\partial z}$

13. $\dfrac{\partial F}{\partial r} = \dfrac{\partial f}{\partial x}\dfrac{\partial X}{\partial r} + \dfrac{\partial f}{\partial y}\dfrac{\partial Y}{\partial r}$; $\dfrac{\partial F}{\partial s} = \dfrac{\partial f}{\partial x}\dfrac{\partial X}{\partial s} + \dfrac{\partial f}{\partial y}\dfrac{\partial Y}{\partial s}$; $\dfrac{\partial F}{\partial t} = \dfrac{\partial f}{\partial x}\dfrac{\partial X}{\partial t} + \dfrac{\partial f}{\partial y}\dfrac{\partial Y}{\partial t}$

14. (a) $\dfrac{\partial F}{\partial r} = \dfrac{\partial f}{\partial x}$; $\dfrac{\partial F}{\partial s} = \dfrac{\partial f}{\partial x}$; $\dfrac{\partial F}{\partial t} = \dfrac{\partial f}{\partial y}$

  (b) $\dfrac{\partial F}{\partial r} = \dfrac{\partial f}{\partial x} + 2r\dfrac{\partial f}{\partial y}$; $\dfrac{\partial F}{\partial s} = \dfrac{\partial f}{\partial x} + 2s\dfrac{\partial f}{\partial y}$; $\dfrac{\partial F}{\partial t} = \dfrac{\partial f}{\partial x} + 2t\dfrac{\partial f}{\partial y}$

  (c) $\dfrac{\partial F}{\partial r} = \dfrac{1}{s}\dfrac{\partial f}{\partial x}$; $\dfrac{\partial F}{\partial s} = \dfrac{-r}{s^2}\dfrac{\partial f}{\partial x} + \dfrac{1}{t}\dfrac{\partial f}{\partial y}$; $\dfrac{\partial F}{\partial t} = \dfrac{-s}{t^2}\dfrac{\partial f}{\partial y}$

15. $a_k(\vec{T}) = D_k f[\vec{U}(\vec{T})]$ for $k = 1, 2, 3, \ldots, n$

4.18 Exercises (page 194)

1. $n = 2$

2. $\partial f/\partial x = -1/(2y + 2z + 1)$; $\partial f/\partial y = -2(y + z)/(2y + 2z + 1)$; $\partial^2 f/(\partial x \partial y) = 2/(2y + 2z + 1)^3$

3. $\partial^2 z/(\partial x \partial y) = [\sin(x + y)\cos^2(y + z) + \sin(y + z)\cos^2(x + y)]/\cos^3(y + z)$

4. $\dfrac{\partial f}{\partial x} = -\dfrac{D_1F + 2x\,D_2F}{D_1F + 2z\,D_2F}$; $\dfrac{\partial f}{\partial y} = -\dfrac{D_1F + 2y\,D_2F}{D_1F + 2z\,D_2F}$

5. $D_1F = f'[x + g(y)]$; $D_2F = f'[x + g(y)]g'(y)$; $D_{1,1}F = f''[x + g(y)]$; $D_{1,2}F = f''[x + g(y)]g'(y)$; $D_{2,2}F = f''[x + g(y)][g'(y)]^2 + f'[x + g(y)]g''(y)$

8. $\partial X/\partial v = (1 + xu)/(x - y)$; $\partial Y/\partial u = (1 - yv)/(x - y)$; $\partial Y/\partial v = (1 + yu)/(y - x)$

9. $\partial X/\partial y = -(1 + xu)/(1 + u)$; $\partial V/\partial u = (1 - yv)/(1 + yu)$; $\partial V/\partial y = (1 - x)/(1 + u)$

10. $\dfrac{\partial X}{\partial v} = \dfrac{\partial(F, G)}{\partial(y, v)}\bigg/\dfrac{\partial(F, G)}{\partial(x, y)}$; $\dfrac{\partial Y}{\partial u} = \dfrac{\partial(F, G)}{\partial(u, x)}\bigg/\dfrac{\partial(F, G)}{\partial(x, y)}$; $\dfrac{\partial Y}{\partial v} = \dfrac{\partial(F, G)}{\partial(v, x)}\bigg/\dfrac{\partial(F, G)}{\partial(x, y)}$

11. $\vec{T} = \pm\dfrac{1}{\sqrt{751}}(24\,\vec{i} - 4\sqrt{7}\,\vec{j} + 3\sqrt{7}\,\vec{k})$

12. $2\vec{i} + \vec{j} + \sqrt{3}\,\vec{k}$, or any scalar multiple thereof

4.20 Exercises (page 199)

1. $f(x, y, z) = (x^2 + y^2 + z^2)/2 + C$

2. $f(x, y, z) = x^2/2 - y^2/2 + xz - yz + C$

3. $\vec{V}$ is not a gradient

4. $\vec{V}$ is not a gradient

5. $\vec{V}$ is not a gradient

6. $f(x, y, z) = y^2\sin x + xz^3 - 4y + 2z + C$

7. $f(x, y, z) = x + 2x^2y - x^3z^2 + 2y - z^3 + C$

8. $f(x, y) = x^2e^y + xy - y^2 + C$

9. $f(x, y) = x\sin y + y\cos x + (x^2 + y^2)/2 + C$

10. $f(x, y) = x\sin(xy) + C$

11. (b) $f(x, y) = \dfrac{ar^{n+1}}{n+1} + C$ if $n \neq -1$; $f(x, y) = a \log r + C$ if $n = -1$
12. $9x^2 - 18xy + 16y^2 - 7 = 0$
13. $x^2 - y^2 + 2xz - 2yz + 9 = 0$
15. (a) $v(x, y) = e^x \sin y$
    (b) $v(x, y) = -\sin x \sinh y$
    (c) $v(x, y) = \arctan(y/x)$ if $x > 0$; $v(x, y) = \pi/2$ if $x = 0, y > 0$; $v(x, y) = -\pi/2$ if $x = 0, y < 0$; $v(x, y) = \arctan(y/x) + \pi$ if $x < 0, y > 0$; $v(x, y) = \arctan(y/x) - \pi$ if $x < 0, y < 0$

4.23 Exercises (page 209)

1. Absolute minimum at $(0, 1)$
2. Saddle point at $(0, 1)$
3. Saddle point at $(0, 0)$
4. Absolute minimum at each point of the line $y = x + 1$
5. Saddle point at $(1, 1)$
6. Absolute minimum at $(1, 0)$
7. Saddle point at $(0, 0)$
8. Saddle point at $(0, 0)$; relative maximum at $(2, 3)$
9. Saddle point at $(0, 0)$; relative minimum at $(1, 1)$
10. Saddle points at $(n\pi + \pi/2, 0)$, where n is any integer
11. Absolute minimum at $(0, 0)$; saddle point at $(-1/4, -1/2)$
12. Absolute minimum at $(-1/26, -3/26)$; absolute maximum at $(1, 3)$
13. Absolute maximum at $(\pi/3, \pi/3)$; absolute minimum at $(2\pi/3, 2\pi/3)$; relative maximum at (π, π); relative minimum at $(0, 0)$; saddle points at $(0, \pi)$ and $(\pi, 0)$
14. Saddle point at $(1, 1)$
15. Absolute maximum at each point of the circle $x^2 + y^2 = 1$; absolute minimum at $(0, 0)$
17. (c) Relative maximum at $(2, 2)$; no relative minima; saddle points at $(0, 3)$, $(3, 0)$, and $(3, 3)$
18. Maximum value is $1/4$; no minimum
19. Maximum is 2; minimum is 1
20. (a) Maximum is $\dfrac{\sqrt{a^2 + b^2}}{ab}$ at $(b(a^2 + b^2)^{-1/2}, a(a^2 + b^2)^{-1/2})$; minimum is $-\dfrac{\sqrt{a^2 + b^2}}{ab}$ at $(-b(a^2 + b^2)^{-1/2}, -a(a^2 + b^2)^{-1/2})$
    (b) Minimum is $a^2 b^2/(a^2 + b^2)$ at $\left(\dfrac{ab^2}{a^2 + b^2}, \dfrac{a^2 b}{a^2 + b^2}\right)$; no maximum
21. Maximum is $1 + \sqrt{2}/2$ at the points $(n\pi + \pi/8, n\pi - \pi/8)$, where n is any integer; minimum is $1 - \sqrt{2}/2$ at $(n\pi + 5\pi/8, n\pi + 3\pi/8)$, where n is any integer
22. Maximum is 3 at $(1/3, -2/3, 2/3)$; minimum is -3 at $(-1/3, 2/3, -2/3)$
23. $(0, 0, 1)$ and $(0, 0, -1)$
24. 1
25. $(1, 0, 0)$, $(0, 1, 0)$, $(-1, 0, 0)$, $(0, -1, 0)$
26. $\dfrac{a^a b^b c^c}{(a + b + c)^{a+b+c}}$ at $\left(\dfrac{a}{a + b + c}, \dfrac{b}{a + b + c}, \dfrac{c}{a + b + c}\right)$
27. Let $x^* = \dfrac{1}{n}\displaystyle\sum_{i=1}^{n} x_i$, $y^* = \dfrac{1}{n}\displaystyle\sum_{i=1}^{n} y_i$, $u_i = x_i - x^*$. Then $a = \left(\displaystyle\sum_{i=1}^{n} y_i u_i\right)\Big/\left(\displaystyle\sum_{i=1}^{n} u_i^2\right)$, and $b = y^* - ax^*$

28. Let $x^* = \dfrac{1}{n}\displaystyle\sum_{i=1}^{n} x_i$, $y^* = \dfrac{1}{n}\displaystyle\sum_{i=1}^{n} y_i$, $z^* = \dfrac{1}{n}\displaystyle\sum_{i=1}^{n} z_i$, $u_i = x_i - x^*$, $v_i = y_i - y^*$, and let

$$\Delta = \begin{vmatrix} \sum u_i^2 & \sum u_i v_i \\ \sum u_i v_i & \sum v_i^2 \end{vmatrix},$$

where the sums are for $i = 1, 2, \ldots, n$. Then

$$a = \frac{1}{\Delta}\begin{vmatrix} \sum u_i z_i & \sum u_i v_i \\ \sum v_i z_i & \sum v_i^2 \end{vmatrix}, \quad b = \frac{1}{\Delta}\begin{vmatrix} \sum v_i z_i & \sum u_i v_i \\ \sum u_i z_i & \sum u_i^2 \end{vmatrix}, \quad c = z^* - ax^* - by^*$$

29. $m^2 = \dfrac{A + C - \sqrt{(A - C)^2 + 4B^2}}{2(AC - B^2)}$

31. $abc\sqrt{3}/2$

32. $5 \log r + 3 \log \sqrt{3}$

4.26 Miscellaneous exercises (page 217)

2. One example: $f(x, y) = 3x$ when $x = y$, $f(x, y) = 0$ otherwise

3. $D_1 f(0, 0) = 0$; $D_2 f(0, 0) = -1$; $D_{2,1} f(0, 0) = 0$; $D_{1,2} f(0, 0)$ does not exist

5. $F'''(t) = \dfrac{\partial^3 f}{\partial x^3}[X'(t)]^3 + 3\dfrac{\partial^3 f}{\partial x^2 \partial y}[X'(t)]^2 Y'(t) + 3\dfrac{\partial^3 f}{\partial x \partial y^2} X'(t)[Y'(t)]^2$

$\qquad + \dfrac{\partial^3 f}{\partial y^3}[Y'(t)]^3 + 3\dfrac{\partial^2 f}{\partial x^2} X'(t)X''(t) + 3\dfrac{\partial^2 f}{\partial x \partial y}[X''(t)Y'(t) + X'(t)Y''(t)]$

$\qquad + 3\dfrac{\partial^2 f}{\partial y^2} Y'(t)Y''(t) + \dfrac{\partial f}{\partial x} X'''(t) + \dfrac{\partial f}{\partial y} Y'''(t)$,

assuming the mixed partial derivatives are independent of the order of differentiation

6. 8

8. $\partial x / \partial u = \partial x / \partial v = 0$

11. A sphere with center at the origin and radius $\sqrt{2}$

13. $9/4$ at the points $(-1/2, \pm \sqrt{3}/2)$; $-1/4$ at $(1/2, 0)$

14. $2\sqrt{b - 1}$ if $b > 2$; $|b|$ if $b \le 2$

15. $f(x) = x^2$

16. $(4 \pm \sqrt{5})/\sqrt{2}$

17. Angle is $\pi/3$; width across the bottom is $c/3$; maximum area is $c^2/(4\sqrt{3})$

20. (a) $\phi'(t) = A'(t)\displaystyle\int_c^{B(t)} f[A(t), y]\, dy + B'(t)\displaystyle\int_a^{A(t)} f[x, B(t)]\, dx$

(b) $\phi'(t) = 2t\, e^{t^2}\,(2e^{t^2} - e^a - e^c)$

Chapter 5

5.3 Exercises (page 223)

1. $-14/15$

2. $4/3$

3. 0

4. $-2\pi a^2$

5. $1/35$

6. 40

8. $\pi a^3/4$

9. $2a^3$

10. $a = (3c/2)^{1/2}$

5.6 Exercises (page 227)

1. $-369/10$
2. $23/6$
3. -2π
4. 0
5. $1 + \sqrt{2}$
6. $256a^3/15$
7. $2\pi^2 a^3 (1 + 2\pi^2)$
8. $[(2 + t_0^2)^{3/2} - 2\sqrt{2}]/3$
9. (a) $-2\sqrt{2}\,\pi$
   (b) $-\pi$
10. 5
11. $\bar{x} = \dfrac{6ab^2}{3a^2 + 4\pi^2 b^2}\,; \bar{y} = -\dfrac{6\pi ab^2}{3a^2 + 4\pi^2 b^2}$
12. $2\pi/3$
13. $\dfrac{600 - 36\sqrt{2} - 49\log(9 - 4\sqrt{2})}{64[6\sqrt{2} + \log(3 + 2\sqrt{2})]}$
14. (b) $4a^3$
15. $I_x = (a^2 + b^2)^{1/2}[\pi a^4 + (4\pi^3 - \pi/2)a^2 b^2 + 32\pi^5 b^4/5]$
    $I_y = (a^2 + b^2)^{1/2}[\pi a^4 + (4\pi^3 + \pi/2)a^2 b^2 + 32\pi^5 b^4/5]$

5.9 Exercises (page 233)

2. (b) $(2e^{2\pi} - 5e^{\pi} - 5\pi - 3)/10$
3. (b) 3
4. $8/5$
6. $-4b^2 + 8\pi b - 4$; minimum occurs when $b = \pi$

5.11 Exercises (page 236)

3. $\phi(x, y) = \arctan(y/x)$ if $x > 0$; $\phi(x, y) = \pi/2$ if $x = 0$ and $y > 0$; $\phi(x, y) = -\pi/2$ if $x = 0$ and $y < 0$; $\phi(x, y) = \arctan(y/x) + \pi$ if $x < 0$ and $y > 0$; $\phi(x, y) = \arctan(y/x) - \pi$ if $x < 0$ and $y < 0$

5.14 Exercises (page 241)

1. $x^2/2 + 2xy + y^2/2 = C$
2. $x^2 y = C$
3. $x^3/3 - xy - y/2 + (\sin 2y)/4 = C$
4. $\cos 2x \sin 3y = C$
5. $x^3 y + 4x^2 y^2 - 12e^y + 12ye^y = C$
6. $\int Q(x)e^{\int P(x)dx}\, dx - ye^{\int P(x)dx} = C$
8. (a) $x + y = Cy^2$
   (b) $y^3/x^3 - 3\log|x| = C$
9. (a) $6(xy)^{1/2} - (y/x)^{3/2} = C$; $(x^5 y)^{-1/2}$ is an integrating factor
   (b) $x + e^{-x}\sin y = C$; $e^{-x}\cos y$ is an integrating factor
10. $x^3 y^4 + x^4 y^5 = C$, $10x^3 y^4 + x^5 y^5 = C$, respectively; $x^2 y^3$ is a common integrating factor

5.17   Exercises (page 248)

   1. (a) -4
      (b) 4
      (c) 8
      (d) 4π
      (e) $3\pi/2$
   2. 0
   3. $n = 3$
   4. $-\pi$
   9. $g(x, y) = \pm [P^2(x, y) + Q^2(x, y)]^{1/2}$

5.19   Exercises (page 252)

   1. (b) 0
   2. $0, 2\pi, -2\pi$
   3. As many as three
   4. As many as seven
   5. (a) -3
   6. 2π

5.21   Exercises (page 259)

   1. (a) div $\vec{F}(x, y, z) = 2x + 2y + 2z$; curl $\vec{F}(x, y, z) = \vec{0}$
      (b) div $\vec{F}(x, y, z) = 0$; curl $\vec{F}(x, y, z) = 2\vec{i} + 4\vec{j} + 6\vec{k}$
      (c) div $\vec{F}(x, y, z) = -x \sin y$; curl $\vec{F}(x, y, z) = \vec{i} + \vec{j}$
      (d) div $\vec{F}(x, y, z) = ye^{xy} - x \sin(xy) - 2xz \sin(xz^2)$;
          curl $\vec{F}(x, y, z) = z^2 \sin(xz^2)\vec{j} - [xe^{xy} + y \sin(xy)]\vec{k}$
      (e) div $\vec{F}(x, y, z) = 2x \sin y + 2y \sin(xz) - xy \sin z \cos(\cos z)$;
          curl $\vec{F}(x, y, z) = [x \sin(\cos z) - xy^2 \cos(xz)]\vec{i} - y \sin(\cos z)\vec{j} + [y^2z \cos(xz) - x^2 \cos y]\vec{k}$
   2. $\vec{0}$
   4. $n = -3$
   5. No such vector field
   10. One such field is $\mu(x, y, z) = (xyz)^{-2}$

5.24   Exercises (page 263)

   1. (a) , (c), and (e) are false; all others true
   4. $\operatorname{div}(\vec{V} \times \vec{r}) = 0$; $\operatorname{curl}(\vec{V} \times \vec{r}) = (c + 1)\vec{V}$
   6. $16(a + b)$

5.26   Exercises (page 267)

   1. $(3x - 2z)\vec{j} - x\vec{k}$ is one such field
   2. $(x^2/2 - xy - yz + z^2/2)\vec{j} + (x^2/2 - xz)\vec{k}$ is one such field
   3. $(x^2y/2 + z^2/2)\vec{j} + \nabla f(x, y)$ for some f independent of z
   5. $\vec{G}(x, y, z) = \dfrac{yz}{r(x^2 + y^2)}\vec{i} - \dfrac{xz}{r(x^2 + y^2)}\vec{j}$ satisfies curl $\vec{G} = r^{-3}\vec{r}$ at all points not on the z-axis
   6. $f(r) = Cr^{-3}$
   9. $\vec{F}(x, y, z) = -\tfrac{1}{3}(z^3\,\vec{i} + x^3\,\vec{j} + y^3\,\vec{k})$, $\vec{G}(x, y, z) = \tfrac{1}{3}\nabla(x^3y + y^3z + z^3x)$

Chapter 6

6.3 Exercises (page 282)

1. $(a_2b_3 - a_3b_2)(x - x_0) + (a_3b_1 - a_1b_3)(y - y_0) + (a_1b_2 - a_2b_1)(z - z_0) = 0$;
   $$\frac{\partial \vec{r}}{\partial u} \times \frac{\partial \vec{r}}{\partial v} = (a_2b_3 - a_3b_2)\vec{i} + (a_3b_1 - a_1b_3)\vec{j} + (a_1b_2 - a_2b_1)\vec{k}$$

2. $x^2/a^2 + y^2/b^2 = z$; $\dfrac{\partial \vec{r}}{\partial u} \times \dfrac{\partial \vec{r}}{\partial v} = -2bu^2 \cos v\, \vec{i} - 2au^2 \sin v\, \vec{j} + abu\, \vec{k}$

3. $x^2/a^2 + y^2/b^2 + z^2/c^2 = 1$;
   $$\frac{\partial \vec{r}}{\partial u} \times \frac{\partial \vec{r}}{\partial v} = abc \sin u \left(\frac{\sin u \cos v}{a}\, \vec{i} + \frac{\sin u \sin v}{b}\, \vec{j} + \frac{\cos u}{c}\, \vec{k} \right)$$

4. $z = f(\sqrt{x^2 + y^2})$; $\dfrac{\partial \vec{r}}{\partial u} \times \dfrac{\partial \vec{r}}{\partial v} = -uf'(u) \cos v\, \vec{i} - uf'(u) \sin v\, \vec{j} + u\, \vec{k}$

5. $y^2/a^2 + z^2/b^2 = 1$; $\dfrac{\partial \vec{r}}{\partial u} \times \dfrac{\partial \vec{r}}{\partial v} = b \sin v\, \vec{j} + a \cos v\, \vec{k}$

6. $(\sqrt{x^2 + y^2} - a)^2 + z^2 = b^2$;
   $$\frac{\partial \vec{r}}{\partial u} \times \frac{\partial \vec{r}}{\partial v} = b(a + b \cos u)(\cos u \sin v\, \vec{i} + \cos u \cos v\, \vec{j} + \sin u\, \vec{k})$$

7. $|abc| \cosh v \left[\left(\dfrac{\sin^2 u}{a^2} + \dfrac{\cos^2 u}{b^2} \right) \cosh^2 v + \dfrac{\sinh^2 v}{c^2} \right]^{1/2}$

8. $\sqrt{128v^2 + 4}$

9. $|u - v| \sqrt{36u^2v^2 + 9(u + v)^2 + 4}$

10. $\sqrt{2u^4 + u^2}$

6.5 Exercises (page 287)

2. $\pi a^2 \sqrt{3}$

3. $(2\pi - 4)a^2$

4. 4

5. (a) A circular paraboloid
   (b) $-2u^2 \cos v\, \vec{i} - 2u^2 \sin v\, \vec{j} + u\vec{k}$
   (c) $n = 6$

6. $\sqrt{2}\, \pi a^2/4$

7. $2\pi\sqrt{6}$

8. $2\pi a^2(3\sqrt{3} - 1)/3$

9. $4\pi^2 ab$

6.9 Exercises (page 296)

1. $4\pi/3$

3. $\bar{x} = \bar{y} = \bar{z} = a/2$

4. $1/2$

7. 0

8. 0

9. 0

10. $\pi \sqrt{2}$

12. On the axis of the cone, at a distance $\frac{1}{4}\alpha(1 - \cos \alpha)/[1 - \cos (\alpha/2)]$ from the center of the sphere.

6.12 Exercises (page 303)

1. 0
2. $-\pi$
3. -4
4. 4/3
14. (c) $3\pi/2$

6.16 Exercises (page 313)

1. 3
2. (a) 144π
   (b) -16π
   (c) 128π
3. (a) $3|V|$
   (b) $9|V|\,\bar{z}$
   (c) $|V|\,\bar{x}$
   (d) $4I_z$
15. 8π

Chapter 7

7.3 Exercises (page 323)

1. $x = \dfrac{\sqrt{6}}{2k}\displaystyle\int \dfrac{dy}{\sqrt{A^3 - y^3}} + B$

2. $x = \dfrac{\sqrt{6}}{2k}\displaystyle\int \dfrac{dy}{\sqrt{A^3 + y^3}} + B$

3. $y = \log|Ax + B|$

4. $y = -x + \log|1 + Ae^{2x}| + B$

5. $x = \displaystyle\int \dfrac{dy}{\sqrt{y^4 - 2y^2 + A}} + B$

6. $y = Ae^{x^2/2} - 4x + B$

7. $y = x + A[x\sqrt{1 - x^2} + \arcsin x] + B$

8. $y = Ax + (A^2 + 1)\log|x - A| + B$; singular solution $y = C - \tfrac{1}{2}x^2$

9. $x = \dfrac{\sqrt{2}}{k}\displaystyle\int \dfrac{dy}{\sqrt{A^2 - y^4}} + B$

10. $x = \dfrac{\sqrt{2}}{k}\displaystyle\int \dfrac{dy}{\sqrt{y^4 + A}} + B$

12. $Ax^2 + y^2 = B$

13. $\log x = \dfrac{Ay}{x} + A^2\log\left(\dfrac{y}{x} - A\right) + B$, and $y = Cx$

14. $y = Ax\tan(B - A\log x)$, or $y = Ax\tanh(B + A\log x)$, or $y = Cx$

15. $y = x^2(A\log x + B)^2$

16. $f(x) = \arcsin(e^x/\sqrt{2}) - \pi/4 \ (x \le \log\sqrt{2})$

17. $y = \dfrac{a^{-1/k}(a - x)^{1+1/k}}{2(1 + 1/k)} - \dfrac{a^{1/k}(a - x)^{1-1/k}}{2(1 - 1/k)} + \dfrac{ak}{k^2 - 1}$ if $k > 1$;

   $y = \dfrac{(a - x)^2}{4a} - \dfrac{a}{2}\log\left(1 - \dfrac{x}{a}\right) - \dfrac{a}{4}$ if $k = 1$

18. $s(t) = \frac{1}{2}gt^2 - ct + c\left(t - \frac{w}{k}\right)\log\left(1 - \frac{kt}{w}\right)$

19. $s(t) = ct + c\left(\frac{w}{k} - t\right)\log\left(1 - \frac{kt}{w}\right)$

20. $s(t) = \frac{wv_0}{k}\log\frac{w}{w - kt}$

7.7   Exercises (page 333)

1. $y = e^x(A \cos \sqrt{2}x + B \sin \sqrt{2}x)$
2. $y = Ae^x + Be^{-3x}$
3. $y = e^x(A \cos x + B \sin x)$
4. $y = e^x(A \cos 2x + B \sin 2x)$
5. $y = (A + Bx)e^{-x}$
6. $y = (A + Bx)e^x$
7. $y = \frac{5}{3} - \frac{2}{3}e^{-3x/2}$
8. $y = -\cos(5x - 15)$
9. $y = \frac{a}{2}e^{b(x-1)} + \frac{b}{2}e^{a(x-1)}$, where $a = 2 - \sqrt{5}$, $b = 2 + \sqrt{5}$
10. $y = 2e^{-2x}(\cos x + \sin x)$
11. $u(x) = 6(e^{4x} - e^{-x})/5$; $v(x) = e^x - e^{-5x}$
12. $u(x) = \frac{1}{2}e^{2x-\pi}\sin 5x$; $v(x) = \frac{5}{6}e^{-2x-\pi}\sin 3x$
15. $u(x) = e^{-x^2}$; $Q(x) = 4x^2 + 2$
16. $k = n^2\pi^2$; $f_k(x) = C \sin n\pi x$ $(n = 1, 2, 3, \ldots)$
17. (a) $y'' - y = 0$
    (b) $y'' - 4y' + 4y = 0$
    (c) $y'' + y' + \frac{5}{4}y = 0$
    (d) $y'' + 4y = 0$
    (e) $y'' - y = 0$

7.9   Exercises (page 340)

1. $y = Ae^x + Be^{-x} - x$
2. $y = e^x(A \cos \sqrt{2}x + B \sin \sqrt{2}x) - \frac{8}{27} + \frac{2}{9}x + \frac{2}{3}x^2 + \frac{1}{3}x^3$
3. $y = Ae^x + B - 2x - x^2 - \frac{1}{3}x^3$
4. $y = Ae^{-x} + B + \frac{1}{3}x^3$
5. $y = Ae^x + Be^{4x} + \frac{9}{32} + \frac{1}{8}x + \frac{1}{4}x^2$
6. $y = Ae^{2x} + Be^{-3x} - \frac{7}{12} + \frac{1}{2}x - x^2 - \frac{1}{3}x^3$
7. $y = (A + Bx - \log x)e^{-x}$
8. $y = A \sin x + (B + \log|\csc x + \cot x|) \cos x - 2$
9. $y = Ae^x + Be^{-x} + (e^x - e^{-x})\log(1 + e^x) - xe^x - 1$
10. $y = (A + \frac{1}{3}x)e^x - \frac{1}{6} + \frac{1}{3}e^{-x} + (B + \frac{1}{3})e^{-2x} - \frac{1}{3}(e^x + e^{-2x})\log(1 + e^x)$
11. $y = \begin{cases} (A + Bx)e^{-3x} + \frac{1}{9} & \text{when } 1 < x < 2, \\ (a + bx)e^{-3x} & \text{when } x < 1 \text{ or } x > 2 \end{cases}$
13. $y = (A + \frac{1}{4}x)e^{2x} + Be^{-2x}$
14. $y = (x - \frac{4}{3})e^x + Ae^{-2x} + B$
15. $y = \frac{1}{4}e^{2x} + (A + \frac{1}{3}x - \frac{1}{9})e^x + Be^{-2x}$
16. $y = (A + Bx + \frac{1}{3}x^3)e^x + x + 2$
18. $y = A \cos 2x + B \sin 2x + x \cos x + \frac{2}{3} \sin x$
19. $y = A \sin x + (B - \frac{1}{2}x) \cos x$
20. $y = A + Be^{3x} - \frac{1}{5}e^{2x}(3 \sin x + \cos x)$

21. $y = A \sin x + B \cos x + \frac{1}{40} e^{2x}(3 \sin 3x - \cos 3x)$

22. (a) $1/(2\pi\sqrt{2})$

   (b) $R < \sqrt{2}$

24. $y = (A + Bx^3)e^x + (x^2 - 2x + 2)e^{2x}$

25. $y = Ae^{4x} \int e^{-4x - x^3/3} \, dx + Be^{4x}$

26. $y = Ax^{1/2} + Bx^{-1/2}$

27. $y = Ae^x + Bx^2 e^{-x} - x$

28. $y = A(x^2 - 2) + B/x$

29. $y = x^{-2}[A + B(x - 1)^3 + \frac{1}{9}x^3 + \frac{2}{3}x^2 - \frac{7}{6}x + \frac{1}{2} - (x - 1)^3 \log|x - 1|]$

30. $a = 1, -1; \quad y = [Ae^{g(x)} + Be^{-g(x)}]/x$

7.11   Exercises (page 347)

7. (b) $y = \sum_{i=0}^{n-1} k_i u_i$

7.13   Exercises (page 350)

1. $y = c_1 + c_2 e^{-x} + c_3 e^{3x}$

2. $y = c_1 + c_2 e^x + c_3 e^{-x}$

3. $y = c_1 + (c_2 + c_3 x)e^{-2x}$

4. $y = (c_1 + c_2 x + c_3 x^2)e^x$

5. $y = (c_1 + c_2 x + c_3 x^2 + c_4 x^3)e^{-x}$

6. $y = c_1 e^{2x} + c_2 e^{-2x} + c_3 \cos 2x + c_4 \sin 2x$

7. $y = e^{\sqrt{2}x}(c_1 \cos \sqrt{2}x + c_2 \sin \sqrt{2}x) + e^{-\sqrt{2}x}(c_3 \cos\sqrt{2}x + c_4 \sin \sqrt{2}x)$

8. $y = c_1 e^x + e^{-x/2}(c_2 \cos \frac{1}{2}\sqrt{3}x + c_3 \sin \frac{1}{2}\sqrt{3}x)$

9. $y = e^{-x}[(c_1 + c_2 x)\cos x + (c_3 + c_4 x)\sin x]$

10. $y = (c_1 + c_2 x)\cos x + (c_3 + c_4 x)\sin x$

11. $y = c_1 + c_2 x + (c_3 + c_4 x)\cos \sqrt{2}x + (c_5 + c_6 x)\sin \sqrt{2}x$

12. $y = c_1 + c_2 x + (c_3 + c_4 x)\cos 2x + (c_5 + c_6 x)\sin 2x$

13. $f(x) = \dfrac{1}{2m^2} (e^{mx} - \cos mx - \sin mx)$

16. (a) $y^{(4)} - 5y'' + 4y = 0$

   (b) $y''' + 6y'' + 12y' + 8y = 0$

   (c) $y^{(4)} - 2y''' + y'' = 0$

   (d) $y^{(4)} - 2y''' + y'' = 0$

   (e) $y^{(5)} - 2y^{(4)} + y''' = 0$

   (f) $y^{(4)} + 8y''' + 33y'' + 68y' + 52y = 0$

   (g) $y^{(4)} - 2y'' + y = 0$

   (h) $y^{(6)} + 4y'' = 0$

7.16   Exercises (page 358)

1. $y_1 = -2x - x^2 - \frac{1}{3}x^3$

2. $y_1 = \frac{1}{4}xe^{2x}$

3. $y_1 = (x - \frac{4}{3})e^x$

4. $y_1 = \frac{1}{3} \sin x$

5. $y_1 = \frac{1}{2}x^2 e^x + e^{2x}$

6. $y_1 = \frac{1}{2}xe^x$

7. $y_1 = x \cosh x$

8. $y_1 = \frac{1}{24}x^4 e^{-x}$

9. $50y_1 = (11 - 5x) e^x \sin 2x + (2 - 10x) e^x \cos 2x$

10. $y_1 = -(\frac{5}{8}x + \frac{3}{8}x^2 + \frac{1}{12}x^3)e^{-x}$

12. $y_1 = \dfrac{x^m e^{\alpha x}}{p_A^{(m)}(\alpha)}$

15. (b) $2D$

    (c) $3D^2$

    (d) nD^{n-1}

16. $y = Ae^x + Be^{-x} + \frac{1}{2}e^x \displaystyle\int \frac{e^{-x}}{x}\,dx - \frac{1}{2}e^{-x}\displaystyle\int \frac{e^x}{x}\,dx$

17. $y = (A + \frac{1}{2}x) \sin 2x + (B + \frac{1}{4}\log|\cos 2x|)\cos 2x$

18. $y = Ae^x + Be^{-x} + \frac{1}{2}\sec x$

19. $y = (A + Bx)e^x + e^{ex} - xe^x \displaystyle\int e^{ex}\,dx + e^x \displaystyle\int xe^{ex}\,dx$

20. $y = -\dfrac{1}{8}\log|x| + \dfrac{1}{3}e^x \displaystyle\int \frac{e^{-x}}{x}\,dx - \dfrac{1}{4}e^{2x}\displaystyle\int \frac{e^{-2x}}{x}\,dx$

$$+ \dfrac{1}{24}e^{4x}\int \frac{e^{-4x}}{x}\,dx + Ae^x + Be^{2x} + Ce^{4x}$$

7.18 Exercises (page 366)

2. $f(x) = u_1(x) \ (\alpha = 1)$

3. (a) $A = (a - b)/2, \ B = (a + b)/2$

    (b) $\dfrac{d}{dt}\left[(t^2 - 1)\dfrac{dy}{dt} \right] - \alpha(\alpha + 1)y = 0$, where $\alpha = 1$ or -2, and $x = (t + 1)/2$

4. $u_1(x) = 1 + \displaystyle\sum_{m=1}^{\infty} (-1)^m 2^m \frac{\alpha(\alpha - 2) \cdots (\alpha - 2m + 2)}{(2m)!} x^{2m}$ for all x;

$u_2(x) = x + \displaystyle\sum_{m=1}^{\infty} (-1)^m 2^m \frac{(\alpha - 1)(\alpha - 3) \cdots (\alpha - 2m + 1)}{(2m + 1)!} x^{2m+1}$ for all x

5. $u_1(x) = 1 + \displaystyle\sum_{m=1}^{\infty} \frac{(-1)^m}{(3m + 2)(3m - 1) \cdots 8 \cdot 5} x^{3m}$ for all x;

$u_2(x) = x^{-2}\left(1 + \displaystyle\sum_{n=1}^{\infty} \frac{(-1)^n}{3^n n!} x^{3n} \right)$ for all $x \neq 0$

6. $y = x^2 \left(\dfrac{1}{6} + \displaystyle\sum_{n=1}^{\infty} \frac{(\alpha - 2)(\alpha - 3) \cdots (\alpha - n - 1)}{n!(n + 3)!} x^n \right)$ for all x

11. (b) $f(x) = \frac{1}{5}P_0(x) + \frac{4}{7}P_2(x) + \frac{8}{35}P_4(x)$

15. (b) $\dfrac{2n}{4n^2 - 1}$

7.20 Exercises (page 375)

5. $J_{-3/2}(x) = -\left(\dfrac{2}{\pi x} \right)^{1/2} \left(\dfrac{\cos x}{x} + \sin x \right)$

9. (a) $y = x^{1/2} [c_1 J_{1/3}(\tfrac{2}{3}x^{3/2}) + c_2 J_{-1/3}(\tfrac{2}{3}x^{3/2})]$

    (b) $y = x^{1/2} [c_1 J_{1/4}(\tfrac{1}{2}x^2) + c_2 J_{-1/4}(\tfrac{1}{2}x^2)]$

    (c) $y = x^{1/2} [c_1 J_\alpha(2\alpha x^{1+m/2}) + c_2 J_{-\alpha}(2\alpha x^{1+m/2})]$, where $\alpha = 1/(m + 2)$, provided that $1/(m + 2)$ is not an integer; otherwise replace the appropriate J by K

    (d) $y = x^{1/2} [c_1 J_\alpha(\tfrac{1}{2}x^2) + c_2 J_{-\alpha}(\tfrac{1}{2}x^2)]$, where $\alpha = \sqrt{2}/8$

10. $y = g_\alpha$ satisfies $x^2 y'' + (1 - 2c)xy' + (a^2 b^2 x^{2b} + c^2 - \alpha^2 b^2)y = 0$

    (a) $y = x^{-5/2} [c_1 J_5(2x^{1/2}) + c_2 K_5(2x^{1/2})]$

    (b) $y = x^{-5/2} [c_1 J_{5/2}(x) + c_2 J_{-5/2}(x)]$

    (c) $y = x^{-5/2} [c_1 J_1(\tfrac{2}{3}x^{5/2}) + c_2 K_1(\tfrac{2}{3}x^{5/2})]$

    (d) $y = x [c_1 J_0(2x^{1/2}) + c_2 K_0(2x^{1/2})]$

★7.25 Exercises (page 385)

1. (a) $2i$

    (b) $-i$

    (c) $\tfrac{1}{2} - \tfrac{1}{2}i$

    (d) $18 + i$

    (e) $-\tfrac{1}{5} + \tfrac{3}{5}i$

    (f) $1 + i$

    (g) 0

    (h) $1 + i$

2. (a) $\sqrt{2}$

    (b) 5

    (c) 1

    (d) 1

    (e) $\sqrt{2}$

    (f) $\sqrt{65}$

4. (a) $2e^{i\pi/2}$

    (b) $3e^{-i\pi/2}$

    (c) $e^{\pi i}$

    (d) e^{0i}

    (e) $2\sqrt{3}e^{5\pi i/6}$

    (f) $e^{i\pi/4}$

    (g) $2\sqrt{2}e^{i\pi/4}$

    (h) $2\sqrt{2}e^{-i\pi/4}$

    (i) $\tfrac{1}{2}\sqrt{2}e^{-i\pi/4}$

    (j) $\tfrac{1}{2}e^{-i\pi/2}$

8. (b) $z = 2n\pi i$ where n is any integer

10. (c) $\tfrac{1}{2}\sqrt{3} + \tfrac{1}{2}i, -\tfrac{1}{2}\sqrt{3} + \tfrac{1}{2}i, -i$

    (d) $a + bi, -a - bi, -b + ai, b - ai$, where $a = \tfrac{1}{2}\sqrt{2 + \sqrt{2}}$ and $b = \tfrac{1}{2}\sqrt{2 - \sqrt{2}}$

    (e) $a - bi, -a + bi, b + ai, -b - ai$, where a and b are as in (d)

Chapter 8

8.4 Exercises (page 394)

2. (a) No

    (b) Yes

(c) Yes
(d) No
(e) Yes
(f) No
(g) Yes

3. (a) Neither
   (b) Seminorm
   (c) Seminorm
   (d) Neither
   (e) Seminorm
   (f) Norm
   (g) Neither
   (h) Neither

7. (a), (b), (c)

8.7 Exercises (page 401)

1. (a) $P(x) = \frac{1}{6}(x^2 + 13x + 12)$
   (b) $P(x) = \frac{1}{2}(x^2 - 5x + 6)$
   (c) $P(x) = -\frac{1}{6}(x^3 - 6x^2 + 5x - 6)$
   (d) $P(x) = 2x^3 + x^2 - x - 2$
   (e) $P(x) = -5x^3 - x^2 + 10x - 5$

2. $P(x) = \dfrac{1}{640}(9x^4 - 196x^2 + 640)$

4. (a) $Q(x) = 2x^3 + 3x^2 - x - 3$
   (b) $Q(x) = 4x^3 + 7x^2 - 3x - 7$

5. (a) $P(32) = \dfrac{31}{21}$; $f(32) - P(32) = \dfrac{43}{42}$

   (b) $P(32) = \dfrac{992}{255}$; $f(32) - P(32) = -\dfrac{709}{510}$

   (c) $P(32) = \dfrac{43}{15}$; $f(32) - P(32) = -\dfrac{11}{30}$

   (d) $P(32) = -\dfrac{403}{1530}$; $f(32) - P(32) = \dfrac{2114}{765}$

7. (a) $L_0(x) = \dfrac{1}{72}(u - 1)(u - 3)(u - 4)(u - 6)$; $L_1(x) = -\dfrac{1}{30}u(u - 3)(u - 4)(u - 6)$;

   $L_2(x) = \dfrac{1}{18}u(u - 1)(u - 4)(u - 6)$; $L_3(x) = -\dfrac{1}{24}u(u - 1)(u - 3)(u - 6)$;

   $L_4(x) = \dfrac{1}{180}u(u - 1)(u - 3)(u - 4)$

   (b) $P(2.6) = 20$

8. (b) $x \geq 1.581$
   (c) $h \leq 0.0006$

14. (d) Let $B_0(x) = 1$ and let $B_n(x) = (x - x_0)(x - x_0 - nh)^{n-1}/n!$ for $n \geq 1$; the one and only polynomial P of degree $\leq n$ satisfying the conditions $P(x_0) = c_0$, $P'(x_1) = c_1$, $P''(x_2) = c_2, \ldots, P^{(n)}(x_n) = c_n$ is given by $P(x) = c_0 B_0(x) + \cdots + c_n B_n(x)$

8.11 Exercises (page 411)

4. (b) $\phi_{k+1}(x) = \dfrac{\sqrt{(2k + 1)(2k + 3)}}{k + 1} x\phi_k(x) - \dfrac{k}{k + 1}\sqrt{\dfrac{2k + 3}{2k - 1}}\, \phi_{k-1}(x)$, where $\phi_k = P_k/\|P_k\|$

5. (b) $\displaystyle\sum_{k=0}^{m} P_k^2(x) = \frac{p_m}{p_{m+1}} [P_m(x)P'_{m+1}(x) - P_{m+1}(x)P'_m(x)]$

6. (a) Let $a_0 = \dfrac{1}{2}\displaystyle\int_{-1}^{1} f(t)\,dt$, $a_1 = \dfrac{3}{2}\displaystyle\int_{-1}^{1} t\,f(t)\,dt$, $a_2 = \dfrac{5}{2}\displaystyle\int_{-1}^{1} \dfrac{3t^2-1}{2} f(t)\,dt$,

   $a_3 = \dfrac{7}{2}\displaystyle\int_{-1}^{1} \dfrac{5t^3-3t}{2} f(t)\,dt$. Then for $k = 1$: $A_0 = a_0$, $A_1 = a_1$; for $k = 2$:
   $A_0 = a_0 - a_2/2$, $A_1 = a_1$, $A_2 = 3a_2/2$; for $k = 3$: $A_0 = a_0 - a_2/2$, $A_1 = a_1 - 3a_3/2$,
   $A_2 = 3a_2/2$, $A_3 = 5a_3/2$

   (b) $\|f - T_2\|^2 = \int_{-1}^{1} f^2(t)\,dt - 2A_0^2 - \frac{2}{3}A_1^2 - \frac{2}{5}A_2^2 - \frac{4}{3}A_0A_2$,
   $\|f - T_3\|^2 = \int_{-1}^{1} f^2(t)\,dt - 2A_0^2 - \frac{2}{3}A_1^2 - \frac{2}{5}A_2^2 - \frac{2}{7}A_3^2 - \frac{4}{3}A_0A_2 - \frac{4}{5}A_1A_3$

7. $\dfrac{1}{2} + \dfrac{5}{8} P_2(x) - \dfrac{3}{16} P_4(x) = \dfrac{15}{128}(1 + 14x^2 - 7x^4)$

8. (c) $S_0(x) = \frac{1}{2}$; $S_1(x) = \frac{1}{2} + \frac{3}{2}x$; $S_2(x) = -\frac{3}{4} + \frac{3}{2}x + \frac{15}{4}x^2$; $S_3(x) = -\frac{3}{4} - \frac{15}{4}x + \frac{15}{4}x^2 + \frac{35}{4}x^3$

11. (a) $\|P - f\|^2 = \dfrac{n-1}{n} - \dfrac{\log^2 n}{n-1}$

    (b) $P(x) = \left(\dfrac{12}{(n-1)^2} - \dfrac{6(n+1)}{(n-1)^3}\log n\right)x + \dfrac{4(n^3-1)\log n}{(n-1)^4} - \dfrac{6(n+1)}{(n-1)^2}$;
    $\|P - f\|^2 = 36 \log 2 - 28 \log^2 2 - \frac{23}{2} = 0.0007$ when $n = 2$

12. (a) $\|P - f\|^2 = \dfrac{1}{2n}[(n-2)e^{2n} + 4e^n - n - 2]$

    (b) $P(x) = (18 - 6e)x + 4e - 10$; $\|P - f\|^2 = 20e - \frac{7}{2}e^2 - \frac{57}{2} = 0.0038$

8.14 Exercises (page 420)

6. $Q(x) = -\dfrac{5}{2}x^4 + \dfrac{35}{16}x^3 - \dfrac{25}{32}x^2 + \dfrac{25}{256}x - \dfrac{1}{512}$

11. (b) $U_0(x) = 1$, $U_1(x) = 2x$, $U_2(x) = 4x^2 - 1$, $U_3(x) = 8x^3 - 4x$, $U_4(x) = 16x^4 - 12x^2 + 1$,
    $U_5(x) = 32x^5 - 32x^3 + 6x$

8.17 Exercises (page 427)

1. 10.067
   $\searrow$
   $\quad$ 0.08367
   $\nearrow \qquad \searrow$
   10.318 $\qquad\qquad$ 0.01733; $P(2.5) = 25.261$
   $\searrow \qquad \nearrow$
   $\quad$ 0.17033
   $\nearrow$
   10.829

2. (a) 102
   $\searrow$
   $\quad$ -30
   $\nearrow \qquad \searrow$
   12 $\qquad\quad$ 5; $P(2) = -8$
   $\searrow \qquad \nearrow$
   $\quad$ -5
   $\nearrow$
   -3

   (b) $Q(2) = -2.23$

5. (b) $f(x_0, x_1, \ldots, x_n) = \displaystyle\sum_{k=0}^{n} u(x_0, x_1, \ldots, x_k)v(x_k, x_{k+1}, \ldots, x_n)$

8.19 Exercises (page 432)

4. (b)

8	-5040	13068	-13132	6769	-1960	322	-28	1		
9	40320	-109584	118124	-67284	22449	-4536	546	-36	1	
10	-3628800	1026576	-1172700	723680	-269325	63273	-9450	870	-45	1

(c) $1 + 2x + 2x^2 - 3x^3 + x^4$

5. (c)

8	1	127	966	1701	1050	266	28	1	
9	1	255	3025	7770	6951	2646	462	36	1
10	1	511	9330	34105	42525	22827	5880	750	45	1

(d) $-1 + 6x^{(1)} + 16x^{(2)} + 9x^{(3)} + x^{(4)}$

7. (a) $\frac{4}{3}n^3 + \frac{11}{2}n^2 + \frac{61}{6}n$

(b) $\frac{1}{4}n^4 + \frac{5}{6}n^3 + \frac{3}{4}n^2 + \frac{1}{6}n$

(c) $\frac{1}{4}n^4 + \frac{3}{2}n^3 + \frac{11}{4}n^2 + \frac{3}{2}n$

(d) $\frac{1}{5}n^5 + \frac{1}{2}n^4 + \frac{1}{3}n^3 - \frac{1}{30}n$

8.22 Exercises (page 441)

1. (a) $0.693773 - \epsilon$, where $0.000208 \le \epsilon \le 0.001667$. This gives the inequalities $0.6921 < \log 2 < 0.6936$

   (b) $n = 578$

2. (a) $c = \sqrt{3}/3$

   (b) $c_1 = \dfrac{a+b}{2} + \dfrac{b-a}{2}\dfrac{\sqrt{3}}{3}$, $c_2 = \dfrac{a+b}{2} - \dfrac{b-a}{2}\dfrac{\sqrt{3}}{3}$

3. (a) $c = \sqrt{2}/2$

   (b) $c_1 = \dfrac{a+b}{2} + \dfrac{b-a}{2}\dfrac{\sqrt{2}}{2}$, $c_2 = \dfrac{a+b}{2} - \dfrac{b-a}{2}\dfrac{\sqrt{2}}{2}$

4. $a = 2 + \sqrt{2}$, $b = 2 - \sqrt{2}$

5. $c = \sqrt{\dfrac{3}{2}}$

7. (d) $\displaystyle\int_a^b f(x)\,dx = \frac{b-a}{18}\left[5f\left(\frac{b+a}{2} - \frac{b-a}{2}\sqrt{\frac{3}{5}}\right) + 8f\left(\frac{b+a}{2}\right)\right.$
$$\left. + 5f\left(\frac{b+a}{2} + \frac{b-a}{2}\sqrt{\frac{3}{5}}\right)\right]$$

10. (a) $\log 2 = 0.693254 - \epsilon$, where $0.000016 \le \epsilon \le 0.000521$; this leads to the inequalities $0.69273 < \log 2 < 0.69324$

   (b) $\log 2 = 0.69315023 - \epsilon$, where $0.00000041 \le \epsilon \le 0.00001334$; this leads to the inequalities $0.693136 < \log 2 < 0.693149$

11. (d) $\log 2 = 0.693750 - \epsilon$, where $0.000115 \le \epsilon \le 0.003704$; this leads to the inequalities $0.69004 < \log 2 < 0.69364$

Chapter 9

★9.3 Exercises (page 462)

1. (a) $K = 2$

   (b) $K = \frac{2}{3}\sqrt[3]{2}$

(c) $K = e$

(d) $K = 4$

(e) $K = 3$

(f) $K = 2 \, ||P|| \, \max\{|d|, |c|\} + ||Q||$, where $||P|| = \max\limits_{a \le x \le b} |P(x)|$ and $||Q|| = \max\limits_{a \le x \le b} |Q(x)|$

2. (a) $y = 0$

(b) $y = 0$

(c) $y = 0$

(d) $y(2 - x^2) = 2$

(e) $y(3 - x^2) = 2$

(f) $y(2 - x^2) = 2$

3. $y = e^{x - x^2}$ if $x \ge 0$; $y = e^{x^2 - x}$ if $x \le 0$

5. $(3x^2 - y^2)^2 = Cy$

9.5   Exercises (page 468)

1. (a) $Y(x) = e^x$

(b) $Y_n(x) = 2e^x - \sum\limits_{k=0}^{n} \dfrac{x^k}{k!}$ if n is odd; $Y_n(x) = \sum\limits_{k=0}^{n} \dfrac{x^k}{k!}$ if n is even

2. $Y_3(x) = \dfrac{x^2}{2} + \dfrac{x^5}{20} + \dfrac{x^8}{160} + \dfrac{x^{11}}{4400}$

3. $Y_3(x) = x + \dfrac{x^4}{4} + \dfrac{x^7}{14} + \dfrac{x^{10}}{160}$

4. $Y_3(x) = \dfrac{x^3}{3} + \dfrac{4x^7}{63} + \dfrac{8x^9}{405} + \dfrac{184x^{11}}{51975} + \dfrac{4x^{13}}{12285}$

5. (a) $Y_2(x) = 1 + x + x^2 + \dfrac{2x^3}{3} + \dfrac{x^4}{6} + \dfrac{2x^5}{15} + \dfrac{x^7}{63}$

(b) $M = 2$; $c = \frac{1}{2}$

(c) $Y(x) = 1 + x + x^2 + \dfrac{4x^3}{3} + \dfrac{7x^4}{6} + \dfrac{6x^5}{5} + \cdots$

6. (a) $Y_4(x) = x + \dfrac{x^3}{3} + \dfrac{2x^5}{15} + \dfrac{17x^7}{315} + \dfrac{38x^9}{2835} + \dfrac{134x^{11}}{51975} + \dfrac{4x^{13}}{12285} + \dfrac{x^{15}}{59535}$

(d) $Y(x) = \tan x = x + \dfrac{x^3}{3} + \dfrac{2x^5}{15} + \dfrac{17x^7}{315} + \dfrac{62x^9}{2835} + \cdots$ for $|x| < \dfrac{\pi}{2}$

8. $Y_3(x) = 2 + x^2 + x^3 + \dfrac{3x^5}{20} + \dfrac{x^6}{10}$; $Z_3(x) = 3x^2 + \dfrac{3x^4}{4} + \dfrac{6x^5}{5} + \dfrac{3x^7}{28} + \dfrac{3x^8}{40}$

9. $Y_3(x) = 5 + x + \dfrac{x^4}{12} + \dfrac{x^6}{6} + \dfrac{2x^7}{63} + \dfrac{x^9}{72}$;

$Z_3(x) = 1 + \dfrac{x^3}{3} + x^5 + \dfrac{2x^6}{9} + \dfrac{x^8}{8} + \dfrac{11x^9}{324} + \dfrac{7x^{11}}{264}$

10. (e) $Y_n(x) = 0$; $\lim\limits_{n \to \infty} Y_n(x) = 0$

(f) $Y_n(x) = \begin{cases} x^2 & \text{if } x \ge 0 \\ -x^2 & \text{if } x \le 0 \end{cases}$; $\lim\limits_{n \to \infty} Y_n(x) = \begin{cases} x^2 & \text{if } x \ge 0 \\ -x^2 & \text{if } x \le 0 \end{cases}$

(g) $Y_n(x) = \dfrac{2x^n}{3^n}$; $\lim\limits_{n \to \infty} Y_n(x) = 0$

(h) $Y_n(x) = \begin{cases} x^2 & \text{if } x \ge 0 \\ -x^2 & \text{if } x \le 0 \end{cases}$; $\lim\limits_{n \to \infty} Y_n(x) = \begin{cases} x^2 & \text{if } x \ge 0 \\ -x^2 & \text{if } x \le 0 \end{cases}$

INDEX

517

Index

PRINTED IN THE UNITED STATES OF AMERICA